essentials of human sexuality

essentials of human sexuality

SECOND CANADIAN EDITION

SPENCER A. RATHUS
Montclair State University

JEFFREY S. NEVID
St. John's University

LOIS FICHNER-RATHUS
The College of New Jersey

SUE WICKS McKENZIE
Dawson College

MARY BISSELL
Sex Information and Education Council of Canada (SIECCAN)

PEARSON

Toronto

National Library Cataloguing in Publication

Essentials of human sexuality / Spencer A. Rathus ... [et al.]. — 2nd Canadian ed.

Includes bibliographical references and index.
ISBN 0-205-41247-5

1. Sex—Textbooks. I. Rathus, Spencer A.

HQ21.E85 2004   306.7   C2004-903074-4

ISBN 0-205-41247-5

Vice President, Editorial Director: Michael J. Young
Acquisitions Editor: Ky Pruesse
Executive Marketing Manager: Judith Allen
Supervising Developmental Editor: Suzanne Schaan
Production Editor: Avivah Wargon
Copy Editor: Gilda Mekler
Production Coordinator: Patricia Ciardullo
Page Layout: Christine Velakis
Permissions/Photo Research: Sandy Cooke
Art Director: Julia Hall
Interior Design: Gillian Tsintziras/Julia Hall
Cover Design: Julia Hall
Cover Image: Getty Images

1 2 3 4 5   09 08 07 06 05

Printed and bound in the United States.

Statistics Canada information is used with the permission of the Minister of Industry, as Minister responsible for Statistics Canada. Information on the availability of the wide range of data from Statistics Canada can be obtained from Statistics Canada's Regional Offices, its World Wide Web site at http://www.statcan.ca and its toll-free access number, 1-800-263-1136.

To our students—past, present, and future. You make it all worthwhile.

— S.W.M.

Brief Contents

Contents

Preface

There are more things in heaven and earth, Horatio,
Than are dreamt of in your philosophy.
SHAKESPEARE, *HAMLET*, V.i.174–175

There are indeed more kinds of people in this world and more ways in which people experience their sexuality than most of us might imagine. Human sexuality may be intimately related to human biology, but it is embedded within the sociocultural fabric of human society. For this reason, a core theme of the Second Canadian Edition of *Essentials of Human Sexuality* is its multicultural perspective. In this text, students learn to examine a broad view of sexual experience and the latest scientific findings in the field, and are encouraged to analyze their own thoughts and perceptions about sexuality and sexual experience. The text is specifically designed to be accessible, useful, and compelling, while careful updates ensure it reflects the most current and relevant research available.

Themes of the Text

The four main themes that thread throughout *Essentials of Human Sexuality* are the rich diversity found in gender roles, sexual attitudes, and sexual behaviours and customs; critical thinking; making responsible sexual decisions; and sexual health.

Diversity

The majority of colleges and universities have as their mission the broadening of students' perspectives so that they will appreciate and tolerate human diversity. Canada is a nation of hundreds of different ethnic and religious groups, many of whom endorse culturally distinctive beliefs about appropriate gender roles for men and women and about sexual practices and customs. Diversity is even greater within the global village of the world's more than 200 nations and myriad distinctive subcultures. This text incorporates a multicultural, multiethnic perspective that reflects the diversity of sexual experience in our society and around the world and expands a student's understanding of the range of cultural differences in sexual attitudes and behaviour. Discussion of diversity encourages respect for people holding diverse beliefs and attitudes. The book encourages students to question what is appropriate for women and men in terms of social roles and sexual conduct in light of cultural traditions and standards. The Second Canadian Edition has been revised to

ensure the inclusion of *A World of Diversity* boxes in every chapter, thus reiterating the importance of this theme. It also includes new material on sexual orientation, including human rights issues around the world and the latest legal developments relating to same-sex marriage in Canada.

Critical Thinking

Today, colleges and universities are encouraging students to become critical thinkers. But students are inundated with so much information about gender and sexuality—from politicians, theologians, community leaders, newspapers, films and television programs, the Internet, and other media—that it can be difficult to sort out truth from fiction.

Critical thinking means being skeptical of information that is presented in print or uttered by authority figures or celebrities. Critical thinking requires thoughtfully analyzing and probing claims and arguments in light of evidence. Moreover, it requires a willingness to challenge conventional wisdom. It means scrutinizing definitions of terms and evaluating the premises or assumptions that underlie arguments.

"Thinking Critically About Human Sexuality" is addressed in a major section in Chapter 1. In the same chapter, a new *Applications* box—"Of Course It's True; I Saw It on the Internet"—gives students guidelines for evaluating credibility in one of the most frequently consulted, yet often unmediated and unreliable, sources of information available. Throughout the book we continue to raise issues that demand critical thinking. These issues are intended to stimulate student interest in analyzing and evaluating their beliefs and attitudes toward gender roles and sexuality against accumulated scientific evidence.

Responsible Sexual Decision Making

Students are also encouraged to make responsible sexual decisions. There are psychological and physical dangers in "going with the flow" or being passive about one's sexuality. We do not encourage students to be sexually active (such a decision is personal). On the other hand, we do encourage students to actively make their own sexual decisions on the basis of accurate information.

Decision making is deeply intertwined with our sexual experience. For example, we need to decide:

- whom to date
- how and when to become sexually intimate
- whether to practise contraception
- which contraceptive method(s) to use
- how to protect ourselves against AIDS and other sexually transmitted infections

Throughout the book students are provided with the information they need to make responsible decisions about their physical health, the gender roles they will enact, sexual practices, birth control, and prevention of sexually transmitted infections.

Sexual Health

The text emphasizes issues relating to sexual health. There is extensive coverage of such topics as HIV/AIDS and other STIs, innovations in contraception and reproductive technologies, breast and prostate cancer, menstrual distress, and diseases that affect the reproductive tract. The text encourages students to take an active role in health promotion. For example, it includes applications that will help students examine their breasts and testes for abnormalities, reduce the risk of HIV infection, and cope with menstrual discomfort.

Coverage

Essentials of Human Sexuality, Second Canadian Edition, provides a comprehensive review of the latest scientific findings in the field. It helps students acquire a broader view of human sexual experience by examining multiple perspectives on human sexuality—historical, biological, psychological, cultural, and sociological.

The Core of the Text

The text covers topics relating to human sexuality including research methods, sexual anatomy and physiology, sexual arousal and behaviour, gender roles, attraction and love, intimate relationships and communication, sexual orientation, conception and contraception, prenatal development and childbirth, sexual behaviour across the life span, sexual dysfunctions and sex therapy, sexually transmitted infections, atypical variations in sexual behaviour, sexual coercion, and commercial sex.

The text also emphasizes pressing issues that are likely to confront or concern today's students. These include sexual harassment, acquaintance sexual assault, interfaith couples, contraception, and the threat of AIDS.

Features

A World of Diversity

The feature *A World of Diversity* highlights the rich variety of human sexual customs and practices in our own society and around the world. Viewing human sexuality in a multicultural context helps students better understand how cultural beliefs, values, and attitudes can influence the expression of sexuality. Students may come to understand that their partners, who may not share their ethnic or religious heritage, may feel differently than they do about sexual intimacy. A new box on "Human Rights and Sexual Orientation" (Chapter 8) looks at controversies in countries as diverse as Egypt, Russia, Uganda, Saudi Arabia, Iran, the U.S., and El Salvador, and discusses efforts to include sexual orientation in the Universal Declaration of Human Rights. Among the many topics featured in the *World of Diversity* boxes are: "Around the World in 80 Ways—A Preview," "Circumcision: From Symbol to Science to Controversy," "Female Circumcision," and "On AIDS and Prostitution in Thailand."

Applications

Hands-on applications give students concrete advice for enhancing their sexual health and sexual experience. Useful information covered in the *Applications* boxes of this text includes "Breast Self-Examination," "Reducing the Risk of Sexual Assault," "Preventing AIDS and Other Sexually Transmitted Infections," and "Talking to Your Children About Sex." "Does Breast Cancer Screening Work?" (a new box in Chapter 2) helps students evaluate the significance of recent, widely reported studies for decisions they make about their own personal health care. Reporting of the latest data and developments leads to solid advice in such boxes such as "Self-Examination of the Testes," "Optimizing the Chances of Conception," and "How to Respond to an Exhibitionist."

Learning Aids

Perhaps more than anything else a textbook is a teaching tool—a device for presenting material in a way that stimulates learning and critical thinking. *Essentials of Human Sexuality*, Second Canadian Edition, was designed to maximize this goal by means of several pedagogical aids:

Chapter Outlines

Each chapter begins with an outline that organizes the subject matter for the student. Headings were created to be succinct and to promote student interest in the topics they address.

"Did You Know That... ?"

Every chapter begins with a series of queries regarding sexual knowledge. For instance, "Did you know that the graham cracker came into being as a means to help young men control their sexual appetites?" and "Did you know that opposites do not usually attract—we are more likely to be attracted to people who share our views and tastes than to people who disagree with them?"

This feature lays the groundwork for basics within a chapter's subject matter and at the same time challenges some of the widespread myths.

Running Glossary

Research shows that most students do not make use of end-of-textbook glossaries. Searching for the meaning of a term is often a cumbersome task that distracts the reader from the subject matter. This textbook has a running glossary—key terms are boldfaced within the text and defined in the margins alongside the related text. Meanings are immediately accessible and the reader can maintain concentration on the material.

Weblinks

Weblinks in the margins of every chapter direct students to valuable Internet resources for additional information, both theoretical and practical. All addresses have been checked for currency and are provided electronically on the Companion Website for *Essentials of Human Sexuality* at **www.pearsoned.ca/Rathus**.

Summing Up

New to the Second Canadian Edition, succinct prose-format reviews highlight the key points covered in each chapter. As well, interactive (fill-in-the-blank) reviews are provided electronically on the text's Companion Website at **www.pearsoned.ca/Rathus**.

Chapter Quiz with Answer Key

Each chapter concludes with a multiple-choice test that allows students to check their knowledge. This unique study system is designed to help students acquire complex terms and fully understand key concepts. The Answer Key is now printed on a separate page at the end of the text to discourage "peeking" as students test themselves.

What's New in the Second Canadian Edition

This book has been updated for Canadian students with current and relevant information, including the most recent data available from sources such as Statistics Canada and Health Canada. In particular, the numerous figures and tables throughout the text have been carefully updated. As in the first edition, studies from Canadian sources have replaced, where available, information from the National Health and Social Life Study (NHSLS), but where there is no comparable Canadian study to replace

the NHSLS, many of its findings have been retained, as they serve to illuminate our own experience. This edition also focuses on Canadian laws and on the historical background to some of the major issues that we face today: birth control, abortion, sexual assault, pornography, and prostitution.

Chapter-by-Chapter Highlights

Chapter 1 A new *Applications* box, "Of Course It's True; I Saw It on the Internet!" considers how students can analyze the information they find online and helps them develop critical thinking skills. The discussion of social changes in the twentieth century looks at cohabitation, the collapse of barriers against women, and same-sex marriage. The research overview includes a new section on Canadian information sources that relate to sexual behaviour.

Chapter 2 Current Canadian incidence and mortality figures are provided for cervical, ovarian, and breast cancer. The text looks at new studies on the relationship between breast cancer rates and use of the birth control pill, with a practical perspective offered in the new *Applications* box "Does Breast Cancer Screening Work?" The discussion of hormone replacement therapy considers recent studies on its risks and effectiveness, as well as current recommendations from the Society of Obstetricians and Gynecologists of Canada. The *World of Diversity* box on "Female Circumcision" has been significantly revised and updated.

Chapter 3 Statistics on Canadian deaths from prostate cancer have been added. The discussion of tests for prostate cancer includes new material on their effectiveness, and the *Applications* box on "Self-Examination of the Testes" has been updated with recommended procedures from the Canadian Cancer Society. A new *World of Diversity* box on "Circumcision: From Symbol to Science to Controversy" looks at the cultural background of the procedure, as well as current perspectives.

Chapter 4 Vancouver researcher Rosemary Basson's intimacy model is introduced in the section on the sexual response cycle, looking at why women may engage in sexual relations for reasons other than sexual satisfaction. The results of recent Canadian surveys enrich the discussions of masturbation, sexual fantasies, and oral sex.

Chapter 5 Information on Supermale syndrome (men with extra Y chromosomes) is updated in the section on sex chromosomal abnormalities, debunking the belief that XYY-chromosome men have a greater propensity towards violence. New material on Poly-X or Superfemale syndrome (women with at least three X chromosomes) has also been added. The discussion of gender identity looks at the implications of the well-known case of the Canadian boy who was raised as a girl after his penis was damaged during circumcision. The implications of recent Canadian studies on aggressiveness in girls and gender typing by very young children are also considered.

Chapter 6 Do opposites attract? This discussion has been updated with the results of a 2003 study showing relationships between similar couples last longer than those of dissimilar couples, as well as a 2000 study showing similarity is more important for women than for men. Material on Sternberg's "Triangular Theory of Love" has been updated with Sternberg's own criticisms of his theory's limitations.

Chapter 7 The section on jealousy has been significantly updated with Statistics Canada data on jealousy as a form of emotional abuse and as a reported factor in spousal homicides, as well as coverage of a new (2004) Canadian paper on jealousy in adolescent relationships.

Chapter 8 This chapter has been extensively updated and a special effort has been made to ensure the information is as current as possible—for example, new material on same-sex marriage rulings in Canadian and U.S. courts was being added right up to the time the book went to press. This chapter also looks at the most recent surveys on attitudes to same-sex marriage, while the section on homophobia includes results of a 2003 Canadian survey that details which groups are most likely to be accepting of homosexuality. The discussion of homosexuality and the law points out that same-sex behaviour remains illegal in 83 countries and is punishable by death in seven, while a new *World of Diversity* box on "Human Rights and Sexual Orientation" looks at human rights issues for gay men and lesbians in a diverse range of countries.

Chapter 9 The updated *Applications* box on "Optimizing the Chances of Conception" cites a new study showing a wide variation in when ovulation may occur. The implications of Bill C-56 (2002) are reviewed in the discussions of artificial insemination and surrogate motherhood. New material on polycystic ovary syndrome (PCOS) has been added to the section on female fertility problems.

Chapter 10 New material on the contraceptive patch and injections has been added to the chapter, as well as information on the withdrawal of Norplant from the Canadian market (2002) and the availability of morning-after pills without prescription in B.C. and Quebec. The section on advantages and disadvantages of oral contraception looks at a recent study on whether there is a relationship between the Pill and breast cancer. Recent research is presented indicating that spermicides containing nonoxynol-9 facilitate, rather than prohibit, the transmission of HIV.

Chapter 11 The section on sex education looks at recent Canadian data on the age at which teens first have intercourse and compares the results to ages in the U.S., France, and Britain. The chapter includes updated statistics on teen condom use and pregnancy rates, and looks closely at the consequences of teen pregnancies, including recent Canadian and U.S. research on the benefits of providing support to pregnant teens. The 2001 census results on rates of cohabitation—including same-sex couples—are considered.

Chapter 12 The chapter considers some recent studies of lack of sexual desire and dyspareunia (a sexual pain disorder) that challenge previously held assumptions about women's sexuality. The section on relationship problems looks at a recent Canadian study that indicates couples who experience greater relationship satisfaction are less likely to report sexual problems.

Chapter 13 The introductory paragraph sets the stage for student readers by contrasting the low rates of HIV among youth versus high rates of less publicized STIs like chlamydia and human papilloma virus. Throughout the chapter, updated rates are provided for specific STIs, including chlamydia, gonorrhea, syphilis, shigellosis, and HIV/AIDS.

Chapter 14 The chapter introduction notes that the APA's 1973 decision to stop classifying homosexuality as a sexual disorder is just one example of how of definitions of sexual variations change. The *Applications* box on "How to Respond to an Exhibitionist" is updated with Canadian research on the probability that the exhibitionist will go on to commit other sexual or violent offences.

Chapter 15 The discussion of acquaintance sexual assault includes new material on how myths influence perceptions of whether sexual assault has occurred. Throughout the chapter, the most recent Canadian data is cited for reported sexual assault rates, rates of reporting sexual assault, sexual assault rates on men, sexual assault rates by women, and sexual abuse of children. The question of whether team sports encourage sexual aggression or tend to attract males with aggressive tendencies is explored in the section on sociocultural factors.

Chapter 16 A 1988 study in the previous edition, indicating that most (female) prostitutes found sex with customers satisfying, has been challenged by recent research; the chapter looks at a more recent survey of female, male, and transgendered prostitutes that reports female prostitutes are the least likely to report experiencing sexual satisfaction. The section on characteristics of female prostitutes includes a Montreal study that looked at rates of running away from home, experience of sexual abuse, and rates of injection drug use among prostitutes compared to other street youth. The *World of Diversity* box on "Aids and Prostitution in Thailand" has been revised to note the impact of the global sex tourism industry and discusses poverty as a decisive factor when clients pressure prostitutes to have sex without a condom.

Supplements

For Instructors

The *Instructor's Resource CD-ROM* includes the following items:

- *Instructor's Manual.* This manual provides instructors with a rich resource of teaching aids, including activities, teaching tips, and additional lecture material.
- *Test Item File.* This test bank will help instructors create tests and exams. It is available in both Microsoft Word and TestGen formats (see below).
- *Pearson TestGen.* TestGen is a special computerized version of the Test Item File that enables instructors to view and edit the existing questions, add questions, generate tests, and print the tests in a variety of formats. Powerful search and sort functions make it easy to locate questions and arrange them in any order desired. TestGen also enables instructors to administer tests on a local area network, have the tests graded electronically, and have the results prepared in electronic or printed reports.

Some of these resources can also be downloaded from Pearson Education Canada's Instructor Central website; this is a protected site for instructors only. An access code is required; apply online at **www.pearsoned.ca/instructor** or contact your local sales representative for details.

For Students

The Companion Website at **www.pearsoned.ca/Rathus** offers students an online study aid. It provides a wealth of exercises and self-tests that allow students to review and learn at their own pace. As well, students can explore numerous links to the Internet to enrich their understanding of the topics covered.

Acknowledgments

The authors owe a great debt of gratitude to the many researchers and scholars whose contributions to the body of knowledge in the field of human sexuality are represented in these pages. Underscoring the interdisciplinary nature of the field, we have drawn upon the work of scholars in such fields as psychology, sociology, medicine, anthropology, theology, and philosophy, to name a few. We are also indebted to the many researchers who have generously allowed us to quote from their work and reprint tabular material representing their findings.

Canadian authors Sue McKenzie and Mary Bissell are especially grateful to the following individuals for their helpful comments, which fuelled the changes in the Second Canadian Edition: Wendy L. Bourque (St. Thomas University); Judith Grad (Concordia University); Jim Katz (John Abbott College); Evelyn J. Kita (Niagara College); Nicki Monahan (George Brown College); and Dawn Moore (Algonquin College). Thanks also to those who reviewed the Second Canadian Edition anonymously, and to the reviewers whose comments helped shaped the First Canadian Edition: Steve Balz (Niagara College); E. Sandra Byers (University of New Brunswick); Terry Humphreys (University of British Columbia); Jean Jablonski (Humber College); Nicki Monahan (George Brown College); David E. Reagan (Camosun College); Christopher Roney (King's College); B.J. Rye (St. Jerome's University); Laurie Schnirer (University of Alberta); and Bryan Teixeira (Camosun College).

The Canadian authors also wish to thank the staff at Pearson Education Canada, including acquisitions editors Christine Cozens and Ky Pruesse; developmental editors Lesley Mann and Suzanne Schaan; production editor Avivah Wargon; freelance copy editor Gilda Mekler; designer Julia Hall; production coordinator Trish Ciardullo; formatter Christine Velakis; and marketing manager Judith Allen.

Sue McKenzie thanks her daughter Catherine for taking her through the complexities of the Criminal Code of Canada, as well as her colleagues and students for many helpful suggestions. She also thanks her husband, Bob, for living with the textbook for so long.

Spencer A. Rathus
Jeffrey S. Nevid
Lois Fichner-Rathus
Sue Wicks McKenzie
Mary Bissell

A Great Way to Learn and Instruct Online

The Pearson Education Canada Companion Website is easy to navigate and is organized to correspond to the chapters in this textbook. Whether you are a student in the classroom or a distance learner you will discover helpful resources for in-depth study and research that empower you in your quest for greater knowledge, and maximize your potential for success in the course.

Companion Website

[**www.pearsoned.ca/rathus**]

PEARSON

Jump to...   http://www.pearsoned.ca/rathus   Home   Search   Help   Profile

Companion Website

Home >

Pearson Education Canada Companion Website

Essentials of Human Sexuality, Second Canadian Edition, by Rathus et al.

Student Resources

The modules in this section provide students with tools for learning course material. These modules include:
- Multiple-Choice Quizzes
- Essay Questions
- Internet Links

In the quiz modules, students can send answers to the grader and receive instant feedback on their progress through the Results Reporter. Coaching comments and references to the textbook may be available to ensure that students take advantage of all available resources to enhance their learning experience.

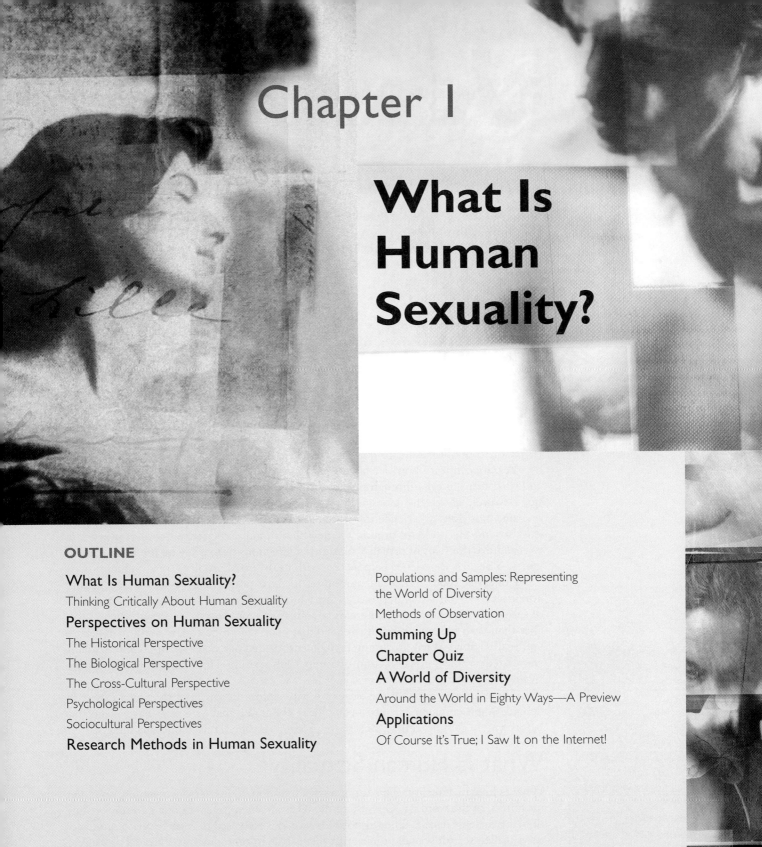

Chapter 1

What Is Human Sexuality?

Did You Know That...

- In ancient Greece, a mature man would take a sexual interest in an adolescent boy, often with the blessing of the boy's parents?
- The first illustrated sex manual was produced in China more than 2000 years ago?
- The Hindus believed that sexual fulfillment was one way to become reincarnated at a higher level of existence?
- The graham cracker came into being as a means to help young men control their sexual appetites?
- You could study the sexual behaviour of millions of people and still not obtain an accurate picture of the sexual behaviour of the general population?
- Until 1969, it was illegal to provide information about birth control or sell contraceptives in Canada?
- More Canadian women than men think that the birth control pill is a good thing?
- Masters and Johnson created a transparent artificial penis containing photographic equipment to study female sexual response?

We are about to embark on the study of human sexuality. But why, you may wonder, do we need to *study* human sexuality? Isn't sex something to *do* rather than to *talk about*? Isn't sex a natural function? Don't we learn what we need to know from personal experience or from our parents or our friends?

Yes, we can learn how our bodies respond to sexual stimulation—what turns us on and what turns us off—through personal experience. Personal experience teaches us little, however, about the biological processes that bring about sexual response and orgasm. Nor does experience inform us about the variations in sexual behaviour that exist around the world, or around the neighbourhood. Experience does not prepare us to recognize the signs of sexually transmitted infections or to evaluate the risks of pregnancy. Nor does experience help us deal with most sexual problems or dysfunctions.

Concerns about AIDS and unwanted teenage pregnancies have focused greater attention today on the importance of sex education. Many children receive some form of sex education as early as elementary school. You may know more about human sexuality than your parents or grandparents did at your age, or do today. But how much do you really know? What, for example, happens inside your body when you are sexually stimulated? What causes erection or vaginal lubrication? How do our sexual responsiveness and interests change as we age?

These are just a few of the issues we will explore in this book. We also expect to debunk some common but erroneous ideas about sex that you may have picked up before you began this course. Before we proceed further, let us define our subject.

What Is Human Sexuality?

What is human sexuality? This is not a trick question. Consider the meaning, or rather meanings, of the word *sex*. One use of the term *sex*, then, refers to our **gender**, or state of being male or female. The word *sex* (or *sexual*) is also used to refer to anatomic structures, called sex (or sexual) organs, that play a role in reproduction or sexual pleasure.

We may also speak of sex when referring to physical activities involving our sex organs for purposes of reproduction or pleasure: masturbation, hugging, kissing, **coitus**, and so on. Sex also relates to **erotic** feelings, experiences, or desires, such as sexual fantasies and thoughts, sexual urges, or feelings of sexual attraction to another person. We will use the term *gender* in this text to refer to the state of being male or female, as in **gender identity** and **gender roles**.

Gender One's personal, social, and legal status as male or female.

Coitus (co-it-us or co-EET-us). Sexual intercourse.

Erotic Arousing sexual feelings or desires. (From the Greek word for love, *eros*.)

Gender identity The psychological sense of being male or female.

Gender roles Complex clusters of ways in which males and females are expected to behave within a given culture.

Human sexuality is defined as the ways in which we experience and express ourselves as sexual beings. Our awareness of ourselves as females or males is part of our sexuality, as is the capacity we have for erotic experiences and responses.

Human sexuality, like biology, psychology, and sociology, is also a science. It is an interdisciplinary enterprise that draws upon the scientific expertise of anthropologists, biologists, medical researchers, sociologists, and psychologists, to name but a few of the professional groups involved in the field. These disciplines all have contributions to make, since sexual behaviour reflects our biological capabilities and our psychological characteristics as well as social and cultural influences.

People's sexual attitudes, experiences, and behaviours are shaped to a large extent by their cultural traditions and beliefs. Consider some of the fascinating findings in this chapter's *World of Diversity* feature.

> **Human sexuality** The ways in which we experience and express ourselves as sexual beings.

Thinking Critically About Human Sexuality

We are inundated with so much information about sex that it is often difficult to separate truth from fiction. Newspapers, TV shows, and popular books and magazines

Applications

"Of Course It's True; I Saw It on the Internet!"

In many ways, the internet has revolutionized the way we do research. If you want to find out about a topic, all you have to do is "Google" it. In the bad old days, students (including your authors) spent hours in the library looking up references, wandering through the stacks inhaling the dust of ages, only to find that the book or journal that we desperately needed for the term paper due tomorrow had been checked out by someone else. Today, sitting at your desk in your favourite chair, at the click of a mouse, you can find all the information you need for that paper. Or can you? It is true that, thanks to the internet, we have access to more information than we could process in a lifetime. But is it accurate? Just because we found it on the internet, is it really true?

Unfortunately, not all students are asking themselves this question. In an informal survey of college students, 29% said that they always accepted information found on the web as accurate, and only 34% said that they would look for further information to verify accuracy (Weiler, 2001).

To further assess both college students' internet research skills and their ability to critically evaluate information found on the web, Leah Graham and Panagiotis Metaxas of Wellesley College (Graham & Metaxas, 2003) asked 180 students in a "Computers and the Internet" class to research specific questions. Questions were chosen to represent areas where the potential for misinformation abounds, including advertising claims, political lobby groups, and scams. The researchers were interested in both the accuracy of the information that students found and whether they made any attempt to verify its validity.

Although the students were not directed to limit their research to the internet, only 2% cited non-internet sources. Most students used a single search engine, even though no one search engine can sift through all the information available on a given topic. Students were susceptible to advertising claims and potentially misleading government information as well. When asked about "major innovations" in the field of computers, most students went directly to the MicrosoftWeb site for their answers. Only 12% went to other sources as well. Over 60% of the students accepted as accurate information from US government websites and anti-tobacco sites without double-checking, and 48% said that they would use the data and cite the source in a research paper. Only 21% felt that the information should be checked for accuracy. And students in their fourth year were no more internet-savvy than first-year students.

So how can you tell if information that you find on the internet is accurate? First, check your sources. Many colleges and universities subscribe to research services such as ProQuest, EBSCO, and PsychInfo. You can increase the accuracy of your results by searching only peer-reviewed material, except when you need population statistics, for which sites like Statistics Canada's are usually the best source, or up-to-date information on new drugs or medical treatments, for which newspapers and newsmagazines are often the best source. If you find what looks like a research article on a webpage, look for the author's affiliation, a description of the research methodology used, and the presence or absence of references to other research. (Note, however, that there is no guarantee that the author has cited other research accurately. When in doubt, check). Information should also be as current as possible.

Apply the same critical thinking skills that you use to evaluate information in newspapers and magazines and on television: keep an open mind, accept ambiguity, ask questions, be aware of biases (including your own), and always look for other explanations.

contain features about sex that contradict one another, contain half-truths, or draw misleading conclusions. A scientific approach to human sexuality encourages people to think critically about false claims and findings that are presented as truths. To help students evaluate claims, arguments, and widely held beliefs, most colleges encourage *critical thinking*. One aspect of critical thinking is skepticism—not taking things for granted. It means being skeptical of things that are presented in print, uttered by authority figures or celebrities, or passed along by friends. Another aspect of critical thinking is thoughtful analysis and probing of claims and arguments. Critical thinking requires willingness to challenge the "common-sense" beliefs that many of us take for granted. It means scrutinizing definitions of terms and evaluating the premises of arguments and their logic. It also means finding *reasons* to support your beliefs, rather than relying on feelings. When people think critically, they maintain open minds. They suspend their beliefs until they have obtained and evaluated the evidence. (The *Applications* box on the previous page discusses techniques to evaluate the accuracy of information found on the internet and in other media.)

Perspectives on Human Sexuality

Human sexuality is a complex topic. No single theory or perspective can capture all its nuances. In this book we explore human sexuality from many perspectives. In this section we introduce a number of perspectives—historical, biological, cross-cultural, psychological, and sociocultural.

A World of Diversity

Around the World in Eighty Ways—A Preview

Like other aspects of human behaviour, sexual beliefs and behaviours vary widely around the world. North America alone has hundreds of different ethnic and religious groups, which vary in their sexual customs, attitudes, and beliefs. This diversity extends to the entire "global village" of the world's nearly 200 nations and to each nation's own distinctive subcultures.

The *World of Diversity* features that appear throughout this text explore the rich variety of sexual expression found worldwide. Seeing sexuality in contexts other than our own can help us understand the role of a culture's beliefs, values, and attitudes in our own and others' expressions of sexuality. It can help us understand why our partners, who may not share the same ethnic or religious heritage, may have different beliefs about sexual intimacy. Exploring diversity can also help us understand cultural differences related to gender, sexual orientation, sexual attraction, sexual jealousy, premarital sex, teenage pregnancy, and risks of sexually transmitted infections.

People in some societies believe, for instance, that a brother and sister who eat at the same table are engaging in a mildly erotic type of act. The practice is therefore forbidden (Davenport, 1977). In contemporary Islamic societies, female sexuality is often viewed as dangerous. If women's behaviour and attire are not kept under strict control, they can be "fatal attractions" for men (Kammeyer et al., 1990). What is sexually arousing, too, varies from culture to culture. Among the Abkhasians in the southern part of what used to be the Soviet Union, men regard the female armpit as highly arousing. A woman's armpits are, therefore, a sight for her husband alone (Kammeyer et al., 1990).

Of course, one glaring reason for today's heightened interest in understanding sexuality in a broader perspective is the worldwide AIDS epidemic. Any effort to end this scourge requires that we open our eyes to cultural attitudes and traditions that may increase the risk of transmission of the infection.

If we take a quick tour of the world of diversity within our own borders and beyond, we find that:

- Kissing is practised nearly universally as a form of petting in Canada, but it is unpopular in Japan and unknown among some cultures in Africa and South America.
- Some societies encourage sexual experimentation and even sexual intercourse among children and adolescents, while others punish any form of childhood sexual play.
- In many places, there remains a tendency to blame the victims of crimes—especially victims of sexual assault—rather than the perpetrators. In the strongly patriarchal society of Islamic Pakistan for example, the so-called Hudood Ordinance has actually resulted in prison sentences for some women who have brought rape charges against men. Hudood grants more credibility to the testimony of men than to that of women. An accused man may claim that any sexual contact between himself and the woman making the accusations was consensual, and the court will be inclined to believe him. Women too are also frequently prevented from testifying in court. The result has

The Historical Perspective

History places our sexual behaviour in context. It informs us as to whether our sexual behaviour reflects trends that have been with us through the millennia or the customs of a particular era.

Prehistoric Sexuality: From Female Idols to Phallic Worship Information about life among our Stone Age ancestors is drawn largely from cave drawings, stone artifacts, and the customs of modern-day preliterate peoples. From such sources, historians and anthropologists infer a prehistoric division of labour. By and large, men hunted for game. Women nurtured children and gathered edible plants and nuts and crabs and other marine life that wandered along the shore or swam in shallow waters.

Art produced in the Stone Age, some 20 000 years ago, suggests the worship of women's ability to bear children and perpetuate the species (Fichner-Rathus, 1995). Primitive statues and cave drawings portray women with large, pendulous breasts, rounded hips, and prominent sex organs. Most theorists regard the figurines as fertility symbols.

As the ice sheets of the last ice age retreated (about 11 000 B.C.) and the climate warmed, hunters and gatherers became farmers and herders. Villages sprang up around fields. Men tended the livestock. Women became farmers. As people grew aware of the male role in reproduction, **phallic worship** sprang into being. The penis was glorified in art as a plough, an axe, or a sword. **Phallic symbols** played roles in religious ceremonies in ancient Egypt. Ancient Greek art revered phalluses, rendering them sometimes as rings and sometimes as necklaces. Some phalluses were given wings, suggesting the power ascribed to them. In ancient Rome, a large phallus was carried like a float in a parade honouring Venus, the goddess of love.

Women in Prehistory: The "Venus" of Willendorf
http://witcombe.sbc.edu/ willendorf/willendorfgoddess. html
A photo and discussion of the famous fertility figure the Venus of Willendorf.

Phallic worship Worship of the penis as a symbol of generative power.

Phallic symbols Images of the penis.

been that women who bring charges of rape are sometimes prosecuted for adultery and jailed if found guilty, while their assailants go free (Schork, 1990). Since 1999, there have been several unsuccessful attempts to revise or repeal the Hudood Ordinance, but they have been unsuccessful, and groups working to improve the status of women in Pakistan are not optimistic ("NGOs sceptical," 2003).

- Sex was typically considered "indecent and unmentionable" in Russia, according to Kon (1995), "a subject only for the degenerate underground." However, since the collapse of the Soviet Union, sex has apparently been escaping into the mainstream of Russian life. In today's Russia, newspapers and television regularly cover prostitution and pornography as well as the traditional bus accidents (Schillinger, 1995). As sex has grabbed the Russian imagination, the incidences of premarital sex and sexual assault have also apparently risen (Kon, 1995).

- Although public figures may occasionally voice public condemnation of premarital sexual relations, the majority of people in Canada engage in them without fear of government reprisal. In China, however, where the results of a national survey showed that about half of the population engages in premarital relations, a male college student was expelled from a Beijing university when it became known that he had engaged in premarital sexual relations (Southerland, 1990). Other students report that the punishment was typical. There has, however, been a loosening up of social control of sexual behaviour and increasing tolerance for premarital sexuality in recent years (Herold & Byers, 1994; Zhang, et al., 1999).

- Perhaps in response to feelings of guilt or remorse, many Japanese women who have abortions place miniature stone statues known as *mizuko-jizo* in Buddhist temples in memory of their aborted fetuses. They sometimes decorate the statues with bibs or little hats and surround them with little stuffed animals, baby food, and pacifiers—all

in the belief that it keeps the souls of their aborted fetuses warm and entertained (Bumiller, 1990).

- Canada has its romantic Valentine's Day, but in Japan Christmas Eve is a time of sexual devotion. On Christmas Eve everyone, especially single women, must have a date. It is a time for men and women to express love and devotion through expensive presents, dinners at the best restaurants, and overnight visits to fancy hotels (Japanese Life Style, 2003).

Incest taboo The prohibition against intercourse and reproduction among close blood relatives.

The **incest taboo** may have been the first human taboo (Tannahill, 1980). All human societies apparently have some form of incest taboo (Ember & Ember, 1990). Yet, brother–sister marriages were permitted among the rulers of ancient Egypt and among the royal families of the Incas and of Hawaii, even though they were generally prohibited among commoners.

The Ancient Hebrews The ancient Hebrews viewed sex as a fulfilling experience intended to fulfill the divine injunction to "be fruitful and multiply." Childlessness and the development of a repulsive abnormality, such as a boil, were grounds for divorce. Male–male and female–female sexual behaviour were strongly condemned. But sex within marriage was believed to strengthen marital bonds and solidify the family.

Women among the ancient Hebrews were expected to be good wives and mothers. A wife was considered the property of her husband. A wife could be stoned to death for adultery. A woman might have to share her husband with his secondary wives and concubines.

The Ancient Greeks The classical or golden age of ancient Greece lasted for about 200 years, from about 500 B.C. to 300 B.C. Within this relatively short span lived the philosophers Socrates, Plato, and Aristotle; the playwrights Aristophanes, Aeschylus, and Sophocles; the natural scientist Archimedes; and the lawgiver Solon. Like the Hebrews, the Greeks valued family life. The Greeks expressed sexual interests openly. They admired the well-developed body and enjoyed nude wrestling among men in the arena. Erotic encounters and off-colour jokes characterized the plays of Aristophanes and other playwrights. The Greeks held that the healthy mind must dwell in a healthy body. They cultivated muscle and movement along with mind.

Three aspects of Greek sexuality are of particular interest to our study of sexual practices in the ancient world: male–male sexual behaviour, pederasty, and prostitution. The Greeks viewed men and women as **bisexual**. Male–male *sex* was deemed normal. However, only a few male–male *relationships*, such as relationships between soldiers and between adolescents and older men, received the stamp of social approval.

Bisexual Sexually responsive to either gender. (From the Latin *bi-*, meaning "two.")

Pederasty Sexual love of boys. (From the Greek *paidos*, meaning "boy.")

Pederasty means love of boys. Greek men might take on an adolescent male as a lover and pupil. Families were generally pleased if their adolescent sons attracted socially prominent mentors.

Prostitution flourished at every level of society. Prostitutes ranged from refined **courtesans** to **concubines** (slaves). Courtesans could play musical instruments, dance, engage in witty repartee, or discuss the latest political crisis. They were also skilled in the arts of love. No social stigma was attached to visiting a courtesan. Their clients included philosophers, playwrights, politicians, and generals.

Courtesan A prostitute—especially the mistress of a noble or wealthy man. (From Italian roots meaning "court lady.")

Women in general held a low social status in society. The women of Athens had no more legal or political rights than slaves. They were subject to the authority of their male next-of-kin before marriage and to their husbands afterwards. They received no formal education and were consigned most of the time to women's quarters in their homes. All in all, the women of the ancient world were treated as *chattels*—property.

Concubine A secondary wife, usually of inferior legal and social status. (From Latin roots meaning "lying with.")

The Ancient Romans Much is made of the sexual excesses of the Roman emperors and ruling families. The emperor Caligula sponsored orgies. Sexual excesses were found more often among the upper classes of palace society than among average Romans, however. Unlike their counterparts in ancient Greece, Romans viewed male–male sexual behaviour as a threat to the integrity of the Roman family. Thus, it was not held in favour. Although Roman women were more likely than their Greek counterparts to share their husbands' social lives, they were still considered to be the property of their husbands.

The Early Christians Early Christian views on sexuality were largely shaped by Saint Paul and the church fathers in the first century and by Saint Augustine in the latter part of the fourth century. The early Christians sought to restrict sex to marriage. They saw temptations of the flesh as distractions from spiritual devotion to God. Paul preached that celibacy was closer to the Christian ideal than marriage.

Christians, like Jews before them, demanded virginity of brides. Masturbation and prostitution were condemned as sinful. Early Christians taught that men should love their wives with restraint, not passion. The goal of procreation should govern sexual behaviour—the intellect should rule the flesh. Divorce was outlawed. Masturbation, male–male sexual behaviour, female–female sexual behaviour, oral–genital contact, anal intercourse—all were viewed as abominations in the eyes of God.

Islam Islam, the dominant religion in the Middle East, was founded by the Prophet Muhammad. Muhammad was born in Mecca, in what is now Saudi Arabia, in about A.D. 570. The Islamic tradition treasures marriage and sexual fulfillment in marriage. Premarital intercourse invites shame and social condemnation. In some fundamentalist Islamic states, it incurs the death penalty.

The family is the backbone of Islamic society. Celibacy is frowned upon (Ahmed, 1991). Muhammad decreed that marriage represents the only road to virtue (Minai, 1981). Islamic tradition permits a sexual double standard, however. Men may take up to four wives, but women are permitted only one husband. Public social interactions between men and women are severely restricted. In traditional Islamic cultures, social dancing between the genders is shunned. Women are expected to keep their heads and faces veiled in public and to avoid all contact, even a handshake, with men other than their husbands.

Women supporters of the Islamic religious alliance in Lahore, Pakistan. Women in traditional Islamic cultures must keep their heads and faces veiled in public.

The Far East In the cultures of the Far East, sexuality was akin to spirituality. To the Taoist masters of China, sex was a sacred duty. It was a form of worship that was believed to lead toward immortality. Sex was to be performed well and often if one were to achieve harmony with nature.

The Chinese culture was the first to produce a detailed sex manual, which came into use about 200 years before the birth of Jesus. The man was expected to extend intercourse as long as possible, thereby absorbing more of his wife's natural essence, or *yin*. Yin would enhance his own masculine essence, or *yang*. Taoists believed that it was wasteful for a man to "spill his seed." Masturbation, acceptable for women, was ruled out for men. The "good wife," like her Western counterparts, was limited largely to the domestic roles of child rearing and homemaking.

The ancient Hindus of India cultivated sexual pleasure as a spiritual ideal. From the fifth century onward, temples show sculptures of gods, heavenly nymphs, and ordinary people in erotic poses (Gupta, 1994). Hindu sexual practices were codified in a sex manual, the *Kama Sutra*. The *Kama Sutra* illustrates sexual positions, some of which would challenge a contortionist. It holds recipes for alleged aphrodisiacs. This manual remains the most influential sex manual ever produced. It is believed to have been written by the Hindu sage Vatsyayana sometime between the third and fifth centuries A.D., at about the time that Christianity was taking shape in the West as an organized religion.

The Hindus believed that sex was a religious duty, not a source of shame or guilt. In the Hindu doctrine of *karma* (the passage or transmigration of souls from one place to another), sexual fulfillment was regarded as one way to become reincarnated at a higher level of existence. Indian society grew more restrictive toward sexuality after about A.D. 1000 (Tannahill, 1980).

An Illustration from the Kama Sutra. The Kama Sutra, an Indian sex manual believed to have been written sometime between the third and fifth centuries A.D., contains graphic illustrations of sexual techniques and practices.

The Protestant Reformation During the Reformation, Martin Luther (1483–1546) and other Christian reformers such as John Calvin (1509–1564) split off from the Roman Catholic Church and formed their own sects, which led to the development of the modern Protestant denominations. Luther disputed many Roman Catholic doctrines on sexuality. He believed that priests should be allowed to marry and rear children. Calvin rejected the Roman church's position that sex in marriage was permissible only for the purpose of procreation. To Calvin, sex strengthened the marriage bond and helped relieve the stresses of everyday life. The Protestant Reformation encouraged a more accepting view of sexuality, although it maintained strict adherence to the belief that sex was permissible only in the context of marriage.

Shaping the Present: From Repression to Revolution Early settlers brought to the New World the religious teachings that had dominated Western thought and culture for centuries. Whatever their differences, each religion stressed the ideal of family life and viewed sex outside of marriage as immoral or sinful. A woman's place, by and large, was in the home and in the fields, not in the university. McGill University, founded in 1821, did not admit women into its medical school until 1917. Not until the twentieth century did Canadian women gain the right to vote.

The middle and later parts of the nineteenth century are generally called the Victorian period, named after Queen Victoria of England. Victoria assumed the throne in 1837 and ruled until her death in 1901. Her name has become virtually synonymous with sexual repression. Victorian society in Europe and North America, on the surface at least, was prim and proper. Even the legs of pianos were draped with cloth for the sake of modesty. Many women viewed sex as a marital duty to be performed for procreation or to satisfy their husbands' cravings

Women were assumed not to experience sexual desires or pleasures. "I would say," observed Dr. William Acton (1814–1875), an influential English physician, in 1857, "that the majority of women (happily for society) are not much troubled with sexual feeling of any kind."

It was widely believed among medical authorities in England and North America that sex drains the man of his natural vitality. Physicians thus recommended that intercourse be practised infrequently, perhaps once a month or so. The Reverend Sylvester Graham (1794–1851) preached that ejaculation deprived men of the "vital fluids" they need to maintain health and vitality. Graham preached against "wasting the seed" by masturbation or frequent marital intercourse. (How frequent was frequent? In Graham's view, intercourse more than once a month could dangerously deplete the man's vital energies.) Graham recommended that young men control their sexual appetites by adopting a diet of simple foods based on whole-grain flours. To this day, his name is identified with a type of cracker he developed for this purpose in the 1830s, the graham cracker, derived from unbolted wheat (graham flour).

In the twentieth century, social change swept through Western culture at a dizzying pace. Sexual behaviours and attitudes that would have been unthinkable a couple of generations ago—such as cohabitation ("living together")—have become commonplace. The social barriers that had restricted women's roles have largely broken down.

The Foundations of the Scientific Study of Sexuality Against this backdrop of sexual repression, scientists and scholars first began to approach sexuality as an area of legitimate scientific study. An early important contributor to the science of human sexuality was the English physician Havelock Ellis (1859–1939). Ellis compiled a veritable encyclopedia of sexuality: *Studies in the Psychology of Sex*. Ellis challenged the prevailing view by arguing that sexual desires in women were natural and healthy. He argued that a gay male or lesbian sexual orientation was a naturally occurring variation within the spectrum of normal sexuality, and not an aberration.

Another influential **sexologist**, the German psychiatrist Richard von Krafft-Ebing (1840–1902), described individuals with sexual deviations in his book *Psychopathia Sexualis*. His writings contain vivid descriptions of deviations ranging from sado-masochism (sexual gratification through inflicting or receiving pain) and bestiality (sex with animals) to yet more bizarre and frightening forms, such as necrophilia (intercourse

Sexologist A person who engages in the scientific study of sexual behaviour.

with dead people). Krafft-Ebing viewed sexual deviations as mental diseases that could be studied and perhaps treated by medical science.

At about the same time, a Viennese physician, Sigmund Freud (1856–1939), was developing a theory of personality that has had an enormous influence on modern culture and science. Freud believed that the sex drive is our principal motivating force. Alfred Kinsey (1894–1956), an Indiana University zoologist, conducted the first large-scale studies of sexual behaviour in the 1930s and 1940s. The results of his surveys were published in two volumes, *Sexual Behavior in the Human Male* (1948) and *Sexual Behavior in the Human Female* (1953). The publication of these books unleashed a torrent of criticism. A congressional committee in the 1950s went so far as to claim that Kinsey's work undermined the moral fibre of the nation, rendering it more vulnerable to a Communist takeover (Gebhard, 1976). Even so, Kinsey and his colleagues made sex a scientifically respectable field of study and helped lay the groundwork for greater openness in talking about sex.

The Sexual Revolution The period of the mid-1960s to the mid-1970s is often referred to as the sexual revolution. Dramatic changes occurred in North American sexual attitudes and practices during the "Swinging Sixties." There was a major social upheaval, not only in sexual behaviour, but also in science, politics, fashion, music, art, and cinema. The so-called hippie generation, disheartened by commercialism and the Vietnam War, tuned in (to rock music on the radio), turned on (to drugs), and dropped out (of mainstream society). Films became sexually explicit. Hard rock music bellowed the message of rebellion and revolution.

The sexual revolution gained momentum from the war in Vietnam, the bomb (fear of the nuclear bomb), the pill (the introduction of the birth-control pill), and the tube (TV, that is). The pill enabled people to engage in recreational or casual sex, rather than procreative sex (Asbell, 1995). Pop psychology movements, like the Human Potential Movement of the 1960s and the 1970s (the "Me Decade"), spread the message that people should get in touch with and express their genuine feelings, including their sexual feelings. "Doing your own thing" became one catchphrase. "If it feels right, do it" became another. Popular books encouraged people to explore their sexuality. As film scenes of lovemaking became more commonplace, movie ratings were developed to alert parents not only to violence, but also to sexually explicit scenes and language.

The Sexual Counterrevolution—and After By the 1980s, a conservative reaction to this climate of sexual freedom developed as critics urged a return to "family values." Schools (especially in the U.S., but also in some parts of Canada) promoted abstinence for teenagers. Casual sex was on the wane—in part because of fear of AIDS, in part as a pendulum swing back toward commitment and romance. Some of the aspects of sexual behaviour that preoccupied the media in the 60s and 70s fell by the wayside—we no longer hear much about mate-swapping (swinging) or "open marriages." Yet there is evidence that the pendulum may be swinging back again. Between 1975 and 1995, the proportion of Canadians who felt that premarital sex is "not wrong at all" increased from 39 to 57 percent, while those who believed that it is "always wrong" decreased in number from 19 to 13 percent (Bibby, 1995). In particular, more teens are sexually active today, and at younger ages (see Chapter 11). And after a period of significant decline in the percentage of AIDS cases attributed to men having sex with men, rates began to increase again in the late 1990s. One recent study (Canadian Press Newswire, 2000) found that some men are having unsafe sex in the belief that a cure for HIV is imminent (see Chapter 13).

Notwithstanding these pendulum shifts, looking at the sexual behaviour and attitudes since the 1960s, we can argue that in addition to increased incidence of premarital sex, at least two other features of the sexual revolution have become permanent parts of our social fabric: the liberation of female sexuality and a greater willingness to discuss sex openly. As well, recent court decisions in Ontario, Quebec, and British Columbia striking down the traditional definition of marriage have paved the way for federal legislation that will—it is anticipated—make same-sex marriage a permanent part of the Canadian social fabric.

What, then, does history tell us about sex? Is there a universal standard for defining sexual values, or are there many standards? All societies have some form of an incest taboo. Other sexual practices—masturbation, sex with many partners, male–male or

History and Concept of Sexology
http://www.kinseyinstitute.org/resources/sexology.html
Excerpts from The Birth of Sexology: A Brief History in Documents.

female–female sexual behaviour, prostitution and so on—have been condemned in some societies, tolerated by others, and encouraged by still others. Some societies accept non-procreative sex; others have outlawed it. Most societies have placed a value on procreative sex within the context of an enduring relationship, usually in the form of marriage.

The Biological Perspective

The biological perspective focuses on the roles of genes, hormones, the nervous system, and other biological factors in human sexuality. Sex serves the biological function of reproduction. People are endowed with anatomic structures and physiological capabilities that make sexual behaviour possible—and, for most people, pleasurable.

The biology of sex informs us about the mechanisms of reproduction, sexual arousal, and sexual response. The biology of sex teaches that erection occurs when the penis becomes engorged with blood. It teaches that vaginal lubrication is the result of a "sweating" action of the vaginal walls. It teaches that orgasm is a spinal reflex as well as a psychological event.

Some scientists suggest that there is a genetic basis to social behaviour, including sexual behaviour, among humans and other animals. The theory of **sociobiology** proposes that **genes** may transmit not only physical traits but also dispositions toward *behaviour* that enhances reproductive success. Genes govern sexual maturation and the production of sex hormones. Hormones, in turn, are largely responsible for regulating the sexual behaviour of other animal species. We may carry behavioural tendencies that helped our prehistoric ancestors survive and reproduce successfully, even if these traits are no longer adaptive in modern culture (Bjorklund & Kipp, 1996).

To what extent does biology govern sexual behaviour? Is sex controlled by biological instincts? Or are psychosocial factors, such as culture, experience, and decision-making ability, more important? The sexuality of other species is largely governed by biological processes, but *human* sexuality involves a complex interaction of biological and psychosocial factors. Biology indicates what is possible, and often, what is pleasurable or painful. Biology is not destiny, however. It does not imply what is proper and improper or determine our sexual decisions. Religious tradition, cultural and personal values, and learning and experience guide these decisions.

The Cross-Cultural Perspective

The cross-cultural perspective, like the historical perspective, provides insight into the ways in which cultural beliefs affect sexual behaviour and attitudes. Historians are limited in their sources to the eyewitness accounts of others and the shards of information that can be gleaned from fading relics. Anthropologists, however, can observe other cultures firsthand. Interest in the cross-cultural perspective on sexuality was spurred by the early-twentieth-century work of the anthropologists Margaret Mead (1901–1978) and Bronislaw Malinowski (1884–1942).

Sociobiology The theory that dispositions toward behaviour patterns that enhance reproductive success may be genetically transmitted.

Genes The basic units of heredity, which consist of chromosomal segments of DNA.

Sociobiology **www.ship.edu/~cgboeree/ sociobiology.html** An explanation of the main points of the theory of sociobiology.

Are Today's Young People More or Less Liberal in the Expression of Their Sexuality Than People in Earlier Generations? Today the threat of AIDS hangs over every sexual encounter. While many young people today are selective in their choice of partners and take precautions to make sex safer, more teenagers are engaging in sexual activity, and at younger ages, than in previous generations.

In *Sex and Temperament in Three Primitive Societies* (1935), Mead laid the groundwork for recent psychological and sociological research challenging gender-role stereotypes. In most cultures characterized by a gender division of labour, men typically go to business or to the hunt, and—when necessary—to war. In such cultures, men are perceived as strong, active, independent, and logical. Women are viewed as passive, dependent, nurturant, and emotional. Mead concluded that these stereotypes are not inherent in our genetic heritage. Rather, men and women learn to behave in ways that are expected in their particular culture.

Malinowski lived on the Trobriand island of Boyawa in the South Pacific during World War I. There he gathered data on two societies of the South Pacific, the Trobrianders and the Amphett Islanders. The Amphett Islanders maintained strict sexual prohibitions, whereas the Trobrianders enjoyed greater freedom. Trobrianders, for example, encouraged their children to masturbate. Boys and girls were expected to begin to engage in intercourse when they were biologically old enough. According to custom, they would pair off, exchange a coconut, a bit of betel nut, a few beads, or some fruit from the bush. Then they would go off together and engage in intercourse (Malinowski, 1929, p. 488). Adolescents were expected to have multiple sex partners until they married. Malinowski found the Trobrianders less anxiety-ridden than the Amphett Islanders. He attributed the difference to their sexual freedom, thus making an early plea to relax sexual prohibitions in Western society.

Cross-Cultural Commonalities and Differences in Sexual Behaviour
In 1951, Clellan Ford, an anthropologist, and Frank Beach, a psychologist, reviewed sexual behaviour in nearly 200 preliterate societies around the world. They found great variety in sexual customs and beliefs. They also found some common threads. For example, kissing was quite common across the cultures they studied, although not universal. The Thonga of Africa were one society that did not practise kissing. Upon witnessing two European visitors kissing each other, members of the tribe commented that they could not understand why Europeans "ate" each other's saliva and dirt. The frequency of sexual intercourse also varies from culture to culture, but intercourse is relatively more frequent among young people everywhere.

Societies differ in their attitudes toward childhood masturbation. Some societies, such as the Hopi Native Americans of the southwest United States, ignore it. Trobrianders encourage children to stimulate themselves. Other societies condemn it.

The cross-cultural perspective illustrates the importance of learning in human sexual behaviour. Societies differ widely in their sexual attitudes, customs, and practices. The members of all human societies share the same anatomic structures and physiological capacities for sexual pleasure, however. The same hormones flow through their arteries. Were human sexuality completely or predominantly determined by biology, we would not find such diversity.

Psychological Perspectives

Psychological perspectives focus on the many psychological influences—perception, learning, motivation, emotion, personality, and so on—that affect our sexual behaviour and our experience of ourselves as female or male. Some psychological theorists, such as Freud, focus on the motivational role of sex in human personality. Others focus on how our experiences and mental representations of the world affect our sexual behaviour.

Freud and Psychoanalytic Theory
Freud, a Viennese physician, formulated a grand theory of personality termed **psychoanalysis**. Freud believed that we are all born with biologically based sex drives. These drives must be channelled through socially approved outlets if family and social life are to carry on without undue conflict. He hypothesized that conflicts between sexuality and society become internalized in the form of an inner conflict between two opposing parts of the personality—the **id**, which is the repository of biologically based drives or "instincts" (such as hunger, thirst, elimination, sex, and aggression), and the **ego**, which represents reason and good sense. The ego seeks social-

Sigmund Freud *Freud's theory of personality, emphasizing the sex drive as our principal motivating force, has had an enormous influence on modern culture and science.*

Sigmund Freud and the Freud Archives
http://users.rcn.com/brill/ freudarc.html
This site provides a comprehensive listing of links on Freud and his work.

Psychoanalysis The theory of personality originated by Sigmund Freud, which proposes that human behaviour represents the outcome of clashing inner forces.

Id In Freud's theory, the mental structure that is present at birth, embodies physiological drives, and is fully unconscious.

Ego In Freud's theory, the second mental structure to develop, which is characterized by self-awareness, planning, and delay of gratification.

Superego In Freud's theory, the third mental structure, which functions as a moral guardian and sets forth high standards for behaviour.

Unconscious mind Those parts or contents of the mind that lie outside of conscious awareness.

Defence mechanisms In psychoanalytic theory, automatic processes that protect the ego from anxiety by disguising or ejecting unacceptable ideas and urges.

Repression The automatic ejection of anxiety-evoking ideas from consciousness.

Erogenous zones Parts of the body, including but not limited to the sex organs, that are responsive to sexual stimulation.

Psychosexual development In psychoanalytic theory, the process by which sexual feelings shift from one erogenous zone to another as a human being matures.

Oedipus complex In psychoanalytic theory, a conflict of the phallic stage in which the boy wishes to possess his mother sexually and perceives his father as a rival in love. (The analogous conflict for girls is the Electra complex.)

Behaviourists Learning theorists who argue that a scientific approach to understanding behaviour must refer only to observable and measurable behaviours.

ly appropriate outlets for satisfying the basic drives that arise from the id. Your id, for example, prompts you to feel sexual urges. Your ego attempts to find ways of satisfying those urges without incurring condemnation from others or from your own moral conscience, which Freud called the **superego**. How these internal conflicts are resolved, in Freud's view, largely determines our ability to love, work, and lead well-adjusted lives.

Freud proposed that the mind operates on conscious and unconscious levels. The conscious level corresponds to our state of present awareness. The **unconscious mind** refers to the darker reaches of the mind that lie outside our direct awareness. The ego shields the conscious mind from awareness of our baser sexual and aggressive urges by means of **defence mechanisms** such as **repression**, or motivated forgetting.

Although many sexual impulses are banished to the unconscious, they continue to seek expression. One avenue of expression is the dream, through which sexual impulses may be perceived in disguised, or symbolic, form. The therapists and scholars who follow in the Freudian tradition are quite interested in analyzing dreams, and many dream objects, including snakes, knives, caves, tunnels, crossing a bridge, and riding a roller coaster are considered symbols of the genitals and/or sexual behaviour.

Freud introduced new and controversial ideas about people as sexual beings. For example, he originated the concept of **erogenous zones**—the idea that many parts of the body, not just the genitals, are responsive to sexual stimulation.

According to Freud's theory of **psychosexual development**, children undergo five stages of development: oral, anal, phallic, latency, and genital, which are named according to the predominant erogenous zones of each stage. One of Freud's most controversial beliefs was that children normally harbour erotic interests. He theorized that it was normal for children to progress through stages of development in which the erotic interest shifts from one erogenous zone to another, as, for example, from the mouth to the anus. He believed that the suckling of the infant in the oral stage was an erotic act. So too was learning to control the processes of elimination during the anal stage. Freud believed that it was normal for children to develop erotic feelings toward the parent of the other gender during the phallic stage. Freud termed these incestuous urges and feelings of rivalry the **Oedipus complex**. Freud's theories, although controversial, had a major impact on scientific research in a number of fields, including personality theory and child development. However, a major criticism is the continuing failure to find empirical evidence in support of the theories.

Learning Theories To what extent does sexual behaviour reflect experience? Would you have the same sexual attitudes and do the same things if you had been reared in another culture? We think not. Even within the same society, family and personal experiences can shape unique sexual attitudes and behaviours. While psychoanalytic theory plumbs the depths of the unconscious, learning theorists focus on the environmental factors that shape behaviour.

Behaviourists such as John B. Watson (1878–1958) and B. F. Skinner (1904–1990) emphasized the importance of rewards and punishments in the learning process. In psychology, events (such as rewards) that increase the frequency or likelihood of behaviour are termed reinforcements. Children left to explore their bodies without parental condemnation will learn what feels good and tend to repeat it. The Trobriand child who is rewarded for masturbation and premarital coitus through parental praise and encouragement will be more likely to repeat these behaviours (at least openly!) than the child in a more sexually restrictive culture, who is punished for the same behaviour. When sexual behaviour (like masturbation) feels good, but parents connect it with feelings of guilt and shame, the child is placed in conflict and may vacillate between masturbating and swearing off it.

Of course parental punishment does not necessarily eliminate childhood masturbation or teenage sexual behaviour. Punishment tends to suppress behaviour, but not necessarily eliminate it. People can (and do) learn to engage in prohibited behaviours secretly. If as young children we are severely punished for sexual exploration, we may come to associate sexual stimulation *in general* with feelings of guilt or anxiety. Such early learning experiences can set the stage for sexual dysfunctions in adulthood.

Social-learning theorists also use the concepts of reward and punishment, but they emphasize the importance of mental activity (anticipations, thoughts, plans, and so on) and learning by observation. Observational learning, or **modelling**, refers to acquiring knowledge and skills through observing others. Observational learning includes seeing models in films or on television, hearing about them, and reading about them.

Sociocultural Perspectives

Sexual behaviour is determined not only by biological and psychological factors, but also by social factors. Social factors contribute to the shaping of our sexual attitudes, beliefs,

> **Social-learning theory** A cognitively oriented learning theory in which observational learning, values, and expectations play key roles in determining behaviour.
>
> **Modelling** Acquiring knowledge and skills by observing others.

TABLE 1.1 Number of sex partners since age 18 as found in the NHSLS* study

Social Characteristics	Number of Sex Partners (%)					
	0	1	2–4	5–10	11–20	21+
Gender						
Male	3.4	19.5	20.9	23.3	16.3	16.6
Female	2.5	31.5	36.4	20.4	6.0	3.2
Age						
18–24	7.8	32.1	34.1	15.4	7.8	2.8
25–29	2.2	25.3	31.3	22.2	9.9	9.0
30–34	3.1	21.3	29.3	25.2	10.8	10.3
35–39	1.7	18.9	29.7	24.9	14.0	10.8
40–44	0.7	21.9	27.6	24.2	13.7	12.0
45–49	2.0	25.7	23.8	25.1	9.6	13.9
50–54	2.4	33.9	27.8	18.0	9.0	9.0
55–59	1.3	40.0	28.3	15.2	8.3	7.0
Marital Status						
Never married (not cohabiting)	12.3	14.8	28.6	20.6	12.1	11.6
Never married (cohabiting)	0.0	24.6	37.3	15.7	9.7	12.7
Married	0.0	37.1	28.0	19.4	8.7	6.8
Education						
Less than high school	4.2	26.7	36.0	18.6	8.8	5.8
High school graduate	3.4	30.2	29.1	20.0	9.8	7.4
Some college	2.1	23.9	29.4	23.3	11.9	9.3
College graduate	2.1	24.1	25.8	23.9	11.1	13.0
Advanced degree	3.5	24.6	26.3	22.8	9.6	13.2
Religion	16.2					
None	2.6	22.8	29.0	20.3	15.9	15.9
Liberal, moderate Protestant	2.3	29.8	31.2	23.0	12.4	8.3
Conservative Protestant	2.9	27.2	30.4	20.4	9.5	7.0
Catholic	.3.8	24.1	29.2	22.7	8.1	9.1
Jewish†	0.0		13.0	29.6	16.7	16.7

*National Health and Social Life Survey, conducted by a research team centred at the University of Chicago.
†These sample sizes are quite small.

Source: Adapted from Laumann, E. O., Gagnon, J. H., Michael, R. T., & Michaels, S. (1994). *The Social Organization of Sexuality: Sexual Practices in the United States.* Chicago: University of Chicago Press, Table 5.1C, p. 179.

| TABLE 1.2 Number of partners in the past year by age and gender (data collected Dec. 1994–Jan. 1995) | | | | | | | | | |

Number of Sex Partners	15 – 19		20 – 24		25 – 29		30 – 45	
	M%	F%	M%	F%	M%	F%	M%	F%
Total Population								
(Regardless of Relationship and Sexual Activity Status) 0	54.6	56.3	21.8	18.7	7.3	6.6	6.8	7.6
1	22.4	28.5	49.2	64.4	69.0	83.6	83.9	86.3
2+	20.2	13.1	26.7	16.2	20.3	9.2	6.2	5.3
(Single only; Regardless of sexual activity status) 0	55.2	57.5	27.9	28.2	15.0	19.9	26.4	34.4
1	24.6	27.2	37.4	49.3	39.6	57.2	42.4	48.0
2+	20.2	13.1	31.8	21.7	38.4	22.0	24.6	15.7
(Regardless of Relationship status; sexually active only) 1	56	67	58	81	71	92	86	96
2	16	22	11	10	14	5	4	2
3-5	16	11	15	6	9	4	4	1
6+	12	0	12	3	6	0	3	0

Source: Maticka-Tyndale, E. (1997). Reducing the incidence of sexually transmitted disease through behavioural and social change. *The Canadian Journal of Human Sexuality, 6,* 89–105. By Permission.

and behaviour. Whereas anthropologists contribute to our understanding of cross-cultural variance in sexuality, sociocultural theorists focus on differences in sexuality among the subgroups of a society, as defined, for example, by differences in religion, race/ethnicity, country of origin, socioeconomic status, marital status, age, educational level, and gender. Consider the issue of the numbers of sex partners people have. Tables 1.1 and 1.2 report the results of two surveys concerning the number of sex partners people report.

Consider gender. Males, according to the survey, report having greater numbers of sex partners than females do. Throughout the text, we will be focusing on gender differences and why men seem generally more likely than women to seek a wide range of sexual experience.

People in the oldest age groups covered appear to have had somewhat fewer sex partners than younger people. This is not surprising, as older respondents entered adulthood early in the sexual revolution and may have been exposed to more conservative sexual attitudes. The Canadian study (Table 1.2) also shows that people over 30 are less likely to have had multiple partners during the preceding year, possibly because of more conservative attitudes or simply because they are more likely to be married or in a long-term relationship. We shall find this sort of age difference, or age gradient, throughout the text as well.

Level of education is also connected with sexual behaviour. Generally speaking, it would appear that education has something of a liberalizing influence. People with some college or university education, or who have completed college or university, are likely to have more sex partners than those who attended only grade school or high school.

Ethnicity is also connected with sexual behaviour. Throughout this book, discussions of diversity will address differences between various cultural groups around the world.

Research Methods in Human Sexuality

Human sexuality is a science. Scientists base their knowledge on research evidence, rather than on intuition, faith, or superstition. Scientists are critical thinkers both by training and by nature. They question prevailing assumptions and theories about sexual behaviour. Scientists recognize that they cannot gain perfect knowledge. They know that one era's "truths" may become another era's ancient myths and fallacies.

There are many practical applications to the research being carried out in the field of human sexuality. For example, research into the effects of sexuality education and STI prevention programs may help educators design the most effective curriculum possible. Research advances in retroviral therapy have significantly extended the lives of people with HIV infections. The latest form of emergency contraception, Plan B, and the newest addition to the roster of contraceptive devices, the patch, are direct results of research.

Populations and Samples: Representing the World of Diversity

Researchers undertake to learn about **populations**. Populations are complete groups of people or animals. Many researchers have attempted to learn about people in Canada, for example. (In 2002, there were over 31 million of us—a sizable population.) Other researchers may identify adults, or adolescents, as their population. Still other researchers study differences in sexual behaviour between ethnic groups. These groups are termed the *populations of interest*, or *target populations*. It would be expensive and difficult to try to study every individual in these populations.

Because of the impossibility of studying all members of a population, scientists select individuals from the population and study them. The individuals who participate in research are said to form a **sample**. However, we cannot truly learn about a population unless the sample *represents* that population. A *representative sample* is a research sample of participants who accurately represent the population of interest. If our samples do not represent the target populations, we cannot extend or **generalize** the results of our research to the populations of interest. If we wished to study the sexual behaviour of only one group, our population would consist of all members of that group. If we used only college students as our sample, our sample would not represent all Canadians.

Sampling Methods One way of acquiring a representative sample is through random sampling. A **random sample** is one in which every member of the target population has an equal chance of participating.

Magazine mail-in surveys and internet polls may boast that they have thousands of respondents, but size alone does not mean that a sample is representative. If you have ever wondered why two polls on the same topic released on the same day have different results, it is usually because of sampling differences.

Researchers overcome biased sampling by drawing *random* or *stratified random samples* of populations. In a random sample, every member of a population has an equal chance of participating. The problem with a random sample is that small sections of the population may be missed. In a **stratified random sample**, known subgroups of a population are represented in proportion to their numbers in the population. For example, about 3.5% of the Canadian population is Chinese-Canadian. Researchers could therefore decide that 3.5% of their sample must be Chinese-Canadian if they are to represent all people in Canada.

Another problem is **volunteer bias**. That is, sexual research is almost invariably conducted with people who volunteer to participate. Volunteers may differ from people who refuse to participate. For example, volunteers tend to be more open about their sexuality than the general population. They may even tend to exaggerate behaviours that others might consider deviant or abnormal.

Methods of Observation

Once scientists have chosen those they will study, they observe them. In this section, we consider several methods of observation: the case-study method, the survey method, naturalistic observation, participant observation, and laboratory observation.

The Case-Study Method A **case study** is a carefully drawn, in-depth biography of an individual or a small group. The focus is on understanding one or several individuals as fully as possible by unravelling the interplay of various factors in their backgrounds.

Population A complete group of organisms or events.

Sample Part of a population.

Generalize To go from the particular to the general.

Random sample A sample in which every member of a population has an equal chance of participating.

Stratified random sample A random sample in which known subgroups in a population are represented in proportion to their numbers in the population.

Volunteer bias A slanting of research data that is caused by the characteristics of individuals who volunteer to participate, such as willingness to discuss intimate behaviour.

Case study A carefully drawn, in-depth biography of an individual or a small group of individuals that may be obtained through interviews, questionnaires, and historical records.

Alfred Kinsey. *Kinsey and his colleagues conducted the first large-scale scientific study of sexual behaviour in the United States.*

Survey A detailed study of a sample obtained by means such as interviews and questionnaires.

The Kinsey Institute for Research in Sex, Gender, and Reproduction
http://www.indiana.edu/~kinsey/
The Kinsey Institute website supports interdisciplinary research and the study of human sexuality.

In most case studies, the researcher comes to know the individual or group through interviews conducted over a prolonged period of time. The interviewing pattern tends to build upon itself with a good deal of freedom, as opposed to the one-shot, standardized set of questions used in survey questionnaires.

Researchers may also conduct case studies by interviewing people who have known the individuals or by examining public records. Sigmund Freud, for example, drew upon historical records in his case study of the Renaissance inventor and painter Leonardo da Vinci. Freud concluded that Leonardo's artistic productions represented the sublimating, or channelling, of male–male sexual impulses.

Despite the richness of material that may be derived from the case-study approach, it has drawbacks. People often have gaps in memory, especially for childhood events. Clinicians and interviewers may unintentionally guide people into saying what they expect to hear. Then, too, researchers may inadvertently colour people's reports when they jot them down—shape them subtly in ways that reflect their own views.

The Survey Method **Surveys** typically gather information about behaviour through questionnaires or interviews. Researchers may interview or administer questionnaires to thousands of people from particular population groups to learn about their sexual behaviour and attitudes. Interviews such as those used by Kinsey and his colleagues (1948, 1953) have the advantages of face-to-face contact and of giving the interviewer the opportunity to probe—that is, to follow up on answers that seem to lead toward useful information. A skilled interviewer may be able to set a respondent at ease and establish a sense of trust or rapport that encourages self-disclosure.

Questionnaires are less expensive than interviews. The major expenses in using questionnaires involve printing and distribution. Questionnaires can be administered to groups of people at once, and respondents can return them anonymously. Anonymity may encourage respondents to disclose intimate information. Questionnaires, of course, can be used only by people who can read and record their responses. Interviews can be used even with people who cannot read or write. But interviewers must be trained, sometimes extensively, and then paid for their time.

Many of these surveys have *something* to offer to our understanding of human sexuality, but some are more methodologically sound than others. None perfectly represents the population at large, however. Most people consider their sexuality to be among the most intimate, private aspects of their lives. People who willingly agree to be polled as to their political preferences may resist participation in surveys concerning their sexual behaviour. Let us consider the sampling techniques of several major studies in greater depth.

American Surveys (1): The Kinsey Reports Kinsey and his colleagues (1948, 1953) interviewed 5300 males and 5940 females in the United States between 1938 and 1949. They asked a wide array of questions on various types of sexual experiences, including masturbation, oral sex, and coitus that occurred before, during, and outside of marriage. For obvious reasons, Kinsey could not use more direct observational methods, such as sending his researchers to peer through bedroom windows. Kinsey chose not to try to obtain a random sample. He believed that a high refusal rate would wreck the chances of accurately representing the general population. Instead, he adopted a group sampling approach. He recruited study participants from the organizations and community groups to which they belonged, such as college fraternities and sororities. He contacted representatives of groups in diverse communities and tried to persuade them to secure the cooperation of fellow group members. If he showed these individuals that they would not be subjected to embarrassment or discomfort, Kinsey hoped that they would persuade other members to participate. Kinsey understood that the groups he solicited were not necessarily representative of the general population. He believed, however, that his sampling approach was dictated by practical constraints. Even so, he made an attempt to sample as broadly as possible from the groups he solicited. In some cases he obtained full participation. In other cases he obtained a large enough proportion of the group membership to at least ensure representativeness of the group. Still, visible minorities, people in rural areas, older people, the poor, and Catholics and Jews were all underrepresented in Kinsey's samples.

To his credit, Kinsey took measures to instill candour in the people he interviewed. For one, study participants were assured of the confidentiality of their records. For another, Kinsey's interviewers were trained to conduct the interviews in an objective and matter-of-fact style. To reduce the tendency to slant responses in a socially desirable direction, participants were reassured that the interviewers were not passing judgment on them.

Kinsey checked the **reliability** of his data by evaluating the consistency of the responses given by several hundred interviewees who were reexamined after at least 18 months. Their reports of the **incidence** of sexual activities (for example, whether or not they had ever engaged in premarital or extramarital coitus) were highly reliable. That is, participants tended to give the same answers on both occasions. But reports of the **frequency** of sexual activities (such as the number of times one has masturbated to orgasm or the frequency of coitus in marriage) were less consistent. People find it more difficult to compute the frequencies of their activities than to answer whether or not they have ever engaged in them.

Kinsey recognized that consistency of responses across time did not guarantee their **validity**. He could not validate self-reports directly, as one might validate reports that a person is drug-free by means of urine analysis. He could not send his investigators to peer through bedroom windows, so he had to use indirect means to validate the data. One indirect measure was comparison of the reports of husbands and wives. There was a remarkable consistency in the reports of 706 pairs of spouses. It thus appears that their self-reports were accurate.

American Surveys (2): The NHSLS Study The National Health and Social Life Survey was intended to provide general information about sexual behaviour in the United States, and also specific information that might be used to predict and prevent the spread of AIDS. It was conducted by Edward O. Laumann of the University of Chicago and three colleagues—John H. Gagnon, Robert T. Michael, and Stuart Michaels—in the 1990s and published as *The Social Organization of Sexuality: Sexual Practices in the United States* in 1994.

The sample included 3432 people. Of this number, 3159 were drawn from English-speaking adults living in households (not dormitories, prisons, and so forth), ages 18 to 59. The other 273 were purposely obtained by oversampling African-American and Hispanic-American households to obtain more information about these ethnic groups. The sample probably represents the overall U.S. population quite well. However, there may be too few Asian-Americans, Native Americans, and Jews to offer much information about these groups.

The researchers identified samples of households in geographic areas—by addresses, not names. They sent a letter to each household, describing the purpose and methods of the study, and an interviewer visited each household one week later. The people targeted were assured that the purposes of the study were important and that the identities of participants would be kept confidential. Incentives of up to $100 were offered for cooperating. A high completion rate of close to 80% was obtained in this way. All in all, the NHSLS study could be the only one since Kinsey's day that offers a reasonably accurate picture of the sexual practices of the general population of the United States.

Canadian Surveys There are no Canadian surveys comparable to the NHSLS study. However, the General Social Survey, the National Population Health Survey, and the National Longitudinal Survey of Children and Youth, all funded by Statistics Canada, provide information on a number of issues related to human sexual behaviour. Data from these large-scale national surveys are released periodically. In addition, the 1998 Canadian Contraception Study (Fisher, et al., 1999) used a national sample of nearly 1600 women to gather information about frequency of sexual intercourse and sexual problems as well as contraceptive knowledge and use. Information from these surveys will be found throughout this book.

Magazine Surveys Major readership surveys have also been conducted by popular magazines, such as *Psychology Today*, *Cosmopolitan*, *Chatelaine*, and even *Consumer Reports*. Although these surveys all offer some useful information and may be commended for

Reliability The consistency of a measure.

Incidence A measure of the occurrence or the degree of occurrence of an event.

Frequency The number of times an action is repeated within a given period.

Validity With respect to tests, the degree to which a particular test measures the constructs or traits it purports to measure.

Statistics Canada
www.statcan.ca/
Information on issues related to sexual behaviour in Canada is available from Statistics Canada.

attaining large samples (ranging from 20 000 to 106 000!), their sampling techniques are inherently unscientific and biased. Each sample represents, at best, the readers of the magazine in which the questionnaire appeared. Moreover, we learn only about readers who volunteered to respond to these questionnaires. Volunteers tend to be more open and cooperative than people who do not volunteer. So the samples may represent only those readers who were willing to complete and mail in the surveys, and the results should not be applied to the general population.

Some surveys sponsored by media organizations have used representative sampling techniques to provide more accurate information. *Maclean's* magazine periodically surveys Canadians on a number of social issues, including sexual behaviour. Generally, 1600 Canadians are randomly sampled by telephone. Another comprehensive survey was carried out on behalf of the Sun Media Corporation, and included a number of issues including abortion, date rape, prostitution, homosexuality, sex in the media and on the internet, and sexual harassment.

In sum, the accuracy of surveys can be limited by factors such as these:

- Nonrepresentative sampling (Sampling may be biased.)
- Faulty memories of sexual behaviour
- Distortion or concealment of information
- **Social desirability** (Some people try to ingratiate themselves with their interviewers by offering what they believe to be socially desirable answers.)
- Volunteer bias

Social desirability
A response bias to a questionnaire or interview, in which the person provides a socially acceptable response.

Naturalistic observation
A method in which organisms are observed in their natural environments.

Participant observation
A method in which observers interact with the people they study as they collect data.

The Naturalistic-Observation Method In **naturalistic observation**, also called the *field study*, scientists directly observe the behaviour of animals and humans where it happens. Anthropologists, for example, have lived among preliterate societies and reported on their social and sexual customs. Other disciplines, too, have adopted methods of naturalistic observation in their research on human sexuality. Sociologists have observed the street life of prostitutes. Psychologists have observed body language between couples in dating situations.

The Participant-Observation Method In **participant observation**, the investigators learn about people's behaviour by directly interacting with them. Participant observation has been used in studies of male–male sexual behaviour and mate-swapping (swinging). In effect, participation has been the "price of admission" for observation.

The Laboratory-Observation Method In *Human Sexual Response* (1966), William Masters and Virginia Johnson were among the first to report direct laboratory observations of individuals and couples engaged in sexual acts. In all, 694 people (312 men and 382 women) participated in the research. The women ranged from 18 to 78 in age; the men from 21 to 80. There were 276 married couples, 106 single women, and 36 single men. The married couples engaged in intercourse and other forms of mutual stimulation, such as manual and oral stimulation of the genitals. The unmarried people participated in studies that did not require intercourse, such as measurement of female sexual arousal to insertion of a penis-shaped probe and male ejaculation during masturbation. Masters and Johnson reported on similar laboratory observations of sexual response among gay people for their 1979 book, *Homosexuality in Perspective*.

Direct laboratory observation of biological processes was not invented by Masters and Johnson. However, they were confronting a society that was still unprepared to speak openly of sex, let alone to observe people engaged in sexual activity in the laboratory. Masters and Johnson were accused of immorality, voyeurism, and an assortment of other evils. Nevertheless, their methods offered the first reliable set of data on what happens to the body during sexual response. Their instruments permitted them to directly measure vasocongestion (blood flow to the genitals), myotonia (muscle tension), and other physiological responses. Perhaps their most controversial device was a "coition machine." This was a transparent artificial penis outfitted with photographic equipment. It enabled them to study changes in women's internal sexual organs as they became sexually aroused. From these studies, Masters and Johnson observed that it is useful to divide sexual response into four stages (their "sexual response cycle").

Limitations of Observational Research One of the basic problems with naturalistic observation is the possibility that the behaviour under study may be reactive to the measurement itself. This source of bias is referred to as the **observer effect**.

The ethnographer who studies a particular culture or subgroup within a culture may unwittingly alter the behaviour of the members of the group by focusing attention on some facets of their behaviour. Falling prey to social desirability, some people may "straighten out their act" while the ethnographer is present. Other people may try to impress the ethnographer by acting in ways that are more aggressive or sexually provocative than usual. In either case, people supply distorted or biased information. Ethnographers must corroborate self-reported information by using multiple sources. They must also consider whether their own behaviour is more obtrusive than they think.

Observer bias can distort researchers' perceptions of the behaviours they observe. Observers who hold rigid sexual attitudes may be relatively unwilling to examine sexual activities that they consider to be offensive or objectionable. They may unwittingly (or intentionally) slant interviews in a way that presents a "sanitized" view of the behaviour of those they study, or exaggerate or "sensationalize" certain sexual practices to conform to their preconceptions of the sexual behaviour of the people they study.

The method of laboratory observation used by Masters and Johnson may be even more subject to distortion. Unlike animals, which naturalists may observe unobtrusively from afar, people who participate in laboratory observation know that they are being observed and that their responses are being measured. The problem of volunteer bias, troublesome for sex surveys, is even thornier in laboratory observation. How many of us would assent to performing sexual activities in the laboratory while we were connected to physiological monitoring equipment in full view of researchers? Some of the women observed by Masters and Johnson were patients of Dr. Masters who felt indebted to him and agreed to participate. Many were able to persuade their husbands to participate as well. Some were medical students and graduate students who may have been motivated to earn extra money (participants were paid for their time) as well as by scientific curiosity.

Another methodological concern of the Masters and Johnson approach is that observing people engaged in sexual activities may in itself alter their responses. People may not respond publicly in the same way that they would in private. The physiological monitoring equipment may also alter their natural responses. With these constraints in mind, it is perhaps remarkable that the people studied by Masters and Johnson were able to become sexually aroused and reach orgasm.

The Correlational Method

What is the relationship between age and frequency of coitus among married couples? What is the connection between socioeconomic status and teenage pregnancy? In each case, two variables are being related to one another: age and frequency of coitus, and socioeconomic status and rates of teenage pregnancy. Correlational research describes the relationship between variables such as these.

A **correlation** is a statistical measure of the relationship between two variables. In correlational studies, two or more variables are related, or linked to, one another by statistical means. The strength and direction (positive or negative) of the relationship between any two variables is expressed with a statistic called a **correlation coefficient**.

Research has shown relationships (correlations) between marital satisfaction and a host of variables: communication skills, shared values, flexibility, frequency of social interactions with friends, and churchgoing, to name a few. Although such research may give us an idea of the factors associated with marital satisfaction, the experimenters have not manipulated the variables of interest. For this reason we cannot say which, if any, of the factors is causally related to marital happiness. Consider the relationship between churchgoing and marital happiness. Couples who attend church more frequently report higher rates of marital satisfaction (Wilson & Filsinger, 1986). It is possible that churchgoing stabilizes marriages. It is also possible that people who attend church regularly are more stable and committed to marriage in the first place.

Observer effect A distortion of individuals' behaviour caused by the act of observation.

Correlation A statistical measure of the relationship between two variables.

Correlation coefficient A statistic that expresses the strength and direction (positive or negative) of the relationship between two variables.

Correlations may be *positive* or *negative*. Two variables are positively correlated if one increases as the other increases. Frequency of intercourse, for example, has been found to be positively correlated with sexual satisfaction (Blumstein & Schwartz, 1983). That is, married couples who engage in coitus more frequently report higher levels of sexual satisfaction. However, the experimenters did not manipulate the variables. Therefore, we cannot conclude that sexual satisfaction *causes* high coital frequency. It could also be that frequent coitus contributes to greater sexual satisfaction. It is also possible that there is no causal relationship between the variables. Perhaps both coital frequency and sexual satisfaction are affected by other factors, such as communication ability, general marital satisfaction, health, and so on (see Figure 1.1). Similarly, height and weight are positively correlated but do not cause each other. Another factor, growth, contributes to both.

Limitations of the Correlational Method Correlation is not causation. Many variables are correlated but not causally related to one another.

Although correlations do not show cause and effect, they can be used to make predictions. For example, we can predict that people who were sexually traumatized as children are more likely to encounter psychological problems later on. They find it more difficult to establish intimate relationships in adulthood. However, we cannot demonstrate that sexual trauma directly causes these problems. Although correlation does not provide causal knowledge, it permits us to anticipate the needs of victims of sexual assault for treatment services. Knowledge of correlational relationships may also lead to controlled experiments that more directly address questions of cause and effect.

The Experimental Method
The most effective (though not always feasible) method for studying *cause-and-effect relationships* is the **experiment**. Experiments permit scientists to draw conclusions about cause-and-effect relationships because the experimenter is able to control or manipulate the factors or variables of interest directly and to observe their effects.

In an experiment on the effects of alcohol on sexual arousal, for example, a group of participants would receive an intervention, called a **treatment**, such as a dose of alcohol. (In other experiments, the intervention or treatment might involve the administration of a drug, exposure to violent pornography, a program of sex education, etc.). They would then be carefully observed to learn whether this treatment made a difference in their behaviour—in this case, their sexual arousal.

Independent and Dependent Variables In an experiment, the variables (treatments) that are hypothesized to have a causal effect are manipulated or controlled by the researcher. Consider an experiment designed to determine whether or not alcohol stimulates sexual arousal. The design might involve giving one group of participants a certain dosage of alcohol, and then measuring its effects. In such an experimental arrangement, the

Experiment A scientific method that seeks to confirm cause-and-effect relationships by manipulating independent variables and observing their effects on dependent variables.

Treatment In experiments, an intervention that is administered to participants (e.g., a test, a drug, or a sex education program) so that its effects may be observed.

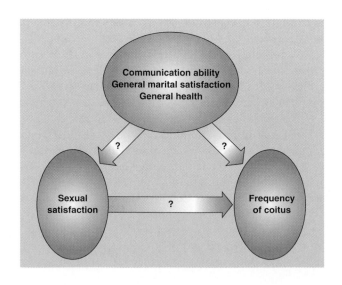

Figure 1.1. What Is the Relationship Between Frequency of Intercourse and Sexual Satisfaction?

Married couples who engage in coitus more frequently report higher levels of sexual satisfaction, but why? Since researchers have not manipulated the variables, we cannot conclude that sexual satisfaction causes high coital frequency. Nor can we say that frequent coitus causes greater sexual satisfaction. Perhaps both variables are affected by other factors, such as communication ability, general marital satisfaction, and general health.

dosage of alcohol is considered an **independent variable**, whose presence and quantity is manipulated by the researchers. The measured results are called **dependent variables**, since changes in their values are believed to depend on the independent variable or variables. In this experiment, measures of sexual arousal would be the dependent variables. Dependent variables are outcomes; they are observed and measured by the researchers, but not manipulated. Sexual arousal might be measured by means such as physiological measurement (gauging the degree of penile erection in the male, for example) or self-report (asking participants to rate their sexual arousal on a rating scale).

In a study of the effects of sex education on teenage pregnancy, sex education would be the independent variable. The incidence of teenage pregnancy would be the dependent variable. Researchers would administer the experimental treatment (sex education) and track the participants for a period of time to determine their pregnancy rates. But how would experimenters know whether or not the treatment had made a difference in the pregnancy rate? One way is to randomly assign people or animals to experimental and control groups.

Experimental and Control Groups Participants in **experimental groups** receive the treatment. Participants in **control groups** do not. Every effort is made to hold all other conditions constant for both groups. By using random assignment and holding other conditions constant, researchers can be reasonably confident that the independent variable (treatment), and not extraneous factors (such as the temperature of the room in which the treatment was administered or differences between the participants in the experimental and control groups), brought about the results.

Random Assignment Why do experimenters assign individuals at random to experimental and control groups whenever possible? Consider a study conducted to determine the effects of alcohol on sexual arousal in response to sexually explicit material, such as adult films. If we permitted study participants to choose whether or not they would drink alcohol, we might not know if it was the alcohol itself that accounted for the results. Some other factor, called a **selection factor**, might discriminate between people who would or would not choose to drink alcohol. One difference might be that people who chose to drink might also have more permissive attitudes toward sexually explicit material than the others. Their permissiveness rather than the alcohol could affect their sexual responsiveness to these stimuli. If this were the case, experimental outcomes might reflect the effects of the selection factor rather than the alcohol.

Experimentation with Animals Researchers frequently undertake studies with other animal species that would be impractical or unethical with people. For example, it may be hypothesized that prenatal sexual hormones "feminize" or "masculinize" the brain to give rise to gender-typed behaviours or predispose the individual to a heterosexual, gay male, or lesbian sexual orientation. The ideal method for examining these hypotheses would be to alter the balance of sex hormones systematically at various stages of fetal development and then monitor individuals' behaviour in subsequent years. However, neither parents nor researchers would be willing to risk the well-being of children through such an experiment. Therefore, studies of this kind have been conducted on animals to try to shed some light on similar processes in people.

To the extent that we share physiological processes with animals, experiments with other species may inform us about ourselves. Because of their physiological similarities to people, rats and monkeys are commonly used in laboratory experiments. But these animals are more similar to humans biologically than psychologically. Thus, we may make some generalizations from them to people concerning the effects of drugs and other biochemical treatments. We cannot, however, assume that their responses provide much of a clue to higher cognitive processes, such as thinking and reasoning.

Limitations of the Experimental Method Although scientists agree that the experimental method provides the strongest evidence of cause-and-effect relationships, experimenters cannot manipulate many variables of interest directly. We may suspect

Independent variable
A condition in a scientific study that is manipulated so that its effects may be observed.

Dependent variables
The measured results of an experiment, which are believed to be a function of the independent variables.

Experimental group
A group of study participants who receive a treatment.

Control group A group of study participants who do not receive the experimental treatment. However, other conditions are held comparable to those of individuals in the experimental group.

Selection factor A bias that may operate in research when people are allowed to determine whether or not they will receive a treatment.

that sexual trauma in the form of sexual assault is a causal factor in the development of psychological or emotional problems. However, we would not expose people to sexual trauma to observe its effects. In the absence of a direct manipulation of the presumed causal factor (sexual assault), we cannot be sure that adjustment problems in sexual assault victims are directly attributable to sexual assault itself, especially when they occur years later. Other factors may be involved, such as insensitive treatment of sexual assault victims by their families or by representatives of the criminal justice system.

Summing Up

What Is Human Sexuality?

The term *human sexuality* refers to gender, sexual behaviour, sexual feelings, and the biology of sex. It concerns the ways we experience and express ourselves as sexual beings. Human sexuality is studied by anthropologists, biologists, medical researchers, psychologists, sociologists, and other scientists. Canadian society embraces a wide range of sexual attitudes and values.

Critical thinking encourages thoughtful analysis of arguments, willingness to challenge conventional beliefs, and an open mind. Critical thinking also involves skepticism, caution in drawing conclusions, and avoidance of oversimplification and generalization.

Perspectives on Human Sexuality

The chapter considered five different perspectives on sexuality:

- A study of history shows little evidence of universal sexual trends. There is evidence that prehistoric peoples worshipped the generative power of women and men. Both Jews and Christians emphasized sex as a means of propagation and generally restricted sex to the context of marriage and family life. Many ancient societies, including the ancient Greeks and Romans, viewed women as property. Some Eastern civilizations equated sexual pleasure with religious experience. Repressive Victorian sexual attitudes gave way to the sexual revolution of the 1960s and 1970s, but the threat of AIDS and other sexually transmitted infections has brought about some changes in sexual attitudes, although not necessarily in behaviour.
- The **biological** perspective focuses on the role of biological processes, including genetic, hormonal, vascular, and neural factors, in explaining human sexual behaviour. Knowledge of biology helps us understand how our bodies respond to sexual stimulation and helps maintain sexual health. Sociobiologists

assert that there is a genetic basis to much human behaviour.

- The **cross-cultural** perspective provides insight into the ways that cultural beliefs affect sexual behaviour. Cross-cultural evidence challenges the notion of the universality of gender-role stereotypes. All cultures place some limits on sexual freedom, but some are more permissive than others.
- The **psychological** perspective focuses on how perception, learning, motivation, emotion, personality, and so on affect gender and sexual behaviour. Freud proposed that biologically based sex drives come into conflict with social codes. Learning theorists focus on the importance of rewards, punishments, and modelling in determining sexual behaviour.
- **Sociocultural** theorists focus on differences in sexual behaviour among different groups in society. They may look at differences related to age, gender, religion, socioeconomic status, education, and ethnic origins, among others.

Research Methods in Human Sexuality

Scientists insist that assumptions about sexual behaviour be supported by evidence based on careful observations in the laboratory or in the field.

Research **samples** should accurately **represent** the **population** of interest. Representative samples are usually obtained through random sampling. Non-random samples may be biased, which limits the validity of the results.

Methods of Observation

Case studies are carefully drawn biographies of individuals or small groups. They attempt to unravel the interplay of various factors in a person's background in order to explain some aspect of their behaviour. **Surveys** typically gat her information about sexual behaviour through either individual interviews or questionnaires administered to large samples of people. There are many sources of bias in surveys. In **naturalistic observation**, scientists directly observe the behaviour of animals and humans where it happens—in the "field." If the observer participates in the activity being observed, this is termed **participant observation**. In the **laboratory observation** method, the behaviour is observed in laboratory settings. **Correlational studies** provide information about the strength and direction of any relationship between two variables. However, they do not demonstrate cause and effect. **Experiments** allow scientists to draw conclusions about cause-and-effect relationships because they directly manipulate the variables of interest in order to measure their effects.

Chapter Quiz

1. Critical thinking involves all of the following EXCEPT
   (a) skepticism.
   (b) challenging common sense.
   (c) evaluating the premises of logic.
   (d) accepting the opinions of authority figures.

2. According to the text, art produced in the Stone Age suggests that people worshipped
   (a) women's ability to bear children.
   (b) a scientific approach to human sexuality.
   (c) bisexuality in men.
   (d) men's ability to father children.

3. According to the text, which of the following is likely to have been the first human taboo?
   (a) The taboo against masturbation.
   (b) The taboo against incest.
   (c) The taboo against oral sex.
   (d) The taboo against anal intercourse.

4. Which of the following cultural groups first produced an illustrated sex manual?
   (a) The Greeks of the golden age.
   (b) The ancient Romans.
   (c) The ancient Chinese.
   (d) The ancient Indians.

5. According to the text, which of the following challenged the prevailing English view by arguing that sexual desires in women were natural and healthy?

(a) Havelock Ellis.
(b) Sylvester Graham.
(c) Sigmund Freud.
(d) Richard von Krafft-Ebing.

6. The theory of _____ proposes that not only physical traits but also dispositions toward behaviour that enhances reproductive success may be transmitted by genes.
   (a) psychology
   (b) sociology
   (c) anthropology
   (d) sociobiology

7. One of Sigmund Freud's most controversial beliefs is that
   (a) children normally harbour erotic interests.
   (b) children tend to ignore unacceptable ideas and impulses.
   (c) children's dreams have symbolic meanings.
   (d) children tend to seek pleasure and avoid painful experiences.

8. Masters and Johnson are best known for using _____ in their research on human sexual response.
   (a) correlational coefficients
   (b) cross-cultural methods
   (c) the laboratory-observation method
   (d) the survey

9. People who agree to participate in psychological research may not represent the general population because of
   (a) obtrusive means of measurement.
   (b) volunteer bias.
   (c) random sampling.
   (d) level of education.

10. Most researchers agree that the best means of learning about cause and effect is
    (a) the experiment.
    (b) the correlational method.
    (c) the survey.
    (d) the case study.

Chapter 2

Female Sexual Anatomy and Physiology

Did You Know That...

- A name for the external genitals, especially the female genitals, is derived from Latin roots that mean "something to be ashamed of"?

- Women, but not men, have a sex organ whose only known function is the experiencing of sexual pleasure?

- Cultures in some parts of Africa and the Middle East ritually mutilate or remove the clitoris?

- The hymen may be torn by horseback riding, strenuous exercise, or even bicycle riding?

- Screening programs have greatly reduced the incidence of cervical cancer in North American women?

- The size of the breasts is largely determined by the amount of fatty tissue in them?

- About 80% of the women with breast cancer have no family history of the disease?

- Exercise and diet help many women cope with menstrual discomfort?

The saying *Vive la différence!* celebrates the differences between men and women. In this chapter we tour the female sex organs. Even generally sophisticated students may fill in some gaps in their knowledge. Most of us know what a vagina is, but how many of us realize that only the female gender has an organ that is exclusively dedicated to pleasure? Or that a woman's passing of urine does not involve the vagina? How many of us know that a newborn girl already has all the **ova** she will ever produce?

Ova Egg cells. (Singular: ovum.)

The Female Sex Organs

External Sex Organs

The external sexual structures of the female are termed the **pudendum** or the **vulva**. *Pudendum* derives from the Latin term *pudendus*. It literally means "something to be ashamed of." *Vulva* is a Latin word that means "wrapper" or "covering." The vulva consists of the *mons veneris*, the *labia majora* and *minora* (major and minor lips), the *clitoris*, and the vaginal opening (see Figure 2.1). Figure 2.2 shows variations in the appearance of women's genitals.

Pudendum The external genitals, especially the female genitals.

Vulva The external sexual structures of the female.

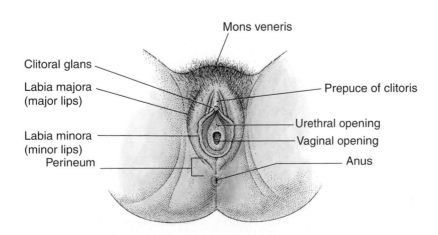

Mons veneris

Clitoral glans

Labia majora (major lips)

Labia minora (minor lips)

Perineum

Prepuce of clitoris

Urethral opening

Vaginal opening

Anus

Figure 2.1. Female External Sex Organs.

This figure shows the vulva with the labia opened to reveal the urethral and vaginal openings.

Figure 2.2. Normal Variations in the Vulva.

The features of the vulva show a great deal of variation. A woman's attitude toward her genitals is likely to reflect her general self-concept and early childhood messages rather than the appearance of her vulva per se.

Mons veneris A mound of fatty tissue that covers the joint of the pubic bones in front of the body, below the abdomen and above the clitoris. (The name is a Latin phrase meaning "hill" or "mount of Venus," the Roman goddess of love. Also known as the *mons pubis,* or simply *mons.*)

Labia majora Large folds of skin that run downward from the mons along the sides of the vulva. (Latin for "large lips" or "major lips.")

Labia minora Hairless, light-coloured membranes, located between the labia majora. (Latin for "small lips" or "minor lips.")

Clitoris A female sex organ consisting of a shaft and glans located above the urethral opening. It is extremely sensitive to sexual sensations.

Corpora cavernosa Masses of spongy tissue in the clitoral shaft that become engorged with blood and stiffen in response to sexual stimulation. (Latin for "cavernous bodies.")

Prepuce The fold of skin covering the glans of the clitoris (or penis). (From Latin roots meaning "before a swelling.")

The Mons Veneris The **mons veneris** consists of fatty tissue that covers the joint of the pubic bones in front of the body, below the abdomen and above the clitoris. At puberty the mons becomes covered with pubic hair that is often thick and curly, but varies from person to person in waviness, texture, and colour. The mons cushions a woman's body during sexual intercourse, protecting her and her partner from the pressure against the pubic bone caused by thrusting. The mons is well supplied with nerve endings, so that caresses of the area can produce pleasurable sexual sensations.

The Labia Majora The **labia majora** are large folds of skin that run downward from the mons along the sides of the vulva. The labia majora of some women are thick and bulging. In other women, they are thinner, flatter, and less noticeable. When close together, they hide the labia minora and the urethral and vaginal openings.

The outer surfaces of the labia majora, by the thighs, are covered with pubic hair and have darker skin than that found on the thighs or labia minora. The inner surfaces of the labia majora are hairless and lighter in colour. Like the mons, the labia are supplied with nerve endings that respond to stimulation and can produce sensations of sexual pleasure. The labia majora also shield the inner portion of the female genitals.

The Labia Minora The **labia minora** are two hairless, light-coloured membranes, located between the major lips. They surround the urethral and vaginal openings. The outer surfaces of the labia minora merge with the major lips. At the top they join at the prepuce (hood) of the clitoris. The labia minora differ markedly in appearance from woman to woman. Rich in blood vessels and nerve endings, the labia minora are highly sensitive to sexual stimulation. When a woman is sexually stimulated they darken and swell, indicating engorgement with blood.

The Clitoris The clitoris is the only sex organ whose only known function is the experiencing of pleasure. **Clitoris** (see Figure 2.1) derives from the Greek word *kleitoris,* meaning "hill" or "slope." The clitoris receives its name from the manner in which it slopes upward in the shaft and forms a mound of spongy tissue at the glans. The body of the clitoris, termed the clitoral shaft, is about 2 cm long and .5 cm wide. The clitoral shaft consists of erectile tissue that contains two spongy masses called **corpora cavernosa** ("cavernous bodies") that fill with blood (become engorged) and become erect in response to sexual stimulation. The stiffening of the clitoris is less apparent than the erection of the penis, because the clitoris does not swing free from the body as the penis does. The **prepuce** (meaning "before a swelling"), or hood, covers the clitoral shaft. It is a sheath of skin formed by the upper part of the labia minora.

The clitoral glans is a smooth, round knob or lump of tissue. It resembles a button and is situated above the urethral opening. The clitoral glans may be covered by the clitoral hood but is readily revealed by gently separating the labia minora and retracting

A World of Diversity

Female Circumcision

Cultures in some parts of Africa and the Middle East ritually remove either the entire clitoris, or the clitoral hood. In some situations, the labia are also removed. Removal of the clitoris, or **clitoridectomy**, is a rite of initiation into womanhood in some of these predominantly Islamic cultures. It may be performed as a puberty ritual in late childhood or early adolescence, or sometimes early in childhood (not at birth, like male circumcision).

The clitoris gives rise to feelings of sexual pleasure in women. Its removal represents an attempt to ensure the girl's chastity since it is assumed that uncircumcised girls are consumed with sexual desires (Ahmed, 1991). One physician in Cairo says, "With circumcision we remove the external parts, so when a girl wears tight nylon underclothes she will not have any stimulation" (cited in MacFarquhar, 1996, p. A3). Some groups in rural Egypt and in the northern Sudan, however, perform clitoridectomies primarily because it is a social custom that has been passed down from ancient times (Toubia, 1994). Some perceive it as part of their faith in Islam. However, neither Islam nor any other religion requires it (MacFarquhar, 1996). Ironically, many young women do not grasp that they are victims. They assume that clitoridectomy is part of being female (Rosenthal, 1994).

Clitoridectomies are often performed under unsanitary conditions without benefit of anaesthesia (Rosenthal, 1993). Medical complications are common, including infections, bleeding, tissue scarring, painful menstruation, and obstructed labour (Toubia, 1994). The procedure is psychologically traumatizing (Toubia, 1994). An even more radical form of clitoridectomy, called *infibulation* or pharaonic circumcision, is practised widely in the Sudan. Pharaonic circumcision involves complete removal of the clitoris along with the labia minora and the inner layers of the labia majora.

After removal of the skin tissue, the raw edges of the labia majora are sewn together. Only a tiny opening is left to allow passage of urine and menstrual discharge. The sewing together of the vulva may be intended to ensure the girls' chastity until marriage. Medical complications are common, including menstrual and urinary problems, and even death. After marriage, the opening is enlarged to permit intercourse. Enlargement is a gradual process that is often made difficult by scar tissue from the circumcision. Hemorrhaging and tearing of surrounding tissues are common consequences. It may take three months or longer before the opening is large enough to allow penile penetration. Mutilation of the labia is now illegal in the Sudan, although the law continues to allow removal of the clitoris. Some African countries have outlawed clitoridectomies, although such laws are rarely enforced (Rosenthal, 1993).

Millions of women in Africa and the Middle East—85 to 114 million by some estimates (Kaplan, 1993)—have undergone removal of the clitoris and the labia minora. Clitoridectomies remain common in nearly 30 countries in Africa, in many countries in the Middle East, and in parts of Malaysia, Yemen, Oman,

Indonesia, and the India-Pakistan subcontinent (Rosenthal, 1995). Thousands of African immigrant girls living in European countries and North America have also had this surgery performed (Dugger, 1996). However, there is some evidence that the incidence of female circumcision is declining, at least in the Sudan (Islam & Uddin, 2001).

Do not confuse male circumcision with this procedure inflicted on girls. *The New York Times* columnist A. M. Rosenthal (1995) calls female circumcision the most widespread existing violation of human rights in the world. The Pulitzer Prize–winning African American novelist Alice Walker has condemned it in her novel *Possessing the Secret of Joy* (1992). She called for its abolition in her book and movie *Warrior Marks*.

Female Circumcision. *Some cultures in Africa and the Middle East ritually remove the clitoris as a rite of initiation into womanhood. Novelist Alice Walker drew attention to the practice in her novel* Possessing the Secret of Joy. *She has called for its abolition in her book and film* Warrior Marks.

Female circumcision has been illegal in Canada since 1997. Yet calls from Westerners to ban the practice in parts of Africa and the Middle East have sparked controversy on grounds of "cultural condescension"—that people in one culture cannot dictate the cultural traditions of another. Yet for Alice Walker, "torture is not culture." As the debate continues, some 2 million African girls continue to undergo ritual circumcision each year.

Clitoridectomy Surgical removal of the clitoris.

Homologous Similar in structure; developing from the same embryonic tissue.

Analogous Similar in function.

the hood. It is highly sensitive to touch because of the rich supply of nerve endings. Because the clitoral glans is highly sensitive to touch, many women prefer to be stroked or stimulated on the mons, or on the clitoral hood, rather than directly on the glans.

In some respects, the clitoris is the female counterpart of the penis. Both organs develop from the same embryonic tissue, which makes them similar in structure, or **homologous**. They are not fully similar in function, or **analogous**, however. Both organs receive and transmit sexual sensations, but the penis is directly involved in reproduction and excretion by serving as a conduit for sperm and urine, respectively. The clitoris, however, is a unique sex organ. It serves no known purpose other than sexual pleasure.

Surgical removal of the clitoral hood is performed on many women in the Near East and Africa. The *World of Diversity* feature examines this practice.

The Vestibule The word *vestibule*, which means "entranceway," refers to the area within the labia minora that contains the openings to the vagina and the urethra. The vestibule is richly supplied with nerve endings and is very sensitive to tactile stimulation.

Urethral opening The opening through which urine passes from the female's body.

The Urethral Opening Urine passes from the female's body through the **urethral opening** (see Figure 2.1), which is connected by a short tube called the urethra to the bladder (see Figure 2.3), where urine collects. The urethral opening lies below the clitoral glans and above the vaginal opening. The urethral opening, urethra, and bladder are unrelated to the reproductive system.

The proximity of the urethral opening to the external sex organs may pose some hygienic problems for women, whether or not they are sexually active. The urinary tract, which includes the urethra, bladder, and kidneys, may become infected from bacteria that are transmitted from the vagina or rectum. In sexually active women, infectious microscopic organisms may also pass from the male's sex organs to the female's urethral opening during sexual intercourse. Manual stimulation of the vulva with dirty hands may also transmit bacteria through the urethral opening to the bladder. Anal intercourse followed by vaginal intercourse may transfer microscopic organisms from the rectum to the bladder and cause infection. For similar reasons, women should first wipe the vulva, then the anus, when using the bathroom.

Cystitis An inflammation of the urinary bladder. (From the Greek *kystis*, meaning "sac.")

Gynecologist A physician who treats women's diseases, especially of the reproductive tract. (From the Greek *gyne*, meaning "woman.")

Cystitis is a bladder inflammation that may stem from any of these sources. Its primary symptoms are burning and frequent urination (also called *urinary urgency*). Pus or a bloody discharge is common, and there may be an intermittent or persistent ache just above the pubic bone. These symptoms may disappear after several days, but consultation with a **gynecologist** is recommended, because untreated cystitis can lead to serious kidney infections. A few precautions may help women prevent serious inflammation of the bladder:

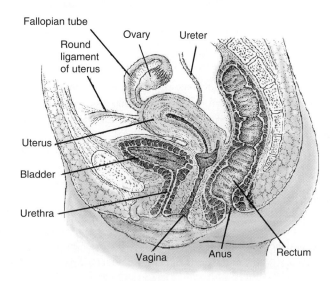

Figure 2.3. The Female Reproductive System.

This cross-section locates many of the internal sex organs that compose the female reproductive system. Note that the uterus is normally tipped forward.

- Drinking two litres of water a day to flush the bladder
- Drinking cranberry juice to maintain an acid environment that discourages growth of infectious organisms (125 mL, two or three times a day—crantinis don't count!)
- Decreasing use of alcohol and caffeine (from coffee, tea, or cola drinks) that may irritate the bladder
- Washing the hands prior to masturbation or self-examination
- Washing one's partner's and one's own genitals before and after intercourse
- Preventing objects that have touched the anus (fingers, penis, toilet tissue) from subsequently coming into contact with the vulva
- Urinating soon after intercourse to help wash away bacteria

The Vaginal Opening One does not see an entire vagina, but rather the vaginal opening, or **introitus**, when one parts the labia minora. The introitus lies below and is larger than the urethral opening. Its shape resembles that of the **hymen.**

The hymen is a fold of tissue across the vaginal opening that is usually present at birth and may remain at least partly intact until a woman engages in coitus. For this reason the hymen has been called the "maidenhead." Its presence has been taken as proof of virginity, and its absence as evidence of coitus. However, some women are born with incomplete hymens, and other women's hymens are torn accidentally during such activities as horseback riding, strenuous exercise, or gymnastics—or even bicycle riding. A punctured hymen is therefore poor evidence of coital experience. A flexible hymen may also withstand many coital experiences, so its presence does not guarantee virginity.

Figure 2.4 illustrates various vaginal openings. The first three show common shapes of hymens among women who have not had coitus. The fifth drawing shows a parous ("passed through") vaginal opening, typical of a woman who has delivered a baby. Now and then the hymen consists of tough fibrous tissue and is closed, or imperforate, as in the fourth drawing. An imperforate hymen may not be discovered until after puberty, when menstrual discharges begin to accumulate in the vagina. In these rare cases, a simple surgical incision will perforate the hymen.

The Perineum The **perineum** incorporates the skin and underlying tissue between the vaginal opening and the anus. The perineum is rich in nerve endings. Stimulation of the area may heighten sexual arousal. Many physicians make a routine perineal incision during labour, called an **episiotomy**, to facilitate childbirth.

Structures That Underlie the External Sex Organs Figure 2.5 shows what lies beneath the skin of the vulva. The vestibular bulbs and Bartholin's glands are active during sexual arousal and are found on both sides (shown on the right in Figure 2.5). Muscular rings (**sphincters**) that constrict bodily openings such as the vaginal and anal openings are also found on both sides.

The clitoral **crura** are wing-shaped, leglike structures that attach the clitoris to the pubic bone beneath. The crura contain corpora cavernosa, which engorge with blood and stiffen during sexual arousal.

Introitus The vaginal opening. (From the Latin for "entrance.")

Hymen A fold of tissue across the vaginal opening that is usually present at birth and usually remains at least partly intact until a woman engages in coitus. (Greek for "membrane.")

Perineum The skin and underlying tissue that lie between the vaginal opening and the anus. (From Greek roots meaning "around" and "to empty out.")

Episiotomy A surgical incision in the perineum that may be made during childbirth to protect the vagina from tearing. (From the Greek roots *epision*, meaning "pubic region," and *tome*, meaning "cutting.")

Sphincters Ring-shaped muscles that surround body openings and open or close them by expanding or contracting. (From the Greek for "that which draws close.")

Crura Anatomical structures resembling legs that attach the clitoris to the pubic bone. (Singular: *crus*. A Latin word meaning "leg" or "shank.")

Annular hymen   Septate hymen   Cribriform hymen   Imperforate hymen   Parous introitus (after childbirth)

Figure 2.4. Appearance of Various Types of Hymens, and the Introitus (at right) As It Appears Following Delivery of a Baby.

Figure 2.5. Structures That Underlie the Female External Sex Organs.

If we could see beneath the vulva, we would find muscle fibres that constrict the various body openings, plus the crura ("legs") of the clitoris, the vestibular bulbs, and Bartholin's glands.

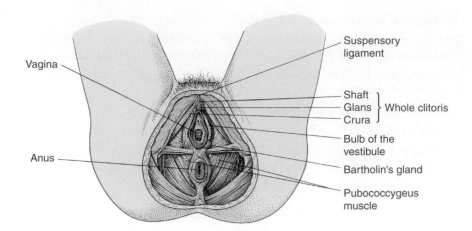

Vestibular bulbs Cavernous structures that extend downward along the sides of the introitus and swell during sexual arousal.

Bartholin's glands Glands that lie just inside the minor lips and secrete fluid just before orgasm.

The Canadian Women's Health Network **www.cwhn.ca/indexeng.html** This site has extensive links to information on women's reproductive health.

Vagina The tubular female sex organ that contains the penis during sexual intercourse and through which a baby is born. (Latin for "sheath.")

The **vestibular bulbs** are attached to the clitoris at the top and extend downward along the sides of the vaginal opening. Blood congests them during sexual arousal, swelling the vulva and lengthening the vagina. This swelling contributes to coital sensations for both partners.

Bartholin's glands lie just inside the minor lips on each side of the vaginal opening. They secrete a couple of drops of lubrication just before orgasm. This lubrication is not essential for coitus. In fact, the fluid produced by the Bartholin's glands has no known purpose. If the glands become infected and clogged, however, a woman may notice swelling and local irritation. It is wise to consult a gynecologist if these symptoms do not fade within a few days.

It was once believed that the source of the vaginal lubrication or "wetness" that women experience during sexual arousal was produced by the Bartholin's glands. It is now known that engorgement of vaginal tissues during sexual excitement results in a form of "sweating" by the lining of the vaginal wall. During sexual arousal the pressure from this engorgement causes moisture from the many small blood vessels that lie in the vaginal wall to be forced out and to pass through the vaginal lining, forming the basis of the lubrication. In less time than it takes to read this sentence (generally within 10 to 30 seconds), beads of vaginal lubrication or "sweat" appear along the interior lining of the vagina in response to sexual stimulation, in much the same way that rising temperatures cause water to pass through the skin as perspiration.

Pelvic floor muscles permit women to constrict the vaginal and anal openings. They contract automatically, or involuntarily, during orgasm, and their tone may contribute to coital sensations.

Internal Sex Organs

The internal sex organs of the female include the innermost parts of the vagina, the cervix, the uterus, and two ovaries, each connected to the uterus by a fallopian tube (see Figures 2.3, 2.6). These structures comprise the female reproductive system.

The Vagina The **vagina** extends back and upward from the vaginal opening (see Figure 2.3). It is usually 7 to 12 cm long at rest. Menstrual flow and babies pass from the uterus to the outer world through the vagina. During coitus, the penis is contained within the vagina.

The vagina is commonly pictured as a canal or barrel, but when at rest, it is like a collapsed muscular tube. Its walls touch like the fingers of an empty glove. The vagina expands in length and width during sexual arousal. The vagina can also expand to allow insertion of a tampon, as well as the passage of a baby's head and shoulders during childbirth.

The vaginal walls have three layers. The inner lining, or *vaginal mucosa*, is made visible by opening the labia minora. It is a mucous membrane similar to the skin that lines the inside of the mouth. It feels fleshy, soft, and corrugated. It may vary from very dry

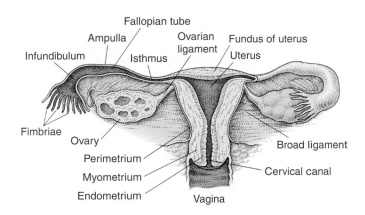

Figure 2.6. Female Internal Reproductive Organs.

This drawing highlights the relationship of the uterus to the fallopian tubes and ovaries. Note the layers of the uterus, the ligaments that attach the ovaries to the uterus, and the relationship of the ovaries to the fimbriae of the fallopian tubes.

Applications

Preventing Vaginitis

Vaginitis refers to any vaginal inflammation, whether it is caused by an infection, an allergic reaction, or chemical irritation. Vaginitis may also stem from use of birth-control pills or antibiotics that alter the natural body chemistry, or from other factors, such as lowered resistance (from fatigue or poor diet). Changes in the natural body chemistry or lowered resistance permit microscopic organisms normally found in the vagina to multiply to infectious levels. Vaginitis may be recognized by an abnormal or unpleasant smelling discharge, itching, burning of the vulva, and, sometimes, urinary urgency. Women with vaginitis are advised to seek medical attention, but here are some suggestions that may help prevent vaginitis (Boston Women's Health Book Collective, 1992):

- Wash your vulva and anus regularly with mild soap. Pat dry (taking care not to touch the vulva after dabbing the anus).
- Wear cotton panties. Nylon underwear retains heat and moisture that cause harmful bacteria to flourish.
- Avoid pants that are tight in the crotch.
- Be certain that sex partners are well-washed. Condoms may also reduce the spread of infections back and forth between sex partners.
- Use a sterile, water-soluble jelly such as K-Y jelly if artificial lubrication is needed for intercourse. Do not use Vaseline. Birth-control jellies can also be used for lubrication.
- Avoid intercourse that is painful or abrasive to the vagina.
- Avoid diets high in sugar and refined carbohydrates since they alter the normal acidity of the vagina.
- Women who are prone to vaginal infections may find it helpful to douche occasionally with plain water, a solution of 15 to 30 mL of vinegar in a litre of warm water, or a solution of baking soda and water. Douches consisting of plain (unflavoured) yogurt that contain live cultures may help replenish the "good" bacteria that are normally found in the vagina and that may be destroyed by use of antibiotics. Consult your physician before deciding to douche or to apply any preparations to the vagina.
- Watch your general health. Eating poorly or getting insufficient rest will reduce your resistance to infection.

(especially if the female is anxious about something like examinations) to very wet, in which case fingers slide against it readily. The middle layer of the vaginal wall is muscular. The outer or deeper layer is a fibrous covering that connects the vagina to other pelvic structures.

The vaginal walls are rich with blood vessels but poorly supplied with nerve endings. Unlike the sensitive outer third of the vaginal barrel, the inner two-thirds are so insensitive to touch that minor surgery may sometimes be performed on those portions without anesthesia. The entire vaginal barrel is sensitive to pressure, however, which can be experienced as sexually pleasurable.

The vaginal walls secrete substances that help maintain the vagina's normal acidity (pH 4.0 to 5.0). Normally the secretions taste salty. The odour and taste of these secretions may vary during the menstrual cycle. Although the evidence is not clear, the secretions are thought to contain substances that may act as sexual attractants. Women who frequently **douche** or use feminine deodorant sprays may remove or mask substances that may arouse sex partners. Douching or spraying may also alter the natural chemical balance of the vagina, which can increase the risk of vaginal infections. The

Vaginitis Vaginal inflammation.

Douche Application of a jet of liquid to the vagina as a rinse. (From the Italian *doccia*, meaning "shower bath.")

Cervix The lower end of the uterus. (Latin for "neck.")

Os The opening in the middle of the cervix. (Latin for "mouth.")

Pap test A test of a sample of cervical cells that screens for cervical cancer and certain other abnormalities, but not for STIs. (Named after the originator of the technique, Dr. Papanicolaou.)

Radiotherapy Treatment of a disease by X-rays or by emissions from a radioactive substance.

Uterus The hollow, muscular, pear-shaped organ in which a fertilized ovum becomes implanted and develops until birth.

Fundus The uppermost part of the uterus. (*Fundus* is a Latin word meaning "base.")

Endometrium The innermost layer of the uterus. (From Latin and Greek roots meaning "within the uterus.")

Endometriosis A condition caused by the growth of endometrial tissue in the abdominal cavity or elsewhere outside the uterus. Characterized by menstrual pain, it may cause infertility.

Myometrium The middle, well-muscled layer of the uterus. (*Myo-* stems from the Greek *mys*, meaning "muscle.")

Perimetrium The outer layer of the uterus. (From roots meaning "around the uterus.")

Hysterectomy Surgical removal of the uterus.

normal, healthy vagina cleanses itself through regular chemical secretions that are evidenced by a mild white or yellowish discharge.

The Cervix The **cervix** is the lower end of the uterus. Its walls, like those of the vagina, produce secretions that contribute to the chemical balance of the vagina. The opening in the middle of the cervix, or **os**, is normally about the width of a straw, although it expands to permit passage of a baby from the uterus to the vagina during childbirth. Sperm pass from the vagina to the uterus through the cervical canal.

Cervical cancer is relatively uncommon in Canada and the United States. Both the incidence of cervical cancer and deaths from it have declined over the last 20 years, largely due to screening programs (National Cancer Institute of Canada, 2003). The National Cancer Institute of Canada estimates that, in 2003, 1400 new cases will be diagnosed (National Cancer Institute of Canada, 2003). Cervical cancer is more common among women who have had many sex partners, who became sexually active at a relatively early age, who have lower socioeconomic status, and who smoke. All women are at risk, however.

A **Pap test** examines a sample of cervical cells that are smeared on a slide to screen for cervical cancer and other abnormalities, including early changes due to the effects of the HPV virus. Annual Pap tests along with a pelvic examination are recommended for women who are, or have been, sexually active or who have reached age 18. Most cases of cervical cancer can be successfully treated by surgery and **radiotherapy** if they are detected early. The five-year survival rate for women with cervical cancer is 67%. For women diagnosed with localized cancer, the survival rate is 70% (Canadian Cancer Society, 2000). However, cervical cancer can also be prevented when precancerous changes are detected by Pap smear ("Panel Says," 1996). It is estimated that approximately 420 Canadian women will die from cervical cancer in 2003 (National Cancer Institute of Canada, 2003).

The Uterus The **uterus**, or womb (see Figures 2.3, 2.6), is the organ in which a fertilized ovum becomes implanted and develops until birth. The uterus usually slants forward (is *antroverted*), although about 10% of women have uteruses that tip backward (are *retroverted*). In most instances a retroverted uterus causes no problems, but some women with retroverted uteruses find coitus in certain positions painful. A retroverted uterus normally tips forward during pregnancy.

The uterus is suspended in the pelvis by flexible ligaments. In a woman who has not given birth, it is about 7 cm long, 7 cm wide, and 2.3 cm thick near the top. The uterus expands to accommodate a fetus during pregnancy and shrinks after pregnancy, though not to its original size.

The uppermost part of the uterus is called the **fundus** (see Figure 2.6). The uterus is shaped like an inverted pear. If a ceramic model of a uterus were placed on a table, it would balance on the fundus. The central region of the uterus is called the *body*. The narrow lower region is the cervix, which leads downward to the vagina.

Like the vagina, the uterus has three layers (also shown in Figure 2.6). The innermost layer, or **endometrium**, is richly supplied with blood vessels and glands. Its structure varies according to a woman's age and phase of the menstrual cycle. Endometrial tissue is discharged through the cervix and vagina at menstruation. For reasons not entirely understood, in some women endometrial tissue may also grow in the abdominal cavity or elsewhere in the reproductive system. This condition is called **endometriosis**, and the most common symptom is menstrual pain. If left untreated, endometriosis may lead to infertility.

Cancer of the endometrial lining is called endometrial cancer. Risk factors include obesity, a diet high in fats, early onset of menstruation or late menopause, history of failure to ovulate, and estrogen-replacement therapy (Rose, 1996). For women who obtain hormone-replacement therapy, combining estrogen with progestin mitigates the risk of endometrial cancer (Grodstein et al., 1996; Rose, 1996). A common symptom of endometrial cancer is abnormal uterine staining or bleeding, especially after menopause. The most common treatment is surgery (Rose, 1996). The five-year survival rate for endometrial cancer is up to 95% if it is discovered early and limited to the endometrium (Rose, 1996). (Endometrial cancer is usually diagnosed early because women tend to quickly report postmenopausal bleeding to their doctors.) The survival rate drops when the cancer *metastasizes*, or invades surrounding tissues.

The second layer of the uterus, the **myometrium**, is well muscled. It endows the uterus with flexibility and strength, and creates the powerful contractions that propel a fetus outward during labour. The third or outermost layer, the **perimetrium**, provides an external cover.

One woman in three in Canada has a **hysterectomy** by the age of 55 (National Cancer Institute of Canada, 2000). Most hysterectomy patients are between the ages of 35 and 45. A hysterectomy may be performed when women develop cancer of the uterus, ovaries, or cervix, or other diseases that cause pain or excessive uterine bleeding. A hysterectomy may be partial or complete. A **complete hysterectomy** involves the surgical removal of the ovaries, fallopian tubes, cervix, and uterus. It is usually performed to reduce the risk of cancer spreading throughout the reproductive system. A partial hysterectomy removes the uterus but spares the ovaries and fallopian tubes. Sparing the ovaries allows the woman to continue to ovulate and produce adequate quantities of female sex hormones.

The hysterectomy has become steeped in controversy. In many cases it is possible that less radical medical interventions might successfully treat the problem (Bernstein et al., 1993). Women whose physicians recommend a hysterectomy are advised to seek a second opinion before proceeding.

The Fallopian Tubes Two uterine tubes, also called **fallopian tubes**, are about 10 cm in length and extend from the upper end of the uterus toward the ovaries (see Figure 2.6). The part of each tube nearest the uterus is the **isthmus**, which broadens into the **ampulla** as it approaches the ovary. The outer part, or **infundibulum**, has fringelike projections called **fimbriae** that extend toward, but are not attached to, the ovary.

Ova pass through the fallopian tubes on their way to the uterus. The fallopian tubes are not inert passageways. They help nourish and conduct ova. These tubes are lined with tiny hairlike projections termed *cilia* ("lashes") that help move ova through the tube. The exact mechanisms by which ova are guided are unknown, however. It is tempting to say that ova move at a snail's pace, but a snail would leave them far behind. They journey toward the uterus at about 2 to 3 cm per day. Since ova must be fertilized within a day or two after they are released from the ovaries, fertilization usually occurs in the infundibulum within a couple of inches of the ovaries. The form of sterilization called tubal ligation ties off the fallopian tubes, so that ova cannot pass through them or become fertilized.

In an **ectopic pregnancy**, the fertilized ovum implants itself outside the uterus, most often in the fallopian tube where fertilization occurred. Ectopic pregnancies can eventually burst fallopian tubes, causing hemorrhaging and death. Ectopic pregnancies are thus terminated before the tube ruptures. They are not easily recognized, however, because their symptoms—missed menstrual period, abdominal pain, irregular bleeding—suggest many conditions. Experiencing any of these symptoms is an excellent reason for consulting a gynecologist. Women who have had pelvic inflammatory disease (PID), undergone tubal surgery, or used intrauterine devices (IUDs) are at increased risk of developing ectopic pregnancies (Marchbanks et al., 1988).

The Ovaries The two **ovaries** are almond-shaped organs that are each about 2 to 6 cm long. They lie on either side of the uterus, to which they are attached by ovarian ligaments. The ovaries produce ova (egg cells) and the female sex hormones **estrogen** and **progesterone**.

Estrogen is a generic term for several hormones (such as estradiol, estriol, and estrone) that promote the changes of puberty and regulate the menstrual cycle. Estrogen also helps older women maintain cognitive functioning and feelings of psychological well-being (Sourander, 1994). Progesterone also has multiple functions, including regulating the menstrual cycle and preparing the uterus for pregnancy by stimulating the development of the endometrium (uterine lining). Estrogen and progesterone levels vary with the phases of the menstrual cycle.

Complete hysterectomy Surgical removal of the ovaries, fallopian tubes, cervix, and uterus.

Fallopian tubes Tubes that extend from the upper uterus toward the ovaries and conduct ova to the uterus. (After the Italian anatomist Gabriel Fallopio, who is credited with their discovery.)

Isthmus The segment of a fallopian tube closest to the uterus. (A Latin word meaning "narrow passage.")

Ampulla The wide segment of a fallopian tube near the ovary. (A Latin word meaning "bottle.")

Infundibulum The outer, funnel-shaped part of a fallopian tube. (A Latin word meaning "funnel.")

Fimbriae Projections from a fallopian tube that extend toward an ovary. (Singular: *fimbria*. Latin for "fibre" or "fringe.")

Ectopic pregnancy A pregnancy in which the fertilized ovum becomes implanted outside the uterus, usually in the fallopian tube. (*Ectopic* derives from Greek roots meaning "out of place.")

Ovaries Almond-shaped organs that produce ova and the hormones estrogen and progesterone.

Estrogen A generic term for female sex hormones (including estradiol, estriol, estrone, and others) or synthetic compounds that promote the development of female sex characteristics and regulate the menstrual cycle. (From the roots meaning "generating" [-*gen*] and "estrus.")

Progesterone A steroid hormone secreted by the corpus luteum or prepared synthetically that stimulates proliferation of the endometrium and is involved in regulation of the menstrual cycle. (From the root *pro*-, meaning "promoting," and the words *gestation*, *steroid*, and *one*.)

Follicle A capsule within an ovary that contains an ovum. (From a Latin word meaning "small bag.")

Ovarian Cancer Canada **www.ovariancancercanada.ca** More information on ovarian cancer and support for women with ovarian cancer can be found at this website.

Secondary sex characteristics Physical traits that distinguish women from men but are not directly involved in reproduction.

Mammary glands Milk-secreting glands. (From the Latin *mamma*, which means both "breast" and "mother.")

Figure 2.7. A Breast of an Adult Woman.

This drawing reveals the structures underlying the breast, including mammary glands and milk ducts.

The human female is born with all the ova she will ever have (about 2 million), but they are immature in form. Of these, about 400 000 survive into puberty, each of which is contained in the ovary within a thin capsule, or **follicle**. During a woman's reproductive years, from puberty to menopause, ripened ova will be released by their rupturing follicles for possible fertilization. How these ova are selected is among the mysteries of nature. Until recently, it was thought that only a dozen or so follicles developed during each cycle, with only one ovum completing the cycle to maturity and leaving the ovary. However, researchers at the University of Saskatchewan have found that this process of follicular development is repeated several times during each menstrual cycle. Using daily high-resolution ultrasound examinations, Baerwald, Adams, and Pierson tracked ovarian changes in 50 women with normal menstrual cycles. They found that follicle development occurred in waves, and that 40% of the women had more than one major wave (Baerwald et al., 2003). The Canadian Cancer Society estimated that in 2003, 2600 women in Canada would be diagnosed with ovarian cancer, and 1550 would die from it. It most often strikes women between the ages of 40 and 70 and ranks as the fifth leading cancer killer of women, behind lung cancer, breast cancer, colon cancer, and pancreatic cancer (National Cancer Institute of Canada, 2003). Women most at risk are those with blood relatives who had the disease, especially a first-degree relative (mother, sister, or daughter). Other risk factors are also important, since about 9 women in 10 who develop ovarian cancer do not have a family history of it. Researchers have identified several risk factors that increase the chances of developing the disease: never having given birth, prolonged use of talcum powder between the anus and the vagina, infertility, a history of breast cancer, and a diet rich in meat and animal fats. Questions have been raised as to whether the use of clomiphene, a fertility drug, increases the risk of ovarian cancer (Del Priore et al., 1995; Whittemore, 1994).

Early detection is the key to fighting ovarian cancer. When it is detected before spreading beyond the ovary, 90% of victims survive. However, the overall survival rate is only 40% (Canadian Cancer Society, 2000). Unfortunately, ovarian cancer is often "silent" in the early stages, showing no obvious signs or symptoms. The most common sign is enlargement of the abdomen, which is caused by the accumulation of fluid. Periodic, complete pelvic examinations are important. The Pap test, which is useful in detecting cervical cancer, does not reveal ovarian cancer. The Canadian Cancer Society (2000) advises women over the age of 40 to have a cancer-related checkup every year.

Surgery, radiation therapy, and drug therapy are treatment options. Surgery usually includes the removal of one or both ovaries, the uterus, and the fallopian tubes.

The Breasts

In some cultures the breasts are viewed merely as biological instruments for feeding infants. In our culture, however, breasts have taken on such erotic significance that a woman's self-esteem may become linked to her bustline.

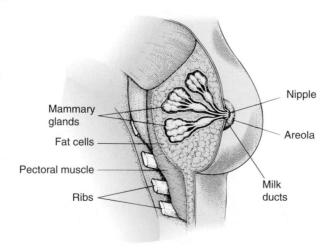

Mammary glands

Fat cells

Pectoral muscle

Ribs

Nipple

Areola

Milk ducts

The breasts are **secondary sex characteristics**. That is, like the rounding of the hips, they distinguish women from men, but they are not directly involved in reproduction. Each breast contains **mammary glands** (Figure 2.7). Each gland opens at the nipple through its own duct. The mammary glands are separated by soft, fatty tissue. It is the amount of this fatty tissue, not the amount of glandular tissue,

Figure 2.8. Normal Variations in the Size and Shape of the Breasts of Adult Women.

The size and shape of the breasts have little bearing on ability to produce milk or on sensitivity to sexual stimulation. Breasts have become highly eroticized in our culture.

that largely determines the size of the breasts. Women vary little in their amount of glandular tissue, so breast size does not determine the quantity of milk that can be produced.

The nipple, which lies in the centre of the **areola**, contains smooth muscle fibres that contract to make the nipple erect. The areola, or area surrounding the nipple, darkens during pregnancy and remains darker after delivery. Oil-producing glands in the areola help lubricate the nipples during breast-feeding. Milk ducts conduct milk from the mammary glands through the nipples. Nipples are richly endowed with nerve endings, so that stimulation of the nipples heightens sexual arousal for many women. Figure 2.8 shows normal variations in the size and shape of the breasts of adult women.

Women can prompt their partners to provide breast stimulation by informing them that their breasts are sensitive to stimulation. They can also guide a partner's hands in ways that provide the type of stimulation they desire. The breasts vary in sensitivity with the phases of the menstrual cycle, and some women appear less responsive to breast stimulation than others. However, some less sensitive women may learn to enjoy breast stimulation by focusing on breast sensations during lovemaking in a relaxed atmosphere.

Areola The dark ring on the breast that encircles the nipple.

Breast Cancer

Breast cancer struck about 21 000 women and took some 5300 lives in Canada in 2003. It is the second leading cause of cancer deaths among women, after lung cancer (Canadian Cancer Society, 2003a). In Canada, it is estimated that 1 woman in 9 will develop breast cancer ("Chance of breast cancer," 1993). The disease takes the lives of nearly 3 of 10 women who develop it. It is not cancer in the breast that causes death, but rather its spread to vital body parts, such as the brain, the bones, the lungs, or the liver.

The incidence of breast cancer rose steadily in Canada between 1974 and 1992, perhaps due to an increased use of **mammography**, a specialized X-ray that detects cancerous lumps in the breast. The rate of increase has slowed since then, however (National Cancer Institute of Canada, 2003). Advances in early detection and treatment have led to a decline in the mortality rate. In fact, in 1999, the death rate from breast cancer was at the lowest level since 1950 (National Cancer Institute of Canada, 2003). The five-year survival rate for women whose breast cancers have not metastasized—that is, spread beyond the breast—is 93%, up from 78% in the 1940s (Miller et al., 1996). The five-year survival rate drops to 69% if the cancer has spread to the surrounding region and to 18% if it has spread to distant sites in the body.

The risk of breast cancer increases sharply with age. About four of five cases develop in women over the age of 50 ("Chance of breast cancer," 1993). The National Cancer Institute of Canada estimates that from birth to age 40, 1 in 217 women will develop breast cancer. From birth to age 50 the risk rises to 1 in 63. By age 60, the risk rises to 1 in 24, and by age 75, to 1 in 15 (Canadian Cancer Society, 2000).

Mammography A special type of X-ray test that detects cancerous lumps in the breast.

The Breast Cancer Society of Canada
www.bcsc.ca/
This site provides information on breast health and the society's news and events.

The risk of breast cancer is higher among women with a family history of the disease (Slattery & Kerber, 1993). A study of more than 100 000 women nurses showed that those with mothers or sisters who had breast cancer had nearly twice the chance of developing the disease themselves (Colditz et al., 1993). Women who had both a mother and a sister with the disease had between two and three times greater risk. Still, about 80% of women with breast cancer have no family history of the disease (Brody, 1995a). Only about 6% of the women with breast cancer in the nurses' study had either a mother or sister with the disease (Johnson & Williams, 1993).

Other risk factors include early onset of menstruation (before age 12), late menopause (after age 50), delayed childbearing (after age 30), never giving birth, and heavy drinking of alcohol (Canadian Cancer Society, 2000; Colditz et al., 1995; Fuchs et al., 1995). Many of these factors apparently create greater risk because of prolonged exposure to estrogen. Estrogen stimulates breast development in young women. Earlier onset of menstruation, later menopause, and delayed childbearing are all connected to longer, uninterrupted exposure to high levels of estrogen. Despite the fact that birth-control pills contain estrogen, a review of 54 studies involving more than 150 000 women concluded that there is no connection between using the pill and breast cancer (Gilbert, 1996), although one recent study suggests that women with a strong family history of breast cancer may be at higher risk if they take the pill (Grabrick et al., 2000). Nor has it been shown that a diet high in fats contributes to breast cancer (Hunter et al., 1996).

Detection Women with breast cancer have lumps in the breast, but most lumps in the breasts are not cancerous. Most are either **cysts** or **benign** tumours called **fibroadenomas**. Breast cancer involves lumps in the breast that are **malignant**.

There is no clear-cut way to prevent breast cancer, but early detection and treatment reduce the risk of mortality. The sooner cancer is detected, the less likely it is to have spread to critical organs.

Breast cancer may be detected in a number of ways, including breast self-examination (BSE), medical examination, and mammography. Through mammography, tiny, highly curable cancers can be detected—and treated—before they can be felt by touch (Brody, 1995a). By the time a malignant lump is large enough to be felt by touch, it may have metastasized—that is, splintered off to form colonies elsewhere in the body. A mammogram can detect tiny tumours before metastasis. One study found that 82% of women whose breast cancers were detected early by mammography survived for at least five years following surgery, as compared to 60% of those whose cancers were discovered later. Early detection may offer another benefit. Smaller cancerous lumps can often be removed by **lumpectomy**, which spares the breast. More advanced cancers are likely to be treated by **mastectomy.**

Cyst a saclike structure filled with fluid or diseased material.

Benign Doing little or no harm.

Fibroadenoma A benign, fibrous tumour.

Malignant Leading to invasive and destructive growth and metastasis; severe, tending to become worse.

Lumpectomy Surgical removal of a lump from the breast.

Mastectomy Surgical removal of the entire breast.

Mammography. Early detection is a key to effective treatment of cancer. Mammography uses specialized X-ray technology to detect cancerous lumps in the breast before they can be felt. The goal is to detect tumours before they have metastasized to other parts of the body.

Applications

Does Breast Cancer Screening Work?

Recent research has called into question the effectiveness of both mammograms and breast self-examination in the early detection of breast cancer. As part of the Canadian National Breast Screening Study (2), nearly 40 000 Canadian women between the ages of 50 and 59 were randomly assigned to either a mammogram-only group or a group that combined a mammogram with breast examination. Over the 13 years of the study, 622 women in the combination group and 610 in the mammogram-only group were diagnosed with invasive breast cancer, and approximately equal numbers of women in each group had died of the disease by 1996, suggesting that accompanying annual mammograms with thorough breast examination by trained professionals does not affect mortality (Miller et al., 2000). Although women have been encouraged to examine their breasts for at least 40 years, a 1994 review of research on the effectiveness of breast self-examination concluded that there was not enough evidence to recommend either for or against BSE as a screening method for breast cancer (Morrison, 1994). More recently, Nancy Baxter (2001) reviewed research published since that time and concluded that BSE does not reduce the mortality rate from breast cancer.

Not surprisingly, not all health practitioners agree with this conclusion, and the Canadian Cancer Society is maintaining its recommendation that women practise regular breast self-examination and report the results of any changes to their doctors (Canadian Cancer Society, 2003b).

The Canadian Cancer Society recommends that women between the ages of 50 and 69 have a mammogram every two years. Mammography is not foolproof, however (see the *Applications* box "Does Breast Cancer Screening Work?"). Thus, the chances of early detection are optimized through a combination of monthly breast self-examinations (see the *Applications* box "Guidelines for Breast Self-Examination"), annual breast examinations by a physician, and regular mammograms.

Although breast cancer is much more common among women over 50, it has killed women as young as their twenties (Statistics Canada 2001), so it is never too early to start checking. Men, too, can get breast cancer, although it is less common. A man should also report to his doctor any changes he notices in chest tissue.

Applications

Guidelines for Breast Self-Examination

A woman may wish to undertake an initial breast self-examination with a physician in order to determine the degree of "lumpiness" that seems normal for her. Then she should conduct a breast self-examination at least once a month, preferably about a week after her period ends (when the breasts are least influenced by hormones), so that any changes can be reported promptly to a physician (see Figure 2.9).

The following instructions for breast self-examination are based on Canadian Cancer Society guidelines. Additional material on breast self-examination may be obtained from the Canadian Cancer Society by calling this toll-free number:
    1-800-939-3333.

1. *In the shower.* Examine your breasts during your bath or shower; hands glide more easily over wet skin. Keep your fingers flat, and move gently over every part of each breast. Use the right hand to examine the left breast and the left hand for the right breast. Check for any lump, hard knot, or thickening.

2. *Before a mirror.* Inspect your breasts with your arms at your sides. Next, raise your arms high overhead. Look for any changes in the contour of each breast, a swelling, dimpling of skin, or changes in the nipple. Then rest your palms on your hips and press down firmly to flex your chest muscles. Your left and right breasts will not exactly match—few women's breasts do. Regular inspection shows what is normal for you and will give you confidence in your examination.

3. *Lying down.* To examine your right breast, put a pillow or folded towel under your right shoulder. Place your right arm behind your head—this distributes breast tissue more evenly on the chest. With your left hand, fingers flat, press gently with the finger pads (the top thirds of the fingers) of the three middle fingers in small circular motions around an imaginary clock face. Begin at the outermost top of your right breast for 12 o'clock, then move to 1 o'clock, and so on around the circle back to 12. A ridge of firm tissue in the lower curve of each breast is normal. Then move in 2.5 cm, toward the nipple. Keep circling to examine every part of your breast, including the nipple. This requires at least

Figure 2.9. Woman Examining Her Breasts for Lumps.

three more circles. Now slowly repeat the procedure on your left breast. Place the pillow beneath your left shoulder, your left arm behind your head, and use the finger pads on your right hand.

After you examine your left breast fully, squeeze the nipple of each breast gently between your thumb and index finger. Any discharge, clear or bloody, should be reported to your doctor immediately.

Research shows that many women who know how to do breast self-exami-nations do not do them regularly. Why? There are many reasons, including fear of what one will find and doubts as to whether self-examination will make a difference. But the most frequently mentioned reasons are being too busy or forgetting (Friedman et al., 1994).

The Menstrual Cycle

Menstruation The cyclical bleeding that stems from the shedding of the uterine lining (endometrium).

Ovulation The release of an ovum from an ovary.

Corpus luteum The follicle that has released an ovum and then produces copious amounts of progesterone and estrogen during the luteal phase of a woman's cycle. (From Latin roots meaning "yellow body.")

Endocrine gland A ductless gland that releases its secretions directly into the bloodstream.

Menarche The onset of menstruation; first menstruation. (From Greek roots meaning "months" [*men*] and "beginning" [*arche*].)

Menstruation is the cyclical bleeding that stems from the shedding of the uterine lining (endometrium). Menstruation takes place when a reproductive cycle has not led to the fertilization of an ovum. The word *menstruation* derives from the Latin *mensis*, meaning "month." The human menstrual cycle averages about 28 days in length.

The menstrual cycle is regulated by the hormones estrogen and progesterone, and can be divided into four phases. During the first phase of the cycle, the *proliferative* phase, which follows menstruation, estrogen levels increase, causing waves of ova (egg cells) to ripen within their follicles and endometrial tissue to proliferate in the uterus. During the second phase of the cycle, estrogen reaches peak blood levels, and **ovulation** occurs. Normally only 1 ovum reaches maturity and is released by an ovary during ovulation. Then the third phase—the *secretory*, or *luteal*, phase—of the cycle begins. The luteal phase begins right after ovulation and continues through the beginning of the next cycle.

The term *luteal phase* is derived from **corpus luteum**, the name given the follicle that releases an ovum. The corpus luteum functions as an **endocrine gland** and produces copious amounts of progesterone and estrogen. Progesterone causes the endometrium to thicken, so that it will be able to support an embryo if fertilization occurs. If the ovum goes unfertilized, however, estrogen and progesterone levels plummet. These falloffs trigger the fourth phase, the menstrual phase, which leads to the beginning of a new cycle.

Ovulation may not occur in every menstrual cycle. Anovulatory ("without ovulation") cycles are most common in the years just after **menarche**. They may become frequent again in the years prior to menopause, but they may also occur irregularly among women in their 20s and 30s.

Although the menstrual cycle averages about 28 days, variations among women, and in the same woman from month to month, are quite common. Girls' cycles are often irregular for a few years after menarche. Variations from cycle to cycle tend to occur during the proliferative phase that precedes ovulation. That is, menstruation tends to reliably follow ovulation by about 14 days. Variations of more than two days in the postovulation period are rare.

Although hormones regulate the menstrual cycle, psychological factors can influence the secretion of hormones. Stress can delay or halt menstruation. Anxiety that she may be pregnant and thus miss her period may also cause a woman to be late.

Regulation of the Menstrual Cycle

The menstrual cycle involves finely tuned relationships between structures in the brain—the **hypothalamus** and the **pituitary gland**—and the ovaries and uterus. All these structures are parts of the endocrine system, which means that they secrete chemicals directly into the bloodstream (see Figure 2.10). The ovaries and uterus are also reproductive organs. The chemicals secreted by endocrine glands are called **hormones.** (Other bodily secretions, such as milk, saliva, sweat, and tears, arrive at their destinations by passing through narrow, tubular structures in the body called *ducts*.)

Behavioural and social scientists are especially interested in hormones because of their behavioural effects. Hormones regulate bodily processes such as the metabolic rate, growth of bones and muscle, production of milk, metabolism of sugar, and storage of fats, among others. Several hormones play important roles in sexual and reproductive functions.

The gonads—the **testes** (or testicles) in the male and the ovaries in the female—secrete sex hormones directly into the bloodstream. The female gonads, the ovaries, produce the sex hormones estrogen and progesterone. The male gonads, the testes, produce the male sex hormone **testosterone**. Males and females also produce sex hormones of the other gender, but in relatively small amounts.

The hypothalamus is a pea-sized structure in the front part of the brain. It weighs about 4 to 5 grams and lies above the pituitary gland and below (hence the prefix *hypo-*, for "under") the thalamus. Despite its small size, it is involved in regulating many states of motivation, including hunger, thirst, aggression, and sex. For example, when the rear part of a male rat's hypothalamus is stimulated by an electric probe, the rat runs through its courting and mating sequence. It nibbles at a female's ears and at the back of her neck. When she responds, they copulate. Human sexuality is not so stereotyped or mechanical—although in the cases of some people who are highly routinized in their behaviour, it may appear so.

Hypothalamus A bundle of neural cell bodies near the centre of the brain that are involved in regulating body temperature, motivation, and emotion.

Pituitary gland The gland that secretes growth hormone, prolactin, oxytocin, and others.

Hormone A substance secreted by an endocrine gland that regulates various body functions. (From the Greek *horman*, meaning "to stimulate" or "to excite.")

Testes The male gonads. Singular: testis.

Testosterone The male sex hormone that fosters the development of male sex characteristics and is connected with the sex drive.

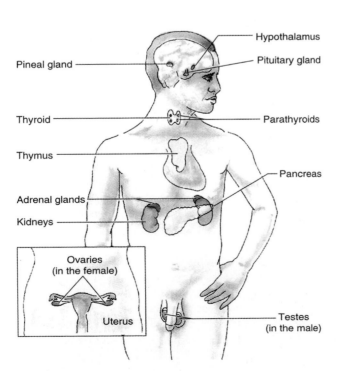

Figure 2.10. Major Glands of the Endocrine System.

The endocrine system consists of glands that secrete chemicals called hormones directly into the bloodstream.

Prolactin A pituitary hormone that stimulates production of milk.

Oxytocin A pituitary hormone that stimulates uterine contractions in labour and the ejection of milk during nursing.

Gonadotropins Pituitary hormones that stimulate the gonads. (Literally, "that which 'feeds' the gonads.")

Follicle-stimulating hormone (FSH) A gonadotropin that stimulates development of follicles in the ovaries.

Luteinizing hormone (LH) A gonadotropin that helps regulate the menstrual cycle by triggering ovulation.

Gonadotropin-releasing hormone (Gn-RH) A hormone secreted by the hypothalamus that stimulates the pituitary gland to release gonadotropins.

Proliferative phase The first phase of the menstrual cycle, which begins with the end of menstruation and lasts about 9 or 10 days. During this phase, the endometrium proliferates.

The pituitary gland, which is about the size of a pea, lies below the hypothalamus at the base of the brain. Because many pituitary secretions regulate other endocrine glands, the pituitary has also been called the *master gland*. Pituitary hormones regulate bone and muscle growth and urine production. Two pituitary hormones are active during pregnancy and motherhood: **prolactin,** which stimulates production of milk; and **oxytocin**, which stimulates uterine contractions in labour and the ejection of milk during nursing. The pituitary gland also produces **gonadotropins** (literally, "that which 'feeds' the gonads") that stimulate the ovaries: **follicle-stimulating hormone (FSH)** and **luteinizing hormone (LH)**. These hormones play central roles in regulating the menstrual cycle.

The hypothalamus receives information about bodily events through the nervous and circulatory systems. It monitors the blood levels of various hormones, including estrogen and progesterone, and releases a hormone called **gonadotropin-releasing hormone (Gn-RH)**, which stimulates the pituitary to release gonadotropins. Gonadotropins, in turn, regulate the activity of the gonads. It was once thought that the pituitary gland ran the show, but it is now known that the pituitary gland is regulated by the hypothalamus. Even the "master gland" must serve another.

Phases of the Menstrual Cycle

We noted that the menstrual cycle has four stages or phases: proliferative, ovulatory, secretory, and menstrual (see Figure 2.11).

The Proliferative Phase
The first phase, or **proliferative phase**, begins with the end of menstruation and lasts about 9 or 10 days in an average 28-day cycle (see Figure 2.11 and Figure 2.12). During this phase the endometrium develops, or "proliferates." This phase is also known as the *preovulatory* or *follicular* phase, because certain ovarian follicles mature and the ovaries prepare for ovulation.

Low levels of estrogen and progesterone are circulating in the blood as menstruation draws to an end. When the hypothalamus senses a low level of estrogen in the blood, it increases its secretion of Gn-RH, which in turn triggers the pituitary gland to release FSH. When FSH reaches the ovaries, it stimulates some follicles (perhaps 10 to 20) to begin to mature. As these follicles ripen, they begin to produce estrogen. Normally, however, only one of them—called the *graafian follicle*—will reach full maturity in the days just preceding ovulation. As the graafian follicle matures, it moves toward the surface of the ovary, where it will eventually rupture and release a mature egg (see Figure 2.12 and Figure 2.13).

Museum of Menstruation and Women's Health
www.mum.org/
This virtual museum provides a wealth of information and arcane facts on menstruation.

Figure 2.11. The Four Phases of the Menstrual Cycle.

The menstrual cycle includes proliferative, ovulatory, secretory (luteal), and menstrual phases.

Figure 2.12. Changes That Occur During the Menstrual Cycle.

This figure shows five categories of biological change: (a) changes in the development of the uterine lining (endometrium), (b) follicular changes, (c) changes in blood levels of ovarian hormones, (d) changes in blood levels of pituitary hormones, and (e) changes in basal temperature. Note the dip in temperature that is connected with ovulation.

Estrogen causes the endometrium in the uterus to thicken to about 3 cm. Glands develop that would eventually nourish an embryo. Estrogen also stimulates the appearance of a thin cervical mucus. This mucus is alkaline and provides a hospitable, nutritious medium for sperm. The chances are thus increased that sperm that enter the female reproductive system at the time of ovulation will remain viable.

The Ovulatory Phase During ovulation, or the **ovulatory phase**, the graafian follicle ruptures and releases a mature ovum near a fallopian tube—not actually into a fallopian tube (see Figure 2.13). The other ripening follicles degenerate and are harmlessly reabsorbed by the body. If two ova mature and are released during ovulation, which happens occasionally, and both are fertilized, fraternal (nonidentical) twins will develop. Identical twins develop when one fertilized ovum divides into two separate **zygotes**.

Ovulatory phase The second stage of the menstrual cycle, during which a follicle ruptures and releases a mature ovum.

Zygote A fertilized ovum (egg cell).

Ovulation is set into motion when estrogen production reaches a critical level. The high level of estrogen is detected by the hypothalamus, which triggers the pituitary to release copious amounts of FSH and LH (see Figure 2.12). The surge of LH triggers ovulation, which usually begins 12 to 24 hours after the level of LH in the body has reached its peak.

The synthetic hormone **clomiphene** is chemically similar to LH and has been used by women who ovulate irregularly to induce reliable ovulation. The induction and accurate prediction of the timing of ovulation increase the chances of conceiving.

A woman's *basal body temperature*, taken by oral or rectal thermometer immediately after awakening, dips slightly at ovulation (see Figure 2.12) and rises by about half a degree Celsius on the day following ovulation. Many women use this information to help them conceive or avoid conceiving. Note, however, that Figure 2.12 is idealized. Many women show greater fluctuations in daily temperature or gradual rises in temperature for about two days after ovulation.

Some women have discomfort or cramping during ovulation, termed **mittelschmerz**. Mittelschmerz is sometimes confused with appendicitis. Mittelschmerz, however, may occur on either side of the abdomen, depending on which ovary is releasing an ovum. A ruptured appendix always causes pain on the right side.

The Secretory Phase
The phase following ovulation is called the postovulatory or **secretory phase**. Some people refer to it as the *luteal phase*, which reflects the name given the ruptured (graafian) follicle—the *corpus luteum*. Figure 2.12 and Figure 2.13 show the transformation of the graafian follicle into the corpus luteum.

Under the influence of LH, the corpus luteum, which has remained in the ovary, begins to produce large amounts of progesterone and estrogen. Levels of these hormones peak at around the 20th or 21st day of an average cycle (see Figure 2.12). These hormones cause the glands in the endometrium to secrete nutrients to sustain a fertilized ovum that becomes implanted in the uterine wall.

If implantation does not occur, the hypothalamus responds to the peak levels of progesterone in the blood by signalling the pituitary to stop producing LH and FSH. Although certainly more complex, this feedback process is similar to that of a thermostat in a house reacting to rising temperatures by shutting down the furnace. The levels of LH and FSH decline rapidly, leading the corpus luteum to decompose. After its decomposition, levels of estrogen and progesterone fall precipitously. In this sense, the corpus luteum sows the seeds of its own destruction: Its hormones signal the brain to shut down secretion of substances that maintain it.

The Menstrual Phase: An End and a Beginning
The **menstrual phase** is the sloughing off of the uterine lining (the endometrium) in the menstrual flow. Menstruation occurs when estrogen and progesterone levels decline to the point where they can no longer sustain the uterine lining. The lining then disintegrates and is discharged from the body along with the menstrual flow. Menstruation itself is the passing of the lining through the cervix and vagina.

The low estrogen levels of the menstrual phase signal the hypothalamus to release Gn-RH, which in turn stimulates the pituitary to secrete FSH. FSH, in turn, prompts ovarian secretion of estrogen and the onset of another proliferative phase. Thus a new cycle begins. The menstrual phase is a beginning as well as an end.

Menstrual flow contains blood from the endometrium (uterine lining), endometrial tissue, and cervical and vaginal mucus. Although the flow can appear persistent and last for five days or more, most women lose only a total of 60–90 mL (4 to 6 tablespoonfuls). A typical blood donor, by contrast, donates 500 mL of blood at a sitting. A woman's blood loss through menstruation is thus usually harmless. Extremely heavy or prolonged (over a week) menstrual bleeding may reflect health problems and should be discussed with a health care provider.

Prior to 1933, women generally used external sanitary napkins or pads to absorb the menstrual flow. In that year, however, **tampons** were introduced and altered the habits of millions of women. Women who use tampons can swim without concern while menstruating, wear more revealing or comfortable apparel, and feel generally less burdened.

Clomiphene A synthetic hormone that is chemically similar to LH and induces ovulation.

Mittelschmerz Pain that occurs during ovulation. (German for "middle pain," reflecting the fact that the pain occurs midway between menstrual periods.)

Secretory phase The third phase of the menstrual cycle, which follows ovulation. Also referred to as the luteal phase, after the corpus luteum, which begins to secrete large amounts of progesterone and estrogen following ovulation.

Menstrual phase The fourth phase of the menstrual cycle, during which the endometrium is sloughed off in the menstrual flow.

Tampon A cylindrical plug of cotton that is inserted into the vagina and left in place to absorb menstrual fluid. (A French word, meaning a gun barrel "plug.")

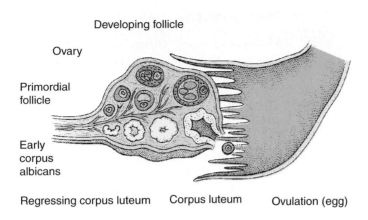

Developing follicle

Ovary

Primordial follicle

Early corpus albicans

Regressing corpus luteum   Corpus luteum   Ovulation (egg)

Figure 2.13. Maturation and Eventual Decomposition of an Ovarian Follicle.

Many follicles develop and produce estrogen during the proliferative phase of the menstrual cycle. Usually only one, the graafian follicle, ruptures and releases an ovum. The graafian follicle then develops into the corpus luteum, which produces copious quantities of estrogen and progesterone. When fertilization does not occur, the corpus luteum decomposes.

Tampons are inserted into the vagina and left in place to absorb menstrual fluid. Tampons have been suspected of causing or exacerbating infections, especially toxic shock syndrome (TSS), an infection that is sometimes fatal. Signs of TSS include fever, headache, sore throat, vomiting, diarrhea, muscle aches, rash, and dizziness. Peeling skin, disorientation, and a plunge in blood pressure may follow.

TSS is caused by the *Staphylococcus aureus* ("staph") bacterium. In 1980, the peak year for cases of TSS, there were 344 recorded cases of TSS in North America and 28 fatalities. The number of TSS cases has declined dramatically since then, with few cases being reported to Health Canada. In 2001, eight Canadians died of TSS (Statistics Canada 2001).

Some researchers believe that concern over TSS has been exaggerated. Nevertheless, many women now use regular rather than superabsorbent tampons to reduce the chance of creating a breeding ground for staph bacteria. Some women alternate tampons during the day with sanitary napkins for overnight. Some change their tampons three or four times a day. Women are encouraged to consult their health care providers about TSS.

Sex During Menstruation

Many couples continue to engage in coitus during menstruation, but others abstain. One study found that people are less likely to initiate sexual activity during menstruation than during any other phase of the woman's cycle (Harvey, 1987). Some people abstain because of religious prohibitions. Others express concern about the "fuss" or the "mess" of the menstrual flow. Despite traditional attitudes that associate menstruation with uncleanliness, there is no evidence that coitus during menstruation is physically harmful to either partner. In fact, menstrual coitus may be helpful to the woman. The uterine contractions that occur during orgasm may help relieve cramping by dispelling blood congestion. Orgasm achieved through masturbation may have the same effect.

Women may be sexually aroused at any time during the menstrual cycle. The preponderance of the research evidence, however, points to a peak in sexual desire in women around the time of ovulation (Kresin, 1993).

Human coital patterns during the phases of the menstrual cycle apparently reflect personal decisions, not hormone fluctuations. Some couples may decide to increase their frequency of coitus at ovulation in order to optimize the chances of conceiving, or to abstain during menstruation because of religious beliefs or beliefs linking menses with uncleanliness. Some may also increase their coital activity preceding menstruation to compensate for anticipated abstinence during menses, or increase coital activity afterwards to make up for deprivation.

Menopause and Sexuality
Menopause does not mark the end of a woman's sex life. Many women, in fact, feel sexually liberated by the biological severing of the traditional link between sexual activity and reproduction.

Menopause The cessation of menstruation.

Climacteric A long-term process, including menopause, that involves the gradual decline in the reproductive capacity of the ovaries.

Osteoporosis Online
www.osteoporosis.ca/
Sponsored by the Osteoporosis Society of Canada, this site provides information for women of all ages—including a 60-second risk quiz.

Osteoporosis A condition characterized by a decline in bone density, such that bones become porous and brittle. (From the Greek *osteon*, meaning "bone," and the Latin *porus*, meaning "pore.")

Hormone-replacement therapy (HRT) Replacement of naturally occurring estrogen, or estrogen and progesterone, with synthetic equivalents, following menopause.

Menopause

Menopause, or the "change of life," is the cessation of menstruation. Menopause is a process that most commonly occurs between the ages of 46 and 50 and lasts for about two years. However, it may begin any time between the ages of 35 and 60. There is at least one case of a woman who became pregnant at age 61.

Menopause is a specific event in a long-term process known as the **climacteric** ("critical period"), which refers to the gradual decline in the reproductive capacity of the ovaries. The climacteric generally lasts for about 15 years, from ages 45 to 60 or so. After about the age of 35, the menstrual cycles of many women shorten, from an average of 28 days to 25 days at age 40 and to 23 days by the mid-40s. By the end of her 40s, a woman's cycles often become erratic, with some periods close together and others missed.

In menopause, the pituitary gland continues to pour normal levels of FSH and LH into the bloodstream, but for reasons that are not well understood, the ovaries gradually lose their capacity to respond. The ovaries no longer ripen egg cells or produce the sex hormones estrogen and progesterone.

The deficit in estrogen may lead to a number of unpleasant physical sensations, such as night sweats and hot flashes (suddenly feeling hot) and hot flushes (suddenly looking reddened). Hot flashes and flushes may alternate with cold sweats, in which a woman feels suddenly cold and clammy. Anyone who has experienced "cold feet" or hands from anxiety or fear will understand how dramatic the shifting patterns of blood flow can be. Hot flashes and flushes stem largely from waves of dilation of blood vessels across the face and upper body. All of these sensations reflect vasomotor instability. That is, there are disruptions in the body mechanisms that dilate or constrict the blood vessels to maintain an even body temperature. Additional signs of estrogen deficiency include dizziness, headaches, pains in the joints, sensations of tingling in the hands or feet, burning or itchy skin, and heart palpitations. The skin usually becomes drier. There is some loss of breast tissue and decreased vaginal lubrication during sexual arousal. Women may also encounter sleep problems, such as awakening more frequently at night and having difficulty falling back to sleep.

Long-term estrogen deficiency has been linked to brittleness and porosity of the bones (**osteoporosis**). In this condition, bones break more readily, and some women develop so-called dowager's hump. Osteoporosis is potentially severely handicapping, even life threatening. The increased brittleness of the bones increases the risk of serious fractures, especially of the hip, and many elderly women never recover from these fractures.

Estrogen deficiency also has psychological effects. It can impair cognitive functioning and feelings of psychological well-being (Sourander, 1994).

Some women who experience severe physical symptoms have been helped by **hormone-replacement therapy (HRT)**, which typically consists of synthetic estrogen and progesterone. These synthetic hormones are used to offset the losses of their naturally occurring counterparts. HRT may help reduce the hot flushes and other symptoms brought about by hormonal deficiencies during menopause. It is helpful in protecting the woman against the development of osteoporosis, but not as effective as other drugs used either alone or in combination with HRT (Greenspan et al., 2003). Although HRT has certainly been helpful to many menopausal women, recent research has raised serious concerns about both the effectiveness and the safety of HRT. A major American study involving more than 16 000 women between the ages of 50 and 79 was terminated three years early because the researchers felt that the risks of HRT outweighed any potential benefits. The study did find a decrease in the incidence of hip and other fractures related to osteoporosis and a nonsignificant decrease in the incidence of colorectal cancer. However, the incidence of coronary heart disease, pulmonary embolism, and other blood clotting disorders increased, and the risk of breast cancer increased in women who remained on combined HRT for more than five years (Manson et al., 2003). For these and other reasons, the Society of Obstetricians and Gynecologists of Canada (SOGC) does not recommend HRT for prevention of heart disease or for routine treatment of hot flashes, night sweats, etc. The SOGC also recommends that women be helped to make informed choices about HRT (Blake et al., 2002).

For those who choose not to use replacement hormones, other drugs are available, when they are needed, to help them deal with menopausal complaints, such as hot flashes.

Your Guide to Menopause
http://www.sogc.org/pub_ed/menop/english/menopause.shtml
The Society of Obstetricians and Gynecologists of Canada provides this public education site with information about menopause, symptoms, and related health issues.

Menstrual Problems

Although menstruation is a natural biological process, the majority of women experience some discomfort prior to or during menstruation. Table 2.1 contains a list of commonly reported symptoms of menstrual problems. The problems we explore in this section include dysmenorrhea, mastalgia, menstrual migraine headaches, amenorrhea, and premenstrual syndrome (PMS).

Dysmenorrhea Pain or discomfort during menstruation, or **dysmenorrhea**, is the most common type of menstrual problem. Most women at some time have at least mild menstrual pain or discomfort. Pelvic cramps are the most common manifestation of dysmenorrhea. They may be accompanied by headache, backache, nausea, or bloated feelings. Women who develop severe cases usually do so within a few years of menarche. **Primary dysmenorrhea** refers to menstrual pain or discomfort in the absence of known organic pathology. Women with **secondary dysmenorrhea** have identified organic problems that are believed to cause their menstrual problems. Their pain or discomfort is caused by, or is secondary to, these problems. Endometriosis, pelvic inflammatory disease, and ovarian cysts are just a few of the organic disorders that can give rise to secondary dysmenorrhea. Yet evidence is accumulating that supposed primary dysmenorrhea is often secondary to hormonal changes, although the precise causes have not been delineated. For example, menstrual cramps sometimes decrease dramatically after childbirth, as a result of the massive hormonal changes that occur with pregnancy.

Painful menstruation was reported by nearly 75% of the participants in a sample of college women (Wildman & White, 1986). The symptoms varied not only from person to person but also according to whether or not the women had been pregnant. Women who had been pregnant reported a lower incidence of menstrual pain but a higher incidence of premenstrual symptoms and menstrual discomfort.

Dysmenorrhea Pain or discomfort during menstruation.

Primary dysmenorrhea Menstrual pain or discomfort that occurs in the absence of known organic problems.

Secondary dysmenorrhea Menstrual pain or discomfort that is caused by identified organic problems.

TABLE 2.1 Common Symptoms of Menstrual Problems

Physical Symptoms	Psychological Symptoms
Swelling of the breasts	Depressed mood, sudden tearfulness
Tenderness in the breasts	Loss of interest in usual social or recreational activities
Bloating	Anxiety, tension (feeling "on edge" or "keyed up")
Weight gain	
Food cravings	Anger
Abdominal discomfort	Irritability
Cramping	Changes in body image
Lack of energy	Concern over skipping routine activities, school, or work
Sleep disturbance, fatigue	
Migraine headache	A sense of loss of control
Pains in muscles and joints	A sense of loss of ability to cope
Aggravation of chronic disorders such as asthma and allergies	

Biological Aspects of Dysmenorrhea Menstrual cramps appear to result from uterine spasms that may be brought about by copious secretion of hormones called **prostaglandins**. Prostaglandins apparently cause muscle fibres in the uterine wall to

Prostaglandins Hormones that cause muscle fibres in the uterine wall to contract, as during labour.

contract, as during labour. Most contractions go unnoticed, but powerful, persistent contractions are discomfiting in themselves and may temporarily deprive the uterus of oxygen, another source of distress. Women with more intense menstrual discomfort apparently produce higher quantities of prostaglandins. Prostaglandin-inhibiting drugs, such as ibuprofen, indomethacin, and aspirin, are thus often of help. Menstrual pain may also be secondary to endometriosis.

Pelvic pressure and bloating may be traced to pelvic edema (Greek for "swelling")—the congestion of fluid in the pelvic region. Fluid retention can lead to a gain of several pounds, sensations of heaviness, and **mastalgia**—a swelling of the breasts that some-times causes premenstrual discomfort. Masters and Johnson (1966) noted that orgasm (through coitus or masturbation) can help relieve menstrual discomfort by reducing the pelvic congestion that spawns bloating and pressure. Orgasm may also increase the menstrual flow and shorten this phase of the cycle.

Headaches frequently accompany menstrual discomfort. Most headaches (in both genders) stem from simple muscle tension, notably in the shoulders, the back of the neck, and the scalp. Pelvic discomfort may cause muscle contractions, thus contributing to the tension that produces headaches. Women who are tense about their menstrual flow are thus candidates for muscle tension headaches. Migraine headaches may arise from changes in the blood flow in the brain, however. Migraines are typically limited to one side of the head and are often accompanied by visual difficulties.

Amenorrhea **Amenorrhea** is the absence of menstruation and is a primary sign of infertility. **Primary amenorrhea** describes the absence of menstruation in a woman who has not menstruated at all by about the age of 16 or 17. **Secondary amenorrhea** describes delayed or absent menstrual periods in women who have had regular periods in the past. Amenorrhea has various causes, including abnormalities in the structures of the reproductive system, hormonal abnormalities, growths such as cysts and tumours, and psychological problems, such as stress. Amenorrhea is normal during pregnancy and following menopause. Amenorrhea may also occur in women who exercise strenuously, such as competitive long-distance runners. It is unclear whether the cessation of menstruation in female athletes is due to the effects of strenuous exercise itself, to related physical factors such as low body fat, to the stress of intensive training, or to a combination of factors.

Mastalgia A swelling of the breasts that sometimes causes premenstrual discomfort.

Amenorrhea The absence of menstruation.

Primary amenorrhea Lack of menstruation in a woman who has never menstruated.

Secondary amenorrhea Lack of menstruation in a woman who has previously menstruated.

Applications

Coping with Menstrual Discomfort

Only a generation ago, PMS was seen as something a woman must put up with. No longer. Today there are many treatment options. These include exercise, dietary control (for example, eating several small meals a day rather than two or three large meals; limiting salt and sugar; vitamin supplements), hormone treatments (usually progesterone), and medications that reduce anxiety or increase the amount of serotonin in the nervous system (Brody, 1996; Steiner et al., 1995). If you have PMS, determine the kinds of symptoms that affect you most by using a PMS calendar or simply by paying close attention. Then check with your physician about the most up-to-date treatment approaches.

Women with persistent menstrual distress may profit from the suggestions listed below. Researchers are exploring the effectiveness of these techniques in controlled studies. For now, you might consider running a personal experiment. Adopt the techniques that sound right for you—all of them, if you wish. Try them out for a few months to see if you reap any benefits.

1. Don't blame yourself! Menstrual problems were once erroneously attributed to women's "hysterical" nature. This is nonsense. Menstrual problems appear, in large part, to reflect hormonal variations or chemical fluctuations in the brain during the menstrual cycle.

2. Keep a menstrual calendar, so that you can track your menstrual symptoms systematically and identify patterns. Clinicians often determine whether PMS is present by asking the woman to track her physical and emotional symptoms over at least two cycles.

3. Develop strategies for dealing with days that you experience the greatest distress—strategies that will help enhance your pleasure and minimize the stress affecting you on those days. Go see a movie or get into that novel you've been meaning to read.

Premenstrual Syndrome (PMS) The term **premenstrual syndrome (PMS)** describes the combination of bodily and psychological symptoms that may afflict women during the four- to six-day interval that precedes their menses each month (see Table 2.2). PMS also appears to be linked with imbalances in serotonin (Steiner et al., 1995), a chemical messenger in the nervous system. Serotonin imbalances are also linked to changes in appetite. In one study, women who suffered from PMS and nonsufferers alike showed increased appetite during the luteal phase, but the increases were greater for women with PMS (Both-Orthman et al., 1988). For many women, premenstrual symptoms persist during menstruation.

Nearly three women in four experience some form of PMS (Brody, 1989). The great majority of cases involve mild to moderate discomfort. Fewer than 10% of women report menstrual symptoms severe enough to impair their social, academic, or occupational functioning (Brody, 1996).

The causes of PMS are unclear, but evidence is accumulating for a biological basis to premenstrual symptoms (Asso & Magos, 1992). Researchers are looking for possible relationships between menstrual problems, including PMS, and chemical imbalances in the body. Researchers have yet to find differences in levels of estrogen or progesterone between women with severe PMS and those with mild or no symptoms (Rubinow &

> **Premenstrual syndrome (PMS)** A combination of physical and psychological symptoms (e.g., anxiety, depression, irritability, weight gain from fluid retention, and abdominal discomfort) that regularly afflicts many women during the four- to six-day interval that precedes their menses each month.

TABLE 2.2 Features of PMS*

Depression	Overeating or cravings for certain foods
Anxiety	Insomnia or too much sleeping
Anger and irritability	Feelings of being out of control or overwhelmed
Loss of interest in usual activities	Physical problems such as headaches, tenderness in the breasts, joint or muscle pain, weight gain or feeling bloated (both from fluid retention)
Difficulty concentrating	
Lack of energy	

*Most women experience only a few of these features, if they experience any at all.

Source: Brody, Jane E. (1996, August 28). PMS Need Not Be the Worry It Was Just Decades Ago. New York Times, p. C9.

---

4. Ask yourself whether you harbour any self-defeating attitudes toward menstruation that might be compounding distress. Do close relatives or friends see menstruation as an illness, a time of "pollution," a "dirty thing"? Have you adopted any of these attitudes—if not verbally, then in ways that affect your behaviour, such as by restricting your social activities during your period?

5. See a doctor about your concerns, especially if you suffer severe symptoms. Severe menstrual symptoms are often secondary to medical disorders such as endometriosis and pelvic inflammatory disease (PID).

Check it out.

6. Develop nutritious eating habits— and continue them throughout the entire cycle (that means always). Consider limiting intake of alcohol, caffeine, fats, salt, and sweets, especially during the days preceding menstruation.

7. Eat several smaller meals (or nutritious snacks) throughout the day, rather than a few highly filling meals.

8. Try vigorous exercise—jogging, swimming, bicycling, fast walking, dancing, skating, even jumping rope. Evidence suggests that exercise helps to relieve and possibly prevent menstrual discomfort (Choi, 1992).

9. Check with your doctor about vitamin and mineral supplements (such as calcium and magnesium). Vitamin B6 appears to have helped some women.

10. Ask your doctor about trying ibuprofen (brand names: Medipren, Advil, Motrin, etc.) or other medicines available over the counter for cramping. Prescription drugs, such as antianxiety drugs or antidepressant drugs, may also be of help (Brody, 1996).

11. Remind yourself that menstrual problems are time-limited. Don't worry about getting through life or a career. Just get through the next couple of days.

Schmidt, 1995). Perhaps it is not hormone levels themselves but the sensitivity of brain centres to these hormones that predisposes some women to PMS.

An alternative explanation of PMS has been proposed by Joan Chrisler and Paula Caplan (2002). They reviewed both the research and popular literature on PMS and suggest that, rather than a medical syndrome, it is a culture-bound syndrome—that is, a collection of "...symptoms and/or experiences that have been categorized as a dysfunction or disease in some societies but not in others" (p. 284). This does not mean that the physical and/or emotional changes women experience are illusory. However, it is only in Western societies that women label their emotional state as abnormal and requiring professional intervention (Chrisler & Caplan, 2002).

Treatments for PMS range from exercise and dietary control (for example, limiting salt and sugar), to use of vitamin supplements, to hormone treatments (usually progesterone), to drugs that increase the amount of serotonin in the nervous system (Steiner et al., 1995). Check with your physician about the most up-to-date research findings.

In this chapter we have explored female sexual anatomy and physiology. In the following chapter, we turn our attention to the male.

Summing Up

The Female Sex Organs

External Sex Organs: The **mons veneris** is a layer of fatty tissue that covers the joining of the pubic bones in the front of the body. The **labia majora** are large folds of skin that run downward from the mons along the sides of the vulva. The **labia minora** are hairless, light-coloured membranes that surround the urethral and vaginal openings. The **clitoris** is the most sensitive of the female sex organs. Its only purpose is sexual stimulation. The **vestibule** contains the openings to both the vagina and urethra. The **urethral opening** allows urine to pass from the bladder out of the body. The **vaginal opening**, or introitus, lies below the urethral opening. The perineum is the area between the vaginal opening and the anus. Underlying structures include the vestibular bulbs, Bartholin's glands, the sphincters, and the pubococcygeus (P-C) muscle.

Internal Sex Organs: The **vagina** allows both menstrual flow and babies to pass from the uterus to the outside world. The **cervix** is the lower end, or neck, of the uterus. The **uterus** is the pear shaped organ in which a fertilized ovum implants and develops until birth. The **fallopian tubes** are two 10-cm long tubes that extend from the upper end of the uterus toward the ovaries. Ova pass through the fallopian tubes on their way to the uterus. Fertilization normally takes place in these tubes. The **ovaries** lie on either side of the uterus and produce ova and the female hormones estrogen and progesterone.

The Breasts

The primary function of the breasts is to provide milk for infants. The breasts contain the mammary glands that produce the milk, a system of ducts to transport the milk to the outside, and fatty tissue. In many cultures, including our own, the breasts have taken on erotic significance that may overshadow their biological function. **Breast cancer** is the second leading cause of death from cancer in Canadian women, after lung cancer. Regular breast self-examination is a good way for women to get to know their breasts and may aid in the early detection of breast cancer.

The Menstrual Cycle

Menstruation is the cyclical bleeding that results from the shedding of the uterine lining if the ovum was not fertilized. It is **regulated** through a finely-tuned relationship between the hypothalamus, the pituitary gland, the ovaries, and the uterus. In response to changes in the levels of estrogen and progesterone, the hypothalamus secretes hormones that regulate the pituitary, which in turn secretes hormones that affect the production of estrogen and progesterone, the maturation of ova, and the development of the endometrium. The menstrual cycle consists of four **phases**. In the **proliferative** phase, which follows menstruation, ova ripen within their follicles, and the lining of the uterus begins to thicken. **Ovulation** is the second phase. In the **postovulatory, secretory,** or **luteal** phase, the corpus luteum secretes progesterone. This hormone, along with estrogen, causes the uterine lining to build up. If fertilization does not occur, a drop in estrogen and progesterone levels triggers the **menstrual** phase. **Menopause** is the cessation of menstruation. Estrogen deficiency during this time may give rise to night sweats, hot flashes, hot flushes, cold sweats, loss of breast tissue, and decreased vaginal lubrication. Although these symptoms may be alleviated by hormone replacement therapy, recent research suggests an increase in the risk of breast cancer as a result.

Common menstrual problems include **dysmenorrhea** (pain and discomfort), **amenorrhea** (absence of menses), and **premenstrual syndrome (PMS).** The causes of PMS are unclear, but many researchers suspect a link between menstrual problems and hormone levels. Women with premenstrual or menstrual discomfort may benefit from a number of active coping strategies, including exercise and changes in dietary habits.

Chapter Quiz

1. The word(s) _____ derive(s) from roots that literally mean "something to be ashamed of."
   (a) clitoris
   (b) mons veneris
   (c) labia majora
   (d) pudendum

2. The _____ is the only sex organ whose only known function is the experiencing of pleasure.
   (a) labia minora
   (b) clitoris
   (c) Bartholin's gland
   (d) cervix

3. Which of the following is NOT a recommended precaution for preventing serious inflammation of the bladder?
   (a) Daily use of antibiotics.
   (b) Drinking two litres of water a day.
   (c) Decreasing use of alcohol and caffeine.
   (d) Preventing objects that have touched the anus from coming into contact with the vulva.

4. An episiotomy is an incision in the
   (a) vulva.
   (b) uterus.
   (c) perineum.
   (d) corpora cavernosa.

5. A Pap test is used to help diagnose cancer of the
   (a) breast.
   (b) cervix.
   (c) endometrium.
   (d) ovaries.

6. A complete hysterectomy involves the surgical removal of all of the following EXCEPT FOR the
   (a) vagina.
   (b) ovaries.
   (c) fallopian tubes.
   (d) cervix.

7. The size of the breasts is largely determined by the
   (a) size of the areola.
   (b) amount of fatty tissue.
   (c) number of mammary glands.
   (d) width of the mammary glands.

8. The five-year survival rate for women whose breast cancers have not metastasized is nearly
   (a) 63%.
   (b) 73%.
   (c) 83%.
   (d) 93%.

9. Which of the following most directly stimulates follicles to begin to mature?
   (a) Gn-RH.
   (b) LH.
   (c) FSH.
   (d) Oxytocin.

10. Following menopause, estrogen-replacement therapy apparently lowers the risk of which of the following?
   (a) breast cancer.
   (b) low blood pressure.
   (c) cardiovascular disorders.
   (d) osteoporosis.

Chapter 3

Male Sexual Anatomy and Physiology

Did You Know That...

- The penis contains neither bone nor muscle?
- Uncircumcised men may be at greater risk than circumcised men of becoming infected by the AIDS virus?
- The father determines the baby's gender?
- The testes churn out about 1000 sperm per second?
- Morning erections have nothing to do with the need to urinate?
- Men cannot will themselves to have erections?
- Black men are at greater risk than white men of developing prostate cancer?
- Many men paralyzed below the waist can attain erection, engage in sexual intercourse, and ejaculate?
- Men can have orgasms without ejaculating?

In this chapter we examine male sexual anatomy and physiology, and we attempt to sort truth from fiction. We see, for example, that despite his lingering doubts, a man's capabilities as a lover do not depend on the size of his penis (at least within broad limits). For a man to judge his sexual prowess on the basis of locker-room comparisons makes about as much sense as choosing a balloon by measuring it when it is deflated.

In our exploration of male sexual anatomy and physiology, as in our exploration of female sexual physiology and anatomy, we begin with the external genitalia and then move inward. Once inside, we focus on the route of sperm through the male reproductive system.

The Penis and Male Sexuality
www.the-penis.com/
A site about the penis with guidance on penis size and health issues and information on male sexuality and male sexual health.

The Male Sex Organs

External Sex Organs

The male external sex organs include the penis and the scrotum (see Figures 3.1, 3.2).

The Penis At first glance, the structure of the **penis** may seem rather simple and obvious, particularly when compared to women's organs. This apparent simplicity may have contributed to cultural stereotypes that men are straightforward and aggressive, whereas women tend to be complicated and, perhaps, mysterious. Yet, as Figure 3.1 shows, the apparent simplicity of the penis is misleading. Much goes on below the surface. Gender stereotypes regarding anatomy are as misleading as those regarding personality (see Chapter 5).

The penis, like the vagina, is the sex organ used in sexual intercourse. Unlike the vagina, however, the penis also serves as a conduit for urine. Semen and urine pass out of the penis through the urethral opening. The opening is called the urethral meatus (me-ATE-us), meaning "passage."

Despite the slang term "boner," the human penis contains no bones. Nor, despite another slang term, "muscle," does the penis contain muscle tissue. However, muscles at the base of the penis, like the muscles surrounding the vaginal and urethral openings in women, are involved in controlling urination and ejaculation.

Rather than bone or muscles, the penis contains three cylinders of spongy material that run its length. The larger two of these cylinders, the **corpora cavernosa** (see Figure 3.1), lie side by side and function like the cavernous bodies in the clitoris. These cylinders fill up with blood and stiffen during sexual arousal. In addition, a **corpus spongiosum** (spongy body) runs along the bottom, or ventral, surface of the penis. It contains the penile urethra that conducts urine through the penis to the urinary opening (urethral meatus) at the tip. At the tip of the penis, the spongy body enlarges to become the glans, or head, of the penis.

Penis The male organ of sexual intercourse. (From the Latin for "tail.")

Corpora cavernosa Cylinders of spongy tissue in the penis that become congested with blood and stiffen during sexual arousal.

Corpus spongiosum The spongy body that runs along the bottom of the penis, contains the penile urethra, and enlarges at the tip of the penis to form the glans.

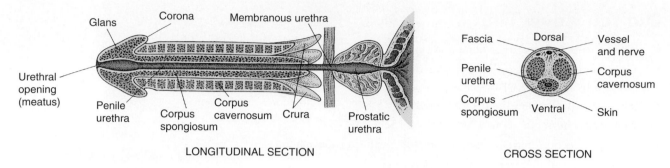

Figure 3.1. The Penis.

During sexual arousal the corpora cavernosa and corpus spongiosum become congested with blood, causing the penis to enlarge and stiffen.

Corona The ridge that separates the glans from the body of the penis. (From the Latin for "crown.")

Frenulum The sensitive strip of tissue that connects the underside of the penile glans to the shaft. (From the Latin *frenum*, meaning "bridle.")

Root The base of the penis, which extends into the pelvis.

Shaft The body of the penis, which expands as a result of vasocongestion.

All three cylinders consist of spongy tissue that becomes engorged (swells) with blood during sexual arousal, resulting in erection. The urethra is connected to the bladder, which is unrelated to reproduction, and to those parts of the reproductive system that transport semen.

The glans of the penis, like the clitoral glans, is extremely sensitive to sexual stimulation. Direct, prolonged stimulation can become irritating, even painful. Men generally prefer to masturbate by stroking the shaft of the penis rather than the glans, although some prefer the latter. The **corona**, or coronal ridge, separates the glans from the body of the penis. It is also quite sensitive to sexual stimulation. After the glans, the parts of the penis that men tend to find most sensitive are the corona and an area on the underside of the penis called the **frenulum**. The frenulum is a thin strip of tissue that connects the underside of the glans to the shaft. Most men find the top part of the penis to be the least sensitive part.

The base of the penis, called the **root**, extends into the pelvis. It is attached to pelvic bones by leglike structures, called *crura*, that are like those that anchor the female's clitoris. The body of the penis is called the penile **shaft**. The penile shaft, unlike the clitoral shaft, is free-swinging. Thus, when sexual excitement engorges the penis with blood, the result—erection—is obvious. The expression "getting shafted," which means being taken advantage of, presumably refers to the penile shaft. Another phrase, "getting screwed," refers more directly to sexual intercourse.

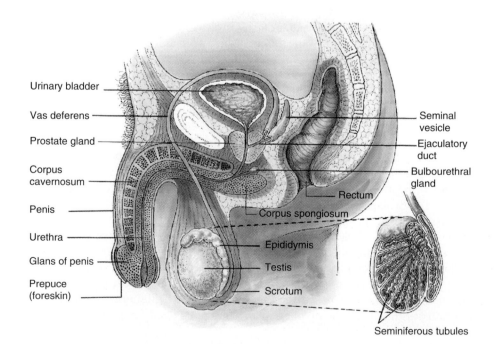

Figure 3.2. The Male Reproductive System.

The external male sex organs include the penis and the scrotum.

The skin of the penis is hairless and loose, allowing expansion during erection. It is fixed to the penile shaft just behind the glans. Some of it, however, like the labia minora in the female, folds over to partially cover the glans. This covering is the prepuce, or **foreskin**. It covers part or all of the penile glans just as the clitoral prepuce (hood) covers the clitoral shaft. The prepuce consists of loose skin that moves freely over the glans. However, at birth, in some males, tough bands of tissue, known as adhesions, cause the foreskin to adhere to the glans. These adhesions generally break by the time a boy is about three years old, although some pediatricians will push the foreskin back and break the adhesions during infancy.

Circumcision **Circumcision** is the surgical removal of the prepuce. Advocates of circumcision believe that it is hygienic because it eliminates a site where smegma might accumulate and bacteria might grow. Opponents of circumcision believe that it is unnecessary because regular cleaning is sufficient to reduce the risk of these problems.

Jews traditionally carry out male circumcision shortly after a baby is born. Muslims also have ritual circumcisions for religious reasons. In North America, circumcision for hygienic reasons is common among people who are neither Jewish nor Muslim (see the World of Diversity box on the next page).

Although it has been suggested that penile cancer, a rare form of cancer, is slightly more common among uncircumcised men, recent research suggests that infection with the virus that causes genital warts and a higher number of sexual partners are more important than circumcision in the development of cancer of the penis (Sherman, et al., 1993). Emerging evidence also suggests that uncircumcised men may be at greater risk than circumcised men of becoming infected by the AIDS virus. Certain cells in the foreskin may be especially susceptible to it (Touchette, 1991). Physicians once agreed that circumcision was the treatment of choice for **phimosis**, a condition in which it is difficult to retract the foreskin of the glans. But today, only a small minority of males with phimosis are circumcised for that reason (Rickwood et al., 2000). Urinary tract infections are more common among uncircumcised male infants than among circumcised infants (Herzog, 1989; Wisell et al., 1987). Still, it has been argued that the risks associated with urinary tract infections in infancy are too low to justify routine circumcision (King, 1988; Lohr, 1989). An Ontario study of nearly 60 000 male infants found that the incidence of urinary tract infections in uncircumcised boys was not as high as previously believed and that approximately 195 circumcisions would have to be performed to prevent one hospitalization for urinary tract infections (To et al., 1998). For these and other reasons, the Canadian Paediatric Society does not recommend routine circumcision of newborn boys.

The foreskin has more than a thousand nerve endings, yet it is generally believed that it has little to do with sexual functioning. A study on adult circumcision found a significant decrease in ability to achieve and maintain an erection and a non-significant decrease in penile sensitivity. However, 47% of the men reported more physical pleasure with intercourse, and said their sex lives were more satisfying after the circumcision (Fink et al., 2002). Another study found no difference between circumcised and uncircumcised men in the sensitivity of the glans of the penis to vibration, pressure, warmth, and cold (Bleustein et al., 2003). Since both of these studies used small, non-random samples, it is hard to draw general conclusions. Men opting for adult circumcision are generally doing so because of a medical condition. It may be that, following infant circumcision, the severed nerves reroute themselves to the glans.

Another argument about the sexual effects of the procedure is that circumcised males may have more difficulty controlling ejaculation since the penile glans is directly exposed to sexual stimulation. As a result, the argument goes, such men would be more likely to suffer from **premature ejaculation**. Common sense—or should we say, common nonsense?—has actually had it both ways: that circumcised men are more and less sensitive to sexual stimulation than the uncircumcised. Perhaps the debate has continued this long because of the virtual absence of well-controlled scientific research comparing the sexual sensitivity of circumcised and uncircumcised men.

Penis Size The belief that the size of the man's penis determines his sexual prowess is based upon the assumption that men with bigger penises are better equipped to satisfy a

Foreskin The loose skin that covers the penile glans. Also referred to as the *prepuce*.

Circumcision Surgical removal of the foreskin of the penis. (From the Latin *circumcidere*, meaning "to cut around.")

Info-Circumcision
www.infocirc.org/
The circumcision Information Resource Centre site provides information about nonreligious infant circumcision and related topics.

Phimosis An abnormal condition in which the foreskin is so tight that it cannot be withdrawn from the glans. (From the Greek *phimos*, meaning "muzzle.")

Premature ejaculation A sexual dysfunction in which the male persistently ejaculates too early to afford the couple adequate sexual gratification.

woman sexually. Zilbergeld (1978) and others point out, however, that women rarely mention penis size as an important element in their sexual satisfaction. Quite regularly they do mention ability to communicate with partners, the emotional atmosphere of the relationship, and sensitivity to employing sexual techniques that enhance their partner's pleasure.

Masters and Johnson (1966) reported that the penises of the 312 male subjects they studied generally ranged in length from a little less than 9 cm to a little more than 10 cm when flaccid (soft). The average erect penis ranges from 13 to 18 cm in length (Reinisch, 1990). There appears to be little relationship between the size of a given penis when flaccid and when erect. Penises that are small when flaccid tend to gain more size when they become erect. Larger flaccid penises gain relatively less (Jamison & Gebhard, 1988). Nor is there a relationship between penis size and body weight, height, or build (Money et al., 1984).

Even when flaccid, the same penis can vary in size. Factors such as cold air or water, or emotions of fear or anxiety can cause the penis (along with the scrotum and testicles)

A World of Diversity

From Symbol to Science to Quandary

Circumcision has been performed for religious, cultural and, more recently, medical reasons. Historically, it has been found worldwide—among African tribes and Australian aboriginal groups, and in India, Egypt (circumcised mummies have been found), the Middle East, Southeast Asia, and Central and South America (Dunsmuir & Gordon, 1999).

As a religious or cultural rite, circumcision has been carried out at birth (in some African societies), at eight days of age (among Jews), or in adolescence or early adulthood as a rite of passage to mark puberty or an approaching marriage.

Circumcision has enormous ritual importance for some cultural groups, including Muslims and Jews, who base the religious commandment to circumcise on God's covenant with Abraham in Genesis 17: 9–13. For observant Jews, circumcision is a solemn religious ceremony accompanied by blessings on the newborn. The child is named and welcomed into a family and the Jewish community. The ceremony is referred to as a covenant, and represents entry into a relationship with God—hence the term *circumcision* can be used metaphorically for achieving a state of holiness, as when Deuteronomy 10:16 calls upon Israel to "circumcise your hearts."

Circumcision also became a cultural identifier. When circumcision was not common among Europeans and North Americans, a circumcised male was quickly recognized as a Jew, and, in times of persecution, sometimes exiled or killed. Jews sometimes referred to non-members of the community as "the uncircumcised." For all these reasons, the practice is heavily laden with emotion. When pediatricians began recommending against routine circumcision, some Jewish parents faced an agonizing decision. Most still consider the ritual a necessary rite of passage.

In Christian Europe, circumcision was attacked by early Fathers of the Church, including Saints Augustine and Jerome. Christian ambivalence toward the practice is shown in the fact that while Luke 2:21 clearly refers to Jesus' circumcision, portrayals of the infant Christ in art before the twentieth century always show him as uncircumcised (Friedman, 2003: 158, 52). By the nineteenth century, however, attitudes began to change as circumcision became a medicalized procedure. Advances in surgical techniques were reflected in increasing numbers of non-Jewish adult men, especially in North America, being circumcised for non-religious reasons. The procedure was prescribed as a treatment for infections of the penis (usually due to gonorrhea), which would cause the foreskin to stick to the head of the penis. Other conditions that circumcision was supposed to prevent or cure included phimosis ("tight foreskin"), priapism (painful, persistent erections), erectile difficulties, sterility, epilepsy, bedwetting,

homosexuality, and masturbation. Darby (2003), in an interesting historical review, suggests that circumcision was promoted as a routine medical procedure primarily to prevent masturbation. According to an 1896 bestselling childcare book entitled *All About Baby*, circumcision would "prevent the vile habit of masturbation" and was "advisable in most cases" (Friedman, 2003, p. 92). It was most often performed on middle- or upper-class boys; in fact, one historian claims that "a circumcised penis soon became a badge of status—proof of one's membership in the American elite." By 1914 circumcision was the most common surgical procedure performed in the United States (Gollaher, 1994, cited in Friedman, 2003, p. 93).

Despite the medical community's best efforts, routine circumcision of newborns never became common practice—except in Great Britain, Canada, and the United States. In Britain, the practice peaked around 1940 at about 30% of males, and has declined since then to less than 5% of males—a figure that many argue is still too high (Rickwood et al., 2000). In the United States, circumcisions have declined from a high of more than 80% in 1980 to 61% in 2002 (Bollinger, 2004). According to the Circumcision Information Resource Centre, less than 17% of male newborns were circumcised in Canada in 1997. Current statistics are not available for all provinces since circumcision is not covered under most health plans, and therefore not tracked.

The penis and scrotum vary a good deal in appearance from one man to another. The penis in the photo to the right is uncircumcised.

to draw closer to the body, reducing its size. The flaccid penis may also grow in size in warm water or when the man is relaxed.

The Scrotum The **scrotum** is a pouch of loose skin that becomes lightly covered with hair at puberty. The scrotum consists of two compartments that hold the testes. Each testicle is held in place by a **spermatic cord**, a structure that contains the **vas deferens**, blood vessels and nerves, and the cremaster muscle. The **cremaster muscle** raises and lowers the testicle within the scrotum in response to temperature changes and sexual stimulation. (The testes are drawn closer to the body during sexual arousal.)

Sperm production is optimal at a temperature that is slightly cooler than the 37 degrees Celsius that is desirable for most of the body. Typical scrotal temperature is about 3 degrees lower than body temperature. The scrotum is loose-hanging and flexible. It permits the testes and nearby structures to escape the higher body heat, especially in warm weather. In the middle layer of the scrotum is the **dartos muscle**, which (like the cremaster) contracts and relaxes reflexively in response to temperature changes. In cold weather, or when a man jumps into a body of cold water, it contracts to bring the testes closer to the body. In warm weather, it relaxes, allowing the testes to dangle farther from the body. The dartos muscle also increases or decreases the surface area of the scrotum in response to temperature changes. Smoothing allows greater dissipation of heat in hot weather. Tightening or constricting the skin surface helps retain heat and gives the scrotum a wrinkled appearance in the cold.

The scrotum is developed from the same embryonic tissue that becomes the labia majora of the female. Thus, like the labia majora, it is quite sensitive to sexual stimulation. It is somewhat more sensitive than the top side of the penis but less so than other areas of the penis.

Internal Sex Organs

The male internal sex organs consist of the testes, the organs that manufacture sperm and the male sex hormone testosterone; the system of tubes and ducts that conduct sperm through the male reproductive system; and the organs that help nourish and activate sperm and neutralize some of the acidity that sperm encounter in the vagina.

The Testes The **testes** (or **testicles**) are the male gonads (*gonad* derives from the Greek *gone*, meaning "seed"). In slang the testes are frequently referred to as "balls" or "nuts." These terms are considered vulgar, but they are reasonably descriptive. They also make it easier for many people to refer to the testes in informal conversation.

The testes serve two functions analogous to those of the ovaries. They secrete sex hormones and produce mature **germ cells**. The germ cells are **sperm**, and the sex hormones are **androgens**. The most important androgen is **testosterone**.

Testosterone Testosterone is secreted by **interstitial cells**, which are also referred to as **Leydig's cells**. Interstitial cells lie between the seminiferous tubules and release

Scrotum The pouch of loose skin that contains the testes. (From the same linguistic root as the word *shred*, meaning "a long, narrow strip," and probably referring to the long furrows on the scrotal sac.)

Spermatic cord The cord that suspends a testicle within the scrotum and contains a vas deferens, blood vessels, nerves, and the cremaster muscle.

Vas deferens A tube that conducts sperm from the testicle to the ejaculatory duct of the penis. (From Latin roots meaning "a vessel" that "carries down.")

Cremaster muscle The muscle that raises and lowers the testicle in response to temperature changes and sexual stimulation.

Dartos muscle The muscle in the middle layer of the scrotum that contracts and relaxes in response to temperature changes.

Testes The male gonads. (Singular: testis.)

Testicles Testes.

Germ cell A cell from which a new organism develops. (From the Latin *germen*, meaning "bud" or "sprout.")

Sperm The male germ cell. (From a Greek root meaning "seed.")

Androgens Male sex hormones. (From the Greek *andros*, meaning "man" or "males," and *-gene*, meaning "born.")

Testosterone The male sex hormone that fosters the development of male sex characteristics and is connected with the sex drive.

Interstitial cells Cells that lie between the seminiferous tubules and secrete testosterone. (*Interstitial* means "set between.")

Leydig's cells Another term for interstitial cells.

Secondary sex characteristics Physical traits that distinguish men from women but are not directly involved in reproduction.

Seminiferous tubule   Interstitial cells

Figure 3.3. Interstitial Cells.

Testosterone is produced by the interstitial cells, which lie between the seminiferous tubules in each testis. Sperm (seen in the middle of the diagram) are produced within the seminiferous tubules.

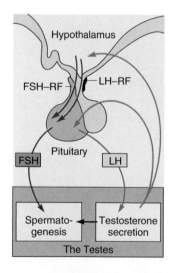

Hypothalamus

FSH–RF   LH–RF

Pituitary

FSH   LH

Spermato-   Testosterone
genesis   secretion

The Testes

Figure 3.4. Hormonal Control of the Testes.

Several endocrine glands—the hypothalamus, the pituitary gland, and the testes—keep blood testosterone levels at a more or less constant level. Low testosterone levels signal the hypothalamus to secrete LH-releasing hormone (LH-RH). Like dominoes falling in a line, LH-RH causes the pituitary gland to secrete LH, which in turn stimulates the testes to release testosterone. Follicle-stimulating hormone—releasing hormone (FSH-RH) from the hypothalamus causes the pituitary to secrete FSH, which in turn causes the testes to produce sperm cells.

testosterone directly into the bloodstream (see Figure 3.3). Testosterone stimulates prenatal differentiation of male sex organs, sperm production, and development of **secondary sex characteristics**, such as the beard, deep voice, and growth of the muscle mass.

In men, several endocrine glands—the hypothalamus, pituitary gland, and testes (see Figure 3.4)—keep blood testosterone levels at a more or less even level. This contrasts with the peaks and valleys in levels of female sex hormones during the phases of the menstrual cycle. Testosterone levels vary slightly with stress, time of day or month, and other factors, but a feedback loop among the endocrine glands keeps them relatively stable.

The same pituitary hormones, FSH and LH, that regulate the activity of the ovaries also regulate the activity of the testes. FSH regulates the production of sperm by the testes. LH stimulates secretion of testosterone by the interstitial cells. Low testosterone levels signal the hypothalamus to secrete a hormone, called LH-releasing hormone (LH-RH). Like dominoes falling in a line, LH-RH causes the pituitary gland to secrete LH, which in turn stimulates the testes to release testosterone into the blood system. LH is also referred to as *interstitial-cell-stimulating hormone*, or ICSH.

When the level of testosterone in the blood system reaches a certain peak, the hypothalamus directs the pituitary gland not to secrete LH. This system for circling information around these three endocrine glands is called a feedback loop. This feedback loop is negative. That is, increases in hormone levels in one part of the system trigger another part to shut down, and vice versa.

The testes usually range between 2.5 and 4.5 cm in length. They are about half as wide as deep. The left testicle usually hangs lower, because the left spermatic cord tends to be somewhat longer.

Is There a Manopause? Men cannot undergo menopause; they have never menstruated. Yet one now and then hears of a so-called male menopause, occasionally referred to as "manopause." Women encounter relatively sudden age-related declines in sex hormones and fertility during menopause. Men experience a gradual decline in testosterone levels as they age, but nothing like the sharp plunge in estrogen levels that women experience during menopause. Testosterone levels begin to fall at about age 40 or 50 and may decline to one-third or one-half of their peak levels by age 80 (Brody, 1995b).

The drop in testosterone levels that occurs as men age may be connected to a variety of age-related symptoms, including reduced muscle mass and strength, accumulation of body fat, reduced energy levels, lowered fertility, and reduced erectile ability. However, despite a decline in testosterone levels, most men remain potent throughout their lives. Little is known about the critical levels of testosterone that are needed to maintain erectile ability. Certain age-related changes, such as reduced muscle mass and strength and increased body fat, may be due not to declining testosterone production but to other factors associated with aging, such as a gradual loss of *human growth hormone*, which helps maintain muscle strength and may prevent fat buildup. Some experts believe that testosterone replacement may help avert erectile problems, bone loss, and frailty (Brody, 1995b). Others worry that excessive use of the hormone may increase the risks of prostate cancer and cardiovascular disease.

Although men do experience a gradual decline in the number and motility of sperm as they age, which reduces their fertility, some viable sperm continue to be produced even into late adulthood. Men can remain sexually active and father children at advanced ages. For both genders, marital satisfaction and attitudes toward aging can affect sexual behaviour as profoundly as physical changes can.

Sperm Each testicle is divided into many lobes. The lobes are filled with winding **seminiferous tubules** (see Figure 3.2). Although packed into a tiny space, these tubules, placed end to end, would span the length of several football fields. Through a process called **spermatogenesis**, these threadlike structures produce and store hundreds of billions of sperm through the course of a lifetime.

Sperm cells develop through several stages. It takes about 72 days for the testes to manufacture a mature sperm cell (Leary, 1990). In an early stage, sperm cells are called

spermatocytes. Each one contains 46 chromosomes, including one X and one Y sex chromosome. Each spermatocyte divides into two spermatids, each of which has 23 chromosomes. Half the **spermatids** have X sex chromosomes, and the other half have Y sex chromosomes. Looking something like tadpoles when examined under a microscope, mature sperm cells, called **spermatozoa**, each have a head, a cone-shaped midpiece, and a tail. The head is about 5 microns (.00005 cm) long and contains the cell nucleus that houses the 23 chromosomes. The midpiece contains structures that provide the energy that the tail needs to lash back and forth in a swimming motion. Each sperm cell is about 50 microns (.0005 cm) long, one of the smallest cells in the body (Thompson, 1993).

During fertilization, the 23 chromosomes from the father's sperm cell combine with the 23 chromosomes from the mother's ovum, furnishing the standard ensemble of 46 chromosomes in the offspring. Among the 23 chromosomes borne by sperm cells is one sex chromosome—an X sex chromosome or a Y sex chromosome. Ova contain X sex chromosomes only. The union of an X sex chromosome and a Y sex chromosome leads to the development of male offspring. Two X sex chromosomes combine to yield female offspring. So the presence of an X or Y sex chromosome from the father determines the baby's gender.

The testes churn out about 1000 sperm per second or about 30 billion—yes, billion—per year (Elmer-Dewitt, 1991). Mathematically speaking, 10 to 20 ejaculations hold enough sperm to populate Earth.

Sperm proceed from the seminiferous tubules through an intricate maze of ducts that converge in a single tube called the **epididymis**. The epididymis lies against the back wall of the testicle and serves as a storage facility for sperm. The epididymis, which is some 5 cm in length, consists of twisted passages that would be 3 to 6 metres in length if stretched end to end. Sperm are inactive when they enter the epididymis. They continue to mature as they slowly make their way through the epididymis for another two to four weeks.

The Vas Deferens
Each epididymis empties into a vas deferens (also called *ductus deferens*). The vas is a thin, cylindrical tube about 40 cm long that serves as a conduit for mature sperm. In the scrotum, the vas deferens lies near the skin surface within the spermatic cord. Therefore, a **vasectomy**, an operation in which the right and left vas deferens are severed, is a convenient means of sterilization. The tube leaves the scrotum and follows a circuitous path up into the abdominal cavity. Then it loops back along the rear surface of the bladder (see Figure 3.5).

Seminiferous tubules Tiny, winding, sperm-producing tubes that are located within the lobes of the testes. (From Latin roots meaning "seed bearing.")

Spermatogenesis Process by which sperm cells are produced and developed.

Spermatocyte An early stage in the development of sperm cells, in which each parent cell has 46 chromosomes, including one X and one Y sex chromosome.

Spermatids Cells formed by the division of spermatocytes. Each spermatid has 23 chromosomes.

Spermatozoa Mature sperm cells.

Epididymis A tube that lies against the back wall of each testicle and serves as a storage facility for sperm. (From Greek roots meaning "upon testicles.")

Vasectomy A sterilization procedure in which the vas deferens is severed, preventing sperm from reaching the ejaculatory duct.

Figure 3.5. Passage of Spermatozoa.

Each testicle is divided into lobes that contain threadlike seminiferous tubules. Through spermatogenesis, the tubules produce and store hundreds of billions of sperm over the course of a lifetime. During ejaculation, sperm cells travel through the vas deferens, up and over the bladder, into the ejaculatory duct, and then through the urethra. Secretions from the seminal vesicles and the bulbourethral glands join with sperm to compose semen.

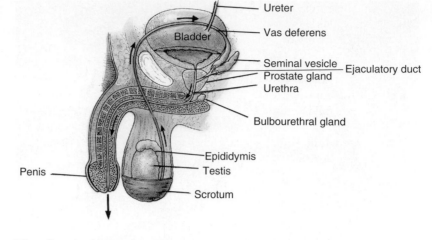

Seminal vesicles Small glands that lie behind the bladder and secrete fluids that combine with sperm in the ejaculatory ducts.

Ejaculatory duct A duct formed by the convergence of a vas deferens with a seminal vesicle through which sperm pass through the prostate gland and into the urethra.

Cilia Hairlike projections from cells that beat rhythmically to produce locomotion or currents.

Prostate gland The gland that lies beneath the bladder and secretes prostatic fluid, which gives semen its characteristic odour and texture.

The Seminal Vesicles The two **seminal vesicles** are small glands, each about 5 cm long. They lie behind the bladder and open into the **ejaculatory ducts**, where the fluids they secrete combine with sperm (see Figure 3.5). A vesicle is a small cavity or sac; the seminal vesicles were so named because they were mistakenly believed to be reservoirs for semen, rather than glands.

The fluid produced by the seminal vesicles is rich in fructose, a form of sugar, which nourishes sperm and helps them become active, or motile. Sperm motility is a major factor in male fertility. Before reaching the ejaculatory ducts, sperm are propelled along their journey by contractions of the epididymis and vas deferens and by **cilia** that line the walls of the vas deferens. Once they become motile, they propel themselves by whipping their tails.

At the base of the bladder, each vas deferens joins a seminal vesicle to form a short ejaculatory duct that runs through the middle of the prostate gland (see Figure 3.5). In the prostate the ejaculatory duct opens into the urethra, which leads to the tip of the penis. The urethra carries sperm and urine out through the penis, but normally not at the same time.

The Prostate Gland The **prostate gland** lies beneath the bladder and approximates a chestnut in shape and size (about 2 cm in diameter). Note the spelling of the name of the gland—pros*tate*, not pros*trate*. (*Prostrate* means lying with one's face on the ground, as in some forms of prayer.) The prostate gland contains muscle fibres and glandular tissue that secrete prostatic fluid. Prostatic fluid is milky and alkaline. It provides the characteristic texture and odour of the seminal fluid. The alkalinity neutralizes some of the acidity of the vaginal tract, prolonging the lifespan of sperm as seminal fluid spreads through the female reproductive system. The prostate is continually active in mature males, but sexual arousal further stimulates secretions. Secretions are conveyed into the urethra by a sievelike duct system. There the secretions combine with sperm and fluid from the seminal vesicles.

A vasectomy prevents sperm from reaching the urethra but does not cut off fluids from the seminal vesicles or prostate gland. A man who has had a vasectomy thus emits an ejaculate that appears normal but contains no sperm.

Cowper's glands Structures that lie below the prostate and empty their secretions into the urethra during sexual arousal.

Bulbourethral glands Another term for Cowper's glands.

Cowper's Glands The **Cowper's glands** are also known as the **bulbourethral glands,** in recognition of their shape and location. These two structures lie below the prostate and empty their secretions into the urethra. During sexual arousal they secrete a drop or so of clear, slippery fluid that appears at the urethral opening. The functions of this fluid are not entirely understood. It may help buffer the acidity of the male's urethra and lubricate the urethral passageway to ease the passage of seminal fluid. The fluid is not produced in sufficient amounts to play a significant role in lubricating the vagina during intercourse.

Fluid from the Cowper's glands precedes the ejaculate and often contains viable sperm. Thus, coitus may lead to pregnancy even if the penis is withdrawn prior to ejaculation. This is one reason why people who practise the "withdrawal method" of birth control are frequently called "parents."

Semen Sperm and the fluids contributed by the seminal vesicles, the prostate gland, and the Cowper's glands make up a whitish fluid called **semen**, or seminal fluid, which is expelled through the tip of the penis during ejaculation. The seminal vesicles secrete about 70% of the fluid that constitutes the ejaculate. The remaining 30% of seminal fluid consists of sperm and fluids produced by the prostate gland and the Cowper's gland. Sperm themselves account for only about 1% of the volume of semen. This is why men with vasectomies continue to ejaculate about as much semen as before, although their ejaculates are devoid of sperm.

Semen is the medium that carries sperm through much of the male's reproductive system and the reproductive tract of the female. Semen contains water, mucus, sugar (fructose), acids, and bases. It activates and nourishes sperm, and the bases help shield sperm from vaginal acidity. The typical ejaculate contains between 200 and 400 million sperm and ranges between 3 and 5 mL in volume. The quantity of semen decreases with age and frequency of ejaculation.

> **Semen** The whitish fluid that constitutes the ejaculate, consisting of sperm and secretions from the seminal vesicles, prostate, and Cowper's glands.

Diseases of the Urogenital System

Because the organs that comprise the urinary and reproductive systems are near each other and share some "piping," they are referred to as the urinogenital or urogenital system. A number of diseases can affect the urogenital system. The type of physician who specializes in their diagnosis and treatment is a **urologist.**

> **Urologist** A physician who specializes in the diagnosis and treatment of diseases of the urogenital system.

Urethritis

Men, like women, are subject to bladder and urethral inflammations, which are generally referred to as **urethritis**. The symptoms include frequent urination (urinary frequency), a strong need to urinate (urinary urgency), burning during urination, and a penile discharge. People with symptoms of urinary frequency and urinary urgency feel the pressing need to urinate repeatedly, even though they may have just done so and may have but another drop or two to expel. The discharge may dry on the urethral opening, in which case it may have to be peeled off or wiped away before it is possible to urinate. The urethra also may become constricted when it is inflamed, slowing or halting urination. It is a frightening sensation for a male to feel the urine rush from his bladder and then suddenly stop at the urethral opening!

> **Urethritis** An inflammation of the bladder or urethra.

Applications

Self-Examination of the Testes

Self-examination (see Figure 3.6) is best performed shortly after a warm shower or bath, when the skin of the scrotum is most relaxed. The man should examine the scrotum for evidence of pea-sized lumps. Each testicle can be rolled gently between the thumb and the fingers. Lumps are generally found on the side or front of the testicle. The presence of a lump is not necessarily a sign of cancer,

but it should be promptly reported to a physician for further evaluation. The Canadian Cancer Society (2003a) lists these warning signals:

1. A lump, usually painless, in one of the testicles.
2. A dull ache in the lower abdomen or groin. (Pain may be absent in cancer of the testes, however.)
3. Sensation of dragging and heaviness in the lower abdomen or scrotum.

Figure 3.6. Testicular Self-Examination.

Preventive measures for urethritis parallel those suggested for cystitis (bladder infection): drinking more water, drinking cranberry juice (125 mL, two or three times a day), and lowering intake of alcohol and caffeine. Cranberry juice is highly acidic, and acid tends to eliminate many of the bacteria that can give rise to urethritis.

Cancer of the Testes

Cancer of the testicles remains a relatively rare form of cancer, accounting for about 800 new cases annually (Canadian Cancer Society, 2003a). It is, however, the most common form of solid-tumour cancer to strike men between the ages of 20 and 34 (Vazi et al., 1989).

There is no evidence that testicular cancer results from sexual overactivity or masturbation. Men who had **cryptorchidism** as children (a condition in which one or both testicles fail to descend from the abdomen into the scrotum) stand about a 40 times greater chance of contracting testicular cancer. Undescended testicles appear to occur more commonly in boys born to mothers who used the hormone diethylstilbestrol (DES) during pregnancy. In the 1940s and 1950s, pregnant women were often prescribed DES to help prevent miscarriages.

Treatments include surgical removal of the diseased testis, radiation, and chemotherapy. The survival rate among cases that are detected early, before the cancer has spread beyond the testes, is 95% (Canadian Cancer Society, 2000). Delayed treatment markedly reduces the chances of survival, because survival is connected with the extent to which the cancer has spread.

The early stages of testicular cancer usually produce no symptoms, other than the mass itself. Because early detection is crucial to survival, men are advised to examine themselves monthly, following puberty (Reinisch, 1990) and to have regular medical checkups. Self-examination may also reveal evidence of sexually transmitted infections and other problems.

Disorders of the Prostate

The prostate gland is tiny at birth and grows rapidly at puberty. It may shrink during adulthood, but usually becomes enlarged past the age of 50.

Benign Prostatic Hyperplasia The prostate gland becomes enlarged in about one-quarter of men past the age of 60 (Walsh, 1996). When enlargement is due to hormonal changes associated with aging rather than other causes, such as inflammation from sexually transmitted diseases, it is referred to as **benign prostatic hyperplasia**.

Because the prostate surrounds the upper part of the urethra (see Figure 3.2), enlargement constricts the urethra. Symptoms such as urinary frequency (including increased frequency of nocturnal urination), urinary urgency, and difficulty starting the flow of urine result. At one time, surgical removal of part of the prostate was used to relieve the pressure on the urethra and increase the flow of urine. Today, chemotherapy is available to improve the flow of urine either by relaxing the smooth muscle of the prostate (with the drug terazosin) or by shrinking an enlarged prostate (with the drug finasteride) (Walsh, 1996).

Cancer of the Prostate A more serious and life-threatening problem is prostate cancer. The National Cancer Institute of Canada (NCIC) estimates that about one man in nine in Canada will develop prostate cancer (NCIC, 2000). Prostate cancer is the most common form of cancer among men, and the second leading cause of cancer deaths in men, after lung cancer. According to the NCIC (2003), 18 800 men will be diagnosed with prostate cancer, and 4200 men will die from the disease.

Prostate cancer involves the growth of malignant prostate tumours that can metastasize to bones and lymph nodes if not detected and treated early. According to the Prostate Cancer Research Foundation of Canada (2000), black men have a higher incidence of prostate cancer than white men. North Americans have a higher incidence of prostate cancer than Asians. Researchers have identified intake of animal fat as a potential risk factor. Men whose diets are rich in animal fats, especially fats from red

Cryptorchidism A condition in which one or both testicles fail to descend from the abdomen into the scrotum.

Benign prostatic hyperplasia Enlargement of the prostate gland due to hormonal changes associated with aging and characterized by symptoms such as urinary frequency, urinary urgency, and difficulty starting the flow of urine.

Prostate Cancer Answers
www.cpcn.org
The Canadian Prostate Cancer Network is the national association of prostate cancer support groups. It promotes early detection as the only current cure for prostate cancer.

www.canadian-prostate.com
The Canadian Prostate Health Council provides information on current and innovative therapies for prostate cancer and other diseases of the prostate.

meat, have a substantially greater chance of developing advanced prostate cancer than do men with a low intake of animal fat. The incidence of prostate cancer also increases with age. Over 60% of all prostate cancers are diagnosed in men between the ages of 60 and 80 (National Cancer Institute of Canada, 2003). Genetic factors may also be involved (Wilson, 1995).

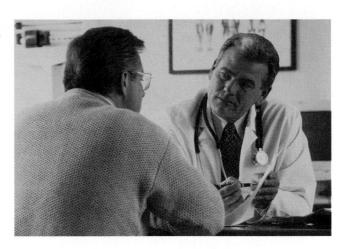

Screening for Prostate Cancer. *Men over 50 should discuss the potential benefits and possible risks of screening for prostate cancer with their doctors.*

The early symptoms of cancer of the prostate may mimic those of benign prostate enlargement: urinary frequency and difficulty in urinating. Later symptoms include blood in the urine, pain or burning on urination, and pain in the lower back, pelvis, or upper thighs (Canadian Cancer Society, 2003b). Most cases occur without noticeable symptoms in the early stages. Rectal examinations are one way to screen for prostate cancer. The physician inserts a finger into the rectum and feels for abnormalities in the prostate gland. The procedure may be uncomfortable, but it is brief and not particularly painful. Unfortunately, many men are reluctant to undergo a rectal examination, even though it is only mildly uncomfortable and may save their lives. Some are embarrassed or reluctant to discuss urinary problems with their physicians. Some may even resist the rectal examination because they associate rectal insertion with male–male sex. Still others are fearful that they may have cancer and choose to remain ignorant. Avoidance of, or ignorance of the need for, annual rectal exams among men is a major contributor to the death rate from prostate cancer.

A blood test may detect evidence of prostate cancer even among men whose prostates feel normal upon physical examination. The blood test measures prostate-specific antigen, or PSA, which is a type of protein that seeps out of the prostate gland when it is cancerous or enlarged. Although both a rectal examination and PSA testing can result in the early detection of prostate cancer, studies have not shown any improvements in survival rates. In some men, prostate cancer is slow-growing and causes few symptoms. However, neither a digital rectal examination nor the PSA test distinguishes between fast and slow prostate cancer, or between prostate cancer and other, benign, conditions. A positive PSA test, for example, would then require other, more invasive tests in order to diagnose prostate cancer. For these reasons, the Canadian Cancer Society recommends that men over 50 discuss with their doctors the potential benefits and possible risks of screening for prostate cancer in order to make informed decisions about their health care.

When a cancerous growth is suspected on the basis of a rectal examination or a PSA blood test, further testing is usually done by ultrasound or biopsy. Early detection is important because treatment is most effective before the cancer has spread ("Early prostate surgery," 1996). The majority of cases of prostate cancer are discovered while they are still localized. The ten-year survival rate is 91% for prostate cancer that has not metastasized (Grover et al., 2000). The survival rate drops dramatically if the cancer has metastasized. Still, the overall survival rate has improved in the past 30 years.

The most widely used treatment for prostate cancer is surgical removal of the prostate gland. However, surgical prostate removal may damage surrounding nerves, leading to problems in controlling the flow of urine or in erection or ejaculation. Recently introduced surgical techniques tend to spare the surrounding nerves and reduce, but not eliminate, the risk of complications. Other treatments include radiation, hormone treatment, and anticancer drugs. Hormone treatment and anticancer drugs may shrink the size of the tumour and relieve pain for long periods of time.

Among older men with slow-growing prostate cancer, physicians often prefer "watchful waiting" to surgery ("Early prostate surgery," 1996). The men frequently die first from causes other than cancer.

Prostatitis Many infectious agents can inflame the prostate, causing **prostatitis**. The chief symptoms are an ache or pain between the scrotum and anal opening and painful

Prostatitis Inflammation of the prostate gland.

ejaculation. Prostatitis is usually treated with antibiotics. Although aspirin and ibuprofen may relieve the pain, men with these symptoms should consult a physician. Painful ejaculation may discourage masturbation or coitus, which is ironic, since regular flushing of the prostate through ejaculation may be helpful in the treatment of prostatitis.

Male Sexual Functions

The male sexual functions of erection and ejaculation provide the means for sperm to travel from the male's reproductive tract to the female's. There the sperm cell and ovum unite to conceive a new human being. Of course, the natural endowment of reproduction with sensations of pleasure helps ensure that it will take place with or without knowledge of these biological facts.

Erection

Erection The enlargement and stiffening of the penis as a consequence of engorgement with blood.

Erection is the engorgement of the penis with blood, such that the penis grows in size and stiffens. The erect penis is an efficient conduit, or funnel, for depositing sperm deep within the vagina.

In mechanical terms, erection is a hydraulic event. The spongy, cavernous masses of the penis are equipped to hold blood. Filling them with blood causes them to enlarge, much as a sponge swells as it absorbs water. Erection involves the cooperation of the vascular (blood) system and the nervous system.

In a few moments—as quickly as 10 or 15 seconds—the penis can double in length, become firm, and shift from a funnel for passing urine to one that expels semen. Moreover, the bladder is closed off when the male becomes sexually aroused, decreasing the likelihood that semen and urine will mix.

Yes, the blood that fills the penis during sexual arousal causes erectile tissue to expand. But what accounts for the firmness of an erection? A sponge that fills with water expands but does not grow hard. It turns out that the two corpora cavernosa are surrounded by a tough, fibrous covering called the *tunica albuginea*. As the rubber of a balloon resists the pressure of pumped-in air, this housing resists expansion, causing the penis to rigidify. The corpus spongiosum, which contains the penile urethra, also engorges with blood during erection. It does not become hard, however, since it lacks the fibrous casing. The penile glans, which is formed by the crowning of the spongiosum at the tip of the penis, turns a dark purplish hue as it becomes engorged, but it too does not stiffen.

Despite the advanced state of biological knowledge, some mechanics of erection are not completely understood. It is not entirely clear, for example, whether penile cavities become engorged because the veins that carry blood away from the penis do not keep pace with the rapid flow of blood entering the penis, or whether the returning blood flow is reduced by compression of the veins at the base of the penis (as stepping lightly on a hose slows the movement of water).

We do know that erection is reversed when more blood flows out of the erectile tissue than flows in, restoring the pre-erectile circulatory balance and shrinking the erectile tissue or spongy masses. The erectile tissue thus exerts less pressure against the fibrous covering, resulting in a loss of rigidity. Loss of erection occurs when sexual stimulation ceases, or when the body returns to a (sexual) resting state following orgasm. Loss of erection can also occur in response to anxiety or perceived threats. Loss of erection in response to threat can be abrupt, as when a man in the throes of passion suddenly hears a suspicious noise in the adjoining room, suggestive of an intruder. Yet the "threats" that induce loss of erection are more likely to be psychological than physical. In our culture, men often measure their manhood by their sexual performance. A man who fears that he will be unable to perform successfully may experience **performance anxiety** that can prevent him from achieving erection or lead to a loss of erection at penetration.

Performance anxiety Feelings of dread and foreboding experienced in connection with sexual activity (or any other activity that might be judged by another person).

The male capacity for erection quite literally spans the life cycle. Erections are common in babies, even within minutes after birth. Evidence from ultrasound studies shows that male fetuses may even have erections months prior to birth. Men who are well into their 80s and 90s continue to experience erections and engage in coitus.

Nor are erections limited to the conscious state. Men have nocturnal erections every 90 minutes or so as they sleep. They generally occur during rapid eye movement (REM) sleep, so named because the sleeper's eyes dart about rapidly under the closed eyelids. REM sleep is associated with dreaming. Erections occur during most periods of REM sleep.

The mechanism of nocturnal erection appears to be physiologically based. That is, erections occur along with dreams that may or may not have erotic content. Morning erections are actually nocturnal erections. They occur when the man is awakened during REM sleep, as by an alarm clock. Men sometimes erroneously believe that a morning erection is caused by the need to urinate. When the man awakens with both an erection and the need to urinate, he may mistakenly assume that the erection was caused by the pressure of the full bladder.

Spinal Reflexes and Sexual Response

Men may become sexually aroused by a range of stimulation, including tactile stimulation provided by their partners, visual stimulation (such as looking at photos of nude models in men's magazines), or even mental stimulation from engaging in sexual fantasies. Regardless of the source of stimulation, the man's sexual responses, erection and ejaculation, occur by **reflex**. Erection and ejaculation are reflexes: automatic, unlearned responses to sexual stimulation. So too are vaginal lubrication and orgasm in women.

The reflexes governing erection and ejaculation are controlled at the level of the spinal cord. Thus, they are considered spinal reflexes. Erections may occur in response to different types of stimulation. Some occur from direct stimulation of the genitals, as from stroking, licking, or fondling the penis or scrotum. Erectile responses to such direct stimulation involve a simple spinal reflex that does not require the direct participation of the brain.

Erections can also be initiated by the brain, without the genitals being touched or fondled at all. Such erections may occur when a man has sexual fantasies, when he views erotic materials, or when he catches a glimpse of a woman in a bikini on a beach. In the case of the "no-hands" type of erections, stimulation from the brain travels to the spinal cord, where the erectile reflex is triggered. To better understand how this reflex works, we need to first explain the concept of the reflex arc.

Reflex A simple, unlearned response to a stimulus that is mediated by the spine rather than the brain.

The Reflex Arc When you withdraw your hand from a hot stove or blink in response to a puff of air, you do so before you have any time to think about it. These responses, like erection, are reflexes that involve sensory neurons and effector neurons (see Figure 3.7). In response to a stimulus like a touch or a change in temperature, sensory neurons or receptors in the skin "fire" and thereby send messages to the spinal cord. The message is then transmitted to effector neurons that begin in the spinal cord and cause muscles to contract or glands to secrete chemical substances. So if you accidentally touched a hot stove, sensory neurons in your fingers or hand would deliver a message to the spinal cord, which would trigger effector neurons to contract muscles that pull your hand away from the stove. The brain does not control this spinal reflex arc. That is not to say that the brain fails to "get the message" shortly afterwards. Sensory messages usually rise from the spinal cord to the brain to make us aware of stimulation. The experience of pain occurs when a message travels from the site of the injury to the spinal cord and then to receiving stations in the brain that interpret the message to produce the sensation of pain. The withdrawal of your hand from a harmful object begins before your brain even gets the message.

In some males, especially adolescents, the erectile reflex is so easily tripped that incidental rubbing of the genitals against his own undergarments, the sight of an attractive passerby, or a fleeting sexual fantasy produces erection. Spontaneous erections may occur under embarrassing circumstances, such as in a high school classroom or on a public beach. In an effort to distract himself from erotic fantasies and to allow an erection to subside, many a male adolescent in the classroom has desperately renewed his interest in his algebra or foreign language textbook.

As men mature they require more penile stimulation to achieve full erection. Partners of men in their 30s and 40s need not feel that their attractiveness has waned if

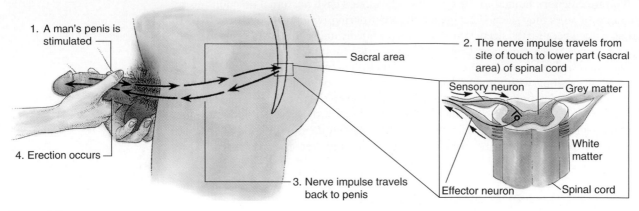

1. A man's penis is
   stimulated

2. The nerve impulse travels from
   site of touch to lower part (sacral
   area) of spinal cord

Sacral area

Sensory neuron — Grey matter

4. Erection occurs

White
matter

Spinal cord

3. Nerve impulse travels
   back to penis

Effector neuron — Spinal cord

Figure 3.7. Reflexes.

Reflexes involve sensory neurons, effector neurons, and, sometimes, interneurons that connect the two in the spinal cord. Reflexes need not involve the brain, although messages to the brain may make us aware when reflexes are occurring. Reflexes are the product of "local government" in the spine. Source: From *Human Sexuality* by S. A. Rathus. Copyright © 1983 by Holt, Rinehart & Winston, Inc. Reprinted by permission of the publisher.

Autonomic nervous system The division of the nervous system that regulates automatic bodily processes, such as heartbeat, pupil dilation, respiration, and digestion. Abbreviated *ANS*.

Sympathetic The branch of the ANS most active during emotional responses, such as fear and anxiety, that spend the body's reserves of energy. The sympathetic ANS largely controls ejaculation.

Parasympathetic The branch of the ANS most active during processes that restore the body's reserves of energy, such as digestion. The parasympathetic ANS largely controls erection.

their lovers no longer have instant "no-hands" erections when they disrobe. It takes men longer to achieve erection as they age, and direct penile stimulation becomes a more critical source of arousal.

The Role of the Autonomic Nervous System Although stimulation that brings about an erection can originate in the brain, this does not mean that erection is a voluntary response, like raising your arm. Whatever the original or dominant source of stimulation—direct penile stimulation or sexual fantasy—erection remains an unlearned, automatic reflex.

Automatic responses, such as erection, involve the division of the nervous system called the **autonomic nervous system** (ANS). *Autonomic* means "automatic." The ANS controls automatic bodily processes such as heartbeat, pupil dilation, respiration, and digestion. In contrast, voluntary movement (like raising an arm) is under the control of the somatic division of the nervous system.

The ANS has two branches, the **sympathetic** and the **parasympathetic**. These branches have largely opposing effects; when they are activated at the same time, their effects become balanced out to some degree. In general, the sympathetic branch is in command during processes that involve a release of bodily energy from stored reserves, such as running, performing some other athletic task, or being gripped by fear or anxiety. The sympathetic branch also governs the general mobilization of the body, such as increasing the heart rate and respiration rate in response to threat.

The parasympathetic branch is most active during processes that restore reserves of energy, such as digestion. When we experience fear or anxiety, the sympathetic branch of the ANS quickens the heart rate. When we relax, the parasympathetic branch curbs the heart rate. The parasympathetic branch activates digestive processes, but the sympathetic branch inhibits digestive activity. Since the sympathetic branch is in command when we feel fear or anxiety, such stimuli can inhibit the activity of the parasympathetic system, thereby slowing down digestive process and possibly causing indigestion.

The divisions of the autonomic nervous system play different roles in sexual arousal and response. The nerves that cause penile arteries to dilate during erection belong to the parasympathetic branch of the autonomic nervous system. It is thus the parasympathetic system that largely governs erection. The nerves governing ejaculation belong to the sympathetic branch, however. One implication of this division of neural responsibility is that intense fear or anxiety, which involves sympathetic nervous system activity, may inhibit erection by counteracting the activity of the parasympathetic nervous system. Since sympathetic arousal is involved in triggering the ejaculatory reflex, anxiety or fear may also accelerate ejaculation, causing premature ejaculation. Intense emotions like fear and anxiety can thus lead to problems in achieving or maintaining erection as well as causing hasty ejaculation.

Because erections seem spontaneous at times, and often occur when the man would rather not have them, it may seem to men that the penis has a mind of its own. Despite this common folk belief, however, the penis possesses no guiding intelligence. It consists of spongy masses of erectile tissue, not the lovely dense grey matter that renders your thought processes so incisive.

Erectile Abnormalities Some men find that their erect penises are slightly curved or bent. Some degree of curvature is perfectly normal, but men with **Peyronie's disease** have excessive curvature that can make erections painful or make it difficult to enjoy coitus. The condition is caused by buildup of fibrous tissue in the penile shaft. Although some cases of Peyronie's disease appear to clear up on their own, most require medical attention.

Some men experience erections that persist for hours or days. This condition is called *priapism*, after Priapus of Greek myth, the son of Dionysus and Aphrodite, who personified male procreative power. Priapism is often caused by leukemia, sickle cell anemia, or diseases of the spinal cord, although in some cases the cause remains unknown. Priapism occurs when the mechanisms that drain the blood that make the penis erect are damaged and so cannot return the blood to the circulatory system. The name of the disorder is truly a misnomer, because Priapus had a voracious sexual appetite. Men with priapism instead suffer from a painful condition that should receive medical attention. Priapism may become a medical emergency, since erection prolonged beyond six hours can starve penile tissues of oxygen, leading to tissue deterioration. Immediate medical intervention in the form of drugs or even surgery may be required to reverse the condition and allow blood to drain from the penis (Spark, 1991).

Ejaculation

Ejaculation, like erection, is a spinal reflex. It is triggered when sexual stimulation reaches a critical point or threshold. Ejaculation generally occurs together with **orgasm**, the sudden muscle contractions that occur at the peak of sexual excitement and result in the abrupt release of sexual tension that had built up during sexual arousal. Orgasm is accompanied by subjective sensations that are generally intensely pleasurable. Ejaculation, however, refers only to the expulsion of semen from the tip of the penis. Orgasm and ejaculation are not synonymous. Nor do they always occur simultaneously. For example, **paraplegics** can ejaculate if the area of the lower spinal cord that controls ejaculation is intact. They do not experience the subjective aspects of orgasm, however, since the sensations of orgasm do not reach the brain.

Conversely, prepubertal boys may experience orgasms even though they emit no ejaculate. Orgasms without ejaculate are termed "dry orgasms." Boys do not begin to produce seminal fluid (and sperm) until puberty. Mature men, too, can experience dry orgasms. They can take the form of "little orgasms" preceding a larger orgasm, or they can follow "wet orgasms" when sexual stimulation is continued but seminal fluids have not been replenished.

Ejaculation occurs in two stages. The first phase, often called the **emission stage**, involves contractions of the prostate, seminal vesicles, and the upper part of the vas deferens (the **ampulla**). The force of these contractions propels seminal fluid into the prostatic part of the urethral tract—a small tube called the **urethral bulb**—which balloons out as muscles close at either end, trapping the semen.

The second stage, which is often referred to as the **expulsion stage**, involves the propulsion of the seminal fluid through the urethra and out of the urethral opening at the tip of the penis. In this stage, muscles at the base of the penis and elsewhere contract rhythmically, forcefully expelling semen. The second stage is generally accompanied by the highly pleasurable sensations of orgasm.

In ejaculation, the seminal fluid is released from the urethral bulb and expelled by forceful contractions of the pelvic muscles that surround the urethral channel and the crura of the penis. The first few contractions are most intense and occur at 0.8-second intervals. Subsequent contractions lessen in intensity. The interval between them gradually increases. Seminal fluid is expelled in spurts during the first few contractions. The contractions are so powerful that seminal fluid may be propelled to distances of 30 to 60 cm,

Peyronie's disease An abnormal condition characterized by an excessive curvature of the penis that can make erections painful.

Orgasm *The climax of sexual excitement.*

Paraplegic A person with sensory and motor paralysis of the lower half of the body.

Emission stage The first phase of ejaculation, which involves contractions of the prostate gland, seminal vesicles, and the upper part of the vas deferens.

Ampulla A sac or dilated part of a tube or canal.

Urethral bulb The small tube that makes up the prostatic part of the urethral tract, which balloons out as muscles close at either end, trapping semen prior to ejaculation.

Expulsion stage The second stage of ejaculation, during which muscles at the base of the penis and elsewhere contract rhythmically, forcefully expelling semen and providing pleasurable sensations.

according to observations made by Masters and Johnson. Some men, however, report that semen travels but a few centimetres or just oozes from the penile opening. The force of the expulsion varies with the condition of the man's prostate, his general health, and his age. More intense orgasms often accompany more forceful ejaculations.

Retrograde Ejaculation Some men experience **retrograde ejaculation**, in which the ejaculate empties into the bladder rather than being expelled from the body. During normal ejaculation an external sphincter opens, allowing seminal fluid to pass out of the body. Another sphincter, this one internal, closes off the opening to the bladder, preventing the seminal fluid from backing up into the bladder. In retrograde ejaculation, the actions of these sphincters are reversed. The external sphincter remains closed, preventing the expulsion of the seminal fluid, while the internal sphincter opens, allowing the ejaculate to empty into the bladder. The result is a dry orgasm. No ejaculate is apparent because semen has backed up into the bladder. Retrograde ejaculation may be caused by prostate surgery (much less so now than in former years), drugs such as tranquillizers, certain illnesses, and accidents. Retrograde ejaculation is usually harmless in itself, since the seminal fluid is later discharged with urine. Infertility can result, however, and there may be some changes in the sensations associated with orgasm. Persistent dry orgasms should be medically evaluated, since their underlying cause may be a threat to health.

> **Retrograde ejaculation**
> Ejaculation in which the ejaculate empties into the bladder. (From the Latin *retrogradi*, meaning "to go backward.")

Summing Up

The Male Sex Organs

External Sex Organs: The male external sex organs include the penis and the scrotum. Both semen and urine pass out of the **penis** through the urethral opening. The penis contains cylinders that fill with blood during sexual arousal. Circumcision (surgical removal of the foreskin) has been carried out for religious and hygienic reasons. In North America, the size of a man's penis is often seen, despite lack of evidence, as a measure of both his masculinity and his ability to please a sexual partner. The **scrotum** (or scrotal sac) contains the testes. Each testicle is held in place by the spermatic cord, which contains the vas deferens.

Internal Sex Organs: The **testes** secrete androgens (male sex hormones) and produce sperm. A negative feedback loop between the testes, the hypothalamus, and the pituitary gland keeps blood testosterone levels more or less constant. Testosterone is produced by Leydig's cells (also known as interstitial cells). **Sperm** are produced in the cells that line the many small seminiferous tubules that make up the testes. They mature and are stored in the epididymis. The **vas deferens** carries the mature sperm out of the testes, where they eventually mix with secretions from the seminal vesicles and prostate gland. The **seminal vesicles'** secretions provide energy for the sperm cells. Secretions from the **prostate gland** give **semen** its characteristic odour and texture. The **Cowper's glands** secrete a small amount of clear fluid that appears at the opening of the urethra before ejaculation.

Diseases of the Urogenital System

Men, like women, are subject to **urethritis** and **cystitis** (urethral and bladder infections). **Testicular cancer** is the most common form of solid-tumour cancer in men between the ages of 20 and 34. Men may also suffer from a number of prostate problems, including infection (**prostatitis**), **prostate cancer**, and **benign enlargement of the prostate** (common in men over 50).

Male Sexual Functions

Erection is an involuntary process by which the penis becomes engorged with blood, increases in size, and stiffens. Erection occurs in response to sexual stimulation and is also common during REM sleep. Erection is controlled by two reflex centres in the spinal cord. Erection and ejaculation also involve the autonomic nervous system (ANS). The parasympathetic branch governs erection, while the sympathetic branch is involved in ejaculation. **Ejaculation** is also a reflex, which is triggered when sexual stimulation reaches a critical level. The emission phase of ejaculation involves contractions of the prostate, seminal vesicles, and vas deferens. In the expulsion stage, semen is propelled through the urethra and out of the penis by rhythmic contractions of muscles at the base of the penis. In retrograde ejaculation, the ejaculate empties into the bladder rather than out of the body.

Chapter Quiz

1. The penis differs from the vagina in that
   (a) the penis is the sex organ used in sexual intercourse.
   (b) the penis serves as a duct for urine.
   (c) the penis develops from embryonic tissue.
   (d) the penis is found in mammals.

2. The penis contains _____ cylinder(s) of spongy material.
   (a) one
   (b) two
   (c) three
   (d) four

3. The condition in which it is difficult to retract the foreskin from the glans is called
   (a) phimosis.
   (b) circumcision.
   (c) priapism.
   (d) cryptorchidism.

4. The Canadian Cancer Society estimates that about 1 man in _____ in Canada will develop prostate cancer.
   (a) 9
   (b) 80
   (c) 800
   (d) 8000

5. The Canadian Cancer Society and other professional groups recommend that men of age _____ and above discuss prostate cancer screening with their doctor.
   (a) 40
   (b) 45
   (c) 50
   (d) 55

6. Erection is the engorgement of the penis with
   (a) semen.
   (b) blood.
   (c) sperm.
   (d) testosterone.

7. Erections generally occur during _____ sleep.
   (a) REM
   (b) non-REM
   (c) deepest
   (d) morning

8. In ejaculation, the seminal fluid is released from the
   (a) vas deferens
   (b) prostate gland
   (c) spinal cord
   (d) urethral bulb

9. The nerves that cause penile arteries to dilate during erection belong to the
   (a) sympathetic nervous system.
   (b) parasympathetic nervous system.
   (c) somatic nervous system.
   (d) central nervous system.

10. Men with _____ have excessive curvature of the penis that can make erections painful or make it difficult to enjoy sexual activity.
    (a) priapism
    (b) phimosis
    (c) Peyronie's disease
    (d) cryptorchidism

Chapter 4

Sexual Response and Behaviour

Did You Know That...

- "Spanish fly" is unlikely to turn your date on but may cure his or her warts?
- Men produce female sex hormones, and women produce male sex hormones?
- Orgasms attained through masturbation may be more intense than those attained through sexual intercourse?
- Many married people masturbate?
- Women are more likely to reach orgasm through masturbation than through sexual intercourse?
- Younger people are more likely to practise oral sex than people over 50? Anal sex is more common among highly educated people?

What turns you on? What sends your heart into your mouth, tightens your throat, and opens the floodgates of desire? The sight of your lover undressing, a photo of Orlando Bloom or J. Lo, a sniff of some expensive perfume, a sip of wine?

Many factors contribute to sexual response and behaviour. Although people's bodies are similar in their potential for sexual response, cultural influences can have profound effects on their sexual behaviour.

Making Sense of Sex: The Role of the Senses in Sexual Arousal

We come to apprehend the world around us through our senses—vision, hearing, smell, taste, and the skin senses, which include that all-important sense of touch. Each of the senses plays a role in our sexual experience.

Vision: The Better to See You With

It was the face of Helen of Troy, not her scent or her melodic voice, that "launched a thousand ships." Men's and women's magazines are filled with pictures of comely members of the other gender. Visual cues can be sexual turn-ons. We may be turned on by the sight of a lover in the nude, disrobing, or dressed in evening wear. Some couples find it arousing to observe themselves making love in an overhead mirror or on videotape. Some people find sexually explicit movies arousing. Others are bored or offended by them.

Smell: Does the Nose Know Best?

Odours can be sexual turn-ons or turn-offs. Most people in the Western world prefer their lovers to be clean and fresh-smelling. People in our society learn to remove or mask odours by the use of soaps, deodorants, and so on. Inclinations to find underarm or genital odours offensive may reflect cultural conditioning and not biological predispositions. In some societies, genital secretions are considered **aphrodisiacs.**

The Skin Senses: Sex as a Touching Experience

The sense of touch has the most direct effects on sexual arousal and response. Any region of the skin can become eroticized. **Erogenous zones** are parts of the body that are especially sensitive to tactile sexual stimulation—to strokes and other caresses. **Primary erogenous zones** are erotically sensitive because they are richly endowed with nerve endings. **Secondary erogenous zones** are parts of the body that become erotically sensitized through experience. For example, a woman might become sexually aroused when her lover gently caresses her shoulders, because such caresses have been incorporated as a regular feature of the couple's lovemaking.

Aphrodisiac Any drug or other agent that is sexually arousing or increases sexual desire. (From *Aphrodite,* the Greek goddess of love and beauty.)

Erogenous zones Parts of the body that are especially sensitive to tactile sexual stimulation.

Primary erogenous zones Erogenous zones that are particularly sensitive because they are richly endowed with nerve endings.

Secondary erogenous zones Parts of the body that become erotically sensitized through experience.

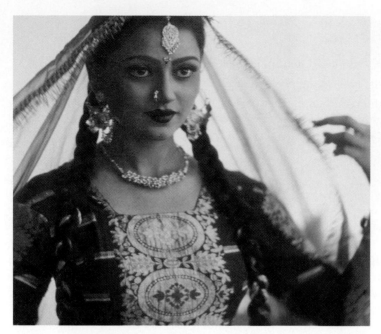

Visual Cues Can Be Sexual Turn-Ons or Turn-Offs. Despite cross-cultural differences in standards of physical attractiveness, a clear complexion has universal appeal.

Primary erogenous zones include the genitals; the inner thighs, perineum, buttocks, and anus; the breasts (especially the nipples); the ears (particularly the earlobes); the mouth, lips, and tongue; the neck; the navel; and, yes, the armpits. Preferences vary somewhat from person to person. Many women, for example, report little sensation when their breasts are stroked or kissed.

People are also highly responsive to images and fantasies. This is why the brain is sometimes referred to as the primary sexual organ, or an erogenous zone. Some women report reaching orgasm through fantasy alone (Kinsey et al., 1953). Men regularly experience erection and nocturnal emissions ("wet dreams") without direct stimulation of the genitals.

Technically, the brain is not an erogenous zone. It is not stimulated directly by touch. (The brain perceives touches of the skin, but it does not have sensory neurons to directly gather this information itself.)

Taste: On Savoury Sex

Some people are sexually aroused by the taste of genital secretions, such as vaginal secretions or seminal fluid. We do not know, however, whether these secretions are laced with chemicals that have biologically arousing effects, or whether arousal reflects the meaning that these secretions have to the individual. Others are turned off by them.

Hearing: The Better to Hear You With

Sounds can be turn-ons or turn-offs. The sounds of one's lover, whether whispers, indications of pleasure, or animated sounds that may attend orgasm, may be arousing during the heat of passion. Many people are aroused when their lovers "talk dirty." Spoken vulgarities spur their sexual arousal. Others find vulgar language offensive. Music can contribute to sexual arousal. Music can relax us and put us "in the mood" or have pleasant associations ("They're playing our song!").

Do We Have a "Sixth Sense" for Sex?

For centuries, people have searched for a love potion—a magical formula that could make others fall in love with them or be strongly attracted to them. Some scientists believe that such potions exist in the form of chemical secretions known as pheromones (Berliner, 1993). **Pheromones** are odourless chemicals that in people would be detected through a "sixth sense"—the *vomeronasal organ*. This organ, located in the nose (hence, *nasal*), would detect these odourless chemicals and signal the brain to respond. Pheromones do trigger sexual behaviour in many organisms, from insects to reptiles to mammals (Cobb & Jallon, 1990; Eggert & Muller, 1989; Mason et al., 1989). Pheromones are commonly contained in vaginal secretions and in urine. However, there is no evidence that stimulation of receptors in the vomeronasal organ is related to behavioural changes in humans (Meston & Frohlich, 2000).

Pheromones Chemical substances secreted externally by certain animals, which convey information to, or produce specific responses in, other members of the same species. (From the Greek *pherein*, meaning "to bear [a message]" and *hormone*.)

Aphrodisiacs and Anaphrodisiacs

Aphrodisiacs: Are There Substances That Enhance Sex?

An aphrodisiac is a substance that arouses or increases one's capacity for sexual pleasure or response. You may have heard of "Spanish fly," a supposed aphrodisiac once extracted from a Spanish beetle. (The beetle from which it was taken, *Lytta vesicatoria*, is near extinction.) A few drops in a date's drink were believed to make you irresistible. Spanish fly is toxic, however, not sexually arousing. The active ingredient, cantharidin, is a skin irritant that can burn off warts. It inflames the urethra, producing a burning sensation in the penis that is sometimes misinterpreted as sexual feelings.

Foods that resemble male genitals have been considered aphrodisiacs. They include oysters, clams, bull's testicles ("prairie oysters"), tomatoes, and "phallic" items such as celery stalks, bananas, and even ground-up rhinoceros, reindeer, and elephant horns (which is one derivation of the slang term "horny"). None of these foods or substances, however, has actually been shown to be sexually stimulating.

Drugs and psychoactive substances may have certain effects on sexual arousal and response. The drug yohimbine, an extract from the African yohimbe tree, stimulates blood flow to the genitals (Brody, 1993b). Its aphrodisiac effects remain to be demonstrated, however.

The heart medicine amyl nitrate dilates blood vessels in the brain and genitals, producing sensations of warmth in the pelvis and possibly facilitating erection and prolonging orgasm. It is inhaled from ampoules that "pop" open. "Poppers" can, however, cause dizziness, fainting, and migraine-type headaches.

Certain drugs appear to have aphrodisiac effects by acting on the brain mechanisms controlling sex drive. For example, drugs that affect brain receptors for the neurotransmitter dopamine, such as the antidepressant drug bupropion (trade name: Wellbutrin) and the drug L-dopa, used in the treatment of Parkinson's disease, can increase the sex drive (Brody, 1993b).

The most potent chemical aphrodisiac may be a naturally occurring substance in the body, the male sex hormone testosterone. It is the basic fuel of sexual desire in both genders (Brody, 1993b). In fact, **anti-androgen** drugs have anaphrodisiac effects.

The safest and perhaps most effective method for increasing the sex drive may be exercise. It boosts energy and increases the sex drive in both genders (Brody, 1993b, Meston & Gorzalka, 1995).

Perhaps the most potent aphrodisiac of all is novelty. Partners can make love in novel places, experiment with different techniques, wear provocative clothing, or share or enact fantasies.

Anti-androgen A substance that decreases the levels of androgens in the bloodstream.

Anaphrodisiacs Drugs or other agents that dull sexual arousal or sexual desire.

Anaphrodisiacs

Some substances, such as potassium nitrate (saltpeter), have been considered anaphrodisiacs. Saltpeter is a diuretic that can increase the need for urination and thus make the thought of sex unappealing.

Tranquilizers and central nervous system depressants, such as barbiturates, can lessen sexual desire and impair sexual performance. These drugs may enhance sexual arousal in some people, however, by lessening sexual inhibitions. Antihypertensive drugs, which are used in the treatment of high blood pressure, may produce erectile and ejaculatory difficulties in men and reduction of sexual desire in both genders. Certain antidepressant drugs, such as fluoxetine (brand name: Prozac), amitriptyline (brand name: Elavil), and imipramine (brand name: Tofranil), appear to dampen sex drive (Brody, 1993b; Meston & Gorzalka, 1992). Antidepressants may also impair erectile response and delay ejaculation in men and orgasmic responsiveness in women (Meston & Gorzalka, 1992). (Because they delay ejaculation, some of these drugs are being used to treat premature ejaculation.)

Nicotine, the stimulant in tobacco smoke, constricts the blood vessels. Thus it can impede sexual arousal by reducing the capacity of the genitals to become engorged with blood. Chronic smoking can also reduce the blood levels of testosterone in men, which can in turn lessen sex drive or motivation.

Psychoactive Drugs

Psychoactive drugs, such as alcohol and cocaine, are widely believed to have aphrodisiac effects. Yet their effects may reflect our expectations of them, or their effects on sexual inhibitions, rather than direct stimulation of sexual response.

Alcohol Small amounts of alcohol are stimulating, but large amounts curb sexual response. This fact should not be surprising because alcohol is a depressant. Alcohol reduces central nervous system activity. Large amounts of alcohol can severely impair sexual performance in both men and women.

Alcohol is connected with a liberated social role and thus provides an excuse for dubious behaviour. "It was the alcohol," people can say, "not me." Alcohol can also induce feelings of euphoria. Euphoric feelings may enhance sexual arousal and also wash away qualms about expressing sexual desires. Alcohol also appears to impair the ability to weigh information ("information processing") that might otherwise inhibit sexual impulses (Steele & Josephs, 1990). When people drink, they may be less able to foresee the consequences of misconduct and less likely to make good decisions about engaging in potentially risky behaviours.

Hallucinogens There is no evidence that marijuana and hallucinogenic drugs directly stimulate sexual response. However, fairly to strongly intoxicated marijuana users claim to have more empathy with others, to be more aware of bodily sensations, and to experience time as passing more slowly. These sensations could heighten subjective feelings of sexual response.

Stimulants Stimulants such as amphetamines ("speed," "uppers") have been reputed to heighten arousal and sensations of orgasm. These drugs generally activate the central nervous system but are not known to have specific sexual effects. Nevertheless, arousing the nervous system can contribute to sexual arousal (Palace, 1995). The drugs can also elevate the mood, and perhaps sexual pleasure is heightened by general elation. The downside is that high doses can give rise to irritability, restlessness, hallucinations, paranoid delusions, insomnia, and loss of appetite.

The stimulant cocaine produces a euphoric rush, which tends to ebb quickly. Physically, cocaine constricts blood vessels (reducing the oxygen supply to the heart), elevates the blood pressure, and accelerates the heart rate. Despite the popular belief that cocaine is an aphrodisiac, frequent use can lead to sexual dysfunctions, such as erectile disorder and failure to ejaculate among males, decreased vaginal lubrication in females, and lack of sexual desire (Weiss & Mirin, 1987).

Effects of Alcohol on Sexual Behaviour—A Complex Picture*. Small doses of alcohol can be stimulating and induce feelings of euphoria, both of which would appear to be connected with sexual interest. Alcohol can also reduce fear of consequences of engaging in risky behaviour—sexual and otherwise. Drinkers sometimes say, "It was the alcohol, not me." Alcohol is also expected to be sexually liberating, and people often live up to social and cultural expectations. Yet, as a depressant drug, alcohol biochemically dampens sexual response.*

Sex Hormones: Do They "Goad" Us into Sex?

Hormones are chemical substances that are secreted by the ductless glands of the endocrine system and discharged directly into the bloodstream. The word *hormone* derives from the Greek *horman*, meaning "to stimulate" or "to excite." They very much goad us into sexual activity.

Both men and women produce small amounts of the sex hormones of the other gender in their bodies. Testosterone, the major form of androgen, or male sex hormone, is secreted in small amounts by the adrenal glands (located above the kidneys) in both genders, but in much larger amounts by the testes. The ovaries produce small amounts of androgens but much larger amounts of the female sex hormones estrogen and progesterone. The testes similarly produce small amounts of estrogen and progesterone.

Sex Hormones and Sexual Behaviour

Sex hormones have organizing and activating effects on behaviour. That is, they exert an influence on the type of behaviour that is expressed (an *organizing* effect) and on the frequency or intensity of the drive that motivates the behaviour and the ability to perform the behaviour (an *activating* effect). For example, sex hormones predispose lower animals and possibly people toward stereotypical masculine or feminine mating behaviours (an organizing effect). They also facilitate sexual response and influence sexual desire (activating effects). Testosterone activates the sex drive of both men and women.

Sex Hormones and Male Sexual Behaviour
Evidence of the role of hormones in sex drive is found among men who have declines in testosterone levels as the result of castration. Castration (removal of the testes) is sometimes performed as a medical treatment for cancer of the testes or prostate or other diseases of the male reproductive tract, such as genital tuberculosis. Some convicted sex offenders have voluntarily undergone castration, although in 2002 the Supreme Court of Canada refused to hear the case of a man who wanted his sentence reduced after having this surgery (Canadian Press Newswire, 2002). Men who are castrated usually gradually lose sexual desire (Meston & Frohlich, 2000). They gradually lose the capacities to attain erection and to ejaculate—an indication that testosterone is important in maintaining sexual functioning as well as drive, at least in males.

Though minimal levels of androgens are critical to male sexuality, there is no one-to-one correspondence between hormone levels and the sex drive or sexual performance in adults. In men who have ample supplies of testosterone, sexual interest and functioning depend more on learning, fantasies, attitudes, memories, and other psychosocial factors than on hormone levels. At puberty, however, hormonal variations may play a more direct role in stimulating sexual interest and activity in males. Udry and his colleagues (Udry et al., 1985; Udry et al., 1986; Udry & Billy, 1987) found, for example, that testosterone levels predicted sexual interest, masturbation rates, and the likelihood of engaging in sexual intercourse among teenage boys. A positive relationship has also been found between testosterone levels in adult men and frequency of sexual intercourse (Dabbs & Morris, 1990; Knussman et al., 1986). Moreover, drugs that reduce the levels of androgen in the blood system, called antiandrogens, lead to reductions in sex drive and related fantasies and urges (Berlin, 1983; Money, 1987b).

Sex Hormones and Female Sexual Behaviour
The female sex hormones estrogen and progesterone play prominent roles in promoting the changes that occur during puberty and in regulating the menstrual cycle. Female sex hormones do not appear, however, to play a direct role in determining sexual motivation or response in human females (Meston & Frohlich, 2000). The human female is sexually responsive during all phases of the reproductive (menstrual) cycle—even during menstruation, when ovarian hormone levels are low—and after menopause.

Hormone A substance secreted by an endocrine gland that regulates various body functions. (From the Greek *horman*, meaning "to stimulate" or "to excite.")

Nobel e-Museum
www.nobel.se/chemistry/laureates/1939/press.html
The Nobel Prize in Chemistry 1939 was awarded for research on sex hormones.

There is some evidence, however, that sexual responsiveness in women is influenced by the presence of circulating androgens, or male sex hormones, in their bodies. The adrenal glands of women produce small amounts of androgens, just as they do in males. Women who receive **ovariectomies**, which are sometimes carried out when a hysterectomy is performed, no longer produce female sex hormones. Nevertheless, they continue to experience sex drives and interest as before. Loss of the ovarian hormone estradiol may cause vaginal dryness and make coitus painful, but it does not reduce sexual desire. (The dryness can be alleviated by a lubricating jelly or by estrogen-replacement therapy.) However, women whose adrenal glands and ovaries have been removed (so that they no longer produce androgens) gradually lose sexual desire. An active and enjoyable sexual history seems to ward off this loss, however, providing further evidence of the impact of mental and experiential factors on human sexual response.

A study was conducted with women whose ovaries had been surgically removed ("surgical menopause") as a way of treating disease. The ovaries supply major quantities of estrogen. Following surgery, the women in this study were treated either with estrogen-replacement therapy (ERT), with ERT plus androgens, or with a placebo (an inert substance made to resemble an active drug) (Sherwin et al., 1985). This was a double-blind study. Neither the women nor their physicians knew which drug the women were receiving. The results showed that the combination of androgens and ERT heightened sexual desire and sexual fantasies more than ERT alone or the placebo.

The Sexual Response Cycle

Although we may be culturally attuned to focus on gender differences rather than similarities, Masters and Johnson (1966) found that the physiological responses of men and women to sexual stimulation (whether from coitus, masturbation, or other sources) are quite alike. The sequence of changes in the body that takes place as men and women become progressively more aroused is referred to as the **sexual response cycle**. Masters and Johnson divided the cycle into four phases: *excitement*, *plateau*, *orgasm*, and *resolution*. Figure 4.1 suggests the levels of sexual arousal associated with each phase.

Both males and females experience **vasocongestion** and **myotonia** early in the response cycle. Vasocongestion is the swelling of the genital tissues with blood, which causes erection of the penis and engorgement of the area surrounding the vaginal opening. The testes, nipples, and even earlobes become engorged as blood vessels in these areas dilate.

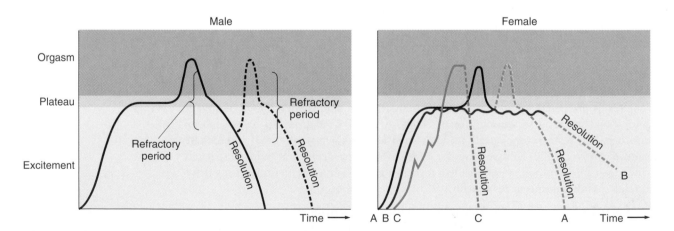

Figure 4.1. Levels of Sexual Arousal During the Phases of the Sexual Response Cycle.

Masters and Johnson divide the sexual response cycle into four phases: excitement, plateau, orgasm, and resolution. During the resolution phase, the level of sexual arousal returns to the prearoused state. For men there is a refractory period following orgasm. As shown by the broken line, however, men can become rearoused to orgasm once the refractory period is past and their levels of sexual arousal have returned to pre-plateau levels. Pattern A for women shows a typical response cycle, with the broken line suggesting multiple orgasms. Pattern B shows the cycle of a woman who reaches the plateau phase but for whom arousal is "resolved" without reaching the orgasmic phase. Pattern C shows the possibility of orgasm in a highly aroused woman who passes quickly through the plateau phase.

Myotonia, or muscle tension, causes voluntary and involuntary muscle contractions, which produce facial grimaces, spasms in the hands and feet, and eventually, the spasms of orgasm. Let us follow these and the other bodily changes that constitute the sexual response cycle.

Excitement Phase

In younger men, vasocongestion during the **excitement phase** produces penile erection as early as three to eight seconds after stimulation begins. Erection may occur more slowly in older men, but the responses are essentially the same. Erection may subside and return as stimulation varies. The scrotal skin thickens, losing its baggy appearance. The testes increase in size. The testes and scrotum become elevated.

In the female, vaginal lubrication may start 10 to 30 seconds after effective stimulation begins. Vasocongestion swells the clitoris, flattens the labia majora and spreads them apart, and increases the size of the labia minora. The inner two-thirds of the vagina expand. The vaginal walls thicken, and because of the inflow of blood, turn from their normal pink to a deeper hue. The uterus becomes engorged and elevated. The breasts enlarge, and blood vessels near the surface become more prominent.

The skin may take on a rosy **sex flush** late in this phase. It varies with intensity of arousal and is more pronounced in women. The nipples may become erect in both genders, especially in response to direct stimulation. Men and women show some increase in myotonia, heart rate, and blood pressure.

Excitement phase The first phase of the sexual response cycle, which is characterized by erection in the male, vaginal lubrication in the female, and muscle tension and increases in heart rate in both males and females.

Sex flush A reddish rash that appears on the chest or breasts late in the excitement phase of the sexual response cycle.

Plateau Phase

A plateau is a level region, and the level of arousal remains somewhat constant during the **plateau phase** of sexual response. Nevertheless, the plateau phase is an advanced state of arousal that precedes orgasm. Men in this phase show a slight increase in the circumference of the coronal ridge of the penis. The penile glans turns a purplish hue, a sign of vasocongestion. The testes are elevated further into position for ejaculation and may reach one and a half times their unaroused size. The Cowper's glands secrete a few droplets of fluid that are found at the tip of the penis (see Figure 4.2).

In women, vasocongestion swells the tissues of the outer third of the vagina, contracting the vaginal opening (thus preparing it to "grasp" the penis) and building the **orgasmic platform** (see Figure 4.3). The inner part of the vagina expands fully. The uterus becomes fully elevated. The clitoris withdraws beneath the clitoral hood and shortens.

Coloration of the labia minora appears, which is referred to as the **sex skin**. Further engorgement of the areolas of the breasts may make it seem that the nipples have lost part of their erection (see Figure 4.4). The Bartholin's glands secrete a fluid that resembles mucus.

Plateau phase The second phase of the sexual response cycle, which is characterized by increases in vasocongestion, muscle tension, heart rate, and blood pressure in preparation for orgasm.

Orgasmic platform The thickening of the walls of the outer third of the vagina, due to vasocongestion, that occurs during the plateau phase of the sexual response cycle.

Sex skin Reddening of the labia minora that occurs during the plateau phase.

Orgasmic Phase

The orgasmic phase in the male consists of two stages of muscular contractions. In the first stage, contractions of the vas deferens, the seminal vesicles, the ejaculatory duct, and the prostate gland cause seminal fluid to collect in the urethral bulb at the base of the penis (see Figure 4.2). The internal sphincter of the urinary bladder contracts, preventing seminal fluid from entering the bladder in a backward, retrograde ejaculation. The closing off of the bladder also serves to prevent urine from mixing with semen. The collection of semen in the urethral bulb produces feelings of ejaculatory inevitability— the sensation that nothing will stop the ejaculate from "coming." This sensation lasts for about two to three seconds.

In the second stage, the external sphincter of the bladder relaxes, allowing the passage of semen. Contractions of muscles surrounding the urethra and urethral bulb and the base of the penis propel the ejaculate through the urethra and out of the body.

Figure 4.2. The Male Genitals During the Phases of the Sexual Response Cycle.

About one man in four, and about three women in four, show a sex flush, which often does not appear until the plateau phase. Myotonia may cause spasmodic contractions in the hands and feet and facial grimaces. Breathing becomes rapid, like panting, and the heart rate may increase to 100 to 160 beats per minute. Blood pressure continues to rise. The increase in heart rate is usually less dramatic with masturbation than during coitus.

Masters and Johnson
www.mastersandjohnson.
com/
The website of the Masters and Johnson clinic.

Orgasm in the female is manifested by three to fifteen contractions of the pelvic muscles that surround the vaginal barrel. The contractions first occur at 0.8-second intervals, producing, as in the male, a release of sexual tension. Another three to six weaker and slower contractions follow. The spacing of these contractions is generally more variable in women than in men. The uterus and the anal sphincter also contract rhythmically. Uterine contractions occur in waves from the top to the cervix. In both genders, muscles go into spasm throughout the body. Blood pressure and heart rate reach a peak, with the heart beating up to 180 times per minute. Respiration may increase to 40 breaths per minute.

Several studies suggest that the orgasms of both genders may feel quite similar. In one, 48 men and women provided written descriptions of orgasms. The researchers (Proctor et al., 1974) modified the language (for example, changing "penis" to "genitals") so that the authors' genders would not be apparent. They then asked 70 "experts" (psychologists, gynecologists, etc.) to indicate the gender of each author. The ratings were no more reliable than guesswork.

Resolution Phase

Resolution phase The fourth phase of the sexual response cycle, during which the body gradually returns to its prearoused state.

The period following orgasm, in which the body returns to its prearoused state, is called the **resolution phase**. Following ejaculation, the man loses his erection in two stages. The first occurs in about a minute. Half the volume of the erection is lost as blood from the corpora cavernosa empties into the other parts of the body. The second stage occurs over a period of several minutes: The remaining tumescence subsides as the corpus

1. EXCITEMENT PHASE

The clitoral glans and the labia swell due to vasocongestion

Vagina begins to lubricate

Clitoris

Labia majora

Labia minora

Figure 4.3. The Female Genitals During the Phases of the Sexual Response Cycle.

Sensations of pleasure tend to be related to the strength of the contractions and the amount of seminal fluid. The first three to four contractions are generally most intense and occur at 0.8-second intervals (five contractions every four seconds). Another two to four contractions occur at a somewhat slower pace. Rates and patterns vary somewhat from man to man.

2. PLATEAU PHASE

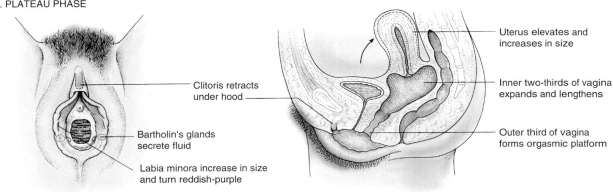

Clitoris retracts under hood

Bartholin's glands secrete fluid

Labia minora increase in size and turn reddish-purple

Uterus elevates and increases in size

Inner two-thirds of vagina expands and lengthens

Outer third of vagina forms orgasmic platform

3. ORGASM PHASE

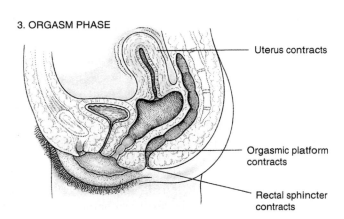

Uterus contracts

Orgasmic platform contracts

Rectal sphincter contracts

4. RESOLUTION PHASE

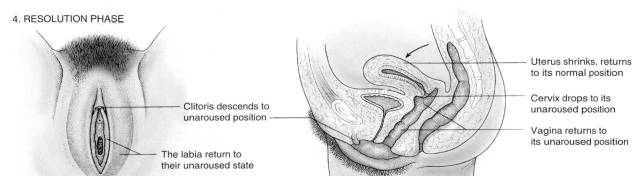

Clitoris descends to unaroused position

The labia return to their unaroused state

Uterus shrinks, returns to its normal position

Cervix drops to its unaroused position

Vagina returns to its unaroused position

Figure 4.4. The Breast During the Phases of the Sexual Response Cycle.

The sensations of orgasm have challenged the descriptive powers of poets. Words like "rush," "warmth," "explosion," and "release" do not adequately capture them. We may assume (rightly or wrongly) that others of our gender experience pretty much what we do, but can we understand the sensations of the other gender?

spongiosum empties. The testes and scrotum return to normal size, and the scrotum regains its wrinkled appearance.

In women orgasm also triggers release of blood from engorged areas. In the absence of continued stimulation, swelling of the areolas decreases; then the nipples return to normal size. The sex flush lightens rapidly. In about 5 to 10 seconds the clitoris descends to its normal position. The clitoris, vaginal barrel, uterus, and labia gradually shrink to their prearoused sizes. The labia minora turn lighter (the "sex skin" disappears) in about 10 to 15 seconds.

Most muscle tension (myotonia) tends to dissipate within five minutes after orgasm in both men and women. Blood pressure, heart rate, and respiration may also return to their prearousal levels within a few minutes. About 30% to 40% of men and women find their palms, the soles of their feet, or their entire bodies covered with a sheen of perspiration. Both men and women may feel relaxed and satiated.

Although the processes by which the body returns to its prearousal state are similar in men and women, there is an important gender difference. Unlike women, men enter a **refractory period** during which they are physiologically incapable of experiencing another orgasm or ejaculation. The refractory period of adolescent males may last only minutes, whereas that of men aged 50 and over may last from several minutes (yes, it could happen) to a day. Women do not undergo a refractory period and so can become quickly rearoused to the point of repeated (multiple) orgasm if they desire and receive continued sexual stimulation (see Figure 4.1).

Myotonia and vasocongestion may take an hour or more to dissipate in people who are aroused but who do not reach orgasm. Persistent pelvic vasocongestion may cause "blue balls" in males—the slang term for a throbbing ache. Women, too, may experience unpleasant pelvic throbbing if they have become highly aroused and do not find release.

Refractory period
A period of time following a response (e.g., orgasm) during which an individual is no longer responsive to stimulation (e.g., sexual stimulation).

Kaplan's Three Stages of Sexual Response: An Alternative Model

Helen Singer Kaplan was a prominent sex therapist and author of several professional books (1974, 1979, 1987) on sex therapy. Where Masters and Johnson had proposed a four-stage physiological model of sexual response, Kaplan developed a three-stage *psychosexual* model consisting of (1) desire, (2) excitement, and (3) orgasm. Kaplan's model is an outgrowth of her clinical experience in working with people with sexual dysfunctions. She believed that their problems could best be classified according to these three phases. Kaplan's model makes it convenient for clinicians to classify sexual dysfunctions involving desire (low or absent desire), excitement (such as problems with erection in the male or lubrication in the female), and orgasm (such as premature ejaculation in the male or orgasmic dysfunction in the female).

Masters and Johnson focus on physiological changes that occur during sexual stimulation. Kaplan's model includes two phases that are primarily physiological (excitement, consisting of initial vasocongestion of the genitals, resulting in erection in the male and vaginal lubrication in the female, and orgasm, marked by pelvic muscular contractions) and one that is primarily psychological (desire). Kaplan's stages of excitement and orgasm are clearly differentiated along physiological lines. (Masters and Johnson's excitement and plateau stages are less clearly differentiated in terms of differences in biological processes. Both primarily involve vasocongestion.)

Masters and Johnson view sexual response as being composed of successive stages; the order is crucial and invariant. Kaplan treats her phases as relatively independent components of sexual response whose sequence is somewhat variable. For example, a person may experience sexual excitement and even orgasm, though sexual desire remains low. Excitement may also precede desire in some situations. For example, people with low sexual desire may find their sexual appetites sparked as their bodies respond to their partners' sexual stimulation. A person who lacks desire, however, might not be motivated to seek sexual stimulation or be able to respond adequately to sexual stimuli.

Kaplan's model is noteworthy for designating desire as a separate phase of sexual response. Problems in lack of sexual interest or desire are among the most common brought to the attention of sex therapists.

Basson's Intimacy Model: A New Alternative Model of Female Sexuality

Both Masters and Johnson's and Kaplan's models of sexual response assume that events proceed in a more or less linear fashion—either from arousal to orgasm or from desire to arousal to orgasm. An alternative model of women's sexual response has been proposed by Rosemary Basson of Vancouver. Dr. Basson, a noted sex therapist and researcher, suggests that for many women, especially in long-term relationships, intimacy, rather than desire, may be the primary motivating factor for sex. That is, women engage in sexual encounters for many reasons other than to satisfy the sexual drive. In long-term relationships, these reasons include

- to feel emotionally closer to the partner
- to feel loved and wanted
- to share sexual feelings and
- to show caring and affection

Based on clinical observations, Basson feels that it is this desire for emotional intimacy that leads a woman to respond positively to sexual stimuli. The subjective experience of sexual arousal depends more on cognitive and affective factors than on genital stimulation. A woman may begin a sexual encounter in a state of "sexual neutrality" (dare we say "indifference"?). If she becomes aroused for any of the intimacy reasons listed above, she may then experience genital or breast stimulation as sexually arousing as well. If this stimulation is pleasant, and effective, and the outcome is positive (lack of discomfort, positive response from partner), the increased feelings of intimacy that result will encourage her to seek out the same experience (Basson, 2001). Basson's model suggests that sexual arousal may precede sexual desire and has implications for therapies for sexual desire disorders in women (see Chapter 12).

Does intimacy precede desire, in woemen? Canadian researcher Rosemary Basson believes that it is a desire for emotional intimacy that leads a woman to respond positively to sexual stimuli.

Controversies About Orgasm

Are women capable of experiencing multiple orgasms? Are men? How many kinds of orgasm are there? Do women ejaculate during orgasm?

Few other topics in human sexuality have aroused more controversies over the years than orgasm. We do not have all the answers, but some intriguing research findings have shed light on some of these continuing controversies.

Multiple Orgasms

Multiple orgasms One or more additional orgasms following the first, which occur within a short period of time and before the body has returned to a pre-plateau level of arousal.

Masters and Johnson (1966) reported that most if not all women are capable of **multiple orgasms**. Though all women may have a biological capability for multiple orgasms, not all women report them. A survey of 720 nurses showed that only 43% reported experiencing multiple orgasms (Darling et al., 1991).

Masters and Johnson define *multiple orgasm* as the rapid occurrence of one or more additional orgasms following the first, before the body has returned to a pre-plateau level of arousal. By this definition, a person would not have experienced multiple orgasms if he or she had two or more successive orgasms that were separated by a return to a prearoused state or a pre-plateau (excitement stage) level of arousal. Yet the lines of demarcation between the excitement and plateau stages of arousal are not always obvious.

By Masters and Johnson's definition, men are not capable of achieving multiple orgasms, because they enter a refractory period following ejaculation during which they are physiologically incapable of achieving another orgasm or ejaculation for a time. Women do not enter a refractory period. Women can continue to have orgasms if they continue to receive effective stimulation (and, of course, are interested in continuing).

Some men have two or more orgasms without ejaculation ("dry orgasms") preceding a final ejaculatory orgasm. These men may not enter a refractory period following their initial dry orgasms and may therefore be able to maintain their level of stimulation at near-peak levels. Some men report multiple orgasms in which dry orgasms follow an ejaculatory orgasm, with little or no loss of erection between orgasms (Dunn & Trost, 1989). Some men report more varied patterns, with ejaculatory orgasms and dry orgasms preceding or following each other in different sequences.

Masters and Johnson found that some women experienced 20 or more orgasms by masturbating. Still, few women have multiple orgasms during most sexual encounters, and many are satisfied with just one per occasion.

How Many Kinds of Orgasms Do Women Have?

The psychoanalyst Sigmund Freud proposed two types of female orgasm: the *clitoral orgasm* and the *vaginal orgasm*. Clitoral orgasms were achieved through direct clitoral stimulation, such as by masturbation. Clitoral orgasms were seen by psychoanalysts (mostly male psychoanalysts, naturally) as emblematic of a childhood fixation—a throwback to an erogenous pattern acquired during childhood masturbation.

The term *vaginal orgasm* referred to an orgasm achieved through deep penile thrusting during coitus and was theorized to be a sign of mature sexuality. Freud argued that women achieve sexual maturity when they forsake clitoral stimulation for vaginal stimulation. This view would be little more than an academic footnote but for the fact that some adult women who continue to require direct clitoral stimulation to reach orgasm, even during coitus, have been led by traditional psychoanalysts to believe that they are sexually "fixated" at an immature stage, or are, at least, sexually inadequate.

Despite Freudian theory, Masters and Johnson (1966) were able to find only one kind of orgasm, physiologically speaking, regardless of the source of stimulation (manual–clitoral or penile–vaginal). By monitoring physiological responses to sexual stimulation, they found that the female orgasm involves the same biological events regardless of how it is attained.

Orgasms experienced through different means may also vary in physiological and subjective intensity. Masters and Johnson (1966) found that orgasms experienced during masturbation were generally more physiologically intense than those experienced during intercourse, perhaps because masturbation allows one to focus only on one's own pleasure and on ensuring that one receives effective stimulation to climax. This does not mean that orgasms during masturbation are more enjoyable or gratifying than those experienced through coitus, however. Given the emotional connectedness we may feel toward our lovers, we are unlikely to break off our relationships in favour of masturbation. Thus, "physiological intensity," as measured by laboratory instruments, does not translate directly into subjective pleasure or fulfillment.

The purported distinction between clitoral and vaginal orgasms also rests on an assumption that the clitoris is not stimulated during coitus. Masters and Johnson showed this to be a false assumption. Penile coital thrusting draws the clitoral hood back and forth against the clitoris. Vaginal pressure also heightens blood flow in the clitoris, further setting the stage for orgasm (Lavoisier et al., 1995).

One might think that Masters and Johnson's research settled the question of whether or not there are different types of female orgasm. Other investigators, however, have proposed that there are distinct forms of female orgasm, yet not those suggested by psychoanalytic theory. For example, Singer and Singer (1972) suggested that there are three types of female orgasm: *vulval*, *uterine*, and *blended*. According to the Singers, the vulval orgasm represents the type of orgasm described by Masters and Johnson (1966) that involves vulval contractions; that is, contractions of the vaginal barrel. Consistent with the findings of Masters and Johnson (1966), they note that the vulval orgasm remains the same regardless of the source of stimulation, clitoral or vaginal.

According to the Singers, the uterine orgasm does not involve vulval contractions. It occurs only in response to deep penile thrusting against the cervix. This thrusting slightly displaces the uterus and stimulates the tissues that cover the abdominal organs. The uterine orgasm is accompanied by a certain pattern of breathing: gasping or gulping of air is followed by an involuntary holding of the breath as orgasm approaches. When orgasm is reached, the breath is explosively exhaled. The uterine orgasm is accompanied by deep feelings of relaxation and sexual satisfaction.

The third type, or blended orgasm, is described as combining features of the vulval and uterine orgasms. It involves both an involuntary breath-holding response and contractions of the pelvic muscles. The Singers note that the type of orgasm a woman experiences—vulval, uterine, or blended—depends on factors such as the parts of the body that are stimulated and the duration of stimulation. Each produces its own kind of satisfaction, and no one type is necessarily better or preferable to any other.

The Singers' hypothesis of three distinct forms of female orgasm remains controversial. Researchers initially scoffed at the idea that orgasms could arise from vaginal stimulation alone. The vagina, after all, especially the inner two-thirds of the vaginal cavity, is relatively insensitive to stimulation (erotic or otherwise). Proponents of the Singers' model counter that the type of uterine orgasm that the Singers described is induced more by pressure resulting from deep pelvic thrusting than by touch.

The G-Spot

A bean-shaped area within the anterior wall of the vagina may have special erotic significance. This area is believed to lie about 2 to 4 cm from the vaginal entrance and to consist of a soft mass of tissue that swells from the size of a dime to a half dollar when stimulated (Davidson et al., 1989). It has been called the **Grafenberg spot**—the "G-spot" for short (see Figure 4.5). The spot can be directly stimulated by the woman's or her partner's fingers or by penile thrusting in the rear entry or the female-superior positions. Some researchers suggest that stimulation of the spot produces intense erotic sensations and that with prolonged stimulation, a distinct form of orgasm occurs. This orgasm is characterized by intense pleasure and, in some cases, by a biological event earlier

Grafenberg spot A part of the anterior wall of the vagina, whose prolonged stimulation is theorized to cause particularly intense orgasms and a female ejaculation. Abbreviated as *G-spot*.

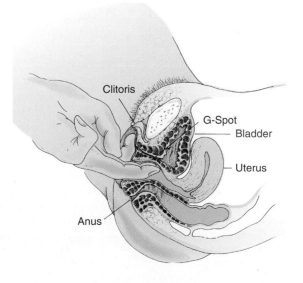

Figure 4.5. The Grafenberg Spot (G-Spot).

thought to be exclusively male in nature: ejaculation (Perry & Whipple, 1981; Whipple & Komisaruk, 1988). These claims, like other claims of distinct forms of female orgasm, are controversial.

The G-spot was named after a gynecologist, Ernest Grafenberg, who first suggested the erotic importance of this area. Grafenberg observed that orgasm in women could be induced by stimulating this area. He also claimed that such orgasms may be accompanied by the discharge of a milky fluid or "ejaculate" from the urethra. In a laboratory experiment, Zaviacic and his colleagues (1988a, 1988b) found evidence of an ejaculate in 10 of 27 women studied. Some researchers believe that this fluid is urine that some women release involuntarily during orgasm (Alzate, 1985). Other researchers believe that it differs from urine (Zaviacic et al., 1988a; Zaviacic & Whipple, 1993).

The existence of the G-spot continues to be debated among researchers. Although many women in the health and counselling professions believe that the G-spot exists and that they have experienced sexual pleasure from stimulation of the area (Davidson et al., 1989), there is considerable confusion as to the precise location of this sensitive area. Despite the fact that references to the G-spot abound, both on the internet and in the popular press, there is very little recent research that confirms its existence. On the other hand, it is currently accepted that some women do experience the release of some fluid with orgasm.

Sexual Behaviour

This section describes sexual techniques and statistical breakdowns of "who does what with whom." There is great variety in human sexual expression. Some of us practise few, if any, of the techniques discussed here. Some of us practise most or all of them. Some of us practise some of them some of the time. Our knowledge of the prevalences of these techniques comes from sex surveys that began with Kinsey and have continued with the work of Hunt, the University of Chicago group, and others.

The human body is sensitive to many forms of sexual stimulation. Yet biology is not destiny: A biological capacity does not impose a behavioural requirement. Cultural expectations, personal values, and individual experience—not only our biological capacities—determine our sexual behaviour. What is right for you is right for you—not necessarily for your neighbour.

Solitary Sexual Behaviour

Various forms of sexual expression do not require a partner. Masturbation is one of the principal forms of one-person sexual expression. Masturbation involves direct stimulation of the genitals. Other forms of individual sexual experience, such as sexual fantasy, may or may not be accompanied by genital stimulation.

Masturbation **Masturbation** may be practised by manual stimulation of the genitals, perhaps with the aid of artificial stimulation, such as a vibrator. It may employ an object, such as a pillow or a **dildo**, that touches the genitals. Even before we conceive of sexual experiences with others, we may learn early in childhood that touching our genitals can produce pleasure.

Pleasure is not the only reason that people masturbate. Other reasons include a wish to relax, a wish to relieve sexual tension, the lack of a partner or a partner's lack of interest, and boredom (Laumann, et al., 1994). Within the Judeo-Christian tradition, masturbation has been condemned as sinful. Until recent years masturbation was thought to be physically and mentally harmful, as well as degrading; in fact, some older dictionaries define masturbation as "self-abuse." Many clergy and medical authorities of the nineteenth century were persuaded that certain foods had a stimulating effect on the sex organs. So one form of advice to parents focused on modifying their children's diets to eliminate foods, notably meat, coffee, tea, and chocolate, that were believed to excite the sex organs, and to substitute "unstimulating" foods in their place, most notably grain products.

Masturbation Sexual self-stimulation.

Dildo A penis-shaped object used in sexual activity.

Porn Flakes: Kellogg, Graham and the Crusade for Moral Fiber
http://www.ibiblio.org/stayfree/10/graham.htm
An amusing and well-researched page discussing Dr. Kellogg and Sylvester Graham and their attempts to curb masturbation through healthful eating habits.

You may have heard of the superintendent of the Battle Creek Sanatorium in Michigan, Dr. J. H. Kellogg (1852–1943). He is better known as the creator of the modern breakfast cereal. Kellogg identified 39 signs of masturbation, including acne, paleness, heart palpitations, rounded shoulders, weak backs, and convulsions. Kellogg believed that sexual desires could be controlled by a diet of simple foods, especially grains, including the corn flakes that have since borne his name.

Despite this history, there is no scientific evidence that masturbation is harmful. Masturbation does not cause insanity, grow hair on the hands, or cause warts or any of the other psychological and physical ills once ascribed to it. Masturbation is physically harmless, save for rare injuries to the genitals due to rough stimulation. Nor is masturbation in itself psychologically harmful, although people who consider masturbation wrong, harmful, or sinful may experience anxiety or guilt if they masturbate or wish to masturbate. These negative emotions are linked to their attitudes toward masturbation, not to masturbation per se (Michael et al., 1994).

Surveys indicate that most people masturbate at some time. The incidence of masturbation is generally greater among men than women. Nearly all of the adult men and about two-thirds of the adult women in Kinsey's samples (Kinsey et al., 1948, 1953) reported that they had masturbated at some time. The NHSLS study also found a notable gender gap in reported frequencies of masturbation (Laumann et al., 1994). Despite the sexual revolution, women may still find masturbation less pleasurable or acceptable than men do. A survey of over 700 students at the University of British Columbia found that while 80% of males had masturbated, only 48% of females said that they had done so (Meston et al., 1996). Women may still be subject to traditional socialization pressures that teach that sexual activity for pleasure's sake is more of a taboo for women than for men. Then, too, women are more likely to pursue sexual activity within the context of a relationship.

Masters and Johnson (1966) found that masturbation was a more reliable means for women to achieve orgasm than coitus, at least for women who accept masturbation as a sexual outlet.

Figure 4.6. Male Masturbation.

Masturbation techniques vary widely, but most men report that they masturbate by manual manipulation of the penis. They tend to grip the penile shaft with one hand and jerk it up and down in a milking motion.

Techniques of Male Masturbation

Sex is like bridge—if you don't have a good partner, you'd better have a good hand.

(CONTEMPORARY BATHROOM GRAFFITI)

Although masturbation techniques vary widely, most men report that they masturbate by manual manipulation of the penis (see Figure 4.6). Typically they take one or two minutes to reach orgasm (Kinsey et al., 1948). Men tend to grip the penile shaft with one hand, jerking it up and down in a milking motion. Some men move the whole hand up and down the penis, while others use just two fingers, generally the thumb and index finger. Men usually shift from a gentler rubbing action during the flaccid or semi-erect state of arousal to a more vigorous milking motion once full erection takes place. Men are also likely to stroke the glans and frenulum lightly at the outset, but their grip tightens and their motions speed up as orgasm nears. At orgasm, the penile shaft may be gripped tightly, but the glans has become sensitive, and contact with it is usually avoided. (Likewise, women usually avoid stimulating the clitoris directly during orgasm because of increased sensitivity.)

Some men use soapsuds (which may become irritating) as a lubricant for masturbation during baths or showers. Other lubricants, such as petroleum jelly or K-Y jelly, may also be used to reduce friction and to simulate the moist conditions of coitus.

A few men prefer to masturbate by rubbing the penis and testicles against clothing or bedding (Kinsey et al., 1948). A very few men rub their genitals against inflatable dolls sold

Figure 4.7. Female Masturbation.

Techniques of female masturbation vary so widely that Masters and Johnson reported never observing two women masturbating in precisely the same way. However, most women masturbate by massaging the mons, labia minora, and clitoral region, either with circular or back-and-forth motions.

in sex shops. These dolls may come with artificial mouths or vaginas that can be filled with warm water to mimic the sensations of coitus. Artificial vaginas are also for sale.

Some men strap vibrators to the backs of their hands. Most men rely heavily on fantasy or erotic photos or videos, but do not use sex-shop devices.

Techniques of Female Masturbation Techniques of female masturbation also vary widely, but some general trends have been noted. Most women masturbate by massaging the mons, labia minora, and clitoral region with circular or back-and-forth motions (Hite, 1976; Kinsey et al., 1953). They may also straddle the clitoris with their fingers, stroking the shaft rather than the glans (see Figure 4.7). The glans may be lightly touched early during arousal, but because of its exquisite sensitivity, it is rarely stroked for any length of time. Women typically achieve clitoral stimulation by rubbing or stroking the clitoral shaft or pulling or tugging on the vaginal lips. Some women also massage other sensitive areas, such as their breasts or nipples, with the free hand. Many women, like men, fantasize during masturbation (Leitenberg & Henning, 1995).

Women usually do *not* masturbate by simulating penile thrusting through the insertion of fingers or phallic objects into their vaginas (Hite, 1976; Kinsey et al., 1953). Hite reported that only 1.5% of her respondents exclusively relied on vaginal insertion as a means of masturbation. Kinsey and his colleagues found that only one in five women had sometimes used vaginal insertions of objects during masturbation. However, anecdotal reports from students and the experience of sex therapists suggest that more women insert objects into the vagina than was previously thought (McKenzie, 2004, Cohen, 2004).

Even when women do use insertion, they usually precede or combine it with clitoral stimulation. Sex shops sell dildos, which women can use to rub their vulvas or to insert vaginally. Penis-shaped vibrators may be used in a similar fashion. Many women masturbate during baths, some by spraying their genitals with water-massage shower heads.

Handheld electrical vibrators provide a massaging action against the genitals that can be erotic. Some women find this type of stimulation too intense, however, and favour vibrators that strap to the back of the hand and cause the fingers to vibrate.

Sexual Fantasy Sexual fantasies can occur without a partner, but many people also fantasize during lovemaking (Leitenberg & Henning, 1995). Some couples find it sexually arousing to share their fantasies or to enact them with their partners. Strictly speaking, however, a fantasy is a private mental experience. Sexual fantasies may be experienced without sexual behaviour, as in erotic dreams or daydreams. Sexual fantasies can also be used to heighten sexual response during masturbation or sexual activity with another person. Masturbators often require some form of mental stimulation, such as fantasy or reading or viewing erotica, to reach orgasm.

Most men and women engage in sexual fantasies from time to time, especially during masturbation (Reinisch, 1990). Men fantasize more often than women do (Hsu et al., 1994). In their U.S. survey, Laumann and his colleagues (1994) found that 54% of men and 19% of women said they thought about sex at least one time a day. Sexual fantasies may be reasonably realistic, such as imagining sexual activity with an attractive classmate. They may involve flights of fancy, such as making love to a movie star. The most common fantasy theme reported among women involves someone they are or have been involved with (Leitenberg & Henning, 1995). In contrast to men's fantasies, women are more likely to focus on the partner's feelings, touching, their own responses to what is happening, and the general feeling tone of the sexual encounter (Leitenberg & Henning, 1995). A study of university students in New Brunswick found that men were more likely to report fantasies of having sex with more than one person at the same time, sex with a stranger, and watching others have sex, while women had more fantasies about undressing provocatively, engaging in sexual activity with a partner contrary to their sexual orientation, and being spanked than men did (Renaud & Byers, 1999). The most common masturbation fantasy reported by both genders in a *Playboy* sample was "having intercourse with a loved one" (Hunt, 1974). But note some interesting gender differences: Men are more likely to assume aggressive, dominant roles. Women are more apt to enact passive, submissive roles (Leitenberg & Henning, 1995; Person et al., 1989). Women are more likely to connect sexual activity to relationships and emotional involvement than men are (Barbach, 1995; Leitenberg & Henning, 1995). Fantasizing about forcing someone into sexual activity, or about being victimized, does not mean that one wants these events to occur (Leitenberg & Henning, 1995; Reinisch, 1990). Women who imagine themselves being sexually coerced remain in control of their fantasies. Real assault victims are not.

Sexual Fantasy. *Sexual fantasies can be a powerful source of sexual stimulation when people are masturbating or making love.*

Sex with Others

Partners' feelings for one another, and the quality of their relationships, may be stronger determinants of their sexual arousal and response than the techniques that they employ. As with other aspects of sharing relationships, communication is the most important "sexual" technique. With the exception of coitus, any (and all) of the behaviours described in this section may be (and are) practised by anyone, regardless of sexual orientation.

Foreplay Various forms of noncoital sex, such as cuddling, kissing, petting, and oral–genital contact, can be used as **foreplay**. Women generally want longer periods of foreplay (and "afterplay") than men do (Denny et al., 1984). Since women usually require a longer period of stimulation during sex with a partner to reach orgasm, increasing the duration of foreplay may increase female coital responsiveness. Kissing, genital touching, and oral–genital contact can also be experienced as ends in themselves, not just as preludes to coitus.

Foreplay Mutual sexual stimulation that precedes sexual intercourse.

Kissing Couples may kiss for its own enjoyment or as a prelude to intercourse or other, more intimate, contact, in which case it is a part of foreplay. In *simple kissing*, the partners keep their mouths closed. Simple kissing may develop into caresses of the lips with the tongue, or into nibbling of the lower lip. In what Kinsey called *deep kissing*, which is also called *French* or *soul kissing*, the partners part their lips and insert their tongues into each other's mouths.

Kissing is not limited to the partner's mouth. Kinsey found that more than nine husbands in ten kissed their wives' breasts. Women usually prefer several minutes of body contact and gentle caresses before desiring to have their partner kiss their breasts, or suck or lick their nipples. Women also usually do not prefer a hard sucking action unless they are highly aroused. Other parts of the body are also often kissed, including the hands and feet, the neck and earlobes, the insides of the thighs, and the genitals themselves.

Touching Touching is a common form of foreplay. Both men and women generally enjoy manual or oral stimulation of the genitals. Women generally prefer that direct caressing of the genitals be focused around the sides of the clitoris rather than directly on the extremely sensitive clitoral glans. Men sometimes assume (often mistakenly) that their partners want them to insert their finger or fingers into the vagina as a form of foreplay. But not all women enjoy this form of stimulation.

Masters and Johnson (1979) noted gender differences with respect to preferences in foreplay. Men typically prefer direct stroking of their genitals by their partner early in lovemaking. Women, however, tend to prefer that their partners caress their genitals after a period of general body contact that includes holding, hugging, and nongenital massage.

Techniques of Manual Stimulation of the Genitals Here again, variability in technique is the rule, so partners need to communicate their preferences. The man's partner may use two hands to stimulate his genitals. One may be used to fondle the scrotum, by gently squeezing the skin between the fingers (taking care not to apply pressure to the testes themselves). The other hand may circle the coronal ridge and engage in gentle stroking of the penis, followed by more vigorous up and down movements as the man becomes more aroused.

The penis may also be gently rolled back and forth between the palms as if one were making a ball of clay into a sausage—increasing pressure as arousal progresses. Note that men who are highly aroused or who have just had an orgasm may find direct stimulation of the penile glans uncomfortable.

The woman may prefer that her partner approach genital stimulation gradually, following stimulation of other body parts. Genital stimulation may begin with light, stroking motions of the inner thighs and move on to the vaginal lips (labia) and the clitoral area. Women may enjoy pressure against the mons pubis from the heel of the hand, or stroking of the labia. Clitoral stimulation can focus on the clitoral shaft or the region surrounding the shaft, rather than the clitoris itself, because of the extreme sensitivity of the clitoral glans.

Some, but not all, women enjoy having a finger inserted into the vagina, which can stroke the vaginal walls or simulate thrusting of the penis. Vaginal insertion is usually not preferred, if at all, until the woman has become highly aroused. Many women desire that their partners discontinue stroking motions while they are experiencing orgasm, but others wish stimulation to continue. Men and women may physically guide their partners' hands or otherwise express their preferences as to the types of strokes they find most pleasurable.

If a finger is to be inserted into the vagina, it should be clean. Fingernails should be well trimmed. Inserting fingers that have been in the anus into the vagina is dangerous. The fingers may transfer microbes from the woman's digestive tract, where they do no harm, to the woman's reproductive tract, where they can cause serious infections.

Breast Stimulation Men are more likely to stimulate women's breasts than to have their own breasts fondled, even though the breasts (and especially the nipples) are erotically sensitive in both genders. Most, but not all, women enjoy breast stimulation. Masters and Johnson report that some women are capable of achieving orgasm from breast stimulation alone.

The hands and the mouth can be used to stimulate the breasts and the nipples. Since the desired type and intensity of breast stimulation varies from person to person, partners need to communicate their preferences.

A World of Diversity

Sexual Behaviour in China

China was never a particularly prudish country. China's tradition of concubines and prostitution predates the birth of Jesus. In its ancient erotic art and fiction, depictions of sex, including oral sex, is quite common (Robert Koch Institute, 2000). This "Golden Age" of Chinese sexuality ended around the end of the seventeenth century, with an increasing emphasis by the government on asceticism in an attempt to enforce chastity on both men and women (Zhang, et al., 1999). Homosexuality and masturbation were condemned as non-procreative behaviours, and continued to be denounced well into the nineteenth century. After the Communists came into power in 1949, China became an even more puritanical society.

Toward the end of the 1970s, along with economic reforms and increased exchanges between Chinese and Western culture, attitudes about sexuality changed again. Sociologist Liu Dalin interviewed 23 000 Chinese over a period of 18 months (Southerland, 1990). China's "Kinsey Report" was the first nationwide sex survey ever conducted in China. It polled twice as many people as Kinsey and his colleagues did. Participants included students, professionals, peasants, even convicted sex offenders drawn from three major cities and 12 provinces. The researchers encountered problems in lack of funds, illiteracy, and reluctance to reveal intimate sexual information. Among their findings: Few couples engaged in extended foreplay. More than one-third of rural women found intercourse painful. Half of young people had engaged in premarital intercourse. Sixty-nine percent of Chinese people approved of extramarital sex—a number considerably higher than that found in North America.

Changing attitudes, especially attitudes about premarital sex and homosexuality, and changing behaviours, have resulted in an increasing incidence of sexually transmitted infections, especially among unmarried individuals. The rate of syphilis increased twentyfold between 1990 and 1998. Gonorrhea and genital warts experienced large, although less dramatic, increases as well. Almost 75% of people diagnosed with an STI in 1998 were unmarried (Digest: STD rates soar in China).

Although, up until now, most cases of HIV in China were acquired through either intravenous drug use or contaminated blood or blood products, men who have sex with men are increasingly at risk (Choi et al., 2003). A study conducted in 2000 on 426 men who have sex with men found that the average number of lifetime sexual partners was 31 and that two-thirds said they never used condoms. Nearly half of the men surveyed had also had sex with women (Beichuan, et al., 2000).

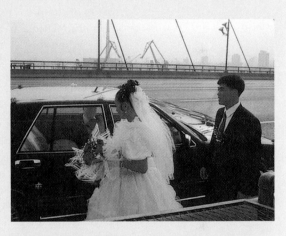

Sex in China. Chastity before marriage is no longer the rule in China. About half of Chinese young people have engaged in premarital sex.

Oral–Genital Stimulation Oral stimulation of the male genitals is called **fellatio**. Fellatio is referred to by slang terms such as "blow job," "sucking," "sucking off," or "giving head." Oral stimulation of the female genitals is called **cunnilingus**, which is referred to by slang expressions such as "eating" (a woman) or "going down" on her.

The popularity of oral–genital stimulation has increased dramatically since Kinsey's day, especially among young couples. Kinsey and his colleagues (1948, 1953) found that at least 60% of married, college-educated couples had experienced oral–genital contact. Such experiences were reported by only about 20% of couples who had only a high school education and 10% who had only a grade school education.

In contrast, the NHSLS study in the 1990s (Laumann et al., 1994) found that about three of four men (77%) and two of three women (68%) report playing the active role in oral sex during their lifetimes. Nearly four men in five (79%) and three of four women (73%) report having been the recipients of oral–genital sex during their lifetimes. Among married couples, 80% of the men and 71% of the women have performed oral sex. Eighty percent of the men and 74% of the women have received oral sex. These are dramatic increases since Kinsey's day.

A poll carried out for the *Toronto Sun* by COMPAS Research in 1998 found that 70% of Canadians said that they had performed oral sex, while 71% said that they had

Fellatio Oral stimulation of the male genitals.

Cunnilingus Oral stimulation of the female genitals.

received it. Males are more likely to report both giving and receiving oral sex (80%) than females (61% said that they had given oral sex to their partner, while 60% said that they had received it). Younger Canadians are more likely to have experienced oral sex—more than 82% of respondents in their 20s and 83% of respondents in their 30s said that they had received oral sex, versus 67% of those in their 40s and 49% of those aged 50 and over. In addition, single, divorced, and widowed respondents were more likely to have both given and received oral sex (76% and 78%) than married respondents (66% and 67%). Canadians living in British Columbia and Quebec were more likely to have both given and received oral sex than those in Ontario (76% versus 65%). Although more males said that they had experienced oral sex than females, more women refused to answer the question (17%) than men (6%), suggesting that this is still an uncomfortable and possibly an embarrassing topic (COMPAS, 1998). Oral–genital stimulation can be a prelude to intercourse or a sexual end in itself. If orgasm is reached through oral–genital stimulation, a woman may be concerned about tasting or swallowing a man's ejaculate. There is no scientific evidence that swallowing semen is harmful to one's health unless the semen carries infectious micro-organisms.

Techniques of Fellatio Although the word *fellatio* is derived from a Latin root meaning "to suck," a sucking action is generally not highly arousing. The up-and-down movements of the penis in the partner's mouth, or the licking of the penis, are generally the most stimulating. Gentle licking of the scrotum may also be highly arousing.

The mouth is stimulating to the penis because it contains warm, moist mucous membranes, as does the vagina. Muscles of the mouth and jaw can create varied pressure and movements. Erection may be stimulated by gently pulling the penis with the mouth (being careful never to touch the penis with the teeth) and simultaneously providing manual stimulation, as described earlier.

Higher levels of sexual arousal or orgasm can be promoted by moving the penis in and out of the mouth, simulating the motion of the penis in the vagina during intercourse. The speed of the motions can be varied, and manual stimulation near the base of the penis (firmly encircling the lower portion of the penis or providing pressure behind the scrotum) can also be stimulating.

Some people may gag during fellatio, a reflex that is triggered by pressure of the penis against the back of the tongue or against the throat. Gagging may be avoided if the man's partner grasps the shaft of the penis with one hand and controls the depth of penetration. Gagging is less likely to occur if the partner performing fellatio is on the top, rather than below, or if there is verbal communication about how deep the man may comfortably penetrate. Gagging may also be overcome by allowing gradually deeper penetrations of the penis over successive occasions while keeping the throat muscles relaxed.

Techniques of Cunnilingus Women can be highly aroused by their partner's tongue because it is soft, warm, and well lubricated. In contrast to a finger, the tongue can almost never be used too harshly. A woman may thus be more receptive to direct clitoral contact by a tongue. Cunnilingus provides such intense stimulation that many women find it to be the best means for achieving orgasm. Some women cannot reach orgasm in any other way (Hite, 1976).

In performing cunnilingus, the partner may begin by kissing and licking the woman's abdomen and inner thighs, gradually nearing the vulva. Gentle tugging at or sucking of the labia minora can be stimulating, but the partner should take care not to bite. Many women enjoy licking of the clitoral region, and others desire sucking of the clitoris itself. The tongue may also be inserted into the vagina where it may imitate the thrusts of intercourse.

"69" The term *sixty-nine*, or *soixante-neuf* in French, describes simultaneous oral–genital stimulation (see Figure 4.8). The numerals 6 and 9 are used because they resemble two partners who are upside-down and facing each other.

The "69" position has the psychologically positive feature of allowing couples to experience simultaneous stimulation, but it can be an awkward position if two people are

Figure 4.8. Simultaneous Oral–Genital Contact.

The "69" position allows partners to engage in simultaneous oral–genital stimulation.

not similar in size. Some couples avoid 69 because it deprives each partner of the opportunity to focus fully on receiving or providing sexual pleasure. A person may find it distracting when receiving stimulation to have to focus on providing effective stimulation to someone else.

The 69 technique may be practised side by side or with one partner on top of the other. But here again there are no strict rules, and couples often alternate positions.

Sexual Intercourse: Positions and Techniques
Sexual intercourse, or *coitus* (from the Latin *coire*, meaning "to go together"), is sexual activity in which the penis is inserted into the vagina. Intercourse may take place in many different positions. We focus on four commonly used positions: the male-superior (man-on-top) position, the female-superior (woman-on-top) position, the lateral-entry (side-entry) position, and the rear-entry position. Then we will discuss anal intercourse.

The Male-Superior (Man-on-Top) Position The male-superior position ("superiority" is used purely in relation to body position, but has sometimes been taken as a symbol of male domination) has also been called the **missionary position**. In this position the partners face one another. The man lies above the woman, perhaps supporting himself on his hands and knees rather than applying his full weight against his partner (see Figure 4.9). Still, movement is easier for the man than for the woman, which suggests that he is in charge.

Many students of human sexuality suggest that it is preferable for the woman to guide the penis into the vagina, rather than having the man do so. The woman can feel the location of the vaginal opening and determine the proper angle of entry. To accomplish this, the woman must feel comfortable "taking charge" of the couple's lovemaking. With the breaking down of the traditional stereotype of the female as passive, women are feeling more comfortable taking this role.

The Female-Superior (Woman-on-Top) Position In the female-superior position the couple face one another with the woman on top. The woman straddles the male from above, controlling the angle of penile entry and the depth of thrusting (see Figure 4.10). Some women maintain a sitting position; others lie on top of their partners. Many women vary their position.

Missionary position The coital position in which the man is on top. Also termed the *male-superior position.*

Figure 4.9. The Male-Superior Coital Position.

In this position the couple face one another. The man lies above the woman, perhaps supporting himself on his hands and knees rather than allowing his full weight to press against his partner. The position is also referred to as the missionary position.

The Lateral-Entry (Side-Entry) Position In the lateral-entry position, the man and woman lie side by side, facing one another (see Figure 4.11).

The Rear-Entry Position In the rear-entry position, the man faces the woman's rear. In one variation (see Figure 4.12), the woman supports herself on her hands and knees while the man supports himself on his knees, entering her from behind. In another, the couple lie alongside one another and the woman lifts one leg, draping it backward over her partner's thigh. The latter position is particularly useful during the later stages of pregnancy.

Use of Fantasy During Coitus Most married people have coital fantasies (Davidson & Hoffman, 1986). Fantasies allow couples to inject sexual variety, even offbeat sexual escapades, into their sexual activity without being unfaithful. There does not appear to be any connection between sexual dissatisfaction with one's relationship and the use of coital fantasies (Davidson & Hoffman, 1986). Thus they are not a form of compensation for an unrewarding sexual relationship.

Coital fantasies, like masturbation fantasies, are used to enhance sexual arousal and run a gamut of themes. They include making love to another partner, group sex, orgies, images of past lovers or special erotic experiences, and making love in fantastic and wonderful places.

Anal Intercourse Anal intercourse is practised by both male–female couples and male–male couples. It involves insertion of the penis into the rectum. The rectum is richly endowed with nerve endings and is thus highly sensitive to sexual stimulation. Anal intercourse is also referred to as lovemaking in the "Greek style" because of bisexuality in ancient Greece among males. Both women and men may reach orgasm through receiving the penis in the rectum and thrusting.

In anal intercourse, the penetrating male usually situates himself behind his partner. (He can also lie above or below his partner in a face-to-face position.) The receiving partner can supplement anal stimulation with manual stimulation of the clitoral region or penis to reach orgasm.

Women often report wanting their partner's fingers in the anus at the height of passion or at the moment of orgasm. A finger in the rectum at time of orgasm can heighten sexual sensation because the anal sphincters contract during orgasm. Although some men also want a finger in the anus, many resist because they associate anal penetration with the female role or with male–male sexual activity.

Figure 4.10. The Female-Superior Coital Position.

The woman straddles the male from above, controlling the angle of penile entry and the depth of thrusting. The female-superior position puts the woman psychologically and physically in charge. The woman can ensure that she receives adequate clitoral stimulation from the penis or the hand. The position also tends to be less stimulating for the male and may thus help him to control ejaculation.

Many couples are repulsed by the idea of anal intercourse. They view it as unnatural, immoral, or risky. Yet others find anal sex to be an enjoyable sexual variation, though perhaps not a regular feature of their sexual diet.

The NHSLS survey found that 1 man in 4 (26%) and 1 woman in 5 (20%) reported having engaged in anal sex at some time during their lives (Laumann et al., 1994). Yet only about 1 person in 10 (10% of the men and 9% of the women) had engaged in anal sex during the past year. As with oral sex, there was a higher incidence of anal sex among more highly educated people in the NHSLS survey. For example, about 30% of the college graduates had engaged in anal sex, as compared with 20% of high school graduates. Education appears to be a liberating experience in sexual experimentation.

Many couples kiss or lick the anus in their foreplay. This practice is called **anilingus**. Oral–anal sex carries a serious health risk, however. Micro-organisms causing intestinal diseases and various sexually transmitted infections can be spread through oral–anal contact.

Anilingus Oral stimulation of the anus.

Many couples today hesitate to engage in anal intercourse because of the fear of AIDS and other sexually transmitted infections (STIs). HIV (the virus that causes AIDS) and other micro-organisms causing STIs such as gonorrhea, syphilis, and hepatitis can be spread by anal intercourse, because small tears in the rectal tissues may allow the microbes to enter the recipient's blood system. Women incur a greater risk of contracting HIV from anal intercourse than from vaginal intercourse—just as receptive anal intercourse in gay men carries a high risk of infection (Voeller, 1991). However, partners who are both infection-free are at no risk of contracting HIV or other STI-causing organisms through anal or vaginal intercourse, or any other sexual act.

Researchers may also be hesitant to ask questions about anal sex. For example, the 1996 study of UBC students included questions about *fantasies* about anal intercourse (37% of males and 11% of females reported these), but did not ask about the actual

Figure 4.11. The Lateral-Entry Coital Position.

In this position the couple face each other side by side. Each partner has relatively free movement and easy access to the other. Because both partners rest easily on the bedding, it is an excellent position for prolonged coitus or for coitus when couples are fatigued.

practice of this behaviour (Meston et al., 1996). Nor did the 1998 COMPAS survey of the sexual habits of Canadians. Data from the first Canadian author's students suggests that, although few students actually engage in anal intercourse, many would like to try it (McKenzie, unpublished data, 2004).

Applications

Advantages and Disadvantages of Various Positions of Sexual Intercourse

Each of the coital positions has some advantages and disadvantages.

The Male-Superior (Man-on-Top) Position

The male-superior position has the advantage of permitting the couple to face one another so that kissing is easier. The woman may run her hands along her partner's body, stroking his buttocks and perhaps cupping a hand beneath his scrotum to increase stimulation as he reaches orgasm.

But the male-superior position makes it difficult for the man to caress his partner while simultaneously supporting himself with his hands. So the position may not be favoured by women who enjoy having their partners provide man-

ual clitoral stimulation during coitus. This position can be highly stimulating to the man, which can make it difficult for him to delay ejaculation. The position also limits the opportunity for the woman to control the angle, rate, and depth of penetration. It may thus be more difficult for her to attain the type of stimulation she may need to achieve orgasm, especially if she favours combining penile thrusting with manual clitoral stimulation. Finally, this position is not advisable during the late stages of pregnancy. At that time the woman's distended abdomen would force the man to arch severely above her, lest he place too much pressure against the woman's abdomen.

The Female-Superior (Woman-on-Top) Position

In the female-superior position the woman is psychologically, and to some degree physically, in charge. She can move as rapidly or as slowly as she wishes with little

effort, adjusting her body so as to vary the angle and depth of penetration. She can reach behind her to stroke her partner's scrotum, or lean down to kiss him.

As in the male-superior position, kissing is relatively easy. This position has additional advantages. The man may readily reach the woman's buttocks or clitoris in order to provide manual stimulation. Assuming that the woman is shorter than he is, it is rather easy for him to stimulate her breasts orally (a pillow tucked behind his head may help). The woman can, in effect, guarantee that she receives adequate clitoral stimulation, either by the penis or manually by his hand or her own. This position thus facilitates orgasm in the woman.

The female-superior position tends to be less stimulating for the male than the male-superior position. While this may be a disadvantage for some men, it can be an advantage for a man who needs

Figure 4.12. The Rear-Entry Coital Position.

The rear-entry position is highly erotic for men who enjoy viewing and pressing their abdomens against their partners' buttocks. Some couples feel uncomfortable about the position because of its association with animal mating patterns. The position is also impersonal in that the partners do not face one another. Moreover, some couples dislike the feeling that the man is psychologically in charge because he can see his partner but she cannot readily see him.

help to control ejaculation. The position is commonly used by couples who are learning to overcome sexual difficulties.

The Lateral-Entry (Side-Entry) Position

This position has the advantages of allowing each partner relatively free movement and easy access to the other. The man and woman may kiss freely, and they can stroke each other's bodies with a free arm. The position is not physically taxing, because both partners are resting easily on the bedding. Thus it is an excellent position for prolonged coitus or for coitus when couples are somewhat fatigued.

There are disadvantages to this position. First, inserting the penis into the vagina while lying side by side may be awkward. Many couples thus begin coitus in another position and then change into the lateral-entry position—often because they wish to prolong coitus. Second, one or both partners may have an arm lying beneath the other that will "fall asleep" or become numb because of the constricted blood supply. Third, women may not receive adequate clitoral stimulation from the penis in this position. Of course, such stimulation may be provided manually (by hand) or by switching to another position after a while. Fourth, it may be difficult to achieve deeper penetration of the penis. The lateral position is useful during pregnancy (at least until the final stages, when the distension of the woman's abdomen may make lateral entry difficult).

The Rear-Entry Position

The rear-entry position may be highly stimulating for both partners. Men may enjoy viewing, and pressing their abdomens against, their partner's buttocks. The man can reach around or underneath to provide additional clitoral or breast stimulation, and the woman may reach behind (if she is on her hands and knees) to stroke or grasp her partner's testicles. The version in which the couple lie alongside one another and the woman lifts one leg, draping it backward over her partner's thigh, is particularly useful during the later stages of pregnancy.

Potential disadvantages to this position include the following: First, this position is the mating position used by most other mammals, which is why it is sometimes referred to as *doggy style*. Some couples may feel uncomfortable about using the position because of its association with animal mating patterns. The position is also impersonal in the sense that the partners do not face one another, which may create a sense of emotional distance. Since the man is at the woman's back, the couple may feel that he is very much in charge—he can see her, but she cannot readily see him. Physically, the penis does not provide adequate stimulation to the clitoris. The penis also tends to pop out of the vagina from time to time.

Summing Up

Making Sense of Sex: The Role of the Senses in Sexual Arousal

Each sense plays a role in sexual experience, but some senses are more involved than others. **Vision** plays a major role in sexual attraction. Visual cues can be sexual turn-ons or turn-offs. In humans, the sense of **smell** is less important in governing sexual arousal than in other mammals, but particular odours can be either arousing or off-putting. Many organisms are sexually aroused by naturally produced chemicals (pheromones), but their role in human sexual behaviour remains unclear. The sense of **touch** has the most direct effects on sexual arousal and response. Areas especially responsive to tactile stimulation are known as erogenous zones. Some people are aroused by the **taste** of genital secretions. **Sounds,** too, can be turn-ons or turn-offs.

Aphrodisiacs and Anaphrodisiacs

Alleged aphrodisiacs such as Spanish fly and foods that in some way resemble the genitals have not been shown to facilitate sexual arousal or response. Some **psychoactive drugs** (including alcohol and cocaine) are thought to have aphrodisiac effects. However, this may be due either to our expectations of them or to their ability to lower inhibitions, rather than to any direct effects on sexual response. Alcohol is often used as an excuse for questionable behaviour, and frequent cocaine use can lead to sexual dysfunctions. Some drugs and other substances, called **anaphrodisiacs**, diminish sexual drive or capacity

Sex Hormones: Do They "Goad" Us into Sex?

Sex hormones have organizing and activating effects on behaviour. Men and women normally produce one genuine aphrodisiac: testosterone. Female sex hormones do not appear to play a direct role in determining sexual motivation or response, but levels of testosterone in the blood have been associated with sexual interest in women.

The Sexual Response Cycle

Masters and Johnson found that both men and women have the same physiological responses to sexual stimulation. Vasocongestion and myotonia occur early in the sexual response cycle. The **excitement phase** is characterized by erection in the male and vaginal lubrication in the female. The **plateau phase** is an advanced stage of sexual arousal preceding orgasm. The **orgasmic phase** is characterized by rhythmic contractions of the pelvic musculature. Ejaculation in men occurs in two stages. In women, orgasm is manifested by contractions of the muscles that surround the vagina. In the **resolution phase**, the body returns to a prearoused state. Men experience a **refractory period**, where repeat erection is impossible. **Kaplan's three stage model** is an alternative model of sexual arousal, focusing on desire, excitement, and orgasm. Kaplan's psychosexual model makes it easier for clinicians to classify and treat sexual dysfunctions. **Basson's intimacy model** suggests that, for women, desire may follow arousal.

Controversies About Orgasm

Many women, and some men, are capable of **multiple orgasms:** more than one orgasm before returning to a prearoused state. Freud assumed that women were capable of two kinds of orgasm: clitoral and vaginal. Masters and Johnson's research found only one type of orgasm regardless of the type of stimulation used. Singer and Singer suggest that women can experience three types of orgasm: vulval, uterine, and blended. The **G-Spot** may have special erotic significance. Some researchers suggest that prolonged stimulation of this area produces an intensely pleasurable orgasm accompanied by some type of ejaculation.

Sexual Behaviour

Solitary sexual behaviours include **masturbation** and **sexual fantasy:** Within the Judeo-Christian tradition, masturbation has been condemned as sinful. While medicine and psychiatry until recently considered masturbation to be physically or mentally harmful, contemporary sex therapists consider it a harmless behaviour. Surveys indicate that most people have masturbated at some time in their lives. Sexual fantasies may occur during masturbation or during sex with another person. The content of sexual fantasies covers a broad range. Many people fantasize about sexual activities they would not actually engage in.

People may engage in many different **sexual behaviours with others. Foreplay, kissing, touching, breast stimulation and oral–genital stimulation** may be enjoyed for their own sake or as a prelude to intercourse. Women generally prefer longer periods of foreplay than men do. Men prefer direct stroking of the genitals, while women usually enjoy indirect rather than direct stimulation of the clitoris. Both men and women enjoy and are aroused by touch in a number of areas of the body, commonly known as erogenous zones. Both men and women enjoy oral and manual stimulation of the breast area. Oral sex is more common among younger Canadians than among those over 50. It is one of the sexual behaviours that many people are reluctant to admit to. Couples use a variety of positions when they engage in **sexual intercourse**, including male-superior, female-superior, lateral-entry and rear-entry.

Chapter Quiz

1. According to the text, pheromones are detected through
   (a) vision.
   (b) tactile sensations.
   (c) the sense of taste.
   (d) the vomeronasal organ.

2. According to the text, the _____ is/are an example of a secondary erogenous zone.
   (a) earlobes
   (b) perineum
   (c) shoulders
   (d) genital organs

3. According to the text, the most potent chemical aphrodisiac may be
   (a) Spanish fly.
   (b) testosterone.
   (c) yohimbine.
   (d) amyl nitrate.

4. Erection first occurs during the _____ phase of Masters and Johnson's sexual response cycle.
   (a) excitement
   (b) plateau
   (c) desire
   (d) resolution

5. The sex skin occurs during the _____ phase of Masters and Johnson's sexual response cycle.
   (a) excitement
   (b) plateau
   (c) desire
   (d) resolution

6. According to Freudian theory, how many types of female orgasm are there?
   (a) One.
   (b) Two.
   (c) Three.
   (d) Four.

7. According to the text, techniques of female masturbation vary widely, but women most commonly
   (a) insert phallic objects in the vagina.
   (b) massage the mons, labia, and the shaft of the clitoris.
   (c) rub the glans of the clitoris.
   (d) apply a vibrator to the glans of the clitoris.

8. According to surveys, the incidence of oral sex has _____ since Kinsey's day.
   (a) risen slightly
   (b) fallen
   (c) stayed about the same
   (d) risen dramatically

9. Which of the following coital positions is also known as the missionary position?
   (a) The male-superior position.
   (b) The female-superior position.
   (c) The lateral-entry position.
   (d) The rear-entry position.

10. Some couples may feel uncomfortable about using the _____ position because of its association with animal mating patterns.
    (a) male-superior position
    (b) female-superior position
    (c) lateral-entry position
    (d) rear-entry position

Chapter 5

Gender Identity and Gender Roles

Did You Know That...

- If male sex hormones were not present during critical stages of prenatal development, we would all develop female?

- Some people have attempted to change their genders through gender-reassignment surgery?

- Women act as aggressively as men do when they are provoked and they believe that the social climate will accept aggressive behaviour from them?

- One reason that women live longer than men do is that men often ignore physical symptoms until a readily treatable problem becomes serious or life-threatening?

- The genitals of boys with Dominican Republic syndrome resemble those of girls at birth, but at puberty they quickly come to look like those of men?

- A two-and-a-half-year-old child may know that he is a boy but think that he can grow up to be a mommy?

- Adolescent girls who show a number of masculine traits are more popular than girls who thoroughly adopt the traditional feminine gender role?

This chapter addresses the biological, psychological, and sociological aspects of gender. First we focus on sexual differentiation—the process by which males and females develop distinct reproductive anatomy. We then turn to gender roles—the complex behaviour patterns that are deemed "masculine" or "feminine" in a particular culture. The chapter examines empirical findings on actual gender differences, which may challenge some of the preconceptions that many of us hold regarding the differences between men and women. We next consider gender typing—the processes by which boys come to behave in line with what is expected of men (most of the time) and girls with what is expected of women (most of the time). We shall also explore the concept of psychological androgyny, which applies to people who display characteristics associated with both genders.

Prenatal Sexual Differentiation

Let us trace the development of **sexual differentiation**. When a sperm cell fertilizes an ovum, 23 **chromosomes** from the male parent normally combine with 23 chromosomes from the female parent. The **zygote**, the beginning of a new human being, is only .15 mm long. Yet this tiny being already bears the stamp of a unique individual—one who will have black or blond hair, grow bald or develop a widow's peak, become male or female.

The chromosomes from each parent combine to form 23 pairs. The 23rd pair are the sex chromosomes. An ovum carries an X sex chromosome, but a sperm carries either an X or a Y sex chromosome. If a sperm with an X sex chromosome fertilizes the ovum, the newly conceived person will normally develop as a female, with an XX sex chromosomal structure. If the sperm carries a Y sex chromosome, the child will normally develop as a male (XY).

After fertilization, the zygote divides repeatedly. After a few short weeks one cell has become billions of cells. At about three weeks a primitive heart begins to drive blood through the embryonic bloodstream. At about five to six weeks, when the **embryo** is only .5 cm to 1 cm long, primitive gonads, ducts, and external genitals whose gender cannot be distinguished visually have formed (see Figure 5.1 and Figure 5.2). Each embryo possesses primitive external genitals, a pair of sexually undifferentiated gonads, and two sets of primitive duct structures, the Müllerian (female) ducts and the Wolffian (male) ducts.

During the first six weeks or so of prenatal development, embryonic structures of both genders develop along similar lines and resemble primitive female structures. At

Sexual differentiation The process by which males and females develop distinct reproductive anatomy.

Chromosome One of the rodlike structures, found in the nucleus of every living cell, that carries the genetic code in the form of genes.

Zygote A fertilized ovum (egg cell).

Embryo The stage of prenatal development that begins with implantation of a fertilized ovum in the uterus and concludes with development of the major organ systems at about two months after conception.

About Gender
www.gender.org.uk/
A comprehensive website on gender roles, gender variance, and gender identity, with information on sexual differentiation and the developing embryo in Part 5.

about the seventh week after conception, the genetic code (XX or XY) begins to assert itself, causing changes in the gonads, genital ducts, and external genitals. The Y sex chromosome causes the testes to begin to differentiate. Ovaries begin to differentiate if the Y chromosome is absent. Some rare individuals who have only one X sex chromosome instead of the typical XY or XX arrangement also become females (though their reproductive systems don't develop fully), since they too lack the Y chromosome (Angier, 1990).

Thus, the basic blueprint of the human embryo is female. The genetic instructions in the Y sex chromosome cause the embryo to deviate from the female developmental course. "Adams" develop from embryos that otherwise would become "Eves."

By about the seventh week of prenatal development, the Y sex chromosome stimulates the production of *H-Y* antigen, a protein that fosters the development of testes. Strands of tissue begin to organize into seminiferous tubules. Female gonads begin to develop somewhat later than male gonads. The forerunners of follicles that will bear ova are not found until the fetal stage of development, about 10 weeks after conception. Ovaries begin to form at 11 or 12 weeks.

The Role of Sex Hormones in Sexual Differentiation

Androgens Male sex hormones. (From the Greek *andros*, meaning "man" or "males," and *-gene*, meaning "born.")

Testosterone The male sex hormone that fosters the development of male sex characteristics and is connected with the sex drive.

Without the influence of male sex hormones, or **androgens**, we would all develop into females (Federman, 1994). Once the testes develop in the embryo, they begin to produce androgens. The most important androgen, **testosterone**, spurs differentiation of the male (Wolffian) duct system (see Figure 5.1). Each Wolffian duct develops into an epididymis, vas deferens, and seminal vesicle. The external genitals, including the penis, begin to take shape at about the eighth week of development under the influence of another androgen, *dihydrotestosterone* (DHT). Yet another testicular hormone, one secreted during the fetal stage, prevents the Müllerian ducts from developing into the female duct system. It is appropriately termed the Müllerian inhibiting substance (MIS).

Small amounts of androgens are produced in female fetuses, but they are not normally sufficient to cause male sexual differentiation. In female fetuses, the relative absence of androgens causes degeneration of the Wolffian ducts and prompts development of female sexual organs. The Müllerian ducts evolve into fallopian tubes, the uterus, and the upper two-thirds of the vagina. These developments occur even in the absence of female sex hormones. Although female sex hormones are crucial in puberty, they are not involved in fetal sexual differentiation. If a fetus with an XY sex chromosomal structure failed to produce testosterone, it would develop female sexual organs.

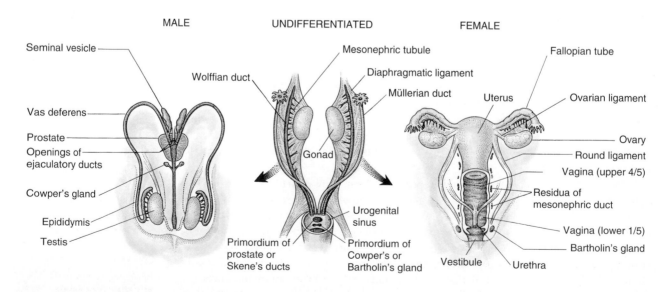

Figure 5.1. Development of the Internal Sexual Organs from an Undifferentiated Stage at About Five or Six Weeks Following Conception.

UNDIFFERENTIATED

Glans area
Urethral fold
Urethral groove
Lateral buttress
Anal pit
Anal tubercle

Genital tubercle

Figure 5.2. Development of the External Sexual Organs from an Undifferentiated Stage at About Five or Six Weeks Following Conception.

45–50 mm

MALE   FEMALE

Glans
Site of future origin of prepuce
Urethral fold
Urogenital groove
Lateral buttress (corpus or shaft)
Labioscrotal swelling
Urethral folds partly fused (perineal raphé)
Anal tubercle
Anus

FULLY DEVELOPED

MALE   FEMALE

Urethral meatus
Glans penis
Prepuce
Shaft or body of penis (corpus)
Penoscrotal raphé
Scrotum

Clitoral shaft
Prepuce
Clitoral glans
Urethral meatus
Labia minora
Labia majora
Vagina

Perineal raphé
Perineal tissues including external sphincter

Descent of the Testes and the Ovaries

The testes and ovaries develop from slender structures high in the abdominal cavity. By about 10 weeks after conception, they have descended so that they are almost even with the upper edge of the pelvis. The ovaries remain there for the rest of the prenatal period. Later they rotate and descend farther to their adult position in the pelvis. About four months after conception the testes normally descend into the scrotal sac through the **inguinal canal**. After their descent, this passageway is closed.

In a small percentage of males, one or both testes remain undescended. They remain in the abdomen at birth. The condition is termed **cryptorchidism**. In most cases of cryptorchidism, the testes migrate to the scrotum during infancy. In still other cases the testes descend by puberty. Men with undescended testes are usually treated through surgery or hormonal therapy, since the condition places them at higher risk for cancer of the testes. Sperm production is also impaired because the undescended testes are subjected to a higher-than-optimal body temperature, causing sterility.

Sex Chromosomal Abnormalities

Abnormalities of the sex chromosomes can have profound effects on sexual characteristics, physical health, and psychological development. **Klinefelter's syndrome**, a condition that affects about 1 in 500 males, is caused by an extra X sex chromosome, so

Inguinal canal A fetal canal that connects the scrotum and the testes, allowing their descent. (From the Latin *inguinus*, meaning "near the groin.")

Cryptorchidism The condition in which one or two testicles fail to descend from the abdomen into the scrotum.

Klinefelter's syndrome A sex-chromosomal disorder in males caused by an extra X sex chromosome.

Supermale syndrome
A sex chromosomal disorder in males caused by an extra Y sex chromosome.

Turner syndrome A sex-chromosomal disorder in females caused by loss of some X chromosome material.

Poly-X or superfemale syndrome A sex chromosomal disorder in females caused by cells with at least three X chromosomes.

that the man has an XXY rather than an XY pattern. Men with this pattern fail to develop appropriate secondary sex characteristics. They have enlarged breasts, poor muscular development, and, because they fail to produce sperm, they are infertile. They also tend to be mildly retarded. **Supermale syndrome** is found in approximately 1 in 1000 male births. Men with this condition have one or more extra Y chromosomes (XYY, XYYY, and XYYYY combinations have all been identified). They are significantly taller than average. It was once thought that the extra Y chromosome was related to an increased propensity towards violence and aggression, but studies of large numbers of XYY males have shown this not to be true (Shaffer et al., 1999).

Turner syndrome occurs in 1 in 2000–5000 girls. It is caused by the loss of some X sex chromosome material. These girls develop typical external genital organs, but they are short in stature and their ovaries do not develop or function normally, so they are infertile. Girls with Turner syndrome tend to be involved in fewer social activities and to have more academic problems than other girls (Rovet & Ireland, 1994). However, they do not have major social or behavioural problems. In **"Poly-X"** or **superfemale syndrome**, which is found in 1 in 1000 female births, cells have at least three X chromosomes, although more may be present. Girls with this condition do not differ physically from other females and the uterus, ovaries, and other female internal structures develop normally. There may be some intellectual deficits and developmental delays, which increase with the number of X chromosomes present (Shaffer, et al., 1999).

Prenatal Sexual Differentiation of the Brain

The brain, like the genital organs, undergoes prenatal sexual differentiation. Testosterone causes cells in the hypothalamus of male fetuses to become insensitive to the female sex hormone estrogen. In the absence of testosterone, as in female fetuses, the hypothalamus develops sensitivity to estrogen.

Sensitivity to estrogen is important in the regulation of the menstrual cycle of women after puberty. The hypothalamus detects low levels of estrogen in the blood at the end of each cycle and initiates a new cycle by stimulating the pituitary gland to secrete FSH. FSH, in turn, stimulates estrogen production by the ovaries and the ripening of an immature follicle in an ovary. Sexual differentiation of the hypothalamus most likely occurs during the second trimester of fetal development (Pillard & Weinrich, 1986).

Gender Identity

Gender identity The psychological sense of being male or female.

Gender assignment The labelling of a newborn as a male or female.

For all of us, our awareness of being male or being female—our **gender identity**—is one of the most obvious and important aspects of our self-concept. Our gender identity is not an automatic extension of our anatomic gender. Gender identity is a psychological construct, a sense of being male or being female. **Gender assignment** reflects the child's anatomic gender and usually occurs at birth. Gender identity is so important to parents that they may want to know "Is it a boy or a girl?" before they begin to count fingers and toes.

Most children first become aware of their anatomic gender by about the age of 18 months. By 36 months, most children have acquired a rather firm sense of gender identity (Etaugh & Rathus, 1995; McConaghy, 1979). Until that time, however, some children make amusing mistakes, as in the case of the two-year-old who had just gotten her first haircut. When asked if she was a boy or a girl, she said, "I'm a boy. I used to be a girl, but then I had my hair cut." It didn't take long for her to realize that the essential things that made her a girl had not changed.

Nature and Nurture in Gender Identity

What determines gender identity? Are our brains biologically programmed along masculine or feminine lines by prenatal sex hormones? Does the environment, in the form of postnatal learning experiences, shape our self-concept as males or females? Or does gender identity reflect an intermingling of biological and environmental influences?

Gender identity is almost always consistent with chromosomal gender. Such consistency does not certify that gender identity is biologically determined, however. We also tend to be reared as males or females, according to our anatomic genders. How, then, might we sort out the roles of nature and nurture, of biology and the environment?

Clues may be found in the experiences of rare individuals, **pseudohermaphrodites**, who possess the gonads of one gender but external genitalia that are ambiguous or typical of the other gender. Pseudohermaphrodites are sometimes reared as members of the other gender (the gender other than their chromosomal gender). Researchers wondered whether the gender identity of these children would reflect their chromosomal and gonadal gender or the gender according to which they were reared. Before going further with this, let us distinguish between true hermaphroditism and pseudohermaphroditism.

Hermaphroditism

Hormonal errors during prenatal development produce various congenital defects. Some individuals are born with both ovarian and testicular tissue. They are called **hermaphrodites**, after the Greek myth of the son of Hermes and Aphrodite, whose body became united with that of a nymph while he was bathing. True hermaphrodites may have one gonad of each gender (a testicle and an ovary), or gonads that combine testicular and ovarian tissue.

Regardless of their genetic gender, hermaphrodites usually assume the gender identity and gender role of the gender assigned at birth. Figure 5.3 shows a genetic female (XX) with a right testicle and left ovary. This person married and became a stepfather with a firm male identity. The roles of biology and environment remain tangled, however, since true hermaphrodites have gonadal tissue of both genders.

True hermaphroditism is extremely rare. More common is pseudohermaphroditism, which occurs in perhaps 1 infant in 1000. The occurrence of pseudohermaphroditism has given scientists an opportunity to examine the roles of nature (biology) and nurture (environmental influences) in the shaping of gender identity.

Pseudohermaphroditism *Pseudohermaphrodites* ("false" hermaphrodites) have testes or ovaries, but not both. Unlike true hermaphrodites, their gonads (testes or ovaries) match their chromosomal gender. Because of prenatal hormonal errors, however, their external genitals and sometimes their internal reproductive anatomy are ambiguous or resemble those of the other gender.

The most common form of female pseudohermaphroditism is **androgenital syndrome**, in which a genetic (XX) female has female internal sexual structures (ovaries), but masculinized external genitals (see Figure 5.4). The clitoris is so enlarged that it may resemble a small penis. The syndrome occurs as a result of excessive levels of androgens. In some cases the fetus's own adrenal glands produce excess androgen (the adrenal glands usually produce low levels of androgen). In other cases mothers may have received synthetic androgens during their pregnancies. In the 1950s and 1960s, before these side effects were known, synthetic androgens were sometimes prescribed to help prevent miscarriages in women with histories of spontaneous abortions.

Another type of pseudohermaphroditism, **androgen-insensitivity syndrome**, describes genetic (XY) males who had lower-than-normal prenatal sensitivity to androgens. As a result their genitals did not become normally masculinized. At birth their external genitals are feminized, including a small vagina, and their testes are undescended. Because of insensitivity to androgens, the male duct system (epididymis,

Pseudohermaphrodites People who possess the gonads of one gender but external genitalia that are ambiguous or typical of the other gender.

Hermaphrodite A person who possesses both ovarian and testicular tissue. (From the names of the male and female Greek gods Hermes and Aphrodite.)

Androgenital syndrome A form of pseudohermaphroditism in which a genetic female has internal female sexual structures but masculinized external genitals.

Androgen-insensitivity syndrome A form of pseudohermaphroditism in which a genetic male is prenatally insensitive to androgens. As a result his genitals do not become normally masculinized.

Figure 5.3. A True Hermaphrodite.

This genetic (XX) female has one testicle and one ovary and the gender identity of a male.

Dominican Republic syndrome A form of pseudohermaphroditism in which a genetic enzyme disorder prevents testosterone from masculinizing the external genitalia.

vas deferens, seminal vesicles, and ejaculatory ducts) fails to develop. Nevertheless, the fetal testes produce Müllerian inhibiting substance, preventing the development of a uterus or fallopian tubes.

A third type of pseudohermaphroditism is named **Dominican Republic syndrome** because it was first documented in a group of 18 affected boys in two rural villages in that nation (Imperato-McGinley et al., 1974). Dominican Republic syndrome is a genetic enzyme disorder that prevents testosterone from masculinizing the external genitalia. The boys were born with normal testes and internal male reproductive organs, but their external genitals were malformed. Their penises were stunted and resembled clitorises. Their scrotums were incompletely formed and resembled female labia. They also had partially formed vaginas.

Pseudohermaphroditism and Gender Identity

The experiences of pseudohermaphrodites have provided insights into the origins of gender identity. The genitals of girls with androgenital syndrome are normally surgically feminized in infancy. The girls also receive hormone treatments to correct excessive adrenal output of androgens. As a result, they usually acquire a feminine gender identity and develop physically as normal females.

What if the syndrome is not identified early in life, however? Consider the cases of two children who were treated at Johns Hopkins University Hospital. The children both suffered from androgenital syndrome, but their treatments and the outcomes were very different. Each child was genetically female (XX). Each had female internal sex organs. Because of prenatal exposure to synthetic male sex hormones, however, each developed masculinized external sex organs (Money & Ehrhardt, 1972).

The problem was identified in one child (let's call her Abby) in infancy. Her masculinized sex organs were removed surgically when she was two years old. Like many other girls, Abby was tomboyish during childhood, but she was always feminine in appearance and had a female gender identity. She began to develop breasts by the age of 12, but did not begin to menstruate until age 20. She dated boys, and her fantasy life centred around marriage to a man.

The other child (let's call him James) was initially mistaken for a genetic male with stunted external sex organs. The error was discovered at the age of three-and-a-half. By then he had a firm male gender identity, so surgeons further masculinized his external sex organs rather than remove them. At puberty, hormone treatments stoked the development of body hair, male musculature, and other male secondary sex characteristics.

As an adolescent, James did poorly in school. Possibly in an effort to compensate for his poor grades, he joined a gang. He became one of the boys. In contrast to Abby, James was sexually attracted to women.

Both children were pseudohermaphrodites. Both had internal female sexual organs and masculinized external organs, but they were treated and reared differently. In Abby's case, the newborn was designated female, surgically altered to remove the masculinized genitals, and reared as a girl. In James's case, the infant was labelled and reared as a boy. Each child acquired the gender identity of the assigned gender. Environmental influences appeared to play the critical role in shaping the gender identity of these children.

Further evidence for the importance of psychosocial influences on gender identity is found in studies of genetic (XY) males with androgen-insensitivity syndrome. They possess testes but are born with feminine-appearing genitals and are typically reared as girls. They develop a female gender identity and stereotypical feminine interests. They show as much interest in dolls, dresses, and future roles as mothers and housewives as do genetic (XX) girls of the same age and social class (Brooks-Gunn & Matthews, 1979; Money & Ehrhardt, 1972).

The boys with Dominican Republic syndrome also resembled girls at birth and were reared as females. At puberty, however, their testes swung into normal testosterone production, causing startling changes: their testes descended, their voices deepened, their musculature filled out, and their "clitorises" expanded into penises. Of the 18 boys who were reared as girls, 17 shifted to a male gender identity. Sixteen of the 18 assumed a stereotypical masculine gender role. Of the remaining 2, 1 adopted a male gender

Figure 5.4.
Pseudohermaphroditism.

In androgenital syndrome (top photo), a genetic (XX) female has female internal sexual structures (ovaries) but masculinized external genitals. The bottom photo shows a genetic (XY) male with androgen-insensitivity syndrome. The external genitals are feminized, and the person has always lived as a female.

identity but continued to maintain a feminine gender role, including wearing dresses. The other maintained a female gender identity and later sought a sex-change operation to "correct" the pubertal masculinization.

The Dominican transformations suggest that gender identity is malleable. What of the roles of nature and nurture in the formation of gender identity, however? If environmental forces (nurture) were predominant, gender identity would be based on the gender in which the person is reared, regardless of biological abnormalities. With the Dominicans, however, pubertal biological changes led to changes in both gender identity and gender roles. Is nature (biology) then the primary determinant of gender identity? Unfortunately, the Dominican study does not allow clear separation of the effects of nature and nurture. One intriguing hypothesis is that the pubertal surges of testosterone may have activated brain structures that were masculinized during prenatal development. Prenatal testosterone levels in these boys were presumably normal and could have affected the sexual differentiation of brain tissue, even though the genetic defect prevented the hormone from masculinizing the external genitalia.

Consider some other possibilities: Did the children, seeing themselves transforming into men, begin to change their self-concept to be consistent with their anatomic changes? Did the children choose to assume male gender identities because the masculine gender role was positively valued in their culture? Either possibility permits a psychological or cultural explanation of gender identity.

A case described by Money and Erhardt (1972) provides the opportunity to see how gender assignment works out over the long term. Identical twin boys were born in Winnipeg in 1965. One suffered severe damage to his penis at the age of 8 months. The parents, although devastated by this, were assured that the child could be successfully reared as a girl. Surgical procedures to transform their son into their daughter began when the child was 21 months old, with removal of the testes and the creation of a vulva.

At first, all appeared to go well. The child seemed to adapt to her change of name and gender, although she was considered to be a "tomboy." She was given estrogen supplements to bring about breast development and a feminine appearance. The case was often cited as evidence that gender is largely a matter of social assignment. However, at 14, she confided to one of her doctors that she had suspected she was a boy since she was 8. At this time, she stopped taking estrogen, and, refusing to live as a girl, began the process of regaining the identity she had been born with. Her breasts were removed and a penis was constructed. Eventually, he married (Diamond, 1999). After his story was told by John Colapinto in 2000, he went public, appearing on Oprah and other talk shows, trying to prevent surgical reassignment of gender for other children. In May 2004, depressed by the suicide of his twin two years earlier and by the failure of his marriage, he committed suicide. The results of this and other, long-term follow-up studies suggest that biology is more important in the development of gender identity than was previously thought.

Most scientists conclude that gender identity is influenced by complex interactions between biological and psychosocial factors. Some place relatively greater emphasis on psychosocial factors (Money, 1987a; Money & Ehrhardt, 1972). Others emphasize the role of biological factors (Collaer & Hines, 1995). The debate over the relative contributions of nature and nurture is likely to continue.

Transsexualism

In 1953 an ex-GI who journeyed to Denmark for a "sex-change operation" made headlines. She became known as Christine (formerly George) Jorgensen. Since then, thousands of **transsexuals** have undergone gender-reassignment surgery. Among the better known is the tennis player Dr. Renée Richards, formerly Dr. Richard Raskin.

Gender-reassignment surgery cannot implant the internal reproductive organs of the other gender. Instead, it generates the likeness of external genitals typical of the other gender. This can be done more precisely with male-to-female than female-to-male transsexuals. After such operations, people can participate in sexual activity and even attain orgasm, but they cannot conceive or bear children.

The Clarke Institute of Psychiatry Gender Identity Clinic
www.camh.net/care_treat ment/gender_identity_ clinic.html
The website of the Centre for Addiction and Mental Health (CAMH) is a Canadian site providing information on gender identity disorders and links to other gender identity websites.

Sex: Unknown
www.pbs.org/wgbh/nova/ transcripts/2813gender.html
A transcript of a documentary on the case of the Winnipeg boy reared as a girl and links to other resources on intersexuals are provided at this website.

Transsexuals People who have a gender-identity disorder in which they feel trapped in the body of the wrong gender.

Gender dysphoria The subjective experience of incongruity between genital anatomy and gender identity or role.

Transsexuals experience **gender dysphoria**. That is, according to John Money (1994), they have the subjective experience of incongruity between their genital anatomy and their gender identity or role. They have the anatomic sex of one gender but feel that they are members of the other gender. As a result of this discrepancy, they wish to be rid of their own primary sex characteristics (their external genitals and internal sex organs) and to live as members of the other gender. Transsexualism is thought to be rare.

Patterns of sexual attraction do not appear to be central in importance. Some transsexuals report never having had strong sexual feelings. Others are attracted to members of their own (anatomic) gender. They are unlikely to regard themselves as gay or lesbian, however. From their perspective, their lovers are members of the other gender. Still others are attracted to members of the other anatomic gender. Nonetheless, they all want to be rid of their own sex organs and to live as members of the other gender.

Theoretical Perspectives No clear understanding of the nature or causes of transsexualism has emerged (Money, 1994). Views on its origins somewhat parallel those on the origins of a gay male or lesbian sexual orientation, which is surprising, given the fundamental differences that exist between the two.

Psychoanalytic theorists have focused on early parent–child relationships. Male transsexuals, in this view, may have had "close-binding mothers" (extremely close mother–son relationships) and "detached–hostile fathers" (fathers who were absent or disinterested) (Stoller, 1969). Such family circumstances may have fostered intense **identification** with the mother, to the point of an inversion of typical gender roles and identity. Girls with weak, ineffectual mothers and strong, masculine fathers may identify with their fathers, rejecting their own female identities.

Identification In psychoanalytic theory, the process of incorporating within ourselves our perceptions of the behaviours, thoughts, and feelings of others.

There is some evidence that male transsexuals tend to have had unusually close relationships with their mothers during childhood. Female transsexuals tend to have identified more with their fathers and to have perceived their mothers as cold and rejecting (Pauly, 1974). Yet one problem with the psychoanalytic view is that the roles of cause and effect may be reversed. It could be that in childhood, transsexuals gravitate toward the parent of the other gender and reject the efforts of the parent of the same gender to reach out to them and engage them in gender-typed activities. These views also do not account for the many transsexuals whose family backgrounds fail to match these patterns. Moreover, these views lack predictive power. Most children—in fact, the vast majority!—with such family backgrounds do *not* become transsexuals.

Transsexuals may also be influenced by prenatal hormonal imbalances. The brain is in some ways "masculinized" or "feminized" by sex hormones during prenatal development. The brain could be influenced in one direction, even as the genitals are being differentiated in the other direction (Money, 1987a).

Gender Reassignment Gender reassignment for transsexuals has been controversial since its inception. Yet psychotherapy is not considered a reasonable alternative, because it has been generally unsuccessful in helping transsexuals accept their anatomic genders (Roberto, 1983; Tollison & Adams, 1979).

Surgery is one element of gender reassignment. This surgery is covered under provincial Medicare programs in British Columbia, Alberta, Manitoba, Saskatchewan, Quebec, and Newfoundland. Since the surgery is irreversible, health professionals usually require that the transsexual live openly as a member of the other gender for a trial period of at least a year before surgery.

Once the decision is reached, a lifetime of hormone treatments is begun. Male-to-female transsexuals receive estrogen, which fosters the development of female secondary sex characteristics. It causes fatty deposits to develop in the breasts and hips, softens the skin, and inhibits growth of the beard. Female-to-male transsexuals receive androgens, which promote male secondary sex characteristics. The voice deepens, hair becomes distributed according to the male pattern, muscles enlarge, and the fatty deposits in the breasts and hips are lost. The clitoris may also grow more prominent.

Gender-reassignment surgery is largely cosmetic. Medical science cannot construct internal genital organs or gonads. Male-to-female surgery is generally more successful.

A Woman's Place? A Man's Place? Contemporary men and women are entering occupations that had been traditionally associated with the other gender. Women fight fires and pilot aircraft; men pursue careers in nursing and primary education.

The penis and testicles are first removed. Tissue from the penis is placed in an artificial vagina so that sensitive nerve endings will provide sexual sensations.

In female-to-male transsexuals, the internal sex organs (ovaries, fallopian tubes, uterus) are removed, along with the remaining fatty tissue in the breasts. The nipples are moved to keep them at the proper height on the torso. The urethra is rerouted through the enlarged clitoris, or an artificial penis and scrotum are constructed from tissue from the abdomen, the labia, and the perineum through a series of operations. In either case, the patient can urinate while standing, which appears to provide psychological gratification. Although the artificial penis does not stiffen and become erect naturally, a variety of methods, including implants, can be used to allow the artificial penis to approximate erection.

Outcomes of Gender-Reassignment Surgery Following the introduction of gender-reassignment surgery, most reports of postoperative adjustment were positive (Pauly & Edgerton, 1986). Reviewers of the international literature reported in 1984 that about 90% of transsexuals who undergo gender-reassignment surgery experience positive results (Lundstrom et al., 1984). In Canada, a follow-up study of 116 transsexuals (female-to-male and male-to-female) at least one year after surgery found that most of them were content with the results and were reasonably well adjusted (Blanchard et al., 1985). Positive results for surgery were also reported in a study of 141 Dutch transsexuals (Kuiper & Cohen-Kettenis, 1988). Nearly 9 of 10 male-to-female and female-to-male transsexuals in a study of 23 transsexuals reported they were very pleased with the results of their gender-reassignment surgery (Lief & Hubschman, 1993).

There have been cases, however, where the post-operative adjustment was less than positive. A story from Reuters ("A Woman's Life") showed that an Iranian transsexual who had a gender-reassignment surgery (male-to-female) in 1999 soon asked for a reverse surgery. The reason? She could not cope with the restrictions imposed on women in Islamic society.

Male-to-female transsexuals outnumber female-to-males, but postoperative adjustment is apparently more favourable for female-to-males. Nearly 10% of male-to-female cases, as compared to 4% to 5% of female-to-males, have had disturbing outcomes, such as severe psychological disorders, hospitalization, requests for reversal surgery, and even suicide (Abramowitz, 1986). One reason for the relatively better postoperative adjustment of the female-to-male transsexuals may be society's more accepting attitudes toward women who desire to become men (Abramowitz, 1986). Female-to-male transsexuals tend to be better adjusted socially before surgery as well (Pauly, 1974), so their superior postoperative adjustment may be nothing more than a selection factor.

Gender Roles and Stereotypes

In our culture the **stereotypical** female exhibits traits such as gentleness, dependency, kindness, helpfulness, patience, and submissiveness. The masculine **gender-role** stereotype

Stereotype A fixed, conventional idea about a group of people.

Gender roles Complex clusters of ways in which males and females are expected to behave within a given culture.

The Society for the Psychological Study of Men and Masculinity
www.apa.org/divisions/div51/
A discussion and studies on the harmful consequences for men of traditional, restrictive gender roles.

Sexism The prejudgment that because of gender, a person will possess negative traits.

is one of toughness, gentlemanliness, and protectiveness. Females are generally seen as warm and emotional; males as independent, assertive, and competitive. The times are a-changing, somewhat. Women, as well as men, now bring home the bacon, but women are still more often expected to fry it up in the pan and bear the primary responsibility for child rearing (Deaux & Lewis, 1983). In some cultures, however, women are reared to be the hunters and food gatherers while men stay close to home and tend the children.

Sexism

We have all encountered the effects of **sexism**—the prejudgment that because of gender, a person will possess certain negative traits. These negative traits are assumed to disqualify the person for certain vocations or prevent him or her from performing adequately in these jobs or in some social situations.

Sexism may even lead us to interpret the same behaviour in different ways when performed by women or by men. We may see the man as "self-assertive," but the woman as "pushy." We may look upon *him* as flexible, but brand *her* fickle and indecisive. *He* may be rational, whereas *she* is cold. *He* is tough when necessary, but *she* is bitchy. When the businesswoman engages in stereotypical masculine behaviours, the sexist reacts negatively by branding her abnormal or unhealthy.

Sexism may make it difficult for men to act in ways that are stereotyped as feminine. A "sensitive" woman is simply sensitive, but a sensitive man may be seen as a "sissy." A woman may be perceived as polite, whereas a man showing the same behaviour seems passive or weak. Only recently have men begun to enter occupational domains previously restricted largely to women, such as secretarial work, nursing, and teaching in the primary grades. Only recently have the floodgates opened for women into traditionally masculine professions such as engineering, law, and medicine.

Although children of both genders have about the same general learning ability, stereotypes limit their horizons. Children tend to show preferences for gender-typed activities and toys by as early as two or three years of age. If they should stray from them, their peers are sure to remind them of the errors of their ways. How many little girls are discouraged from considering professions like architecture and engineering because they are handed dolls, not blocks and fire trucks? How many little boys are discouraged

---

A World of Diversity

Machismo/Marianismo Stereotypes and Hispanic Culture

Machismo is a cultural stereotype that defines masculinity in terms of an idealized view of manliness. To be macho is to be strong, virile, and dominant. Each Hispanic culture puts its own particular cultural stamp on the meaning of machismo, however. In the Spanish-speaking cultures of the Caribbean and Central America, the macho code encourages men to restrain their feelings and maintain an emotional distance. In my travels in Argentina and some other Latin American countries, however, I have observed that men who are sensitive and emotionally expressive are not perceived as compromising their macho code.

In counterpoint to the macho ideal among Hispanic peoples is the cultural idealization of femininity embodied in the concept of marianismo. The marianismo stereotype, which derives its name from the Virgin Mary, refers to the ideal of the virtuous woman as one who "suffers in silence," submerging her needs and desires to serve those of her husband and children. With the marianismo stereotype, the image of a woman's role as a martyr is raised to the level of a cultural ideal. According to this cultural stereotype, a woman is expected to demonstrate her love for her husband by waiting patiently at home and having dinner prepared for him at any time of day or night he happens to come home, to

have his slippers ready for him, and so on. The feminine ideal is one of suffering in silence and being the provider of joy, even in the face of pain. Strongly influenced by the patriarchal Spanish tradition, the marianismo stereotype has historically been used to maintain women in a subordinate position in relation to men.

Source: This *World of Diversity* feature was written by Rafael Javier, Ph.D. Dr. Javier is associate clinical professor of psychology and director of the Center for Psychological Services and Clinical Studies at St. John's University in Jamaica, New York. Dr. Javier was born in the Dominican Republic and educated in philosophy in the Dominican Republic, Puerto Rico, and Venezuela, and in psychology and psychoanalysis at New York University. He is a practising psychoanalyst and maintains a research interest in psycholinguistics and psychotherapy with ethnic minorities. All rights are reserved by Dr. Javier.

from pursuing child-care and nursing professions because of the funny looks they get from others when they reach for dolls?

Stereotypical expectations concerning "men's work" and "women's work" filter down to the primary grades. For example, according to traditional stereotypes, women are not expected to excel in math. Exposure to such negative expectations may discourage women from careers in science and technology.

Gender Differences: *Vive la Différence* or *Vive la Similitude?*

If the genders were not anatomically different, this book would never have been written. But how do the genders differ in cognitive abilities and personality?

Differences in Cognitive Abilities

A classic review by Eleanor Maccoby and Carol Nagy Jacklin (1974) found persistent evidence of differences between males and females in only four areas. Females are somewhat superior to males in verbal ability, including verbal fluency, spelling, and reading comprehension (Hedges & Nowell, 1995; Halpern, 1997). Far more boys than girls have reading problems, ranging from reading below grade level to severe disabilities. Males generally exceed females in visual–spatial abilities (Voyer et al., 1995), such as the ability to follow a map in an unfamiliar location, to construct a puzzle or assemble a piece of equipment, and to perceive relationships between figures in space (see Figure 5.5).

Differences in math are small and narrowing at all ages (Hyde et al., 1990). Females excel in computational ability in elementary school. Males excel in mathematical problem solving in high school and university (Hyde et al., 1990). According to Byrnes and Takahira (1993), boys' superiority in math does not reflect gender per se. Instead, boys do well because of prior knowledge of math and their strategies for approaching math problems.

In our culture, then, girls are somewhat advanced in their development of verbal abilities. Boys apparently show greater math ability, beginning in adolescence. Three factors should caution us not to attach too much importance to these gender differences, however:

1. In most cases, the differences are small (Hyde & Plant, 1995; Maccoby, 1990; Voyer et al., 1995).

2. These gender differences are group differences. Variation in ability on tests of verbal or math skills is larger within than between the genders (Maccoby, 1990).

3. The small differences that exist may largely reflect environmental influences and cultural expectations (Tobias, 1982). Spatial and math skills are stereotyped in our culture as masculine, whereas reading skills are stereotyped as feminine. In one

Canadian Psychiatric Association: Teaching on Gender Issues
www.cpa-apc.org/ Publications/Position_ Papers/Teaching.asp
This paper takes the position that, since men and women differ in their biology and in their life experiences, psychiatrists who take a gender-neutral approach will not provide optimal care for either male or female patients.

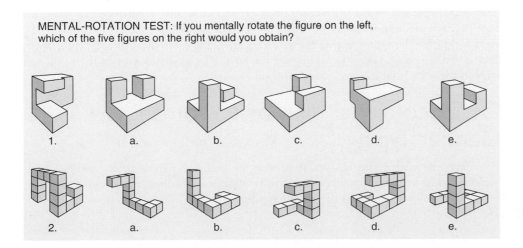

MENTAL-ROTATION TEST: If you mentally rotate the figure on the left, which of the five figures on the right would you obtain?

Figure 5.5. Rotating Geometric Figures in Space.

Visual–spatial skills—for example, the ability to rotate geometric figures in space—have been considered part of the male gender-role stereotype. Gender differences in visual–spatial skills are small, however, and can be modified by training.
Source: From Rathus, S. A., et al. (1990). Psychology. [4th ed.]. Copyright © 1990 by Holt, Rinehart & Winston, Inc. Reprinted by permission of the publishers.

study, however, female introductory psychology students who were given a mere three hours of training in performing visual–spatial skills such as rotating geometric figures performed these tasks as well as men (Stericker & LeVesconte, 1982).

Differences in Personality

There are also many gender differences in personality. According to a meta-analysis of the research literature, females exceed males in extroversion, anxiety, trust, and nurturance (Feingold, 1994). Males exceed females in assertiveness, tough-mindedness, and self-esteem. The assertiveness is connected with aggressiveness, as we see below. The tough-mindedness has unfortunate implications for men's health, as we also see. Two factors may largely account for the relatively lower self-esteem of females:

- Parents, on the average, prefer to have boys.
- Society has created an uneven playing field in which females have to perform better than males to be seen as doing equally well.

Differences in Communication Styles: "He's Just an Old Chatterbox" We have been inundated with cartoons of suburban housewives gossiping across the fence or pouring endless cups of coffee when the "girls" drop by for a chat. Research has shown, however, that in many situations men spend more time talking than women do. Men are also more likely to introduce new topics and interrupt others (Brooks, 1982; Deaux, 1985; Hall, 1984). Girls tend to be more talkative during early childhood than boys. By the time they enter school, however, boys dominate classroom discussions (Sadker & Sadker, 1994). As girls mature, it appears that they learn to "take a back seat" to boys and let the boys do most of the talking when they are in mixed-gender groups (Hall, 1984).

Women, however, are more willing than men to disclose their feelings and personal experiences (Dindia & Allen, 1992). The stereotype of the "strong and silent" male may not discourage men from hogging the conversation, but it may inhibit them from expressing their personal feelings.

Differences in Aggressiveness In almost all cultures (Ford & Beach, 1951; Mead, 1935), it is the males who march off to war and who battle for fame, glory, and shaving-cream-commercial contracts in stadiums and arenas. In most psychological studies on aggression, males have been found to behave more aggressively than females (White, 1983). There is concern, however, that the rate of aggressive and violent behaviours in girls is increasing (Cunningham, 2000).

Differences in Willingness to Seek Health Care Men's life expectancies are shorter, on the average, than women's. Part of the difference, according to a survey of 1500 physicians, is due to women's greater willingness to seek health care ("Doctors tie male mentality," 1995, Catlin, 2000). Men often let symptoms go until a problem that could have been prevented or readily treated becomes serious or life threatening. Women, for example, are much more likely to check themselves for breast cancer than men are to even recognize the symptoms of prostate cancer. Many men, according to the survey, have a "bullet-proof mentality." They are too strong to see the doctor in their 20s, too busy in their 30s, and too frightened later on.

On Becoming a Man or a Woman: Gender Typing

Gender typing The process by which children acquire behaviour that is deemed appropriate to their gender.

We have chronicled the biological process of sexual differentiation, and we have explored some gender differences in cognitive abilities and behaviour. In this section we consider various explanations of **gender typing.**

Biological Perspectives

Biological views on gender typing tend to focus on the roles of genetics and prenatal influences in predisposing men and women to gender-linked behaviour patterns. Biological perspectives have also focused on the possible role of hormones in sculpting the brain during prenatal development.

Sociobiology: It's Only Natural To the sociobiologist, the story of the survival of our ancient ancestors is etched in our genes. Sociobiologists propose that those genes that bestow attributes that increase an organism's chances of surviving to produce viable off-spring are most likely to be transmitted to future generations. We thus possess the genetic remnants of traits that helped our ancestors survive and reproduce (Bjorklund & Kipp, 1996). This heritage, according to sociobiologists, influences our social and sexual behaviour as well as our anatomic features.

According to sociobiologists, men's traditional roles as hunters and warriors, and women's roles as caregivers and gatherers of fruits and vegetables, are bequeathed to us in our genes. Men are better suited to war and the hunt because of physical attributes passed along since ancestral times. Upper-body strength, for example, would have enabled them to throw spears and overpower adversaries. Men also possess perceptual–cognitive advantages that favour aggression. Visual–motor skills, for example, would have enabled men to aim spears or bows and arrows.

Women, it is argued, are genetically predisposed to be empathetic and nurturant because these traits enabled ancestral women to respond to children's needs and enhance the likelihood that their children would flourish and eventually reproduce, thereby transmitting their own genetic legacy to future generations. Prehistoric women thus tended to stay close to home, care for the children, and gather edible plants, whereas men ventured from home to hunt and raid their neighbours' storehouses.

Sociobiology is steeped in controversy. Although scientists do not dispute the importance of evolution in determining physical attributes, many are reluctant to attribute complex social behaviours, such as aggression and gender roles, to heredity. The sociobiological argument implies that stereotypical gender roles—men as breadwinners and women as homemakers, for example—reflect the natural order of things. Critics contend that biology is not destiny, that our behaviour is not dictated by our genes.

Prenatal Brain Organization Researchers have sought the origins of gender-typed behaviour in the organization of the brain. Is it possible that the cornerstone of gender-typed behaviour is laid in the brain before the first breath is taken?

The hemispheres of the brain are specialized to carry out certain functions (Levy, 1985). In most people, the right hemisphere ("right brain") appears to be specialized to perform visual–spatial tasks. The left brain appears to be more essential to verbal functions, such as speech, in most people.

We know that sex hormones are responsible for prenatal sexual differentiation of the genitals and for the gender-related structural differences in the hypothalamus of the developing prenatal brain. Sexual differentiation of the brain may also partly explain men's (slight!) superiority at spatial-relations tasks, such as interpreting road maps and visualizing objects in space. Testosterone in the brains of male fetuses spurs greater growth of the right hemisphere and slows the rate of growth of the left hemisphere. This difference may be connected with the ability to accomplish spatial-relations tasks.

Might boys' inclinations toward aggression and rough-and-tumble play also be prenatally imprinted in the brain? Some theorists argue that prenatal sex hormones may masculinize or feminize the brain by creating predispositions that are consistent with gender-role stereotypes, such as rough-and-tumble play and aggressive behaviour in males (Collaer & Hines, 1995). Money (1987a) allows a role for prenatal dispositions but argues that social learning plays a stronger role in gender typing. He claims that social learning is even potent enough to counteract prenatal predispositions.

Margaret Mead
www.loc.gov/exhibits/mead/
This U.S. Library of Congress website presents archival material related to Mead's life and research.

Cross-Cultural Perspectives

Sociobiology cannot account for differences in gender roles that exist across cultures, especially neighbouring cultures. The anthropologist Margaret Mead (1935) lived among several tribes on the South Pacific island of New Guinea and found that gender roles in these tribes differed not only from those of Western culture, but also from one another.

Among the Mundugumor, a tribe of headhunters and cannibals, both men and women were warlike and aggressive. The women disdained bearing and rearing children because it interrupted participation in warring parties against neighbouring villages. The men and women of the Arapesh tribe, by contrast, were gentle and peaceful. Both genders nurtured the children. The Tchambuli were even more surprising to Western views. The men spent most of their time caring for children, gossiping, bickering, primping and applying makeup, and haggling over prices. Fish was the staple diet of the Tchambuli, and women brought home the daily catch. Women kept their heads shaven, disdained ornaments, and were more highly sexed and aggressive than men.

Whatever the influence of biology on behaviour, biological factors alone do not make men aggressive or independent, or women passive or submissive (Havemann & Lehtinen, 1990). Cultural expectations and learning play a large role.

Psychological Perspectives

Children acquire awareness of gender-role stereotypes by the tender ages of two-and-a half to three-and-a-half (Kuhn et al., 1978, Shaffer et al., 1999), if not earlier. Lisa Serbin and her associates at Concordia University in Montreal have shown that children as young as 18 months have some understanding of gender labels (Serbin et al., 2001). Both boys and girls generally agree, when asked to describe the differences between the genders, that boys build things, play with transportation toys such as cars and fire trucks, enjoy helping their fathers, and hit other children. Both boys and girls also agree that girls enjoy playing with dolls and helping their mothers cook and clean, and are talkative, dependent on others for help, and nonviolent. They perceive the label "cruel" to be a masculine trait, whereas "cries a lot" is perceived as a feminine trait. By the age of three, most children have become aware of the differences in stereotypical ways men and women dress and the types of occupations that are considered appropriate for each gender (Ruble & Ruble, 1982). Psychologists have attempted to explain how children acquire such knowledge and adopt stereotypical behaviour patterns in terms of psychoanalytic, social-learning, and cognitive–developmental theories.

Psychoanalytic Theory Sigmund Freud explained gender typing in terms of identification. Appropriate gender typing, in Freud's view, requires that boys come to identify with their fathers and girls with their mothers. Identification is completed, in Freud's view, as children resolve the **Oedipus complex** (sometimes called the Electra complex in girls).

According to Freud, the Oedipus complex occurs during the phallic period of psychosexual development, from the ages of three to five. During this period the child develops incestuous wishes for the parent of the other gender and comes to perceive the parent of the same gender as a rival. The complex is resolved by the child's forsaking incestuous wishes for the parent of the other gender and identifying with the parent of the same gender. Through identification with the same-gender parent, the child comes to develop gender-typed behaviours that are typically associated with that gender. However, children display stereotypical gender-typed behaviours earlier than Freud would have predicted. Even during the first year, boys are more independent than girls. Girls are more quiet and restrained. Girls show preferences for dolls and soft toys, and boys for hard transportation toys, by the ages of one-and-a-half to three.

Social-Learning Theory Social-learning theorists explain the development of gender-typed behaviour in terms of processes such as observational learning, identification, and socialization. Children can learn what is deemed masculine or feminine by observational learning, as suggested by the results of an experiment by Perry and Bussey (1979). In

Oedipus complex In psychoanalytic theory, a conflict of the phallic stage in which the boy wishes to possess his mother sexually and perceives his father as a rival in love. (The analogous conflict for girls is the *Electra complex*.)

this study, eight- and nine-year-old boys and girls watched adult role models indicate their preferences for each of 16 pairs of items—pairs such as toy cows versus toy horses and oranges versus apples. What the children didn't know was that the expressed preferences were made arbitrarily. The children were then asked to indicate their own preferences for the items represented in the pairs. The boys' choices agreed with the adult men's an average of 14 out of 16 times. Girls chose the pair item selected by the men, on the average, only 3 out of 16 times.

Socialization also plays a role in gender typing. Almost from the moment a baby comes into the world, it is treated according to its gender. Parents tend to talk more to baby girls, and fathers especially engage in more roughhousing with boys (Jacklin et al., 1984). When children are old enough to speak, parents and other adults—even other children—begin to instruct children as to how they are expected to behave. Parents may reward children for behaviour they consider gender-appropriate and punish (or fail to reinforce) them for behaviour they consider inappropriate for their gender.

Parental roles in gender typing are apparently changing. With more mothers working outside the home, daughters today are exposed to more women who represent career-minded role models than was the case in earlier generations. More parents today are encouraging their daughters to become career-minded and to engage in strenuous physical activities, such as organized sports. Many boys today are exposed to fathers who take a larger role than men used to in child care and household responsibilities.

The popular media—books, magazines, radio, film, and especially television—also convey gender stereotypes (Signorelli & Kahlenberg, 2001). The media by and large portray men and women in traditional roles (Signorielli, 1990). Men more often play doctors, lawyers, and police officers. Working women who are married are more likely than men to be portrayed as undergoing role conflict—being pulled in opposite directions by job and family. They are also more likely to be in traditional female jobs than either single women or men (Signorellli & Kahlenberg, 2001).

Social-learning theorists believe that aggression is largely influenced by learning. Boys are permitted, even encouraged, to engage in more aggressive behaviour than girls. When girls act aggressively, they are often told that "this isn't the way girls act."

Cognitive–Developmental Theory
Psychologist Lawrence Kohlberg (1966) proposed a cognitive–developmental view of gender typing. From this perspective, children form concepts about gender and then make their behaviour conform to their gender concepts. These developments occur in stages and are entwined with general cognitive development.

Socialization The process of guiding people into socially acceptable behaviour patterns by means of information, rewards, and punishments.

Socialization. Today, daughters may be exposed to working mothers who are career role models, while boys may be exposed to fathers who take a role in child care and household responsibilities.

Gender Typing. *According to cognitive theories of gender typing, children are motivated to behave in ways that are consistent with their genders. Children seek information as to what behaviours are deemed appropriate for people of their gender.*

Applications

Challenging Gender Roles in Sexual Behaviour

If you are a man, do you feel that it is your responsibility to make dates and initiate sexual relationships? If you are a woman, do you feel that it is your responsibility to serve as the "gatekeeper" in romantic relationships? Regardless of your gender, how do you feel about sexually assertive women? About sexually passive men?

Gender roles have had a profound influence on dating practices and sexual behaviour. Children learn early that women are expected to wait to be asked out and to screen suitors. Men are expected to make the first (sexual) move and women to determine how far advances will proceed. Regrettably, some men refuse to take no for an answer. They feel that they have the right to force their dates into sexual relations.

The view of men as initiators and women as gatekeepers is embedded within the larger stereotype that men are sexually aggressive and women are sexually passive. Men feel pressed not only to initiate sexual encounters, but also to dictate all the "moves" thereafter, just as they are expected to take the lead on the dance floor. According to the stereotype, women are to let men determine the choice, timing, and sequence of sexual positions and techniques. Unfortunately, the stereotype favours men's sexual preferences. It denies women the opportunity to give and receive their preferred kinds of stimulation.

A woman may more easily reach orgasm in the female-superior position, but her partner may prefer the male-superior position. If the man is calling the shots, she may not have the opportunity to reach orgasm. Even the expression of her preferences may be deemed "unladylike."

The stereotypical masculine role also imposes constraints on men. Men are expected to take the lead in bringing their partners to orgasm, but they should not ask their partners what they like because they are expected to be natural experts. ("Real men" not only don't eat quiche; they also need not ask women how to make love.)

Fortunately, more flexible attitudes are emerging. Women are becoming more sexually assertive, and men are becoming more receptive to expressing tenderness and gentleness.

According to another stereotype, men are always sexually ready. Women, however, discover their sexuality only when men ignite their sexual flames. The stereotype denies that "normal" women have spontaneous sexual desires or are readily aroused. Many people view women who are highly interested in sex as sluts or nymphomaniacs.

Are the traditional stereotypes preventing you from expressing your genuine sexual feelings and preferences? If so, what can you do about it?

Gender stability The concept that people retain their genders for a lifetime.

According to Kohlberg, gender typing entails the emergence of three concepts: *gender identity, gender stability,* and *gender constancy*. Gender identity is usually acquired by the age of three. By the age of four or five, most children develop a concept of **gender stability**—the recognition that people retain their genders for a lifetime. Prior to this age, boys may think that they will become mommies when they grow up, and girls, daddies.

The more sophisticated concept of **gender constancy** develops in most children by the age of seven or eight. They recognize that gender does not change, even if people alter their dress or behaviour. So gender remains constant even when appearances change. According to Kohlberg, children are motivated to behave in gender-appropriate ways once they have established the concepts of gender stability and gender constancy. They then make an active effort to obtain information as to which behaviour patterns are considered "masculine" and which "feminine." Once they obtain this information, they imitate the "gender-appropriate" pattern.

Gender Schema Theory: An Information-Processing Approach Gender schema theory proposes that children develop a **gender schema** as a means of organizing their perceptions of the world (Bem, 1981, 1985; Martin & Halverson, 1981). A gender schema is a cluster of mental representations about male and female physical qualities, behaviours, and personality traits. Once children acquire a gender schema, they begin to judge themselves according to traits considered relevant to their genders. In doing so, they blend their developing self-concepts with the prominent gender schema of their culture. Children with self-concepts that are consistent with the prominent gender schema of their culture are likely to develop higher self-esteem than children whose self-concepts are inconsistent.

According to gender schema theory, gender identity itself is sufficient to inspire gender-appropriate behaviour. Once children develop a concept of gender identity, they begin to seek information concerning gender-typed traits and strive to live up to them. Research does suggest that children begin to imitate stereotypical masculine and feminine behaviour patterns once they have developed gender identity. Gender stability and gender constancy are apparently not prerequisites for doing so.

> **Gender constancy** The concept that people's genders do not change, even if they alter their dress or behaviour.
>
> **Gender schema** A cluster of mental representations about male and female physical qualities, behaviours, and personality traits.

Psychological Androgyny: The More Traits, the Merrier?

Most people think of masculinity and femininity as opposite ends of one continuum (Storms, 1980). People tend to assume that the more masculine a person is, the less feminine he or she must be, and vice versa. So a man who exhibits stereotypical feminine traits of nurturance, tenderness, and emotionality is often considered less masculine than other men. Women who compete with men in business are perceived not only as more masculine but also as less feminine than other women.

Some behavioural scientists, such as Sandra Bem, argue that masculinity and femininity are separate personality dimensions. A person who is highly masculine, whether male or female, may also possess feminine traits—and vice versa. People who exhibit "masculine" assertiveness and instrumental skills (skills in the sciences and business, for example) along with "feminine" nurturance and cooperation fit both the masculine and feminine gender-role stereotypes. They are said to show **psychological androgyny** (see Figure 5.6). People high only in assertiveness and instrumental skills fit the masculine stereotype. People high only in traits such as nurturance and cooperation fit the feminine stereotype. People low in the stereotypical masculine and feminine traits are considered "undifferentiated."

People who are psychologically androgynous may be capable of summoning a wider range of masculine and feminine traits to meet the demands of various situations and to express their desires and talents. Researchers, for example, have found psychologically androgynous persons of both genders to show "masculine" independence under group pressures to conform and "feminine" nurturance in interactions with a kitten or baby (Bem, 1975; Bem et al., 1976). Androgynous men and women are more apt to share leadership responsibilities in mixed-gender groups (Porter et al., 1985). By contrast, "masculine" men and women tend to dominate such groups, whereas "feminine" men and women are likely to take a back seat.

> **Psychological androgyny** Possession of stereotypical masculine traits, such as assertiveness and instrumental skills, along with stereotypical feminine traits, such as expressiveness, nurturance, and cooperation.

People who oppose the constraints of traditional gender roles may perceive psychological androgyny as a desirable goal. Some feminist writers, however, criticize psychological androgyny on grounds that the concept is defined in terms of, and thereby perpetuates, belief in the existence of masculine and feminine gender roles (Bem, 1993).

Psychological Androgyny, Psychological Well-Being, and Personal Development

Psychologically androgynous people tend to have higher self-esteem and to be generally better adjusted psychologically than people who are feminine or undifferentiated. Yet it appears that these benefits are more strongly related to the presence of masculine traits than to the combination of masculine and feminine traits (Whitley, 1983; Williams & D'Alessandro, 1994). That is, masculine traits such as assertiveness and independence may be related to psychological well-being, whether or not they are combined with feminine traits such as warmth, nurturance, and cooperation.

There is also evidence that feminine traits, such as nurturance and sensitivity, appear to predict success in intimate relationships—in men as well as in women. Marital happiness as rated by husbands is positively related to femininity in the wives (Antill, 1983). More interestingly, perhaps, ratings of marital happiness from the wives were also positively correlated with their husbands' femininity. Androgynous men are more likely to express tender feelings of love toward their partners and to be more accepting of their partner's faults than are masculine-typed ("macho") men (Coleman & Ganong, 1985). It seems that both genders appreciate spouses who are sympathetic, able to express warmth and tenderness, and nurturant toward children.

Masculine and androgynous adolescents of both genders tend to be more popular and to have higher self-esteem than other adolescents (Lamke, 1982). We might not be surprised, given the prevalence of sexism, that adolescent boys fare better if they possess stereotypical masculine traits. What is more surprising is that adolescent girls also fare better when they exhibit stereotypical masculine traits, such as assertiveness and independence. It seems that young women do not risk having others question their femininity if they exhibit masculine traits, providing more evidence that the constellations of traits we call masculinity and femininity are independent clusters.

Psychological Androgyny and Sexual Behaviour

Some evidence shows psychologically androgynous men and women to be more comfortable with their sexuality than are masculine men and feminine women (Walfish & Mayerson, 1980). Perhaps they can draw upon a broader repertoire of sexual behaviours. They may be comfortable with cuddling and tender holding, and also with initiating and directing sexual interactions. Researchers also find that androgynous women experience orgasm more frequently (Radlove, 1983) and express greater sexual satisfaction (Kimlicka et al., 1983) than feminine women do.

Figure 5.6. A Model of Psychological Androgyny.

Some behavioural scientists argue that masculinity and femininity are independent personality dimensions. People who exhibit "masculine" assertiveness and instrumental skills along with "feminine" nurturance and cooperation are said to be psychologically androgynous. People high in assertiveness and instrumental skills fit only the masculine stereotype. People high only in traits such as nurturance and cooperation fit the feminine stereotype. People low in the stereotypical masculine and feminine patterns are considered undifferentiated.

Source: From Rathus, S. A. and Nevid, J. S. (1989). Psychology and the challenges: Adjustment and growth (4th ed.). Copyright © 1989 by Holt, Rinehart & Winston, Inc. Reprinted by permission of the publisher.

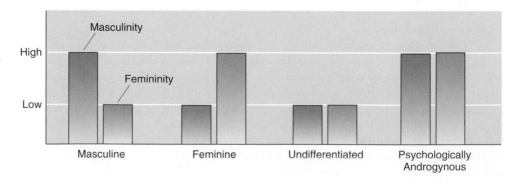

Summing Up

Prenatal Sexual Differentiation

During the first six weeks of prenatal development, embryonic structures develop along similar lines for both genders, and resemble primitive female structures. At about the seventh week after conception, the genetic code (XX or XY) begins to assert itself, causing changes in the gonads, genital ducts, and external genitals. **Testosterone** is responsible for the differentiation of the Wolffian duct system in males. In the absence of testosterone, these ducts degenerate and female sex organs develop. The testes and ovaries develop in the abdominal cavity. The testes usually descend into the scrotal sac about four months after conception. Abnormalities of the sex chromosomes can have profound effects on sexual characteristics, physical health, and psychological development. Examples include Klinefelter's, supermale, Turner, and superfemale syndrome. **Sexual differentiation also occurs in the brain**. Testosterone causes cells in the hypothalamus of male fetuses to become insensitive to estrogen.

Gender Identity

Gender identity is the sense of being male or female. It is almost always consistent with anatomic gender, but the roles of **nature and nurture** are hard to determine. Some individuals—**hermaphrodites**—are born with both ovarian and testicular tissue. Hermaphrodites usually assume the gender identity and gender role of the gender assigned at birth. Pseudohermaphrodites may acquire a gender identity consistent with the gender they are brought up to be. **Transsexuals** harbour a deep sense of discomfort about their anatomic gender. Hormone treatments and gender reassignment surgery provide transsexuals with many of the characteristics of the other gender.

Gender Roles and Stereotypes

Broad cultural expectations of men and women are known as **gender roles**. In North America, the stereotypical female is seen as gentle, dependent, kind, helpful, patient, and submissive. The stereotypical male is tough, competitive, gentlemanly, and protective. **Sexism** is the prejudgment that because of gender, people possess certain negative traits that disqualify them from certain vocations or prevent them from performing certain roles adequately. Stereotypical expectations about "women's work" and "men's work" filter down to young children.

Gender Differences: Vive la Différence or Vive la Similitude?

Boys have historically been seen as excelling in math and spatial-relations skills, while girls have been viewed as excelling in language skills. **Differences in cognitive abilities** are small, however, and cultural expectations play a role. Stereotypical gender preferences for toys and play activities are evident at an early age. There are **differences in personality,** including a tendency for males to be more aggressive than females, but the question is, *why?*

On Becoming a Man or a Woman: Gender Typing

Biological perspectives on gender typing focus on the roles of both genetics and prenatal influences in predisposing men and women to gender-linked patterns. Testosterone in male fetuses affects the growth of the right hemisphere of the brain, which may be connected with the ability to manage spatial-relations tasks. **Cross-cultural** studies have shown that preliterate cultures do not all adopt the same gender roles; even neighbouring cultures may differ. **Psychologists** have attempted to explain gender typing from the perspective of psychodynamic, social-learning, and cognitive-developmental theories. A *gender schema* is a set of mental representations of male and female physical characteristics, behaviours, and personality traits. Children may use gender schemata to organize their perceptions of the world and to judge themselves according to traits considered relevant to their genders.

Psychological Androgyny: The More Traits, the Merrier?

Masculinity and femininity may be two independent personality dimensions. People who combine stereotypical masculine and feminine behaviour patterns are psychologically androgynous. Masculine and androgynous people of both genders tend to be **better adjusted psychologically** than people who are feminine or undifferentiated. They are also more **comfortable with their sexuality** than either masculine men or feminine women.

Chapter Quiz

1. In the embryo, ovaries begin to differentiate if the
    (a) X chromosome is present.
    (b) X chromosome is absent.
    (c) Y chromosome is present.
    (d) Y chromosome is absent.

2. In the embryo, each Wolffian duct develops into all of the following, EXCEPT for
    (a) an epididymis.
    (b) an ovary.

(c) a vas deferens.

(d) seminal vesicles.

3. Pseudohermaphrodites may possess the gonads

   (a) and external genitalia of males.

   (b) and external genitalia of females.

   (c) of one gender but external genitalia that are typical of the other gender.

   (d) and external genitalia that are typical of the other gender.

4. According to the text, _____ experience gender dysphoria.

   (a) people with Dominican Republic syndrome

   (b) hermaphrodites

   (c) pseudohermaphrodites

   (d) transsexuals

5. Which of the following is the most accurate statement about gender differences in mathematics?

   (a) Males excel in computational ability in elementary school.

   (b) Females excel in problem solving in high school and in college.

   (c) Girls outperform boys on standardized math items.

   (d) Differences in math are small and narrowing at all ages.

6. _____ propose that genes bestowing attributes that increase an organism's chances of surviving to produce viable offspring are most likely to be transmitted to future generations.

   (a) Psychologists

   (b) Sociobiologists

   (c) Anthropologists

   (d) Sociologists

7. Margaret Mead found that among the Mundugumor,

   (a) both men and women were warlike and aggressive.

   (b) neither men nor women were warlike and aggressive.

   (c) men but not women were warlike and aggressive.

   (d) women but not men were warlike and aggressive.

8. According to gender schema theory, children blend their developing _____ with the prominent gender schema of their culture.

   (a) embryonic structures

   (b) psychic structures

   (c) self-concepts

   (d) gender identities

9. Sandra Bem argues that masculinity and femininity are

   (a) opposite poles of a single personality dimension.

   (b) separate personality dimensions.

   (c) social requirements that promote the survival of a culture.

   (d) concepts found only in Western societies.

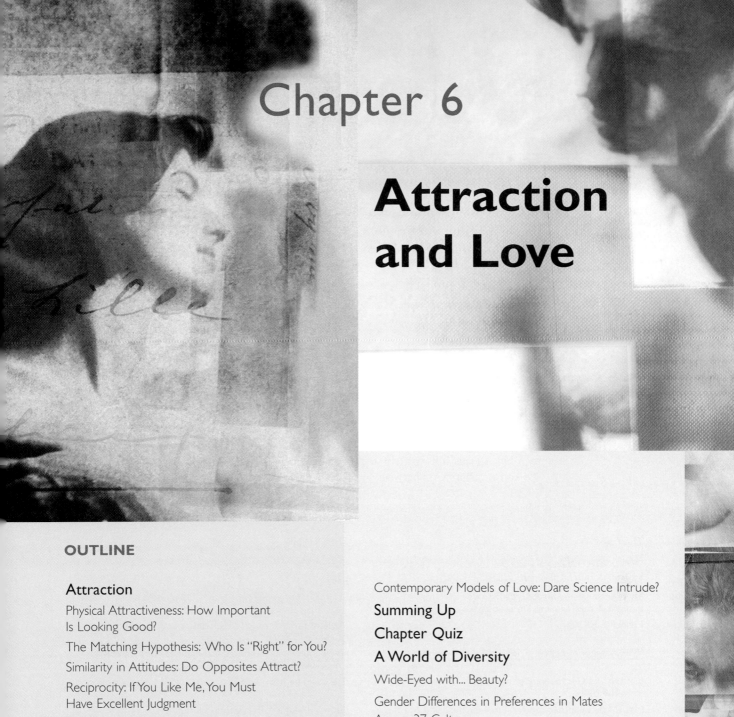

Chapter 6

Attraction and Love

Did You Know That...

- Beauty is not simply "in the eye of the beholder"—there appear to be some universal standards for beauty?

- Young women believe that young men would like them to be thinner than men actually want them to be?

- People are regarded as more attractive when they are smiling?

- Women who are assigned names like Kathy and Jennifer at random are rated as more attractive than women assigned names like Harriet and Gertrude?

- Opposites do not usually attract—we are more likely to be attracted to people who share our views and tastes than to people who disagree with them?

- It is possible to be in love with someone who is not also a friend?

- Many people are lonely because they fear being rejected by others?

Candy and Stretch. A new technique for controlling weight gain? No, these are the names of a couple who have just met at a camera club that doubles as a meeting place for singles.

Candy and Stretch stand above the crowd—literally. She is 180 cm tall, an attractive woman in her early 30s. He is more plain looking, but "wholesome." He is in his late 30s and a full 2 metres tall. Stretch has been in the group for some time. Candy is a new member. Let us follow them as they meet during a coffee break. As you will see, there are some differences between what they say and what they think (Bach & Deutsch, 1970).

	THEY SAY	THEY THINK
Stretch:	Well, you're certainly a welcome addition to our group.	(Can't I ever say something clever?)
Candy:	Thank you. It certainly is friendly and interesting.	(He's cute.)
Stretch:	My friends call me Stretch. It's left over from my basketball days. Silly, but I'm used to it.	(It's safer than saying my name is David Stein.)
Candy:	My name is Candy.	(At least my nickname is. He doesn't have to hear Hortense O'Brien.)
Stretch:	What kind of camera is that?	(Why couldn't a girl named Candy be Jewish? It's only a nickname, isn't it?)
Candy:	Just this old German one of my uncle's. I borrowed it from the office.	(He could be Irish. And that camera looks expensive.)
Stretch:	May I? (He takes her camera, brushing her hand and then tingling with the touch.) Fine lens. You work for your uncle?	(Now I've done it. Brought up work.)
Candy:	Ever since college. It's more than being just a secretary. I get into sales, too.	(Okay, so what if I only went for a year? If he asks what I sell, I'll tell him anything except underwear.)
Stretch:	Sales? That's funny. I'm in sales, too, but mainly as an executive. I run our department.	(Is there a nice way to say used cars? I'd better change the subject.)
	I started using cameras on trips. Last time I was in the Bahamas, I took—	(Great legs! And the way her hips move—)
Candy:	Oh! Do you go to the Bahamas, too? I love those islands.	(So I went just once, and it was for the brassiere manufacturers' convention. At least we're off the subject of jobs.)
Stretch:		(She's probably been around. Well, at least we're off the subject of jobs.)
	I did a little underwater work there last summer. Fantastic colours. So rich in life.	(And lonelier than hell.)
Candy:	I wish I'd had time when I was there. I love the water.	(Look at that build. He must swim like a fish. I should learn.)
		(Well, I do. At the beach, anyway, where I can wade in and not go too deep.)

So begins a relationship. Candy and Stretch have a drink and talk, talk, talk—sharing their likes and dislikes. Amazingly, they seem to agree on everything, from clothing to cars to politics. The attraction they feel is very strong, and neither of them is willing to turn the other off by disagreeing.

They fall in love. Weeks later they still agree on everything, but that doesn't mean they talk honestly about issues.

One of the topics they ignore is birth control. Candy does not take oral contraceptives. (Stretch later claimed that he had assumed she did.) Candy becomes pregnant, and they get married. Only through professional help do they learn each other's genuine feelings. And on several occasions, the union comes close to dissolving.

How do we explain the goings-on in this tangled web of deception? Candy and Stretch felt strongly attracted to each other. What determines who is attractive? Why did Candy and Stretch pretend to agree on everything?

Two possible consequences of attraction are friendship and love. Candy and Stretch "fell in love." What is love? When the first author was a teenager, the answer was, "Five feet of heaven in a ponytail." However, this answer may lack scientific merit. We see that there are different forms of love and that our concepts of love are far from universal.

Attraction

Let us explore some of the factors that determine interpersonal attraction.

Physical Attractiveness: How Important Is Looking Good?

We might like to think of ourselves as so sophisticated that physical attractiveness does not move us. We might like to claim that sensitivity, warmth, and intelligence are more important to us. However, we may never learn about other people's personalities if they do not meet our minimal standards for physical attractiveness. Research shows that physical attractiveness is a major determinant of interpersonal and sexual attraction (Hensley, 1992). For some men and women, physical appearance is the key factor in consideration of partners for dates, sex, and marriage (Hatfield & Sprecher, 1986).

Is Beauty in the Eye of the Beholder? What determines physical attractiveness? Are our standards fully subjective, or is there broad agreement on what is attractive? Cross-cultural studies show that people universally want physically appealing partners (Ford & Beach, 1951). However, is that which appeals in one culture repulsive in others?

In certain African tribes, long necks and round, dislike lips are signs of feminine beauty. Women thus stretch their necks and lips to make themselves more appealing. Women of the Nama tribe persistently tug at their labia majora to make them "beautiful"—that is, prominent and elongated (Ford & Beach, 1951).

In our culture, taller men are considered to be more attractive by women (Hensley, 1994; Sheppard & Strathman, 1989). Undergraduate women prefer their dates to be about 15 cm taller than they are. Undergraduate men, on the average, prefer women who are about 11 cm shorter (Gillis & Avis, 1980). Tall women are not viewed so positively. Shortness, though, is perceived to be a liability for both men and women (Jackson & Ervin, 1992).

Some women of Candy's stature find that shorter men are discouraged from asking them out. Some walk with a hunch, as if to minimize their height. A neighbour of the first and third authors refers to herself as 5 feet 13 inches tall.

Female plumpness is valued in many, perhaps most, preliterate societies (Anderson et al., 1992; Frayser, 1985). Wide hips and a broad pelvis are widely recognized as sexually appealing. In our culture, however, slenderness is in style. Some young women suffer from an eating disorder called **anorexia nervosa**, in which they literally starve themselves to conform to the contemporary ideal. Both genders find slenderness (though not anorexic thinness) attractive, especially for females (Fallon & Rozin, 1985; Franzoi & Herzog, 1987; Rozin & Fallon, 1988).

Living in a Social World: Physical Attraction **www.units.muohio.edu/ psybersite/attraction** An introduction to recent theories on physical attraction.

Anorexia nervosa A potentially life-threatening eating disorder characterized by refusal to maintain a healthy body weight, intense fear of being overweight, a distorted body image, and, in females, lack of menstruation (amenorrhea).

Internet Mental Health:
Anorexia Nervosa
www.mentalhealth.com/dis/
p20-et01.html
This site includes descriptions, diagnoses, and treatments online as well as providing resource material and links.

The hourglass figure is popular in North America. Both males and females rated women of average weight with a waist-to-hip ratio of 0.7 to 0.8 as most attractive and desirable for long-term relationships. Neither very thin nor obese women were found to be as attractive, regardless of the waist-to-hip ratio (Singh, 1994a, 1994b).

Do men idealize the *Penthouse* centrefold? What size busts do men prefer? Women's beliefs that men prefer large breasts may be somewhat exaggerated. The belief that men want women to have bursting bustlines leads many women to seek breast implants in the attempt to live up to an ideal that men themselves don't generally hold (Rosenthal, 1992). Researchers in one study showed young men and women (aged 17 to 25 years) a continuum of male and female figures that differed only in the size of the bust for the female figures and of the pectorals for the male figures (Thompson & Tantleff, 1992). The participants were asked to indicate the ideal size for their own gender and the size they believed the average man and woman would prefer.

The results show some support for the "big is better" stereotype—for both men and women. Women's conception of ideal bust size was greater than their actual average size. Men preferred women with still larger busts, but not nearly as large as the busts women *believed* that men prefer. Men believed that their male peers preferred women with much bustier figures than their peers themselves said they preferred. Ample breast or chest sizes may be preferred by the other gender, but people seem to have an exaggerated idea of the sizes the other gender actually prefers.

Both genders find obese people unattractive, but there are gender differences in impressions of the most pleasing body shape. On the average, male university students think that their present physiques are close to ideal and appealing to women (Fallon & Rozin, 1985). Female university students generally see themselves as much heavier than the figure that is most alluring to men, and heavier still than the figure they perceive as the ideal feminine form. Both genders are wrong about the preferences of the other gender, however. Men actually prefer women to be somewhat heavier than the women imagine they would. Women prefer their men to be a bit leaner than the men would have expected.

Traits and Perceptions of Attractiveness Both genders rate the attractiveness of faces higher when they are shown smiling in photographs than when they are shown in an unsmiling pose (Mueser et al., 1984). (Photographers are not ignorant of this fact.) So there is reason to "put on a happy face" when you meet people socially or ask some-

one out on a date. Context is important, however. It may be more appropriate in a business context to maintain a more serious countenance. The effects of a smile may also be a greater determinant of attractiveness in women than in men (Deutsch et al., 1987).

Gender-role expectations may affect perceptions of attractiveness. Women who viewed videos of prospective dates found men who acted outgoing and self-expressive more appealing than men who were passive (Riggio & Woll, 1984). Another study found that highly feminine women are more likely to be attracted to dominant "macho" men than less feminine women are (Maybach & Gold, 1994). Yet men who viewed videos in the Riggio and Woll (1984) study were put off by outgoing, self-expressive behaviour in women. In yet another study, women rated videos of dom-

Slim Is In. *Pressure to conform to an idealized slender image (left) plays a key role in the development of eating disorders among young women (right).*

inant university men (defined in this study as social control over a troublesome interaction with an instructor) as more appealing than submissive men. Again, male viewers were put off by similarly dominant women (Sadalla et al., 1987). Despite recent changes in traditional gender-role stereotypes, many men still prefer demure women. This is not to suggest that dominant, self-expressive women should stifle themselves to attract traditional men; the relationships would probably rub them both the wrong way.

Names and Perceptions of Attractiveness Names may also affect perceptions of physical appeal. In one study, photographs of women that were randomly assigned names like Kathy, Jennifer, and Christine were rated more attractive than photographs assigned the names Harriet, Gertrude, and Ethel (Garwood et al., 1980). Erwin (1994) replicated this study using photographs of both men and women. The attractive names chosen were Danielle and Alexander and the unattractive names were Tracey and Kenneth. Results showed that the models in the photographs who were paired with attractive names were rated as being more physically attractive than those models paired with unattractive names. This effect was stronger for female photographs than for male ones. In other words, there was a tendency to judge the attractiveness of females on the basis of the names assigned to the photographs while men were more likely to be judged to be attractive based on an assessment of their physical appearance. However, research has found that there is little agreement among people about what names are considered attractive or desirable (Willis & Henderson, 1994). As our society becomes more culturally diverse, names previously considered uncommon or unattractive are increasingly accepted and even valued for their uniqueness.

What Do You Look for in a Long-Term, Meaningful Relationship? Your second author conducted a survey of male and female university students in the early 1980s and found that psychological characteristics such as warmth, fidelity, honesty, and sensitivity were rated higher in importance than physical attractiveness as desirable qualities in a prospective partner for a meaningful, long-term relationship (Nevid, 1984). Physical attractiveness won out when students were asked to consider the qualities that are most important in a partner for a sexual relationship. Overall, however, men placed greater emphasis on the physical characteristics of their partners for both types of relationships than did women. Women placed more value on qualities such as warmth, assertiveness, wit, and ambition. The single most highly desired quality students wanted in long-term partners was honesty.

Although personal qualities may assume more prominent roles in determining partner preferences in long-term relationships, physical appeal probably plays a "filtering" role. Unless a prospective date meets minimal physical standards, we might not look beneath the surface for "more meaningful" traits.

Nevid's results have been replicated in studies on initial attraction and on choice of mates. Women place relatively greater emphasis than men on traits like vocational status, earning potential, expressiveness, kindness, consideration, dependability, and fondness for children. Men give relatively more consideration to youth, physical attractiveness, cooking ability, and frugality (Howard et al., 1987; Sprecher et al., 1994). When it comes to mate selection, females in a sample of students from Germany and the Netherlands also emphasized the financial prospects and status of a potential mate, whereas males emphasized the importance of physical attractiveness (de Raad & Doddema-Winsemius, 1992). A study of more than 200 Korean college students found that in mate selection, women placed relatively more emphasis on education, jobs, and family of origin than men did (Brown, 1994). Men placed relatively more emphasis on physical attractiveness and affection. (Yes, men were more "romantic." Women were more pragmatic.)

Susan Sprecher and her colleagues (1994) surveyed a national probability sample of 13 107 English- or Spanish-speaking people, aged 19 or above, living in households in the United States. In one section of their questionnaire, they asked respondents how willing they would be to marry someone who was older, younger, of a different religion, not likely to hold a steady job, not good-looking, and so forth. Each item was followed by a 7-point scale in which 1 meant "not at all" and 7 meant "very willing." As shown in Table 6.1 on page 123, women were more willing than men to marry someone who was not good-looking. On the other hand, women were less willing to marry someone not likely to hold a steady job.

A World of Diversity

Wide-Eyed with... Beauty?

Some aspects of beauty seem to be largely cross-cultural. Research suggests that people tend to agree on the facial features that they find to be attractive, regardless of ethnicity (Cunningham et al., 1995). They all prefer female faces with large eyes; greater distance between the eyes; small noses; narrower faces with smaller chins; high, expressive eyebrows; larger lower lips; and a well-groomed, full head of hair.

Consider the methodology of a study that compares the facial preferences of people in Japan and England. Perrett (1994) created computer composites of the faces of 60 women. Part A of Figure 6.1 is a composite of the 15 women who were rated the most attractive. He then used computer enhancement to exaggerate the differences between the composite of the 60—that is, the average face—and the composite of the 15 most attractive women. He

found that both Japanese and British men deemed women with large eyes, high cheekbones, and narrow jaws to be the most attractive (Perrett, 1994). Computer enhancement resulted in the image shown in Part B of Figure 6.1. The enhanced composite has still higher cheekbones and a narrower jaw than Part A. Part B was then rated as the most attractive image. Similar results were found for the image of a Japanese woman.

Cunningham and his colleagues (1995) reported historical anecdotes that suggest that the facial preferences of people as diverse as Europeans, Black Africans, Native North Americans, Indians (in India, that is), and Chinese are quite consistent. They quoted from Charles Darwin's 1871 treatise, *The Descent of Man, and Selection in Relation to Sex*:

> Mr. Winwood Reade... who has had ample opportunities for observation [with Black Africans] who have never associated with Europeans is convinced that their ideas of beauty are, on the

whole, the same as ours; and Dr. Rohlfs writes to me the same effect with respect to Borneo and the countries inhabited by the Pullo tribes.... Capt. Burton believes that a woman whom we consider beautiful is admired throughout the world.

Darwin believed that our physical preferences were largely inborn and related to survival of our species. What do you think? Do you believe that "their ideas of beauty are, on the whole, the same as ours"? Or do you think that research hasn't yet ferreted out significant cultural or ethnic differences that might exist? If there is ethnic consistency in these preferences, how would you explain them? For example, do you believe

- that they are merely coincidental?
- that there has been more exchange of ideas among cultures than has been believed?
- that there is something instinctive about them?

A

B

Figure 6.1. What Features Contribute to Facial Attractiveness?

In both England and Japan, features such as large eyes, high cheekbones, and narrow jaws contribute to perceptions of the attractiveness of women. Part A is a computer composite of the faces of 15 women rated as the most attractive of a group of 60. Part B is a computer composite that exaggerates the features of these 15 women. That is, they are developed further in the direction that separates them from the average of the full group.

Are Attractiveness Preferences Inherited? On the surface, gender differences in perceptions of attractiveness seem very sexist—and perhaps they are. Yet some sociobiologists believe that evolutionary forces favour the continuation of gender differences in preferences for mates because certain preferred traits provide reproductive advantages (Bjorklund & Kipp, 1996). Some physical features, like cleanliness, good complexion, clear eyes, good teeth, good hair, firm muscle tone, and a steady gait are

TABLE 6.1 Gender Differences in Mate Preferences

How willing would you be to marry someone who...	Men	Women
• was not "good-looking"?	3.41	4.42†
• was older than you by 5 or more years?	4.15	5.29†
• was younger than you by 5 or more years?	4.54	2.80†
• was not likely to hold a steady job?	2.73	1.62†
• would earn much less than you?	4.60	3.76†
• would earn much more than you?	5.19	5.93†
• had more education than you?	5.22	5.82†
• had less education than you?	4.67	4.08†
• had been married before?	3.35	3.44
• already had children?	2.84	3.11*
• was of a different religion?	4.24	4.31
• was of a different race?	3.08	2.84†

Based on a 7 point scale where 1 = not at all, and 7 = very willing.
*Difference statistically significant at the .01 level of confidence.
†Difference statistically significant at the .001 level of confidence.

Source: Based on information in Susan Sprecher, Quintin Sullivan, & Elaine Hatfield (1994). Mate Selection Preferences: Gender Differences Examined in a National Sample. *Journal of Personality and Social Psychology, 66* (6), 1074–1080.

universally appealing to both genders (Ford & Beach, 1951). Perhaps they are markers of reproductive potential (Symons, 1995). Age and health may be relatively more important to a woman's appeal, since these characteristics tend to be associated with her reproductive capacity: The "biological clock" limits her reproductive potential. Physical characteristics associated with a woman's youthfulness, such as smooth skin, firm muscle tone, and lustrous hair, may thus have become more closely linked to a woman's appeal (Buss, 1994). A man's reproductive value, however, may depend more on how well he can provide for his family than on his age or physical appeal. The value of men as reproducers, therefore, is more intertwined with factors that contribute to a stable environment for child rearing—such as economic status and reliability. Sociobiologists argue that these gender differences in mate preferences may have been passed down through the generations as part of our genetic heritage (Buss, 1994; Symons, 1995).

Men's interest in younger women is apparently universal. It occurs in both preliterate and industrialized societies (Buss, 1994; Symons, 1979). Female jealousy of younger women is another thread that spans cultures. Sexual competition, according to Margaret Mead, generally involves

> the struggle between stronger older men and weaker younger men or between more attractive younger women and more entrenched older ones.

(MEAD, 1967, P. 198)

Sociobiological views of gender differences in mate preferences are largely speculative and not fully consistent with the evidence. Despite gender differences, both men and women report that they place greater weight on personal characteristics than on physical features in judging prospective mates (Buss, 1994). Many women, like men, prefer physically appealing partners (Bixler, 1989). Women also tend to marry men similar to themselves in physical attractiveness as well as socioeconomic standing. Note also that older men are more likely than younger men to die from natural causes. From the standpoint of reproductive advantages, women would thus achieve greater success by marrying fit, younger males who are likely to survive during the child-rearing years than by marrying older, higher-status males. Moreover, similar cultural influences, rather than inherited dispositions, may explain commonalities across cultures in gender differences

A World of Diversity

Gender Differences in Preferences in Mates Across 37 Cultures

What do men in Nigeria, Japan, Brazil, Canada, and the United States have in common? For one thing, men in these countries report that they prefer mates who are younger than themselves. Buss (1994) reviewed survey evidence on the preferred age difference between oneself and one's mate in 37 cultures (representing 33 countries) in Europe, Africa, Asia, Australia, New Zealand, and North and South America. Women, however, preferred older mates (the range was from 1.82 years to 5.1 years).

Gender differences in the preferred age of mates paralleled actual differences in age of men and women at the time of marriage. Men were between two and five years older on the average than their brides at the time of marriage. The smallest age difference at marriage, 2.1 years, was found in Poland. The largest difference, 4.92 years, was found in Greece. Men in the mainland United States are 2.71 years older than women at the time of marriage. In Canada, men are 2.51 years older than their mates, on the average.

Buss finds that in all 37 cultures, men placed greater value on a prospective partner's "good looks" than did women. In contrast, women in 36 of 37 cultures placed greater value on "good earning capacity" of prospective mates.

The consistency of Buss's findings lends credence to the notion that there are widespread gender differences in preferences with respect to age, physical characteristics, and financial status of prospective mates. Generally speaking, men across cultures place greater value on the physical attractiveness and relative youth of prospective mates, whereas women place relatively greater value on the earning capacity of prospective mates. Buss interprets women's preferences for relatively older mates as additional evidence that women appraise future mates on the basis of their ability to provide for a wife and family, since age and income tend to be linked among men.

Despite these gender differences in preferences for mates, Buss finds that both men and women placed greater weight on personal qualities than on looks or income potential of prospective mates. In *all* 37 cultures, the characteristics "kind, understanding" and "intelligent" were rated higher than earning power or physical attractiveness.

in mate preferences. For example, in societies in which women are economically dependent on men, a man's appeal may depend more on his financial resources than on his physical appeal.

The Matching Hypothesis: Who Is "Right" for You?

Do not despair if you are less than exquisite in appearance, along with most of us mere mortals. You may be saved from permanently blending in with the wallpaper by the effects of the **matching hypothesis**. This concept holds that people tend to develop romantic relationships with people who are similar to themselves in physical attractiveness rather than the local Ben Affleck or Halle Berry look-alike.

Researchers have found that people who are dating steadily, engaged, or married tend to be matched in physical attractiveness (Kalick, 1988). Young married couples even tend to be matched in weight (Schafer & Keith, 1990). The central motive for seeking "matches" seems to be fear of rejection by more appealing people (Bernstein et al., 1983).

There are exceptions to the matching hypothesis. Now and then we find a beautiful woman married to a plain or ugly man (or vice versa). How do we explain it? What, after all, would *she* see in *him*? According to one study (Bar-Tal & Saxe, 1976), people judging "mismatched" pairs may tend to ascribe wealth, intelligence, or success to the man. We seek an unseen factor that will balance the physical attractiveness of one partner. For some "mismatched" couples, similarities in attitudes and personalities may balance out differences in physical attractiveness.

Matching hypothesis The concept that people tend to develop romantic relationships with people who are similar to themselves in attractiveness.

Similarity in Attitudes: Do Opposites Attract?

Why do the great majority of us have partners from our own backgrounds? One reason is that marriages are made not in heaven but in the neighbourhood (Michael et al., 1994). That is, we tend to live among people who are similar to us in background, and thus come into contact with them. Another is that we are drawn to people who are similar in their attitudes. People similar in background are more likely to be similar in their attitudes. Similarity in attitudes and tastes is a key contributor to attraction, friendships, and love relationships (Cappella & Palmer, 1990; Griffin & Sparks, 1990; Laumann et al., 1994). Research indicates that partners who are similar in personality report more lasting and satisfying relationships than those who have less in common with each other (Wilson & Cousins, 2003). However, one study suggests that partner similarity is more important for men than for women. The researchers confirmed that partner similarity contributed to marriage stability and quality for both men and women. However, the study reported that high marriage quality, low conflict, and high self-esteem were important predictors of general life satisfaction for men while good general health and high self-esteem were the significant predictors of life satisfaction for women (Arrindell & Luteijn, 2000).

Evidence shows that women place greater weight on attitude similarity as a determinant of attraction to a stranger of the other gender than do men, whereas men place more value on physical attractiveness (Feingold, 1991).

We also tend to *assume* that people we find attractive share our attitudes (Dawes, 1989; Marks et al., 1981). The physical attraction between Candy and Stretch motivated them to pretend that their preferences, tastes, and opinions coincided. When sexual attraction is strong, perhaps we want to think that the kinks in the relationship will be small or that we can iron them out. Let us also note that though similarity may be important in determining initial attraction, compatibility appears to be an even stronger determinant of maintaining an enduring intimate relationship (Vinacke et al., 1988).

Reciprocity: If You Like Me, You Must Have Excellent Judgment

Has anyone told you that you are good-looking, brilliant, and emotionally mature to boot? That your taste is elegant? Ah, what superb judgment!

When we feel admired and complimented, we tend to return these feelings and behaviours. This is called **reciprocity**. Reciprocity is a potent determinant of attraction (Condon & Crano, 1988). We tend to be much more warm, helpful, and candid when we are with strangers who we believe like us (Clark et al., 1989; Curtis & Miller, 1986). We even tend to welcome positive comments from others when we know them to be inaccurate (Swann et al., 1987).

Perhaps the power of reciprocity has enabled many couples to become happy with one another and reasonably well adjusted. By reciprocating positive words and actions, a person can perhaps stoke neutral or mild feelings into robust, affirmative feelings of attraction.

Attraction can lead to feelings of love. Let us now turn to that most fascinating topic.

Love

For thousands of years, poets have sought to capture love in words. Scottish poet Robert Burns wrote that his love was like "a red, red rose." In Sinclair Lewis's novel *Elmer Gantry*, love is "the morning and the evening star." In her book *Emotions*, Canadian author June Callwood proclaimed, "From the beginning of life to its end, love is the only emotion which matters." Love is beautiful and elusive. It shines, brilliant and heavenly. Passion and romantic love are also earthy and sexy, brimming with sexual desire.

Romantic love is hardly unique to our culture. Researchers report finding evidence of romantic love in 147 of the 166 different cultures they studied in a cross-cultural comparison (Jankowiak & Fischer, 1992). Romantic love occurs not only in modern

The Nature of Attraction and Love
http://mentalhelp.net/psyhelp/chap10/chap10c.htm
A clinical psychologist discusses love and attraction with reference to psychological studies and findings.

Reciprocity Mutual exchange.

Who Is Right for You?
Research shows that people tend to pair off with others who are similar in physical characteristics and personality traits.

industrial societies but also in most preliterate societies. The absence of romantic love in the remaining 19 cultures, the investigators suspect, was most probably due to the limitations of their study methods (Gelman, 1993).

Our culture idealizes the concept of romantic love. Thus we readily identify with the plight of the "star-crossed" lovers in *Romeo and Juliet*, who sacrificed for love. We learn that "love makes the world go round" and that "love is everything." In a recent survey of Canadians, being loved was identified as a very important goal for 90% of young adults, 70% of teens, and 84% of adults (Bibby, 2001). Like other aspects of sexual and social behaviour among humans, the concept of love must be understood within a cultural context. Luckily (or miserably), we have such a context in Western culture....

The Greek Heritage

The concept of love can be traced back at least as far as the classical age of Greece. The Greeks distinguished four concepts related to the modern meanings of love: *storge, agape, philia,* and *eros.*

Storge is loving attachment, deep friendship, or nonsexual affection. It is the emotion that binds friends and parents and children. Some scholars believe that even romantic love is a form of attachment that is similar to the types of attachments infants have to their mothers (Hazan & Shaver, 1987).

Agape is similar to generosity and charity. It implies the wish to share one's bounty, and is epitomized by anonymous donations of money. In relationships, it is characterized by selfless giving (Lee, 1988). Agape, according to Lee's research, is the kind of love least frequently found between adults in committed relationships.

Philia is closest in meaning to friendship. It is based on liking and respect, rather than sexual desire. It involves the desire to do and enjoy things with the other person, and to see him or her when one is lonely or bored.

Eros is closest in meaning to our concept of passion. Eros was a character in Greek mythology (transformed in Roman mythology into Cupido, now called Cupid) who would shoot unsuspecting people with his love arrows, causing them to fall madly in love with the person who was nearest to them at the time. Erotic love embraces sudden passionate desire: "love at first sight" and "falling head over heels in love." Passion can be so gripping that one is convinced that life has been changed forever. This feeling of sudden transformation was captured by the Italian poet Dante Alighieri (1265–1321), who exclaimed upon first beholding his beloved Beatrice, *"Incipit vita nuova,"* which can be translated as "My life begins anew." Romantic love can also be earthy and sexy. In fact, sexual arousal and desire may be the strongest component of passionate or romantic love (Berscheid, 1988). Romantic love begins with a powerful physical attraction or feelings of passion, and is associated with strong physiological arousal (Lee, 1988).

Unlike the Greeks, we tend to use the word *love* to describe everything from feelings of affection toward another to romantic ardour to sexual intercourse ("making love"). Still, different types or styles of love are recognized in our own culture, as we shall see.

Romantic Love in Contemporary Western Culture

The experience of romantic love, as opposed to loving attachment or sexual arousal per se, occurs within a cultural context in which the concept is idealized. Western culture has a long tradition of idealizing the concept of romantic love, as represented, for instance, by romantic fairy tales that have been passed down through the generations. In fact, our exposure to the concept of romantic love may begin with hearing the fairy tales of Sleeping Beauty, Cinderella, and Snow White—along with their princes charming. Later, perhaps, the concept of romantic love blossoms with exposure to romantic novels, television and film scripts, and the heady tales of friends and relatives.

During adolescence, strong sexual arousal along with an idealized image of the object of our desires leads us to label our feelings as *love*. We may learn to speak of "love"

Storge (STORE-gay) Loving attachment and nonsexual affection; the type of emotion that binds parents to children.

Agape (AH-gah-pay) Selfless love; a kind of loving that is similar to generosity and charity.

Philia (FEEL-yuh) Friendship love, which is based on liking and respect rather than sexual desire.

Eros The kind of love that is closest in meaning to the modern-day concept of passion.

rather than "lust," because sexual desire in the absence of a committed relationship might be viewed as primitive or animalistic. Being "in love" ennobles attraction and sexual arousal, not only to society but also to oneself. Unlike lust, love can even be discussed at the dinner table. If others think we are too young to experience "the real thing"—which presumably includes knowledge of and respect for the other person's personality traits—our feelings may be called "puppy love" or a "crush."

Western society maintains much of the double standard toward sexuality. Thus, women are more often expected to justify sexual experiences as involving someone they love. Young men usually need not attribute sexual urges to love. So men are more apt to deem love a "mushy" concept. The vast majority of North Americans nonetheless believe romantic love is a prerequisite for marriage. Romantic love is rated by young people as the single most important reason for marriage (Roper Organization, 1985). More than 80% of university students subscribe to the belief that "being in love" is a precondition for marriage (Berscheid, 1988; Simpson et al., 1986). More than half also believe that falling out of love justifies divorce.

Romantic Love. *A survey of single people found that more men than women described themselves as romantic—yet among married people, the results were reversed.*

Which is the more romantic gender? Although the question may well incite an argument in mixed company, the Janus and Janus (1993) survey found that a slightly greater percentage of single men (82%) perceived themselves as being romantic than did single women (77%). Yet among married people, the figures were reversed, with 79% of the women describing themselves as romantic as compared to 72% of the men. Perhaps there is some truth to the stereotype that men are more romantic during the courtship stage of relationships than the marriage stage. Then again, maybe self-perceptions of being romantic don't quite jibe with the reality.

When reciprocated, romantic love is usually a source of deep fulfillment and ecstasy (Hatfield, 1988). How wonderful when love meets its match. When love is unrequited, however, it can lead to emptiness, anxiety, or despair. Romantic love can thus teeter between states of ecstasy and misery (Hatfield, 1988). Perhaps no other feature of our lives can lift us up as high or plunge us as low as romantic love.

Infatuation Versus "True Love": Will Time Tell?
Perhaps you first noticed each other when your eyes met across a crowded room. Or perhaps you met when you were both assigned to the same Bunsen burner in chemistry lab—less romantic, but closer to the flame. However it happened, the meeting triggered such an electric charge through your body that you could not get him (or her) out of your mind. Were you truly in love, however, or was it merely a passing fancy? Was it infatuation or the "real thing"—a "true," lasting, and mutual love? How do you tell them apart?

Perhaps you don't, at least not at first. **Infatuation** is a state of intense absorption in or focus on another person. It is usually accompanied by sexual desire, elation, and general physiological arousal or excitement. Some refer to passion as infatuation. Others dub it a "crush." Both monikers suggest that it is a passing fancy. In infatuation, your heart may pound whenever the other person draws near or enters your fantasies.

For the first month or two, infatuation and the more enduring forms of romantic love are essentially indistinguishable (Gordon & Snyder, 1989). At first, both may be characterized by intense focusing or absorption. Infatuated people may become so absorbed that they cannot sleep, work, or carry out routine chores. Logic and reason are swept aside.

Infatuated people hold idealized images of their love objects and overlook their faults. Caution may be cast to the winds. In some cases, couples in the throes of infatuation rush to get married, only to find a few weeks or months later that they are not well suited.

As time goes on, signs that distinguish infatuation from a lasting romantic love begin to emerge. The partners begin to view each other more realistically and determine whether or not the relationship should continue.

Infatuation A state of intense absorption in or focus on another person, which is usually accompanied by sexual desire, elation, and general physiological arousal or excitement; passion.

Infatuation has been likened to a state of passionate love (Sternberg, 1986) that is based on intense feelings of passion but not on the deeper feelings of attachment and caring that typify a more lasting mutual love. Although infatuation may be a passing fancy, it can be supplanted by the deeper feelings of attachment and caring that characterize more lasting love relationships.

Note, too, that infatuation is not a necessary first step on the path to a lasting mutual love. Some couples develop deep feelings of love without ever experiencing the fireworks of infatuation (Sternberg, 1986). Or sometimes one partner is infatuated while the other manages to keep his or her head below the clouds.

Contemporary Models of Love: Dare Science Intrude?

Despite the importance of love, scientists have historically paid little attention to it. Some people believe that love cannot be analyzed scientifically. Love, they maintain, should be left to the poets, philosophers, and theologians. Yet researchers are now applying the scientific method to the study of love. They recognize that love is a complex concept, involving many areas of experience—emotional, cognitive, and motivational (Sternberg & Grajek, 1984). They have reinforced the Greek view that there are different kinds and styles of love. Let us consider some of the views of love that have emerged from modern theorists and researchers.

Romantic love A kind of love characterized by feelings of passion and intimacy.

Love as Appraisal of Arousal Social psychologists Ellen Berscheid and Elaine Hatfield (Berscheid & Walster, 1978; Walster & Walster, 1978) define **romantic love** in terms of a state of intense physiological arousal and the cognitive appraisal of that arousal as love. The physiological arousal may be experienced as a pounding heart, sweaty palms, and butterflies in the stomach when one is in the presence of or thinking about one's love interest. Cognitive appraisal of the arousal means attributing it to some cause, such as fear or love. The perception that one has fallen in love is thus derived from several simultaneous events: (1) a state of intense physiological arousal that is connected with an appropriate love object (that is, a person, not an event like a rock concert), (2) a cultural setting that idealizes romantic love, and (3) the attribution of the arousal to feelings of love toward the person.

Styles of Love Some psychologists speak in terms of styles of love. Clyde and Susan Hendrick (1986) developed a love attitude scale that suggests the existence of six styles of love among university students. The following is a list of the styles. Each one is exemplified by statements similar to those on the original scale. As you can see, the styles owe a debt to the Greeks:

1. *Romantic love (eros)*: "My lover fits my ideal." "My lover and I were attracted to one another immediately."
2. *Game-playing love (ludus)*: "I keep my lover up in the air about my commitment." "I get over love affairs pretty easily."
3. *Friendship (storge, philia)*: "The best love grows out of an enduring friendship."
4. *Logical love (pragma)*: "I consider a lover's potential in life before committing myself." "I consider whether my lover will be a good parent."
5. *Possessive, excited love (mania)*: "I get so excited about my love that I cannot sleep." "When my lover ignores me, I get sick all over."
6. *Selfless love (agape)*: "I would do anything I can to help my lover." "My lover's needs and wishes are more important than my own."

Most people who are "in love" experience a number of these styles, but the Hendricks (1986) found some interesting gender differences in styles of love. University men are significantly more likely to develop game-playing and romantic love styles. University women are more apt to develop friendly, logical, and possessive love styles. (There were no gender differences in selfless love.) The Hendricks and their colleagues (1988) have also found that both members of a couple tend to experience the same kind of love style. They also showed that couples with romantic and selfless styles of love are more likely to remain together. A game-playing love style leads to unhappiness, however, and is one reason that relationships come to an end.

Sternberg's Triangular Theory of Love Psychologist Robert Sternberg (1986, 1987, 1988) offers a triangular theory of love. In his view there are three distinct components of love:

1. *Intimacy:* the experience of warmth toward another person that arises from feelings of closeness, bondedness, and connectedness to the other. Intimacy also involves the desire to give and receive emotional support and to share one's innermost thoughts with the other.
2. *Passion:* an intense romantic or sexual desire for another person, which is accompanied by physiological arousal.
3. *Decision/commitment:* a component of love that involves both short-term and long-term issues. In the short term there is the issue of deciding that one loves the other person. In the long term there is the issue of one's willingness to make a commitment to maintain the relationship through good times and bad. Decision and commitment need not go hand in hand. Although decision generally precedes commitment, some people become committed to a relationship before they even decide whether they love the other person. Others, however, never make a lasting commitment or openly acknowledge loving the other person.

According to Sternberg's model, love can be conceptualized in terms of a triangle in which each vertex represents one of these basic elements of love (see Figure 6.2). The way the components are balanced can be represented by the shape of the triangle. For example, a love in which all three components were equally balanced would be represented by an equilateral triangle, as in Figure 6.2.

Sternberg believes that couples are well matched if they possess corresponding levels of passion, intimacy, and commitment. Compatibility can be represented visually in terms of the congruence of the love triangles. Figure 6.3(A) shows a perfect match, in which the triangles are congruent. Figure 6.3(B) depicts a good match; the partners are similar in the three dimensions. Figure 6.3(C) shows a mismatch; major differences exist between the partners on all three components. Relationships may run aground when partners are mismatched. A relationship may fizzle, rather than sizzle, when one partner

http://www.tjhsst.edu/Psych/sternberg/
This site summarizes Sternberg's past and current work and provides links to other Sternberg-related pages.

"What's Your Love Story?" www.psychologytoday.com/htdocs/prod/PTOArticle/PTO-20000701-000035.ASP
An article by Robert J. Sternberg on the theory of love as a story.

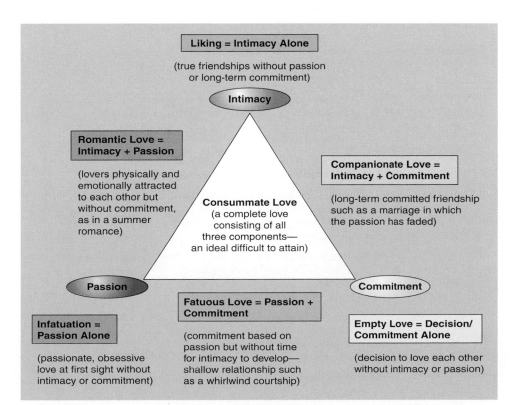

Figure 6.2. The Triangular Model of Love.

According to psychologist Robert Sternberg, love consists of three components, as shown by the vertices of this triangle. Various kinds of love consist of different combinations of these components. Romantic love, for example, consists of passion and intimacy. Consummate love—a state devoutly to be desired—consists of all three.

experiences more passion than the other, or when one wants a long-term commitment when the other's idea of commitment is to stay the night.

According to the Sternberg model, various combinations of the three elements of love characterize different types of love relationships, as shown in Table 6.2 (Sternberg, 1986, 1988). For example, *infatuation* (passionate love) is typified by strong sexual desire, but not by intimacy and commitment. The partners may each feel passionate love for the other, or such feelings may go unrequited.

Liking is very much like friendship. It consists of feelings of closeness and emotional warmth without passion or decision/commitment. Liking is not felt toward passing acquaintances. It is reserved for people to whom one feels close enough to share one's innermost feelings and thoughts. We sometimes develop these intimate relationships without making the commitment to maintaining a long-term relationship that typifies other types of love. Liking may develop into a passionate love, however, or into a more committed form of friendship (called *companionate love* in Sternberg's model).

Should lovers also be friends, or are lovers and friends the twain that never meet? Candy and Stretch's relationship lacked the quality most often associated with true friendship: the willingness to share confidences. Candy and Stretch were "in love" although they were far from friends. Friendship and passionate love do not necessarily overlap. There is nothing that prevents people in love from becoming good friends, however—perhaps even the best of friends. Sternberg's model recognizes that the intimacy we find in true friendships and the passion we find in love are blended in two forms of love—romantic love and consummate love. These love types differ along the dimension of decision/commitment, however.

A

Intimacy

Self — Other

Passion — Decision/Commitment

Perfectly matched involvements

B

Self — Other

Closely matched involvements

C

Other — Self

Severely mismatched involvements

Figure 6.3. Compatibility and Incompatibility, According to the Triangular Model of Love.

Compatibility in terms of Sternberg's types of love can be represented as triangles. Part A shows a perfect match, in which triangles are congruent. Part B depicts a good match; the partners are similar according to the three dimensions. Part C shows a mismatch. Major differences exist between the partners.

TABLE 6.2 Types of Love According to Sternberg's Triangular Model	
1. Nonlove	A relationship in which all three components of love are absent. Most of our personal relationships are of this type—casual interactions or acquaintances that do not involve any elements of love.
2. Liking	A loving experience with another person or friendship in which intimacy is present but passion and commitment are lacking.
3. Infatuation	A kind of "love at first sight" in which one experiences passionate desires for another person in the absence of both intimacy and decision/commitment components of love.
4. Empty love	A kind of love characterized by the decision (to love) and the commitment (to maintain the relationship) in the absence of either passion or intimacy. Stagnant relationships that no longer involve the emotional intimacy or physical attraction that once characterized them are of this type.
5. Romantic love	A loving experience characterized by the combination of passion and intimacy, but without decision/commitment components of love.
6. Companionate love	A kind of love that derives from the combination of intimacy and decision/commitment components of love. This kind of love often occurs in marriages in which passionate attraction between the partners has died down and has been replaced by a kind of committed friendship.
7. Fatuous love	The type of love associated with whirlwind romances and "quickie marriages" in which the passion and decision/commitment components of love are present, but intimacy is not.
8. Consummate love	The full or complete measure of love involving the combination of passion, intimacy, and decision/commitment. Many of us strive to attain this type of complete love in our romantic relationships. Maintaining it is often harder than achieving it.

Source: Adapted from Sternberg, 1988.

Consummate Love. *According to Sternberg, romantic love may develop into a more complete love, called consummate love, in which desire is accompanied by deep intimacy and commitment. Consummate love is the special ideal toward which many Westerners strive.*

Romantic love has both passion and intimacy but lacks commitment. Romantic love may burn brightly and then flicker out. Or it may develop into a more complete love, called *consummate love*, in which all three components flower. Desire is accompanied by a deeper intimacy and commitment. The flames of passion can be stoked across the years, even if they do not burn quite as brightly as they once did. Consummate love is most special, and certainly an ideal toward which many Westerners strive. In *empty love*, by contrast, there is naught but commitment. Neither the warm emotional embrace of intimacy nor the flame of passion exists. With empty love, one's lover is a person whom one tolerates and remains with because of a sense of duty.

Sometimes a love relationship has both passion and commitment but lacks intimacy. Sternberg calls this *fatuous (foolish) love*. Fatuous love is associated with whirlwind courtships that burn brightly but briefly as the partners come to the realization that they are not well matched. Intimacy can develop in such relationships, but couples who rush into marriage often find that the realities of marriage give the lie to their expectations.

In *companionate love*, finally, intimacy and commitment are strong, but passion is lacking. This form of love typifies long-term (so-called Platonic) friendships and marriages in which passion has ebbed but a deep and abiding friendship remains.

Although romantic love may become transformed into companionate love, the process by which this transformation takes place remains vague (Shaver et al., 1988). Companionate love need not be sexless or lacking in romance, however. Although passion may have ebbed, the giving and receiving of sexual pleasure can help strengthen bonds. Partners may feel that their sex lives have even become more deeply satisfying as they seek to please each other by practising what they have learned about each other's sexual needs and wants.

The balance among Sternberg's three aspects of love is likely to shift through the course of a relationship. A healthy dose of all three components—found in consummate love—typifies, for many of us, an ideal marriage. At the outset of marriage, passion may be strong but intimacy weak. Couples may be just getting to know each other's innermost thoughts and feelings. Time alone does not cause intimacy and commitment to grow, however. Some couples are able to peer into each other's deeper selves and form meaningful commitments at relatively early stages in their relationships. Yet some long-married couples may remain distant or waver in their commitment. Some couples experience only a faint flickering of passion early in the relationship. Then it becomes quickly extinguished. For some the flames of passion burn ever brightly. Yet many married couples find that passion tends to fade while intimacy and commitment grow stronger.

Knowing about these components of love may help couples avoid pitfalls. Couples who recognize that passion exerts a strong pull early in a relationship may be less likely to let passion rush them into marriage. Couples who recognize that it is normal for passions to fade may avoid assuming that their love is at an end when it may, in fact, be changing into a deeper, more intimate and committed form of love. This knowledge may also encourage couples to focus on finding ways of rekindling the embers of romance, rather than looking to escape at the first signs that the embers have cooled.

Researchers have tested some facets of the triangular model. One study reported mixed results. As the model would predict, married adults reported higher levels of commitment to their relationships than did unmarried adults (Acker & Davis, 1992). Yet the expected decline in passion over time was found only for women. Critics contend that Sternberg's model does not account for all the nuances and complexities of love (Murstein, 1988). The model tells us little, for example, about the *goals* of love or the *sources* of love. Sternberg himself has pointed out the limitations of his model. As he notes in the article "What's your love story?," his model does not address the question of "What makes a person the kind of lover they are?" (Sternberg, 2000). In fairness, however, Sternberg's model is a major contribution to the scientific study of love, which is only now beginning. Poets, philosophers, and theologians, by comparison, have been writing about love for millennia.

In this chapter we have discussed interpersonal attraction—the force that initiates social contact. In the next chapter we follow the development of social contacts into intimate relationships.

Applications

Coping with Loneliness

In this chapter we have explored feelings of attraction and love. Unfortunately, many people do not experience these feelings. Or, if they do, the feelings are not reciprocated. As a result, many people are lonely.

The causes of loneliness are many and complex. Lonely people tend to have several of the following characteristics:

1. *Lack of social skills.* Lonely people often lack the interpersonal skills needed to make friends or to cope with disagreements.
2. *Lack of interest in other people.*
3. *Lack of empathy.*
4. *Fear of rejection.* This fear is often connected with self-criticism of social skills and expectations of failure in relating to others (Schultz & Moore, 1984).
5. *Failure to disclose personal information to potential friends* (Solano et al., 1982).
6. *Cynicism about human nature* (e.g., seeing people as only out for themselves).
7. *Demanding too much too soon.* They perceive other people as cold and

unfriendly in the early stages of a relationship.
8. *General pessimism.* When we expect the worst, we often get... you guessed it.
9. *An external locus of control.* That is, they do not see themselves as capable of taking their lives into their own hands and achieving their goals.

Psychologists have helped people cope with loneliness by fostering more adaptive ways of thinking and behaving. Lonely people often have distorted views of other people. They may have one or two unfortunate experiences and jump to the conclusion that people are generally selfish and not worth the effort of getting involved. Let's face it: Some people are basically out for themselves, but the expectation that everyone is can perpetuate loneliness by motivating avoidance of social activities.

What can you do to deal with loneliness in your own life? We are all different, and the methods that might help one person may not aid another. But here is a list of suggestions (Rathus & Fichner-Rathus, 1994):

1. *Challenge your feelings of pessimism.* Adopt the attitude that things happen when you make them happen.
2. *Challenge your cynicism about human nature.* Yes, lots of people are selfish and not worth knowing, but if you assume that all people are like that, you can doom yourself to a lifetime of loneliness. Your task is to find people who possess the qualities that you value.
3. *Challenge the idea that failure in social relationships is awful and is thus a valid reason for giving up on them.* Sure, social rejection can be painful, but unless you happen to be George Clooney or Julia Roberts, you may not appeal to everyone. We must all learn to live with some rejection. But keep looking for the people who possess the qualities you value and who will find things of equal value in you.
4. *Follow the suggestions for improving your date-seeking skills spelled out in the Applications in Chapter 7.* Sit down at a table with people in the cafeteria, not off in a corner by

yourself. Smile and say hi to people who interest you. Practise opening lines for different occasions—and a few follow-up lines. Try them out in the mirror.

5. *Make numerous social contacts.* Join committees for student activities. Try intramural sports. Join social-action groups, such as environmental groups and community betterment groups. Join clubs, such as the photography club or the ski club. Get on the school yearbook or newspaper staff.

6. *Be assertive.* Express your genuine opinions.

7. *Become a good listener.* Ask people how they're doing. Ask them for their opinions about classes, politics, the campus events of the day. Then actually listen to what they have to say. Tolerate diverse opinions; remember that no two of us are identical in our outlooks. Maintain eye contact. Keep your face friendly. (No, you don't have to remain neutral and friendly if someone becomes insulting toward a religious or ethnic group.)

8. *Give people the chance to know you.* Exchange opinions and talk about your interests. Yes, you'll turn some people off—who doesn't?—but how else will you learn whether you and another person share common ground?

9. *Fight fair.* Friends will inevitably disappoint you, and you'll want to tell them about it. Do so, but fairly. You can start by asking if it's okay to be open about something. Then say, "I feel upset because you..." You can ask your friend if he or she realized that his or her behaviour upset you. Try to work together to find a way to avoid recurrences. Finish by thanking your friend for helping you resolve the problem.

10. *Remember that you're worthy of friends.* It's true—warts and all. None of us is perfect. We're all unique, but you may connect with more people than you imagine. Give people a chance.

11. *Use your college or university counselling centre.* Many thousands of students are lonely but don't know what to do about it. Others just cannot find the courage to approach others. Counselling centres are very familiar with the problem of loneliness, and you should consider them a valuable resource. You might even ask if there's a group at the centre for students seeking to improve their dating or social skills.

Summing Up

Attraction

Physical attractiveness is a major determinant of sexual attraction. In our culture, slenderness is in style. Both genders consider smiling faces more attractive. Socially dominant men, but not dominant women, are usually found attractive. Women place greater emphasis on such traits as vocational status and earning potential, whereas men give more consideration to physical attractiveness. Some evolutionary psychologists believe that evolutionary forces favour such gender differences in preferred traits because these traits offer reproductive advantages. Both genders value personal traits such as kindness, understanding, and intelligence.

According to the **matching hypothesis,** people tend to develop romantic relationships with people who are similar to themselves in attractiveness. **Similarity in attitudes and tastes** is a strong contributor to attraction, friendships, and love relationships. Through **reciprocity** of positive words and actions, neutral or mild feelings may be stoked into feelings of attraction.

Love

In our culture, we are brought up to idealize the concept of romantic love. The **Greeks** had four concepts related to the modern meanings of love: *storge, agape, philia,* and *eros.* **Western culture** has a long tradition of idealizing the concept of **romantic love**. Most people in Canada see romantic love as a prerequisite to marriage. Early in a relationship, infatuation and more enduring forms of romantic love may be indistinguishable.

Researchers are now applying the **scientific method** to the study of love. Berscheid and Hatfield define romantic love in terms of intense physiological arousal and cognitive appraisal of that arousal as love. Hendrick and Hendrick suggest that there are six styles of love among university students: romantic love, game-playing love, friendship, logical love, possessive love, and selfless love. Sternberg suggests that there are three distinct components of love: intimacy, passion, and commitment. Various combinations of these components typify different kinds of love. Romantic love is characterized by the combination of passion and intimacy.

Chapter Quiz

1. Which of the following is the key factor in choosing dating partners?
   - (a) Attitudinal similarity.
   - (b) Physical appearance.
   - (c) Reciprocity of feelings.
   - (d) Propinquity.

2. Which of the following is found universally attractive in women?
   - (a) A good complexion.
   - (b) Slenderness.
   - (c) Plumpness.
   - (d) Self-assertive behaviour.

3. Which of the following statements about body shape is true of university students?
   - (a) Men generally think that they are too heavy.
   - (b) Men prefer women to be more slender than the women imagine.
   - (c) Women see their own body shapes as being close to ideal.
   - (d) Women prefer men to be more slender than the men imagine.

4. What is the connection between names and perceptions of attractiveness?
   - (a) There is no connection between names and perceptions of attractiveness.
   - (b) Women with unusual names are found to be most attractive.
   - (c) Women with popular names are found to be most attractive.
   - (d) Women with old-fashioned names are found to be most attractive.

5. The central motive for seeking "matches" seems to be
   - (a) desire for compatibility.
   - (b) reciprocity of feelings.
   - (c) the attempt to avoid cognitive dissonance.
   - (d) fear of rejection by more appealing people.

6. Loving attachment, deep friendship, or nonsexual affection describes the concept of
   - (a) agape.
   - (b) eros.
   - (c) storge.
   - (d) philia.

7. _____ is a state of intense absorption in or focusing on another person.
   - (a) Intimacy
   - (b) Infatuation
   - (c) Romantic love
   - (d) Companionate love

8. People who say "I keep my lover up in the air about my commitment," or "I get over love affairs pretty easily" appear to be "in" the _____ style of love.
   - (a) game-playing
   - (b) romantic
   - (c) logical
   - (d) possessive

9. Which of the following is NOT one of Sternberg's components of love?
   - (a) Passion.
   - (b) Mania.
   - (c) Intimacy.
   - (d) Decision/commitment.

10. According to Sternberg, romantic love involves
    - (a) passion and intimacy.
    - (b) ludus and mania.
    - (c) eros and storge.
    - (d) agape and philia.

Chapter 7

Relationships, Intimacy, and Communication

Did You Know That...

- Small talk is a very important "audition" for the formation of a relationship?
- Married people are most likely to have met their spouses through mutual friends?
- It is useful to practise opening lines when you want to develop a relationship?
- You should be careful not to disclose too much too soon with new people?
- People can have intimate relationships without being sexually intimate?
- Men do not naturally know what is pleasing to a woman?
- If you are criticized, the best course may be to acknowledge the criticism and avoid retaliation?
- Disagreements are not necessarily fatal to a relationship?

Will you, won't you, will you, won't you, will you join the dance?
(LEWIS CARROLL, *Alice in Wonderland*)

No man is an island, entire of itself.
(JOHN DONNE)

Canadian love, Canadian love, it's forty below or it's ninety above.
(MARIE-LYNN HAMMOND, from the song "Canadian Love" on the CD *Impromptu*)

In this chapter we first define the stages that lead to intimacy in relationships. We see that not all relationships achieve this level of interrelatedness, even some supposedly deep and permanent relationships such as marriage. Finally, we discuss the ways that communication contributes to relationships and sexual satisfaction, and we enumerate ways of enhancing communication skills.

The ABC(DE)'s of Romantic Relationships

Social-exchange theory The view that the development of a relationship reflects the unfolding of social exchanges—that is, the rewards and costs of maintaining the relationship as opposed to ending it.

ABCDE model Levinger's view, which approaches romantic relationships in terms of five stages: attraction, building, continuation, deterioration, and ending.

Romantic relationships, like people, undergo stages of development. According to **social-exchange theory**, the development reflects the unfolding of social exchanges, which involve the rewards and costs of maintaining the relationship as opposed to dissolving it. During each stage, positive factors sway partners toward maintaining and enhancing their relationship. Negative factors incline them toward letting it deteriorate and end (Karney & Bradbury, 1995).

George Levinger (1980) proposes an **ABCDE model** to describe the stages of romantic relationships: (1) Attraction, (2) Building, (3) Continuation, (4) Deterioration, and (5) Ending.

The A's—Attraction

Attraction occurs when two people become aware of each other and find one another appealing or enticing. We may find ourselves attracted to an enchanting person "across a crowded room," in a nearby office, or in a new class. We may meet others through blind dates, introductions by mutual friends, computer match-ups, or by "accident." Initial feelings of attraction are largely based on visual impressions, though we may also form initial impressions by overhearing people speak or hearing others talk about them.

According to one study (Michael et al., 1994), married people are most likely to have met their spouses through mutual friends (35%) or by self-introductions (32%) (see Figure 7.1). Other sources of introductions are family members (15%) and co-workers, classmates, or neighbours (13%). Mutual friends and self-introductions are also the most common ways of meeting for unmarried couples (Michael et al., 1994).

eMOOtions: Developing Relationships in Cyberspace
www.utm.edu/~moo/
eMOOtion.shtml
This site examines the stages of forming a relationship in cyberspace with reference to George Levinger's ABCDE model.

The B's—Building

Building a relationship follows initial attraction. Factors that motivate us to try to build relationships include similarity in the level of physical attractiveness, similarity in attitudes, and mutual liking and positive evaluations. Factors that may deter us from trying to build relationships include lack of physical appeal, dissimilarity in attitudes, and negative mutual evaluations.

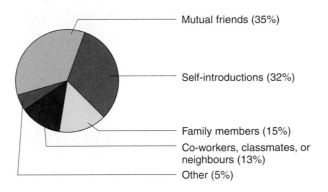

Figure 7.1. How Married People Met Their Partners.

(*Source:* Michael et al., 1994.)

Mutual friends (35%)
Self-introductions (32%)
Family members (15%)
Co-workers, classmates, or neighbours (13%)
Other (5%)

Not-So-Small Talk: An Audition for Building a Relationship In the early stages of building a relationship, we tend to look for overlapping attitudes and interests, and we check out our feelings of attraction. At this point the determination of whether to strive to develop the relationship is often made, at least in part, on the basis of **small talk**. Small talk allows an exchange of information but stresses breadth of topic coverage rather than in-depth discussion. Engaging in small talk may seem phony, but premature self-disclosure of intimate information may repel the other person, as we shall see.

> **Small talk** A superficial kind of conversation that allows exchange of information but stresses breadth of topic coverage rather than in-depth discussion.

Small talk is a trial balloon for friendship. Successful small talk encourages a couple to venture beneath the surface. At a cocktail party, people may flit about from person to person, exchanging small talk, but now and then a couple finds common ground and pairs off.

The "Opening Line": How Do You Get Things Started? One kind of small talk is the greeting, or opening line. We usually precede verbal greetings with eye contact and decide to begin talking if eye contact is reciprocated. Avoidance of eye contact may mean that the person is shy, but it could also signify lack of interest. If you would like to progress from initial attraction to surface contact, try a smile and direct eye contact. If the eye contact is reciprocated, choose an opening line, or greeting:

Verbal salutes, such as "Good morning."

Personal inquiries, such as "How are you doing?"

Compliments, such as "I like your outfit."

References to your mutual surroundings, such as "What do you think of that painting?" or "This is a nice apartment, isn't it?"

References to people or events outside the immediate setting, such as "How do you like this weather we've been having?"

References to the other person's behaviour, such as "I couldn't help noticing you were sitting alone," or "I see you out on this track every Saturday morning."

References to your own behaviour, or to yourself, such as "Hi, my name is Allan Felix" (feel free to use your own name, if you prefer).

The simple "Hi" or "Hello" is very useful. A friendly glance followed by a cheerful hello ought to give you some idea of whether the attraction is reciprocated. If the hello is returned with a friendly smile and inviting eye contact, follow it up with another greeting, such as a reference to your surroundings, the other person's behaviour, or your name.

Exchanging "Name, Rank, and Serial Number" Early exchanges are likely to include name, occupation, marital status, and hometown. This has been likened to exchanging "name, rank, and serial number" with the other person. Each person seeks a sociological profile of the other to discover common ground that may provide a basis for pursuing the conversation. An unspoken rule seems to be at work: "If I provide you with some information about myself, you will reciprocate by giving me an equal amount of information about yourself. Or... 'I'll tell you my hometown if you tell me yours'" (Knapp, 1978, p. 114). If the other person is unresponsive, she or he may not be attracted to you, and you may wish to try someone else. But you may also be awkward in your approach or perhaps turn the other person off by disclosing too much about yourself at once. The *Applications* box below suggests ways of improving date-seeking skills.

Applications

How to Improve Date-Seeking Skills

All right, you know that Mr. or Ms. Right exists. So what do you do? How do you go about making a date?

You can enhance social skills, including date-seeking skills, through the technique of successive approximations. That means practising a series of tasks that are graded in difficulty. You will gain skills and self-confidence as you tackle smaller challenges and progress to more difficult ones. Friends can help you polish your date-seeking skills. They can role-play the prospective date and give honest feedback about your behaviour.

Here is a series of tasks that may help you sharpen your skills. After you achieve success with the easier ones, move on to the more challenging practice levels.

Easy Practice Level

Select a person with whom you are friendly, but one whom you have no desire to date. Practise making small talk about the weather, new films, TV shows, concerts, museum shows, political events, and personal hobbies.

Select a person you might have some interest in dating. Smile when you pass this person at work, school, or elsewhere, and say "Hi." Engage in this activity with other people of both genders to increase your skills at greeting others.

Speak into your mirror, using behaviour rehearsal and role playing.

Pretend you are in the process of sitting next to the person you would like to date, say, at lunch or in the laundry room. Say "Hello" with a broad smile, and introduce yourself. Work on the smile until it looks inviting and genuine. Make some comment about the food or the setting—the cafeteria, the office, whatever. Use a family member or confidant to obtain feedback about the effectiveness of your smile, tone of voice, posture, and choice of words.

Medium Practice Level

Sit down next to the person you want to date, and engage in small talk. If you are in a classroom, talk about a homework assignment, the seating arrangement, or the instructor (be kind). If you are at work, talk about the building or some recent interesting event in the neighbourhood. Ask your intended date how he or she feels about the situation. If you are at a group meeting, such as Parents Without Partners, tell the other person that you are there for the first time and ask for advice on how to relate to the group.

Engage in small talk about the weather and local events. Channel the conversation into an exchange of personal information. Give your "name, rank, and serial number"—who you are, your major field or your occupation, where you're from, why or how you came to the school or company. The other person is likely to reciprocate and provide equivalent information. Ask how he or she feels about the class, place of business, city, hometown, and so on.

Rehearse asking the person out

before your mirror, a family member, or a confidant. You may wish to ask the person out for a cup of coffee or to a film. It is somewhat less threatening to ask someone out to a gathering at which "some of us will be getting together." Or you may rehearse asking the person to accompany you to a cultural event, such as an exhibition at a museum or a concert—it's "sort of" a date, but also less anxiety inducing.

Target Behaviour Level

Ask the person out on a date in a manner consistent with your behaviour rehearsal. If the person says he or she has a previous engagement or can't make it, you may wish to say something like, "That's too bad," or "I'm sorry you can't make it," and add something like, "Perhaps another time." You should be able to get a feeling for whether the person you asked out was just seeking an excuse or has a genuine interest in you and really could not accept the specific invitation.

Before asking the date out again, pay attention to his or her apparent comfort level when you return to small talk on a couple of occasions. If there is still a chance, the person should smile and return your eye contact. The other person may also offer you an invitation. In any event, if you are turned down twice, do not ask a third time. And don't make a catastrophe out of the refusal. Look up. Note that the roof hasn't fallen in. The birds are still chirping in the trees. You are still paying taxes. Then give someone else a chance to appreciate your fine qualities.

Self-disclosure The revelation of personal, perhaps intimate, information.

Self-Disclosure: You Tell Me and I'll Tell You... Carefully

Opening up, or **self-disclosure**, is central to building intimate relationships. But just what sort of information is safe to disclose upon first meeting someone? If you refuse to go beyond the

A World of Diversity

Self-Disclosure: East May Be East and West May Be West, But Here, Perhaps, the Twain Do (Almost) Meet

Research suggests that we should refrain from disclosing certain types of information too rapidly if we want to make a good impression. In one study, confederates of the experimenters (Wortman et al., 1976) engaged in 10-minute conversations with study participants. Some confederates were "early disclosers," who shared intimate information early. Others, "late disclosers," shared intimate information toward the end of the conversation only. In either case, the information was identical. Study participants then rated the disclosers. Early disclosers were rated less mature, secure, well adjusted, and genuine than the late disclosers. Study participants also preferred

to continue relationships with the late disclosers. We may say we value "openness" and "honesty" in our relationships, but it may be a social mistake to open up too soon.

A Japanese study showed similar results. Japanese college students rated actors in a mock conversation more favourably when they disclosed less about themselves (Nakanishi, 1986). Chinese people also responded negatively to others who disclosed early.

Despite such cross-cultural similarities, self-disclosure in general may be viewed less favourably in Eastern cultures. In Japanese society, for example, self-disclosure is often seen as inappropriate in social relationships (Nakanishi, 1986). Not surprisingly,

researchers find that people in the United States tend to disclose much more about themselves in social interactions than do the Japanese.

Do You Dare Let It All Hang Out? *Despite the common belief that one should be honest and open, research suggests that people who self-disclose too much too soon are seen as socially inept. Researchers find that people in Japan tend to disclose less personal information in social interactions than people in the United States do.*

basics, you may look uninterested or as if you are trying to keep things under wraps. If, on the other hand, you spill out the fact that you have a terrible rash on your thigh, it's likely that you have disclosed too much too soon.

If the contact provided by small talk and initial self-disclosure has been mutually rewarding, partners in a relationship tend to develop deeper feelings of liking for each other (Collins & Miller, 1994). Self-disclosure may continue to build gradually through the course of a relationship as partners come to trust each other enough to share confidences and more intimate feelings.

Gender Differences in Self-Disclosure

A woman complains to a friend: "He never opens up to me. It's like living with a stone wall." Women commonly declare that men are loath to express their feelings (Tannen, 1990). Researchers find that men tend to be less willing to disclose their feelings, perhaps in adherence to the traditional "strong and silent" male stereotype (see Chapter 5).

Yet gender differences in self-disclosure tend to be small. Overall, researchers find that women are only slightly more revealing about themselves than men (Dindia & Allen, 1992). We should thus be careful not to rush to the conclusion that men are always more "tight-lipped." The belief that there are large gender differences in self-disclosure appears to be something of a myth.

Stereotypes are also changing—somewhat. We now see depictions in the media of the "new" man as someone who is able to express feelings without compromising his masculinity. We shall have to wait to see whether this "new" sensitive image replaces the rugged, reticent stereotype, or is a passing fancy.

Mutuality: When the "We," Not the "I's," Have It

When feelings of attraction and the establishment of common ground lead a couple to regard themselves as "we"—not just two "I's" who happen to be in the same place at the same time—they have attained what Levinger terms a state of **mutuality**. The development of mutuality favours the continuation and further deepening of the relationship.

Mutuality A phase in building a relationship in which members of a couple come to regard themselves as "we," no longer two "I's" who happen to be in the same place at the same time.

The C's—Continuation

Once a relationship has been established, the couple embarks upon the stage of continuation. Factors that encourage continuation include seeking ways to introduce variety and maintain interest (such as trying out new sexual practices and social activities), showing evidence of caring and positive evaluation (such as sending birthday or Valentine's Day cards), showing lack of jealousy, perceiving fairness in the relationship, and experiencing mutual feelings of general satisfaction.

Factors in this stage that can throw the relationship into a downward spiral include boredom (e.g., falling into a rut in leisure activities, sexual practices, etc.), displaying evidence of negative evaluation (such as bickering, and forgetting anniversaries and other important dates or pretending that they do not exist), perceiving a lack of fairness in the relationship (such as one partner's always deciding how the couple will spend their free time), or experiencing feelings of jealousy and general dissatisfaction.

Jealousy

> O! beware, my lord, of jealousy;
> It is the green-ey'd monster...
>
> (WILLIAM SHAKESPEARE, *Othello*)

Youth, Sexual Jealousy, and Abuse
www.nohurt.org/
edition%203/youth.html
An interview with Rosemary Gartner, Director of the Centre for Criminology at the University of Toronto, discussing reasons for the high rate of partner abuse among young women 18 to 24 years of age.

Thus was Othello, the Moor of Venice, warned of jealousy in the Shakespearean play that bears his name. Yet Othello could not control his feelings and slew his beloved Desdemona. The English poet John Dryden labelled jealousy a "tyrant of the mind." Anthropologists find evidence of jealousy in all cultures, although it may vary in amount and intensity across and within cultures. It appears to be more common and intense among cultures with a stronger machismo tradition, in which men are expected to display their virility.

Sexual jealousy is aroused when we suspect that an intimate relationship is threatened by a rival. Lovers can become jealous when others show sexual interest in their partners or when their partners show an interest (even a casual or nonsexual interest) in another. Jealousy can impair a relationship and produce feelings of mistrust of one's partner or toward potential rivals.

Sexual jealousy may be associated with a range of negative emotions, including fear of losing the loved one and anger toward the rival, the loved one, or both. Jealousy can be a form of emotional abuse in a relationship. In a 1999 Statistics Canada survey, a sample of men and women were asked if their partners' jealousy led to controlling behaviour that prevented them from talking to other men or women. Eleven percent of both men and women reported such behaviour (Statistics Canada, 2000c). Research on adolescent dating relationships has shown that jealousy can precipitate emotional and physical abuse. Unfortunately, many teenagers also believe that jealousy in a partner is proof of love rather than an indication of a potential for abuse (Canadian Association for Adolescent Health, 2004). In extreme cases jealousy can cause depression or give rise to spouse abuse, suicide, or, as with Othello, murder. Statistics on family violence in Canada reveal that in 21% of all spousal homicides jealousy was cited as the motivating factor (Statistics Canada, 2002).

How common is sexual jealousy? Common. In a survey of 103 women at various stages of involvement in an intimate relationship, three out of four reported feelings of jealousy (Pines & Aronson, 1983). Fifty-four percent described themselves as jealous. Women who were in non-monogamous relationships or were dissatisfied with their relationships were more likely to describe themselves as jealous. A typical situation that prompted jealousy was a party at which the woman's partner spent time talking to, or dancing or flirting with, other women.

What causes jealousy? In some cases, people become mistrustful of their current partners because their former partners had cheated. Jealousy may also derive from low self-esteem or a lack of self-confidence. People with low self-esteem may experience sexual jealousy because they become overly dependent on their partners. They may also fear that they will not be able to find another partner if their present lover leaves.

Jealousy. *Sexual jealousy may be associated with a range of negative emotions, including fear of losing the loved one and anger toward the rival, the loved one, or both.*

White (1981) has concluded from his research on jealousy that feelings of inadequacy lead to jealousy in women. In men, the reverse seems to be the case. For men, that is, feelings of jealousy tend to give rise to feelings of inadequacy. It is as if jealousy leads them to question whether they are worthy of their partners' affections. For both men and women, however, feelings of jealousy can lead to perceiving anyone as a rival, which can make them continually mistrustful.

Unfortunately many lovers—including many college and university students—play jealousy games. They let their partners know that they are attracted to other people. They flirt openly and even manufacture tales to make their partners pay more attention to them, to test the relationship, to inflict pain, or to take revenge for a partner's disloyalty.

The D's—Deterioration

Deterioration is the fourth stage of a relationship. It is not a stage that we seek, and is certainly not inevitable. Factors that can deter or slow deterioration include putting time and energy into the relationship, striving to cultivate the relationship, and showing patience—for example, giving the relationship a reasonable opportunity to improve. Factors that foster deterioration include failure to invest time and energy in the relationship, deciding to put an end to it, or simply permitting deterioration to proceed unchecked.

A relationship begins to deteriorate when one or both partners deem the relationship to be less enticing or rewarding than it had been. Couples who work to maintain and enhance their relationships may find that they become stronger and more meaningful.

Active and Passive Responses to Deterioration
When partners perceive their relationship to be deteriorating, they can respond actively or passively. Active responses include trying to enhance the relationship (such as working to improve communication skills, negotiating differences, or seeking professional help) or deciding to end the relationship. A passive response is doing nothing and waiting for something to happen. People can sit back passively and wait for the relationship to improve on its own (once in a great while, it does) or for the relationship to deteriorate to the point where it ends. ("Don't look at me; these things happen.")

It is irrational (and damaging to a relationship) to assume that suitable relationships require no investment of time and effort. No two of us are matched perfectly. Unless one member of a couple does double duty as a doormat, inevitable frictions will surface. When problems arise, it is better to work to resolve them than to act as if they don't exist and hope that they will disappear of their own accord.

The E's—Ending

Ending is the fifth and final stage of a relationship. Like deterioration, it is not inevitable. Various factors can prevent a deteriorating relationship from ending. For example, people who continue to find some sources of satisfaction, who are committed to maintaining the relationship, or who believe that they will eventually be able to overcome their problems are more likely to do what they must to prevent the collapse.

According to social-exchange theory, relationships draw to a close when negative forces hold sway—when the partners find little satisfaction in the affiliation, when the barriers to leaving the relationship are low (that is, the social, religious, and financial constraints are manageable), and especially when alternative partners are available (Karney & Bradbury, 1995).

The swan song of a relationship is not always a bad thing. When people are definitely incompatible, and when genuine attempts to preserve the relationship have failed, ending the relationship can offer each partner a chance for happiness with someone else.

Intimacy

Intimacy Feelings of closeness and connectedness that are marked by sharing of inmost thoughts and feelings.

Intimacy involves feelings of emotional closeness and connectedness with another person and the desire to share each other's inmost thoughts and feelings. Intimate relationships are also characterized by attitudes of mutual trust, caring, and acceptance.

Sternberg's (1986) triangular theory of love (see Chapter 6) regards intimacy as a basic component of romantic love. But people can be intimate and not in love, at least not in romantic love. Close friends and family members become emotionally intimate when they care deeply for each other and share their private feelings and experiences. It is not necessary for people to be *sexually* intimate to have an emotionally intimate relationship. Nor does sexual intimacy automatically produce emotional intimacy. People who are sexually involved may still fail to touch each other's lives in emotionally intimate ways. Even couples who fall in love may not be able to forge an intimate relationship because of unwillingness or inability to exchange inmost thoughts and feelings. Sometimes people share greater emotional intimacy with friends than with their spouses.

Let us now consider some of the factors involved in building and maintaining intimate relationships.

Knowing and Liking Yourself

Some social scientists suggest that an initial step toward intimacy with others is getting to know and like yourself. By coming to know and value yourself, you identify your inmost feelings and needs and develop the security to share them.

Trusting and Caring

Two of the most important ingredients of an intimate relationship are trust and caring. When trust exists in a relationship, partners feel secure that disclosing intimate feelings will not lead to ridicule, rejection, or other kinds of harm. Trust usually builds gradually, as partners learn that it is safe to share confidences. Caring is an emotional bond that allows intimacy to develop. In caring relationships, partners seek to gratify each other's needs and interests.

Tenderness is expressed by putting one's arm around a partner's shoulder to offer support, or by verbalizations of love, caring, and appreciation. In romantic relationships, tenderness also takes the form of kissing, hugging, cuddling, and holding hands.

Being Honest

Since intimacy involves the sharing of one's inmost thoughts and feelings, honesty is a core feature of intimacy. Without honesty, partners see only each other's facades. A person need not, however, be an "open book" to develop and maintain intimacy. Some aspects of experience are kept even from one's most intimate partners, for they may be too embarrassing or threatening to reveal

Building Intimacy. Intimate couples share each other's inmost thoughts and feelings. Intimacy also involves mutual trust, caring, and acceptance.

(Kammeyer et al., 1990). For example, we would not expect partners to disclose every passing sexual fantasy.

Intimate relationships thus usually involve a balance in which some things are revealed and others are not. Total honesty could devastate a relationship. It would not be reasonable, for example, to expect intimate partners to divulge the details of past sexual experiences. The recipient may wonder: "Why is Kimball telling me this? Am I as good a lover as Theresa? Is Kimball still in love with Theresa? What else did Kimball do with Theresa?" Discretion thus also buttresses intimate relationships. Honesty does not require revealing every detail. Nor is intimacy established by brutal criticism, even if it is honest.

Making a Commitment

Have you ever noticed that people may open up to strangers on airplanes or trains, yet find it hard to talk openly with people to whom they are closest? An intimate relationship involves more than the isolated act of baring one's soul to a stranger. Truly intimate relationships are marked by commitment or resolve to maintain the relationship through thick and thin. When we open up to strangers on a plane, we know it is unlikely that we will have to face them again.

This does not mean that intimate relationships require indefinite or lifelong commitments. A commitment, however, carries an obligation that the couple will work to overcome problems in the relationship rather than run for the exit at the first sign of trouble.

Maintaining Individuality When the *I* Becomes *We*

In committed relationships, a delicate balance exists between individuality and mutuality. In healthy unions, a strong sense of togetherness does not eradicate individuality. Partners in such relationships remain free to be themselves. Neither seeks to dominate or submerge himself or herself into the personality of the other. Each partner maintains individual interests, likes and dislikes, needs and goals.

Communicating

Good communication is another hallmark of an intimate relationship. Partners are able to share their most personal thoughts and feelings clearly and honestly. Communication is a two-way street. It embraces sending and receiving messages. The good communicator is thus a skilled listener as well as a clear speaker (Tannen, 1990). We generally associate communication with talk, which involves the use of verbal messages to convey a thought or a feeling. Through talk, the speaker *encodes* a thought or a feeling into words. The listener *decodes* the words to extract the meaning of the message.

Problems in Verbal Communication Problems in verbal communication can arise at several levels:

1. *The speaker may use words differently than the listener, leading to misunderstandings or miscommunication.* For example, the speaker might say, "You look really cute tonight." The listener might object, saying, "You think I look *cute*? What's wrong with the way I look?" The speaker protests, "No, I didn't mean it that way. I meant you look good. Yes, good."

2. *The speaker's words may not match his or her tone of voice, facial expression, or body gestures.* For example, the speaker says, "I *don't mind* if we visit your mother this weekend." But if the tone of voice is sharp or the speaker frowns or shrugs, the listener may conclude that the speaker is not really willing to visit. The listener is particularly likely to place greater weight on *how* something is said rather than on *what* is said when the comment is ambivalent, as in this example, rather than a clear statement such as "I *want* to visit your mother."

How Are Your Communication Skills? **www.bccf.bc.ca/learn/ coup_quiz.html** A questionnaire from BC Council for Families designed to indicate and comment on communication habits.

3. *The speaker may not be able to put into words what he or she truly means or feels.* Sometimes we grasp for words to express our feelings, but they do not come, or those that do come miss the mark.

Nonverbal Communication: The Body Speaks

Though the spoken word is a primary form of communication, we often express our feelings through nonverbal channels as well, such as by tone of voice, gestures, body posture, and facial expressions (Tannen, 1990). People also accentuate the meaning of their words through gestures, raising or lowering their voices, or using a sterner or softer tone of voice.

Nonverbal communication is used not only to accentuate the spoken word, but also to directly express feelings. We are sometimes better able to convey our feelings through body language than by the use of words. A touch or a gaze into someone's eyes may express more about our feelings than words can. Parents express feelings of tenderness and caring toward infants by hugging, holding, and caressing them, and by speaking in a gentle and soothing tone of voice, even though the babies cannot yet grasp the meaning of the words.

Let us examine some aspects of nonverbal communication:

On "Being Uptight" and "Hanging Loose" The ways that people carry themselves offer cues about their feelings and potential actions. People who are emotionally "uptight" often stand or sit rigidly and straight-backed. People who feel more relaxed literally "hang loose."

People who face us and lean toward us are in effect saying that they like us or care about what we are saying. If we overhear a conversation between a couple and see that the woman is leaning toward the man, but he is leaning back and playing with his hair, we tend to infer that he is not accepting what she is saying or has lost interest.

Touching Touching is a powerful form of communication. Women are more apt than men to touch the people with whom they interact. When touching suggests too much intimacy, however, it can be annoying. Touching may also establish "property rights" over one's partner. People may touch their partners in public or hold their hands, not as a sign of affection, but as a signal to others that their partners are taken and that others should keep a respectful distance. Similarly, the wearing of an engagement or wedding ring signals unavailability.

Gazing and Staring: The Look of Love? We gather information about the motives, feelings, and attitudes of others through eye contact. In Western culture, looking other people "squarely in the eye"—at least among men—is positively valued. People who do so appear self-assertive, direct, and candid. When people look away, they may be perceived as shy, deceitful, or depressed. In some Asian cultures, however, looking other people directly in the eye may seem an aggressive invasion.

Unaggressive gazing into another person's eyes—especially the eyes of a person whom one considers attractive—can create deep feelings of intimacy in our culture. In a laboratory study, couples who had just met were instructed to gaze into each other's eyes for two minutes. Afterwards, many reported experiencing feelings of passion (Kellerman et al., 1989). Is this what is meant by "the look of love"?

All in all, there are many ways in which we communicate with others through verbal and nonverbal channels. Let us now look at ways in which partners can learn to communicate better with each other, especially about sex. Many couples, even couples who are able to share deepest thoughts and feelings, may flounder at communicating their sexual needs and preferences. Couples who have lived together for decades may know each other's tastes in food, music, and movies about as well as they know their own but still be hesitant to share their sexual likes and dislikes (Havemann & Lehtinen, 1990). They may also be reluctant, for fear of opening wounds in the relationship, to exchange their feelings about other aspects of their relationship, including each other's habits, appearance, and gender-stereotypical attitudes.

Communication Skills for Enhancing Relationships and Sexual Relations

Marital counsellors and sex therapists might be as busy as the proverbial Maytag repairman if more couples communicated with each other about their sexual feelings. Unfortunately, when it comes to sex, talk may be the most overlooked four-letter word.

Many couples suffer for years because one or both partners are unwilling to speak up. Or problems arise when one partner misinterprets the other. One partner might interpret the other's groans or grimaces of pleasure as signs of pain and pull back during sex, leaving the other frustrated. Improved communication may be no panacea, but it helps. Clear communication can take the guesswork out of relationships, avert misunderstandings, relieve resentments and frustrations, and increase both sexual and general satisfaction with the relationship.

Common Difficulties in Sexual Communication

Why is it so difficult for couples to communicate about sex? Here are some possibilities:

On "Making Whoopee"—Is Sex Talk Vulgar? Vulgarity, like beauty, is to some degree in the eye of the beholder. One couple's vulgarity may be another couple's love talk. Some people may maintain a Victorian belief that any talk about sex is not fit for mixed company, even between intimate partners. Sex, that is, is something you may do, but not something to be talked about. Other couples may be willing in principle to talk about sex, but find the reality difficult because of the lack of an agreeable common language.

How, for example, are they to refer to their genitals or to sexual activities? One partner may prefer to use coarse four-letter (or five-letter) words to refer to them. The other might prefer more clinical terms. A partner who prefers slang for the sexual organs might be regarded by the other as vulgar or demeaning. (But as the forbidden fruit is often the sweetest, some people feel sexually aroused when they or their partners "talk dirty.") One who uses clinical terms, such as *fellatio* or *coitus*, might be regarded as, well, clinical. Some couples try to find a common verbal ground, one that is not vulgar at one extreme, or clinical at the other. They might speak, for example, of "doing it" rather than "engaging in sexual intercourse." Or they might speak of "kissing me down there" rather than practising fellatio or cunnilingus.

In some cases of gross mismatch in partners' choices for the language of love, the differences run much deeper than choice of words.

On Irrational Beliefs Many couples also harbour irrational beliefs about relationships and sex, such as the notion that people should somehow know what their partners want, without having to ask. The common misconception that people should know what pleases their partners undercuts communication. Men, in particular, seem burdened with the stereotype that they should have a natural expertise at sex. Women may feel it is "unladylike" to talk openly about their sexual needs and feelings. Both partners may hold the idealized romantic notion that "love is all you need" to achieve sexual happiness. But such knowledge does not arise from instinct or love. It is learned—or it remains unknown.

A related irrational belief is that "my partner will read my mind." We may erroneously assume that if our partners truly loved us, they would somehow know what types of sexual stimulation we desire. Unfortunately, or fortunately, others cannot read our minds. We must assume the responsibility for communicating our preferences.

Some people communicate more effectively than others, perhaps because they are more sensitive to others' needs or because their parents served as good models of communicators. But communication skills can be acquired at any time. Learning takes time and work, but the following guidelines should prove helpful. These skills can also improve communication in areas of intimate relationships other than the sexual.

Getting Started

How do you bring up tough topics? Here are some ideas.

Talking About Talking You can start by talking about talking. You can inform your partner that it is difficult for you to talk about problems and conflicts: "You know, I've always found it awkward to find a way of bringing things up," or, "You know, I think other people have an easier time than I do when it comes to talking about some things." You can allude to troublesome things that happened in the past when you attempted to resolve conflicts. This approach encourages your partner to invite you to proceed.

Broaching the topic of sex is perhaps the most difficult step in communicating with your partner. Couples who gab endlessly about their finances, their children, their work, and so on, suddenly clam up when sex comes up. So it may be helpful for you and your partner to first agree to talk about talking about sex. You can begin by admitting that it is hard or embarrassing for you to talk about sex. You can say that your sexual relationship is important to you and that you want to do everything you can to enhance it. Gently probe your partner's willingness to set aside time to talk about sex, preferably when you can dim the lights and not be interrupted.

The "right time" may be when you are both relaxed, rested, and not pressed for time. The "right place" can be any place where you can enjoy privacy and go undisturbed. Sex talk need not be limited to the bedroom. Couples may feel more comfortable talking about sex over dinner, when cuddling on the sofa, or when just relaxing together.

Requesting Permission to Bring Up a Topic Another possibility is to request permission to raise an issue. You can say something like this: "There's something on my mind. Do you have a few minutes? Is now a good time to tell you about it?" Or you can say, "There's something that we need to talk about, but I'm not sure how to bring it up. Can you help me with it?"

Giving Your Partner Permission to Say Something That Might Be Upsetting to You You can tell your partner that it is okay to point out ways in which you can become a more effective lover. For example, you can say, "I know that you don't want to hurt my feelings, but I wonder if I'm doing anything that you'd rather I didn't do?"

Active Listening. Effective communication requires listening to the other person's side. We can listen actively rather than passively by maintaining eye contact and ashowing that we understand the other person's feelings and ideas.

Listening to the Other Side

Skilled listening involves skills such as active listening, paraphrasing, the use of reinforcement, and valuing your partner even when the two of you disagree.

Listening Actively To listen actively rather than passively, first adopt the attitude that you may actually learn something—or perceive things from another vantage point—by listening. Second, recognize that even though the other person is doing the talking, you need not sit back passively. In other words, it is not helpful to stare off into space while your partner is talking, or to offer a begrudging "mm-hmm" now and then to be "polite." Instead, you can listen actively by maintaining eye contact and modifying your facial expression to show that you understand his or her feelings and ideas. For example, nod your head when appropriate.

Listening actively also involves asking helpful questions, such as "Would you please give me an example?" or "How did you feel about..."

An active listener does not simply hear what the other person is saying, but also focuses attentively on the speaker's words and gestures to grasp meaning. Nonverbal cues may reveal more about the speaker's inner feelings than the spoken word. Good listeners do not interrupt, change the topic, or walk away when their partners are speaking.

Paraphrasing Paraphrasing shows that you understand what your partner is trying to say. In paraphrasing, you recast or restate the speaker's words to confirm your comprehension. For example, suppose your partner says, "You hardly ever say anything when we're making love. I don't want you to scream or make obligatory grunts, or do something silly, but sometimes I wonder if I'm trying to make love to a brick wall." You can paraphrase it by saying something like this: "So it's sort of hard to know if I'm really enjoying it."

Reinforcing the Other Person for Communicating Even when you disagree with what your partner is saying, you can maintain good relations and keep channels of communication open by saying something like "I really appreciate your taking the time to try to work this out with me" or "I hope you'll think it's okay if I don't see things entirely in the same way, but I'm glad that we had a chance to talk about it."

Showing That You Value Your Partner, Even When the Two of You Disagree When you disagree with your partner, do so in a way that shows that you still value your partner as a person. In other words, say something like "I love you very much, but it annoys me when you..." rather than "You're really contemptible for doing..." By so doing, you encourage your partner to disclose sensitive material without fear of personal attack or the risk of losing your love or support.

Learning About Your Partner's Needs

Listening is basic to learning about another person's needs, but sometimes it helps to go a few steps further.

Asking Questions to Draw the Other Person Out You can ask open-ended questions that allow for a broader exploration of issues, such as these:

> "What do you like best about the way we make love?"
>
> "What sorts of things do I do that bug you?"
>
> "How does it make you feel when I go to bed later than you?"
>
> "Does anything disappoint you about our relationship?"
>
> "Please tell me: What do I do that distracts you when you are studying for a test?"

Closed-ended questions that call for a limited range of responses would be most useful when you're looking for a simple yes-or-no type of response, such as "Would you rather make love with the stereo off?"

Using Self-Disclosure Self-disclosure is essential to developing intimacy. You can also use self-disclosure to learn more about your partner's needs, because communicating your own feelings and ideas invites reciprocation. For example, you might say, "There are times when I feel that I disappoint you when we make love. Should I be doing something differently?"

Granting Permission for the Other Person to Say Something That Might Upset You You can ask your partner to level with you about an irksome issue. You can say that you recognize that it might be awkward to discuss it, but that you will try your best to listen conscientiously and not get too disturbed. You can also limit communication to one such difficult issue per conversation. If the entire emotional dam were to burst, the job of mopping up could be overwhelming.

Providing Information

There are many skilful ways of communicating information, including "accentuating the positive" and using verbal and nonverbal cues. When you want to get something across, remember that it is irrational to expect that your partner can read your mind. He or she can tell when you're wearing a grumpy face, but your expression does not provide much information about your specific feelings. When your partner asks, "What would you like me to do?" responding with "Well, I think you can figure out what I want" or "Just do

Listening with Your Heart as well as Your Ears
http://www.ianr.unl.edu/pubs/family/g1092.htm
A family scientist discusses why listening is important and how to do it effectively.

whatever you think is best" is not very helpful. Only you know what pleases you. Your partner is not a mind-reader.

Accentuating the Positive Let your partner know when he or she is doing something right! Speak up or find another way to express your appreciation. Accentuating the positive is rewarding and also informs your partner about what pleases you. In other words, don't just wait around until your partner does something wrong and then seize the opportunity to complain!

Using Verbal Cues Sexual activity provides an excellent opportunity for direct communication. You can say something like "Oh, that's great" or "Don't stop." Or you can ask for feedback, as in "How does that feel...?"

Feedback provides direct guidance about what is pleasing. Partners can also make specific requests and suggestions.

Using Nonverbal Cues Sexual communication also occurs without words. Couples learn to interpret each other's facial expressions as signs of pleasure, boredom, even disgust. Our body language also communicates our likes and dislikes. Our partners may lean toward us or away from us when we touch them, or relax or tense up; in any case, they speak volumes in silence.

The following exercises may help couples use nonverbal cues to communicate their sexual likes and dislikes. Similar exercises are used by sex therapists to help couples with sexual dysfunctions.

1. *Taking turns petting.* Taking turns petting can help partners learn what turns one another on. Each partner takes turns caressing the other, stopping frequently enough to receive feedback by asking questions like "How does that feel?" The recipient is responsible for giving feedback, which can be expressed either verbally ("Yes, that's it—yes, just like that" or "No, a little lighter than that") or nonverbally, as by making certain appreciative or disapproving sounds. Verbal feedback is usually more direct and less prone to misinterpretation. The knowledge gained through this exercise can be incorporated into the couple's regular pattern of lovemaking.

2. *Directing your partner's hand.* Gently guiding your partner's hand—to show your partner where and how you like to be touched—is a most direct way of communicating sexual likes. While taking turns petting, and during other acts of lovemaking, one partner can gently guide the other's fingers and hands through the most satisfying strokes and caresses. Women might show partners how to caress the breasts or clitoral shaft in this manner. Men might cup their partners' hands to show them how to stroke the penile shaft or caress the testes.

3. *Signalling.* Couples can use agreed-upon nonverbal cues to signal sexual pleasure. For example, one partner may rub the other in a certain way, or tap the other, to signal that something is being done right. The recipient of the signal takes mental notes and incorporates the pleasurable stimulation into the couple's lovemaking. This is a sort of "hit or miss" technique, but even near misses can be rewarding.

Making Requests

A basic part of improving relationships or lovemaking is asking partners to change their behaviour—to do something differently or to stop doing something that hurts or is ungratifying. The skill of making requests now comes to the fore.

Being Specific Be specific in requesting changes. Telling your partner something like "I'd like you to be nicer to me" may accomplish little. Your partner may not know that his or her behaviour is not nice and may not understand how to be "nicer." It is better to say something like "I would appreciate it if you would get coffee for yourself, or at least ask me in a more pleasant way." Or, "I really have a hard time with the way you talk to me in front of your friends. It's as if you're trying to show them that you have control over me or something." Similarly, it may be less effective to say, "I'd like you to be more loving" than to say, "When we make love, I'd like you to kiss me more and tell me how you care about me."

Of course, you can precede your specific requests with openers such as "There's something on my mind. Is this a good time for me to bring it up with you?"

Using "I-Talk" Using the word *I* is an excellent way of expressing your feelings. Psychologists who help people become more assertive often encourage them to use the words *I*, *me*, and *my* in their speech, not just to express their feelings, but to buttress their sense of self-worth.

You are more likely to achieve desired results by framing requests in I-talk than by heaping criticisms on your partner. For example, "I would like it if we spent some time cuddling after sex" is superior to "You don't seem to care enough about me to want to hold me after we make love." Saying "I find it very painful when you use a harsh voice with me" is probably more effective than "Sometimes people's feelings get hurt when their boyfriends [girlfriends] speak to them harshly in front of their friends or families."

You may find it helpful to try out I-talk in front of a mirror or with a confidant before using it with your partner. In this way, you can see whether your facial expression and tone of voice are consistent with what you are saying. Friends may also provide pointers on the content of what you are saying.

Applications

Delivering and Receiving Criticism

> Honest criticism is hard to take, particularly from a relative, a friend, an acquaintance, or a stranger.
>
> Franklin P. Jones

It is difficult enough to be critical of, or to be criticized by, people at work, in school, or casual acquaintances. It is much more difficult to deal with criticism with an intimate partner. The ways in which we criticize loved ones, or respond to criticism from them, can truly make or break love relationships. Here are some hints for delivering and receiving criticism in ways that can enhance rather than destroy relationships.

Delivering Criticism

Delivering criticism effectively is a skill. It requires focusing partners' attention on the problem without inducing resentment or defensiveness, or reducing them to trembling masses of guilt or fear.

Evaluating Your Motives
First, weigh your goals forthrightly. Is your primary intention to punish your partner, or are you more interested in gaining

cooperation? If your goal is punishment, you may as well be coarse and disparaging, but expect to invite reprisals. If your goal is to improve the relationship, however, a tactful approach may be in order.

Picking the Right Time and Place
Deliver criticism privately—not in front of friends or family members. Your partner has a right to be upset when you make criticism public. Making private matters public induces indignation and cuts off communication.

Being Specific
Being specific may be even more important when delivering criticism than when making requests. By being specific about the behaviour that disturbs you, you bypass the trap of disparaging your partner's personality or motives. For example, you may be more effective by saying "I could lose this job because you didn't write down the message" than by saying "You're completely irresponsible" or "You're a flake." Similarly, you may achieve better results by saying "The bathroom looks and smells dirty when you throw your underwear on the floor" rather than "You're a filthy pig." It is more to the point (and less intimidating) to complain

about specific, modifiable behaviour than to try to overhaul another person's personality.

Expressing Displeasure in Terms of Your Own Feelings
Your partner is likely to feel less threatened if you express displeasure in terms of your own feelings than by directly attacking his or her personality. Attacks often arouse defensive behaviour, and sometimes retaliation, rather than enhance relationships. When confronting your partner for failing to be sensitive to your sexual needs when making love, it may be more effective to say "You know, it really upsets me that you don't seem to care about my feelings when we make love" than "You're so wrapped up in yourself that you never think about anyone else."

Keeping Criticism and Complaints to the Here and Now
How many times have you been in an argument and heard things like "You never appreciated me!" or "Last summer you did the same thing!" Bringing up the past during conflicts muddles current issues and heightens resentments. When your partner forgets to jot down the details of the telephone message, it is

more useful to note that "This was a vital phone call" than "Three weeks ago you didn't tell me about the phone call from Chris and as a result I missed out on seeing *Home Alone: The College Years*." It's better to leave alone who did what to whom last year (or even last week). Focus on the present.

Expressing Criticism Constructively

Be sensitive to your partner's needs by avoiding blunt criticisms or personal attacks and by suggesting constructive alternatives. Avoid saying things like "You're really a lousy lover." Say instead, "Can I take your hand and show you what I'd like?" As a rule of thumb, unless you can criticize your partner constructively, it may be best not to criticize at all.

Expressing Criticism Positively

Whenever possible, express criticism positively, and combine it with a concrete request. When commenting upon the lack of affection your partner displays during lovemaking, say, "I love it when you kiss me. Please kiss me more" rather than "You never kiss me when we're in bed and I'm sick of it."

Receiving Criticism

Delivering criticism can be tricky, especially when you want to inspire cooperation. Receiving criticism can be even trickier. Nevertheless, the following suggestions offer some help.

Clarifying Your Goals

When you hear "It's time you did something about...," it is understandable if the hair on the back of your arms does a headstand. After all, it's a blunt challenge. When we are confronted harshly, we are likely to become defensive and think of retaliating. But if your objective is to enhance the relationship, take a few moments to stop and think. To resolve conflicts, we need to learn about the other person's concerns, keep lines of communication open, and find ways of changing problem behaviour.

So when your partner says, "It's about time you did something about the bathroom," stop and think before you summon up your most menacing voice and say, "Just what the hell is that supposed to mean?" Ask yourself what you want to find out.

Asking Clarifying Questions

Just as it's important to be specific when delivering criticism, it helps if you encourage the other person to be specific when you are on the receiving end of criticism. In the example of the complaint about the bathroom, you can help your partner be specific and, perhaps, avert the worst by asking clarifying questions, such as "Can you tell me exactly what you mean?" or "The bathroom?"

Consider a situation in which a lover says something like "You know, you're one of the most irritating people I know." Rather than retaliate and perhaps hurt the relationship further, you can say something like "How about forgoing the character assassination and telling me what I did that's bothering you?" This response assertively requests an end to insults and asks that your partner be specific.

Acknowledging the Criticism

Even when you disagree with a criticism, you can keep lines of communication open and show some respect for your partner's feelings by acknowledging and paraphrasing the criticism.

On the other hand, if you are at fault, you can acknowledge that forthrightly. For example, you can say, "You're right. It was my day to clean the bathroom and it totally slipped my mind" or "I was so busy, I just couldn't get to it." Now the two of you should look for a way to work out the problem. When you acknowledge criticism, you cue your partner to back off a bit and look for ways to improve the situation. But what if your partner then becomes abusive and says something like "So you admit you blew it?" You might then try a little education in conflict resolution. You could say, "I admitted that I was at fault. If you're willing to work with me to find a way to handle it, great; but I'm not going to let you pound me into the ground over it."

Rejecting the Criticism

Now, if you think that you were not at fault, express your feelings. Use I-talk, and be specific. Don't seize the opportunity to angrily point out your partner's shortcomings. By doing so, you may shut down lines of communication.

Negotiating Differences

Negotiate your differences if you feel that there is merit on both sides of the argument. You may want to say something like "Would it help if I...?" And if there's something about your obligation to clean the bathroom that seems totally out of place, perhaps you and your partner can work out an exchange—that is, you get relieved of cleaning the bathroom in exchange for tackling a chore that your partner finds equally odious.

If none of these approaches helps resolve the conflict, consider the possibility that your partner is using the comment about the bathroom as a way of expressing anger over other issues. You may find out by saying something like "I've been trying to find a way to resolve this thing, but nothing I say seems to be helping. Is this really about the bathroom, or are there other things on your mind?"

And notice that we haven't suggested that you seize the opportunity to strike back by saying "Who're you to complain about the bathroom? What about your breath and that pig sty you call your closet?" Retaliation is tempting and may make you feel good in the short run, but it can do a relationship more harm than good in the long run.

Handling Impasses

Communication helps build and maintain relationships, but sometimes partners have profound, substantial disagreements. In fact, it is normal to have disagreements from time to time. Even when their communication skills are superbly tuned, partners now and then reach an impasse.

Opening the lines of communication may also elicit hidden frustrations. These frustrations can lead partners to seriously question the value of continuing the relationship or to agree to consult a helping professional. Though some people feel it is best to "let sleeping dogs lie," the skilful airing of underlying dissatisfactions can be healthful for a relationship. Couples who reach an impasse can follow several courses of action that may be helpful:

Looking at the Situation from the Other Person's Perspective Some of the conflict may be resolved by (honestly!) saying something like "I still disagree with you, but I can understand why you take your position." In this way, you recognize your partner's goodwill and, perhaps, lessen tensions.

Seeking Validating Information On the other hand, if you do not follow your partner's logic, you can say something like "Please believe me: I'm trying very hard to look at this from your point of view, but I can't follow your reasoning. Would you try to help me understand your point of view?"

Taking a Break Sometimes when you reach a stalemate, it helps to allow the problem to "incubate" for a while. If you and your partner put the issue aside for a while, perhaps a resolution will dawn on one of you later on. If you wish, schedule a follow-up discussion so that the issue won't be swept under the rug.

Tolerating Differentness Although we tend to form relationships with people who share similar attitudes, there is never a perfect overlap. A partner who pretends to be your clone will most likely become a bore. Assuming that your relationship is generally rewarding and pleasurable, you may find it possible to tolerate certain differences between yourself and your partner. Respecting other people in part means allowing them to be who they are. When we have a solid sense of who we are as individuals and what we stand for, we are more apt to tolerate differentness in our partners.

Agreeing to Disagree When all else fails, you can agree to disagree on various issues. You can remain a solid, respected individual, and your partner can remain a worthwhile, effective person, even if the two of you disagree from time to time.

Disagreement is not necessarily destructive to a relationship—unless you are convinced that it must be. Two people cannot see everything in the same way. Failure to ever disagree will have to leave at least one partner feeling frustrated now and then.

You can handle an impasse by focusing on the things that you and your partner have in common. Presumably there will be a number of them—perhaps some of them with little feet.

Summing Up

The ABC(DE)'s of Romantic Relationships

Levinger proposes an ABCDE model of romantic relationships. The letters refer to five stages: **attraction, building, continuation, deterioration,** and **ending**. A: The major promoter of *attraction* is propinquity. B: Similarity in the level of physical attractiveness, similarity in attitudes, and liking motivate us to *build* relationships. C: Factors such as variety, caring, positive evaluations, lack of jealousy, perceived fairness in the relationship, and mutual feelings of satisfaction encourage us to *continue* relationships. D: The factors that foster *deterioration* include failure to invest time and energy in the relationship, deciding to put an end to it, and simply permitting deterioration to proceed unchecked. E: Relationships tend to *end* when the partners find little satisfaction in the affiliation, when alternative partners are available, when couples are not committed to preserving the relationship, and when they expect it to falter.

Intimacy

Intimacy involves feelings of emotional closeness with another person and the desire to share each other's innermost thoughts and feelings. An initial step toward intimacy with others is getting to **know and like yourself** so that you can identify your innermost feelings and develop the security to share them. Intimate relationships require **trusting and caring** and tenderness. **Honesty** and commitment are also core features of intimacy. It is important to **maintain individuality** while developing mutuality.

Communication is a two-way street. It embraces sending and receiving messages. We often express feelings through nonverbal channels such as tone of voice, gestures, body posture, and facial expressions.

Communication Skills for Enhancing Relationships and Sexual Relations

A **common difficulty** that couples may find in talking about sex is the lack of an agreeable common language. Many couples also harbour irrational beliefs about relationships and sex.

Ways of **getting started** in communicating include talking about talking, requesting permission to raise an issue, and granting your partner permission to say things that might be upsetting. Skilled **listening** involves elements such as active listening, paraphrasing, reinforcing your partner, and valuing your partner even when you disagree. You can **learn about your partner's needs** by asking questions, using self-disclosure, and asking your partner to level with you about an irksome issue. **Provide information** by "accentuating the positive" and using verbal and nonverbal cues. In **making requests**, it is helpful to take responsibility for what happens, to be specific, to be assertive, and to use "I-talk." You can **handle impasses** by looking at the situation from your partner's point of view, seeking validating information, taking a break, and when all else fails, agreeing to disagree.

Chapter Quiz

1. The view that the development of relationships depends on the balance of the rewards of maintaining it and the costs of dissolving it is termed
   (a) social-exchange theory.
   (b) the ABCDE model.
   (c) stimulus-response theory.
   (d) operant conditioning.

2. According to the text, small talk
   (a) is an insincere way to begin a relationship.
   (b) is an in-depth discussion of important issues.
   (c) promotes premature disclosure of intimate information.
   (d) stresses breadth of topic coverage.

3. Which of the following most accurately describes gender differences in self-disclosure?

   (a) Men are always reluctant to disclose their feelings.
   (b) Women are always willing to disclose their feelings.
   (c) Gender differences in self-disclosure tend to be small.
   (d) Men are usually more willing than women to disclose their feelings.

4. According to the text, jealousy appears to be more common in cultures
   (a) that are wealthy.
   (b) with a strong machismo tradition.
   (c) that are primitive.
   (d) that stress the value of male–female relationships for reproductive purposes.

5. According to the text, it is irrational (incorrect) to assume that
   (a) suitable relationships require no investment of time and effort.
   (b) small talk will lead to the development of a good relationship.
   (c) partners need to work at maintaining good relationships.
   (d) communication skills are important to relationships.

6. Which of the following contributes to the ending of a relationship?
   (a) The partners believe in a religious tradition that encourages maintaining relationships.
   (b) The partners find the relationship to be satisfying.
   (c) The barriers to leaving the relationship are high.
   (d) Alternative partners are available.

7. Which of the following is the most accurate statement about intimacy and relationships?
   (a) It is not necessary for people to be sexually intimate to have an emotionally intimate relationship.
   (b) It is necessary for people to be sexually intimate to have an emotionally intimate relationship.
   (c) People cannot be intimate with one another unless they are in love.
   (d) Intimacy is best established by complete honesty.

8. In healthy, committed relationships
   (a) a delicate balance exists between individuality and mutuality.

(b) a strong sense of togetherness eliminates individuality.

(c) partners seek to submerge their own personalities into the personalities of their partners.

(d) partners do whatever they can to meet all of their partners' sexual desires.

9. According to the text, which of the following is NOT an irrational belief about relationships and sex?

(a) Men should have a natural expertise about sex.

(b) People should know what their partners want without having to communicate.

(c) Sexual knowledge is learned.

(d) It is unladylike for women to express their feelings about sex.

10. The communications skill of active listening includes all of the following EXCEPT

(a) nodding your head when appropriate.

(b) interrupting the speaker.

(c) maintaining eye contact.

(d) asking helpful questions.

Chapter 8

Sexual Orientation

Did You Know That...

- Sexual feelings involving people of one's own gender are common in adolescence and do not mean that one's sexual orientation will be exclusively homosexual in adulthood? Some people are attracted to both men and women?

- Jews and Christians have traditionally referred to male–male sexual activity as the sin of Sodom?

- Among the warlike Sambian people of New Guinea, young males perform fellatio on older males in the belief that it will enable them to acquire the fierce manhood of the headhunter?

- A majority of Canadians favour legalizing same-sex marriages?

- Some heterosexuals seem to hate gay people because they are threatened by the possibility of discovering male–male sexual impulses within themselves?

- The Canadian Human Rights Act prohibits discrimination based on sexual orientation?

Sexual orientation refers to one's erotic attractions toward, and interests in developing romantic relationships with, members of one's own or the other gender. A **heterosexual orientation** refers to an erotic attraction to, and preference for developing romantic relationships with, members of the other gender. (Many gay people refer to heterosexual people as being *straight*, or as *straights*.) Notice that we say *other gender*, not *opposite gender*. Social critics note that many of the problems that arise between men and women are based on the notion that men and women are polar opposites (Bem, 1993). Research and common sense both support the view that men and women are more alike in personality and behaviour than they are different.

Coming to Terms with Terms

A **homosexual orientation** refers to an erotic attraction to, and interest in forming romantic relationships with, members of one's own gender. The term *homosexuality* denotes sexual interest in members of one's own gender and applies to both men and women. Homosexual men are often referred to as **gay males**. Homosexual women are also called **lesbians** or *gay women*. Gay males and lesbians are also referred to collectively as "gays" or "gay people." The term **bisexuality** refers to an orientation in which one is sexually attracted to, and interested in forming romantic relationships with, both males and females.

Now that we have defined the term *homosexuality*, let us note that we will use it only sparingly. Many gay people object to the term *homosexual* because they feel that it draws too much attention to sexual behaviour. Moreover, the term bears a social stigma. As noted by the American Psychological Association's (1991) Committee on Lesbian and Gay Concerns, the word *homosexual* has also been historically associated with concepts of deviance and mental illness. Also, the term is often used to refer to men only and thus renders lesbians invisible. Many gay people would prefer terms such as *gay male* or *lesbian sexual orientation*.

Then, too, the word *homosexual* is ambiguous in meaning—that is, does it refer to sexual behaviour or sexual orientation? In this book, we speak of male–female sexual behaviour (not *heterosexual* behaviour), male–male sexual behaviour, and female–female sexual behaviour.

Classification of Sexual Orientation

Determining a person's sexual orientation might seem to be a clear-cut task. Some people are exclusively gay and limit their sexual activities to partners of their own

Sexual orientation The direction of one's sexual interests—toward members of the same gender, the other gender, or both genders.

Heterosexual orientation Erotic attraction to, and preference for, developing romantic relationships with members of the other gender.

Homosexual orientation Erotic attraction to, and preference for, developing romantic relationships with members of one's own gender. (From the Greek *homos*, meaning "same," not the Latin *homo*, which means "man.")

Gay males Males who are erotically attracted to and desire to form romantic relationships with other males.

Lesbians Females who are erotically attracted to and desire to form romantic relationships with other females. (After Lesbos, the Greek island on which, legend has it, female–female sexual activity was idealized.)

Bisexuality Erotic attraction to, and interest in developing romantic relationships with, both males and females.

A Slice of Contemporary Life. In June 2003 Ontario became one of the few jurisdictions in the world to recognize gay marriages. Here Michael Stark (left) and Michael Leshner, the first gay couple to be legally married in Ontario, celebrate after the ceremony on June 10, 2003.

gender. Others are strictly heterosexual and limit their sexual activities to partners of the other gender. Many people, however, fall somewhere in between. Where might we draw the line between a gay male and lesbian sexual orientation, on the one hand, and a heterosexual orientation, on the other? Where do we draw the line between these orientations and bisexuality? Do we really need to draw lines or should the concept of sexual orientation reflect a blurring of lines and an overlapping of desires and behaviours?

It is possible, indeed not unusual, for heterosexual people to have had some sexual experiences with people of their own gender. Consider a survey of more than 7000 male readers of *Playboy* magazine. Among those reporting sexual experiences with both men and women in adulthood, more than 2 out of 3 perceived themselves to be heterosexual rather than bisexual (Lever et al., 1992). For many of these men, sexual experiences with other men were limited to a brief period of their lives and did not alter their sexual orientations. Lacking heterosexual outlets, prison inmates may have sexual experiences with people of their own gender while they maintain their heterosexual identities. Inmates would form sexual relationships with people of the other gender if they were available, and they return to male–female sexual behaviour upon release from prison. Physical affection also helps some prisoners, male and female, cope with loneliness and isolation. Males who engage in prostitution with male clients may separate their sexual orientation from their "trade." Many fantasize about a female when permitting a client to fellate them. The behaviour is male–male. The person's sexual *orientation* may be heterosexual.

Gay males and lesbians, too, may engage in male–female sexual activity while maintaining a gay sexual orientation. Some gay males and lesbians marry members of the other gender but continue to harbour unfulfilled desires for members of their own gender. Then, too, some people are bisexual but may not have acted upon their attraction to members of their own gender.

Sexual orientation is not necessarily expressed in sexual behaviour. Many people come to perceive themselves as gay or heterosexual long before they ever engage in sexual activity. Some people, gay and heterosexual alike, adopt a celibate lifestyle for religious or ascetic reasons.

Attraction to people of the other gender and people of one's own gender may thus not be mutually exclusive. People may have various degrees of sexual interest in, and sexual experience with, people of either gender. Kinsey and his colleagues recognized that the boundaries between gay male and lesbian sexual orientations, on the one hand, and a heterosexual orientation, on the other, are sometimes blurry. They thus proposed a continuum of sexual orientation between two poles.

The Kinsey Continuum

Kinsey and his colleagues (1948, 1953) conceived a 7-point "heterosexual–homosexual continuum" (see Figure 8.1). People are located on the continuum according to their patterns of sexual attraction and behaviour. People in category 0 are considered exclusively heterosexual. People in category 6 are considered exclusively gay.

What percentage of the population, then, is gay? The percentages depend on the criteria one uses. Kinsey and his colleagues reported that about 4% of men and 1% to 3% of women in their samples were exclusively gay (6 on their scale). A larger percentage of people were considered predominantly gay (scale points 4 or 5) or predominantly heterosexual (1 or 2 on their scale). Some were classified as equally gay and heterosexual in orientation and could be labelled bisexual (scale point 3). Most people were classified as exclusively heterosexual (scale point 0). Table 8.1 indicates the percentage of people who were classified according to the seven categories in Figure 8.1. Percentages varied according to marital status, age, level of education, and other factors. This particular table is based on people aged 20 to 35.

Between the poles of the continuum lie people with various degrees of sexual interest in, and sexual experience with, people of their own gender. Thirty-seven percent of men and 13% of the women told interviewers they had reached orgasm through sexual activity with someone of their own gender at some time after puberty. Fifty percent of men who remained single until age 35 reported they had reached orgasm through sexual activity with other males.

Kinsey's figures for male–male sexual activity may have been exaggerated. For instance, his finding that 37% of males had reached orgasm through sexual activity with other males was based on a sample that included a high proportion of former prisoners. Findings may also have been distorted by the researchers' efforts to recruit known gay people into their samples. Once these sources of possible bias are corrected, the incidence of male–male sexual activity drops from 37% to about 25%.

Kinsey's research also showed that sexual behaviour patterns could shift during a person's lifetime, sometimes dramatically so (Sanders et al., 1990). Sexual experiences or feelings involving people of one's own gender are common, especially in adolescence, and do not mean that one will engage in sexual activity exclusively with people of one's own gender in adulthood (Bullough, 1990).

What did Kinsey find with respect to more enduring patterns of male–male and female–female sexual activity? Estimates based on an analysis of Kinsey's data (Gebhard, 1977) suggest that 13% of the men and 7% of the women, or 10% for both genders combined, were either predominantly or exclusively interested in, and sexually active with, people of their own gender for at least three years between the ages of 16 and 55.

Kinsey's Heterosexual-Homosexual Rating Scale
www.indiana.edu/~kinsey/resources/ak-hhscale.html
This page on the Kinsey Institute website discusses the Kinsey Continuum and provides references for further study.

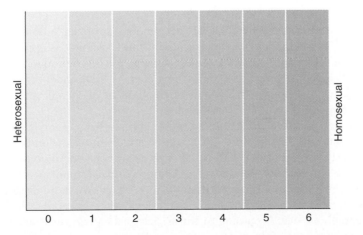

Figure 8.1. The Kinsey Continuum.

Kinsey and his colleagues conceived a 7-point heterosexual–homosexual continuum that classifies people according to their homosexual behaviour and the magnitude of their attraction to members of their own gender. People in category 0, who accounted for most of Kinsey's study participants, were considered exclusively heterosexual. People in category 6 were considered exclusively homosexual.

TABLE 8.1 Percentages of Respondents Aged 20 to 35 at Each Level of the Kinsey Continuum of Sexual Orientation

Rating	Category	Females (%)	Males (%)
0	Entirely heterosexual experience		
	Single	61–72	53–78
	Married	89–90	90–92
	Previously married	75–80	
1–6	At least some sexual experience with people of one's own gender	11–20	18–42
2–6	More than incidental sexual experience with people of one's own gender	6–14	13–38
3–6	Homosexual as much or more than heterosexual	4–11	9–32
4–6	Mostly homosexual	3–8	7–26
5–6	Almost exclusively homosexual	2–6	5–22
6	Exclusively homosexual	1–3	3–16

Source: Adapted from Kinsey, A. C., et al. (1953). *Sexual Behavior in the Human Female*. Philadelphia: W. B. Saunders, p. 488. Reprinted by permission of the Kinsey Institute for Research in Sex, Gender, and Reproduction, Inc.

Current estimates generally find lower percentages of gay people in the population than Kinsey did. Research in the United States, Britain, France, and Denmark finds that about 3% of men surveyed *identify* themselves as gay (Hamer et al., 1993; Laumann et al., 1994). Surveys in the United States, Britain, and France find that larger numbers of men (5% to 11%) and women (2% to 4%) report *engaging in sexual behaviour* with members of their own gender within the past five years (Sell et al., 1995). Surveys show that still larger numbers of men (8% to 9%) and women (8% to 12%) report some *sexual attraction* to members of their own gender, but no sexual interaction since the age of 15 (Sell et al., 1995). A recent Canadian poll indicated that less than 5% of the population had experienced same-sex attraction, while 2.6% of Canadians had had a sexual relationship with a person of the same sex (Léger Marketing, 2003).

Sex surveys reveal only the percentages of people *willing to admit* to certain behaviours or sexual orientations (Cronin, 1993; Isay, 1993). Surveys may omit gay people who hesitate to proclaim their sexual orientation because of social stigma or repression of their sexual feelings.

Challenges to the Kinsey Continuum

Although the Kinsey continuum has been widely adopted by sex researchers, it is not universally accepted. Kinsey believed that exclusive heterosexual and gay sexual orientations lay at opposite poles of one continuum. Therefore, the more heterosexual a person is, the less gay that person is, and vice versa (Sanders et al., 1990).

Viewing gay and heterosexual orientations as opposite poles of one continuum is akin to the traditional view of masculinity and femininity as opposite poles of one continuum, such that the more masculine one is, the less feminine, and vice versa. But we may also regard masculinity and femininity as independent personality dimensions. Similarly, we can regard the sexual orientations of gay people and heterosexuals as separate dimensions, rather than opposites.

Psychologist Michael Storms (1980) suggests that gay and heterosexual orientations are independent dimensions. Thus, one can be high or low on both dimensions simultaneously. Storms (1980) suggests that there are separate dimensions of responsiveness to male–female (**heteroerotic**) stimulation and sexual stimulation that involves someone of the same gender (**homoerotic** stimulation), as shown in Figure 8.2. According to this model, bisexuals are high in both dimensions, whereas people who are low in both are essentially asexual. According to Kinsey, bisexual individuals would be less responsive to stimulation by people of the other gender than heterosexual people are, but more responsive to stimulation by people of their own gender. According to the two-

Heteroerotic Of an erotic nature and involving members of the other gender.

Homoerotic Of an erotic nature and involving members of one's own gender.

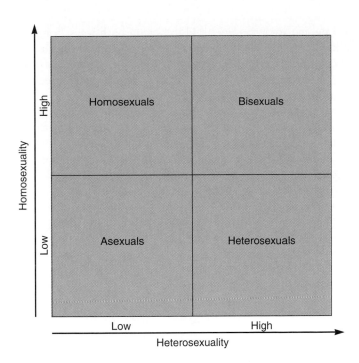

Figure 8.2. Heterosexuality and Homosexuality as Separate Dimensions.

According to this model, homosexuality and heterosexuality are independent dimensions. One can thus be high or low on both dimensions at the same time. Most people are high in one dimension. Bisexuals are high in both dimensions. People who are low in both are considered asexual.

dimensional model, however, bisexual people may be as responsive to stimulation by people of the other gender as heterosexual people are, and as responsive to stimulation by people of their own gender as gay people are.

Moreover, Kinsey considered both overt physical behaviour and psychosexual reactions (such as fantasies and desires) when assigning categories. Thus, two separate and possibly contradictory dimensions of sexual orientation were combined for the purpose of determining one appropriate category (Sell, 1997). Some researchers have since proposed considering the different dimensions of sexual orientation separately. A person could thus score differently on a scale that measures physical behaviour than on one that measures pyschosexual reactions (Bullough, 1990). The components of sexual identity are not always congruous, and thus a person may engage in sexual behaviour or experience sexual desire that is not consistent with his or her professed or assumed sexual identity (Green, 2003; Rothblum, 2000).

Kinsey had argued that the content of erotic fantasies was an excellent gauge of sexual orientation. To test this formulation, Storms (1980) investigated the erotic fantasies of heterosexual, gay, and bisexual people. Kinsey might have predicted that bisexual individuals would have *fewer* heteroerotic fantasies than heterosexual people, and *more* homoerotic fantasies than heterosexual people. But Storms predicted that "bisexuals will report *as much* heteroerotic fantasy as heterosexual people and *as much* homoerotic fantasy as homosexuals" (p. 786).

Storms found that heterosexual students reported significantly more fantasies about the other gender than their own gender. Gay students reported more frequent fantasies about their own gender. Bisexuals, as predicted, reported a high level of both kinds of fantasies. Because Storms did find that many bisexual people show a high level of sexual interest in both men and women, it may be that sexual interest in the other gender and in one's own gender are independent dimensions rather than opposite poles of one continuum.

Bisexuality

Bisexual people are sexually attracted to both males and females. Kinsey and his colleagues considered people rated as 3's to be bisexual (see Figure 8.1). Depending on how one defines bisexuality, perhaps 1% to 4% of the population is bisexual. About 1% of the people (0.8% of the men and 0.9% of the women) surveyed in one study (Laumann et al., 1994) reported having a bisexual *identity*. However, about 4% (3.9% of the men and 4.1% of the women) reported that they were sexually attracted to both women and men.

Bisexual people are sometimes said to "swing both ways," or to be "A/C–D/C" (as in "alternating current" and "direct current"). Some gay people (and some heterosexual people) believe that claims to bisexuality are a "cop-out" that people use to deny being gay. Perhaps they fear leaving their spouses or "coming out" (declaring their gay male or lesbian sexual orientation publicly). Others view bisexuality as a form of sexual experimentation with people of one's own gender by people who are predominantly heterosexual. But many avowed bisexual people disagree. They report that they can maintain erotic interests in, and romantic relationships with, members of both genders. Some authors (e.g., Garber, 1995; Weinberg et al., 1994; Rust, 2002) approach bisexuality as a sexual orientation in its own right, and not simply as a combination of heterosexual and homosexual tendencies.

Perspectives on Gay Male and Lesbian Sexual Orientations

Gay male and lesbian sexual orientations have existed throughout history. In this section we review historical and other perspectives on gay male and lesbian sexual orientations.

Historical Perspectives

In Western culture, few sexual practices have met with such widespread censure as sexual activities with members of one's own gender. Within the Judeo-Christian tradition, male–male and female–female sexual behaviour has been deemed criminal and sinful—an outrage against God and humanity. Many countries, grounded in this religious tradition, pose criminal penalties for sexual practices commonly associated with male–male and female–female sex, such as anal and oral sex.

Jews and Christians have traditionally referred to male–male sexual activity as the sin of Sodom. Hence the origins of the term *sodomy*, which generally alludes to anal intercourse (and sometimes to oral–genital contact). According to the Book of Genesis, the city of Sodom was destroyed by God; however, many theologians maintain that the city was destroyed because of sins of personal pride, excess, and inhospitality rather than because of homosexual behaviour (Spong, 1988). Islamic attitudes condemning homosexuality are, like the attitudes of some Christians, also rooted in an interpretation of the Sodom and Gomorrah story that attributes the destruction of the city to homosexual behaviour (Parrinder, 1996).

Cross-Cultural Perspectives

Ford and Beach (1951) found that in nearly two-thirds of the preliterate societies they studied, male–male sexual interactions were viewed as normal and deemed socially acceptable for some people. The other societies had sanctions against male–male sexual behaviour.

Sexual activities between males are sometimes limited to rites that mark the young male's initiation into manhood. In some preliterate societies, semen is believed to boost strength and virility. Older males thus transmit semen to younger males through oral or anal sexual activities. Among the Sambian people of New Guinea, a tribe of warlike headhunters, 9- to 12-year-old males leave their parents' households and live in a "clubhouse" with other prepubertal and adolescent males. There they undergo sexual rites of passage. To acquire the fierce manhood of the headhunter, they perform fellatio on older males and drink "men's milk" (semen) (Herdt, 1981; Money, 1990; Stoller & Herdt, 1985). The initiate is enjoined to ingest as much semen as he can, "as if it were breast milk or food" (Herdt, 1981, p. 235). Ingestion of semen is believed to give rise to puberty. Following puberty, adolescents are fellated by younger males (Baldwin & Baldwin, 1989). By the age of 19, however, young men are expected to take brides and enter exclusively male–female sexual relationships.

These practices of Sambian culture might seem to suggest that the sexual orientations of males are fluid and malleable. The practices involve *behaviour*, however, and not *sexual orientation*. Male–male sexual behaviour among Sambians takes place within a cultural context that bears little resemblance to consensual male–male sexual activity in Western society. The prepubertal Sambian male does not *seek* sexual liaisons with other males. He is removed from his home, by force if necessary, and thrust into male–male sexual encounters by older males (Baldwin & Baldwin, 1989).

Little is known about female–female sexual activity in non-Western cultures. Evidence of female–female sexual behaviour was found by Ford and Beach in only 17 of the 76 societies they studied. This cross-cultural evidence is consistent with data from our own culture. Here, too, males are more likely than females to develop sexual interests in, or romantic relationships with, members of their own genders (Katz, 1995; Laumann et al., 1994).

Attitudes Toward Sexual Orientation in Contemporary Society

Negative attitudes toward gay people pervade our society (Katz, 1995). One U.S. survey of heterosexual males aged 15 to 19 showed that 9 of 10 felt that sex between men was "disgusting." Three of five could not even see themselves being friends with a gay man (Marsiglio, 1993b).

Seventy-five percent of respondents to a 1987 U.S. survey felt that sexual relations between members of the same gender are "always wrong" (Davis & Smith, 1987). A 2000 Environics poll, however, found that 9 out of 10 Canadians believe that there should be equal job opportunities for homosexuals and two-thirds agree that gay people should be permitted to teach in elementary schools or become members of the clergy. A 2001 Léger poll indicated that 65% of Canadians surveyed agreed that same-sex couples should have access to marriage, and 53% of respondents supported the rights of same-sex couples to adopt (Léger Marketing, 2003).

Some of those who would bar gay people from teaching and other activities believe that gay people, given the chance, will seduce and recruit children into a gay lifestyle. Such beliefs have been used to prevent gay couples from becoming adoptive or foster parents and to deny them custody or visitation rights to their own children following divorce. Some people who would bar gay people from interactions with children fear that the children will be molested. Yet more than 90% of cases of child molestation involve heterosexual male assailants (Gelles & Cornell, 1985; Gordon & Snyder, 1989). Nor are children who are reared or taught by gay men or lesbians more likely to become gay themselves. One study found that 36 of 37 children who were reared by lesbian or transsexual couples developed a heterosexual orientation (Green, 1978). Studies of lesbian mothers and their children have found that parents' sexual orientation has little effect on children's gender development and does not adversely affect their emotional or psychological well-being (Golombok et al., 2003, Dundas & Kaufman, 2000).

Homophobia **Homophobia** takes many forms, including

* use of derogatory names (such as *faggot*).
* telling disparaging "queer jokes."
* barring gay people from housing, employment, or social opportunities.
* taunting (verbal abuse).
* **gay bashing** (physical abuse).

The second part of the word *homophobia* derives from the Greek root word meaning "fear." Although some psychologists link homophobia to fears of a gay male or lesbian sexual orientation within oneself, homophobic attitudes may also be embedded within a cluster of stereotypical gender-role attitudes toward family life (Kerns & Fine, 1994). These attitudes support male dominance and the belief that it is natural and appropriate for women to sacrifice for their husbands and children (Katz, 1995; Marsiglio, 1993b).

Reactions to Child Custody Decisions Involving Homosexuals and Heterosexual Parents
www.cpa.ca/cjbsnew/1995/april/fraser.html
This Canadian study found there was less support for a homosexual than a heterosexual parent in judgments in child custody cases.

Homophobia A cluster of negative attitudes and feelings toward gay people, including intolerance, hatred, and fear. (From Greek roots meaning "fear" [of members of the] "same" [gender].)

Gay bashing Violence against homosexuals.

Homophobic attitudes are more common among males who identify with a traditional male gender role and those who hold a fundamentalist religious orientation (Kerns & Fine, 1994; Marsiglio, 1993b). Similarly, researchers find that college students who hold a conservative political orientation tend to be more accepting of negative attitudes toward gay people than are liberal students (Lottes & Kuriloff, 1992). Generally speaking, heterosexual men are relatively less tolerant of gay people than are heterosexual women (Kerns & Fine, 1994). A recent Canadian poll found that 52% of those surveyed had no moral objection to homosexuality. Younger Canadians were more tolerant of same-sex behaviour than older Canadians. Women, people living in urban areas, and Canadians from higher socioeconomic brackets tended to be more accepting of same-sex behaviour (NFO Cfgroup, 2003).

Perhaps some heterosexual men are threatened by the possibility of discovering male–male sexual impulses within themselves (Freiberg, 1995). Research by Henry Adams and his colleagues (1996) supports this possibility. The Adams group showed men sexually explicit videotapes of male–female, female–female, and male–male sexual activity and measured their sexual response by means of the penile plethysmograph, which measures penile circumference (size of erection). Participants were also asked to report how sexually aroused they felt in response to the videos. The men were also evaluated for their attitudes toward gay males. Nonhomophobic viewers were sexually aroused, according to their penile circumference, only by videos of male–female and female–female sexual activity. The homophobic viewers were also aroused, as assessed by penile circumference, by the video of male–male sexual activity. However, the homophobic men reported that they did not *feel* aroused by the male–male sexual activity, suggesting that they were out of touch with their biological response.

Heterosexism

Heterosexism Oppression based on the assumption that heterosexuality is the norm in society and is therefore superior to gay, lesbian, bisexual, and transgendered sexual orientations.

Heterosexism is a form of discrimination, such as racism and sexism, that reinforces the belief that one group in society (heterosexuals) is superior to other groups (lesbians, gay men, bisexuals, transgendered) simply by virtue of their professed or assumed sexual orientation. It can take the form of overt legal or social discrimination that results in the denial of human rights. Heterosexism can also be more subtle and can be revealed in the assumptions we make about the prevalence of heterosexuality in our society. For example, most media and advertising images promote a view of men and women based on heterosexual ideas of what is attractive. It is assumed that most people want to appear a certain way in order to attract heterosexual partners.

Gay Bashing and the AIDS Epidemic

When AIDS first appeared in North America, it primarily struck the gay male community. Some people believed that the epidemic was a God-sent plague intended to punish gay people for sinful behaviour. In fact, AIDS was initially called GRID—Gay-Related Immune Deficiency. It was not until the early to mid-1980s that the more accurate and less gay-stigmatizing term AIDS (Acquired Immune Deficiency Syndrome) was adopted.

The advent of the epidemic was accompanied by a dramatic rise in the incidence of gay bashing (Freiberg, 1995; Katz, 1995). However, the percentage of gay men who account for new cases of AIDS has been steadily declining (see Chapter 13).

Sexual Orientation and the Law

During the past generation, gay people have organized effectively to fight discrimination and to overturn the laws that have traditionally targeted them. Such laws prohibit "unnatural" sexual acts, even between consenting adults. In 1969, an amendment to the Canadian Criminal Code decriminalized male–male and female–female sexual behaviour. There were differences in the age of consent for males and females, and between heterosexual and homosexual behaviours, which were removed in later reforms. However, anal sex is still prosecutable, even with consent, if one of the participants is under 18, except in a legal marriage.

Many other countries, including Mexico, Holland, Italy, Spain, England, France, and the Scandinavian countries, have decriminalized male–male and female–female sexual activity (Carrera, 1981). However, male-male and female-female sexual behaviour remain illegal in at least 83 countries and are punishable by death in seven countries of the world.

In 2000, Vermont became the first U.S. state to legally recognize civil unions between same-sex couples. The Massachusetts Supreme Court recently ruled that it is

Egale
www.egale.ca
Egale, Equality for Gays and Lesbians Everywhere, is a national organization that promotes equality and justice for lesbian, gay, bisexual, and transgendered people through active lobbying, intervention in the courts, networking, and education.

unconstitutional to deny same-sex couples the right to marry. At the time this book went to press, groups opposed to same-sex marriage were challenging the ruling and threatening the May 2004 deadline for its implementation. The status of gay marriage in Canada is presently being debated. The federal government passed a *Modernization of Benefits and Obligations Act* in 2000, which extended to same-sex couples the same benefits under federal social programs as heterosexual couples. However, a preamble stated that the word *marriage* means "the lawful union of one man and one woman." In 2003, both the Ontario and British Columbia Courts of Appeal overturned this definition of marriage, opening the door to civil marriages for same-gender couples. In both provinces, a number of such marriages have been registered. In March 2004 Quebec became the third province to legalize same-sex marriage. The first such marriage was celebrated 20 days after the decision by Quebec's Court of Appeal. At the time this book went to print, the federal government had submitted draft legislation to the Supreme Court of Canada that would extend civil marriages to same-sex couples throughout Canada. Religious groups have organized campaigns to oppose the legislation; however, polls continue to indicate that a majority of Canadians support same-gender marriage legislation (Léger Marketing, 2001; Ipsos-Reid, 2003; NFO Cfgroup, 2003).

Stereotypes and Sexual Behaviour Among heterosexual people, sexual aggressiveness is linked to the masculine gender role. Sexual passivity is linked to the feminine role. Some heterosexual people assume (often erroneously) that in gay male and lesbian relationships, one partner consistently assumes the masculine role in sexual relations, and the other, the feminine.

Many gay couples vary the active and passive roles, however. Among gay male couples, for example, roles in anal intercourse (*inserter* versus *insertee*) and in fellatio are often reversed. Contrary to popular assumptions, sexual behaviour between lesbians seldom reflects distinct **butch–femme** gender roles. Most lesbians report providing and receiving oral–genital stimulation. Typically, partners alternate roles or simultaneously perform and receive oral stimulation. Many gay people claim that the labels of *masculine* and *feminine* only represent the "straight community's" efforts to pigeonhole them in terms "straights" can understand.

Biological Perspectives

Is sexual orientation an *inborn* trait that is transmitted genetically, like eye colour or height? Does it reflect hormonal influences? Biological perspectives focus on the role of genetics and hormonal influences in shaping sexual orientation.

Genetics and Sexual Orientation Considerable evidence exists that gay male and lesbian sexual orientations run in families (Bailey et al., 1993; Pillard, 1990). In one study, for example, 22% of the brothers of a sample of 51 predominantly gay men were either gay or bisexual themselves. This is nearly four times the proportion expected in the general population (Pillard & Weinrich, 1986). Although such evidence is consistent with a genetic explanation, families also share a common environment.

Twin studies also shed light on the possible role of heredity (Rose, 1995). **Monozygotic (MZ) twins**, or identical twins, develop from a single fertilized ovum and share 100% of their heredity. **Dizygotic (DZ) twins**, or fraternal twins, develop from two fertilized ova. Like other brothers and sisters, DZ twins share only 50% of their heredity. Thus if a gay male or lesbian sexual orientation were transmitted genetically, it should be found about twice as often among identical twins of gay people as among fraternal twins. Since MZ and DZ twins who are reared together share similar environmental influences, differences in the degree of **concordance** for a given trait between the types of twin pairs are further indicative of genetic origins.

Several studies have identified gay men who had either identical (MZ) or fraternal (DZ) twin brothers in order to examine the prevalences of a gay male sexual orientation in their twin brothers (Rose, 1995). Consistent with a genetic explanation, MZ twins do appear to have a higher concordance rate for a gay male sexual orientation than DZ

Gay and Lesbian Emergence: Out in Canada
http://archives.cbc.ca/
**IDD-1-69-599/life_society/
gay_lesbian/**
Multimedia footage from the CBC archives examines the struggle for gay rights in the 1960s and 1970s.

Butch A lesbian who assumes a traditional masculine gender role.

Femme A lesbian who assumes a traditional feminine gender role.

Monozygotic (MZ) twins Twins who develop from the same fertilized ovum; identical twins.

Dizygotic (DZ) twins Twins who develop from different fertilized ova; fraternal twins.

Concordance Agreement.

A World of Diversity

Human Rights and Sexual Orientation

In 1948 the General Assembly of the United Nations adopted and proclaimed the Universal Declaration of Human Rights. This document still stands as a foundational treatise on international human rights. The first article of the Declaration affirms the basic tenet that "all human beings are born free and equal in dignity and rights." The second article outlines the following prohibited grounds for discrimination: race, colour, sex, language, religion, political or other opinion, national or social origin, property, birth, or other status.

What is conspicuously absent from this list is mention of sexual orientation. However, given the fact that the document was drafted in 1948, this omission is not surprising. Historical documents reflect the prevailing attitudes and concerns of the times in which they are written. Societal recognition of sexual diversity is a relatively recent phenomenon, and it is still evolving at an unequal pace in various cultural, religious, and political contexts. As Baird notes in the introduction to her book *The No-Nonsense Guide to Sexual Diversity* (2001), "What is different today is that those who were regularly silenced by history have erupted into it. Across the world, the sexually marginalized have made claim to human rights, equality and justice."

The struggle for human rights is based on the premise that all people, regardless of sexual orientation, are entitled to the "rights and freedoms" outlined in the UN Declaration. However, not all nations accept this interpretation of the universality of human rights. The legal basis for discrimination based on sexual orientation varies from country to country, and even in the absence of formal legal sanctions, cultural and religious prohibitions often exist. Amnesty International, a non-profit organization that campaigns for international human rights, has documented human rights abuses suffered by sexual minorities worldwide. Consider the following examples of abuse compiled by Amnesty International:

- Twenty-one men in Egypt were sentenced to three years in prison for engaging in homosexual activity. The men were eventually acquitted of the charges.
- In Uganda, five gay and lesbian people were arrested, tortured, and forced to flee the country because of their sexual orientation.
- A Russian lesbian was threatened with a forced psychiatric "cure" if she refused to give up custody of her son. She eventually sought asylum in the United States.
- Executions for alleged homosexual activity have taken place in Saudi Arabia, Afghanistan, and Iran. In Iran, an estimated 200 people are executed annually because of their sexual orientation.
- Workers in a lesbian and gay support organization in El Salvador received death threats and had their offices ransacked. Police initially refused to offer protection, but after Amnesty International intervened, measures were taken to ensure the safety of workers and clients.
- An African-American lesbian was ridiculed and raped while in prison custody in the United States.

As these examples show, human rights abuses are not concentrated in any one area of the world but occur in various cultural, religious, and political settings. However, the worldwide struggle for equality and justice for people of all sexual orientations is slowly making gains. The constitutions of South Africa and Ecuador were the first to prohibit discrimination based on sexual orientation. The *Canadian Human Rights Act* also bans discrimination based on sexual orientation. Various countries such as Canada, Sweden, Australia, and South Africa will offer asylum to lesbian, gay, bisexual, and transgendered refugees. Countries seeking membership in the European Union must abolish any legislation that criminalizes same-sex behaviour.

One very significant victory for the human rights campaign for sexual minorities will be the addition of "sexual orientation" in the Universal Declaration of Human Rights. In 2003 a draft resolution proposing such an addition was presented to the UN Commission on Human Rights. The resolution was put forth by Brazil and co-sponsored by 19 European nations. Amnesty International commended the initiative and stated that adoption of the resolution was "the only way to end the intolerable exclusion of lesbian, gay, bisexual and transgendered people from the full protection of the UN system." However, the Brazil resolution, as it came to be known, was blocked by a coalition of Catholic and Islamic countries, and a decision was made to delay discussion of the issue until the next session of the UN in 2004.

Given the movement toward tolerance and inclusion that is slowly gaining legislative momentum in many countries, a universal declaration of human rights for people of all sexual orientations would seem to be inevitable. Regardless of the rights that are defined by law and enshrined in declarations, the ongoing challenge is to ensure that these rights are respected and that the lives of lesbian, gay, bisexual, and transgendered people are valued in all societies.

---

twins. Bailey and Pillard (1991) reported a 52% concordance rate among MZ twin pairs versus a 22% rate among DZ twin pairs in their sample. In another study, researchers reported a concordance rate for a gay sexual orientation of 66% in MZ twins, as compared to 30% among DZ twins (Whitam et al., 1993). Bailey, Dunne, and Martin studied female twins and noted a slightly higher, although not statistically significant, concordance rate for MZ twin pairs (24%) than for DZ twin pairs (11%) (Bailey et al., 2000). But bear in mind that MZ twins are more likely to be dressed alike and treated alike than DZ twins. Thus, their greater concordance for a gay sexual orientation may at least in part reflect environmental factors. The greater concordance between MZ twins may only signify that MZ twins are likely to react more similarly than DZ twins to the same *environmental* influences (Bancroft, 1990).

Researchers have found evidence linking a region on the X sex chromosome to a gay male sexual orientation (Hamer et al., 1993). The researchers cautioned that they had not found a particular gene linked to sexual orientation, just a general location of where the gene may be found. Nor do scientists know how such a gene, or combination of genes, might account for sexual orientation.

Sexologist John Money (1994) agrees that genetic factors may play a role in the development of sexual orientation. However, genetic factors do not fully govern sexual orientation. Most researchers believe that sexual orientation is affected by a complex interplay of biological and psychosocial influences (Barlow & Durand, 1995).

Hormonal Influences and Sexual Orientation Sex hormones strongly influence the mating behaviour of other species (Crews, 1994). Researchers have thus looked into possible hormonal factors in determining sexual orientation in humans.

Testosterone is essential to male sexual differentiation. Thus, the levels of testosterone and its by-products in the blood and urine have been suspected as a possible influence of sexual orientation, at least in males. Research has failed to connect sexual orientation in either gender with differences in the levels of either male or female sex hormones in adulthood (Friedman & Downey, 1994). In adulthood, testosterone appears to have **activating effects**. That is, it affects the intensity of sexual desire, but not the preference for partners of the same or the other gender (Whalen et al., 1990).

What of the possible *prenatal* effects of sex hormones? Experiments have been performed in which pregnant rats were given antiandrogen drugs that block the effects of testosterone. When the drugs were given during critical periods in which the fetuses' brains were becoming sexually differentiated, male offspring were likely to show feminine mating patterns as adults (Ellis & Ames, 1987). The adult males became receptive to mounting attempts by other males and failed to mount females.

Do prenatal sex hormones play a similar role in determining sexual orientation in people? Research with women has not been conclusive. For example, Meyer-Bahlburg and his colleagues (1995) interviewed groups of women exposed prenatally to DES—a synthetic estrogen. They found a slight increase in same-sex fantasy and bisexual behaviour among the DES-exposed group. However, the majority of DES-exposed women identified themselves as heterosexual. The authors concluded that the differences between the DES-exposed group and the control group were "modest" and

The Biology of Sexual Orientation
http://members.aol.com/slevay/page22.html
An overview of the research on sexual orientation, with an emphasis on biological studies.

Activating effects Those effects of sex hormones that influence the level of the sex drive but not sexual orientation.

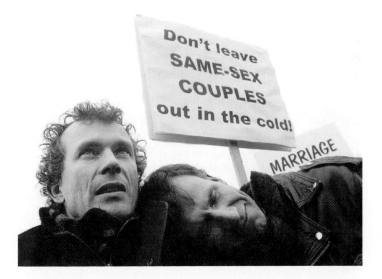

Gay Rights. *Gay men, lesbians, and those who care about them have participated in demonstrations demanding equal access to housing, jobs, and other opportunities.*

"limited to degrees of bisexuality." We do know that the genitals of gay people differentiate prenatally in accord with their chromosomal gender (Whalen et al., 1990). It remains possible that imbalances in prenatal sex hormones may cause brain tissue to be sexually differentiated in one direction even though the genitals are differentiated in the other (Collaer & Hines, 1995).

The Structure of the Brain While there has been no research on the brains of lesbian or bisexual women, evidence suggests that there may be structural differences between the brains of heterosexual and gay men. In 1991, Simon LeVay, a neurobiologist at the Salk Institute in La Jolla, California, carried out autopsies on the brains of 35 men who had died of AIDS—19 gay men and 16 (presumably) heterosexual men. He found that a segment of the hypothalamus in the brains of the gay men was less than half the size of the same segment in the heterosexual men. The same brain segment was larger in the brain tissues of heterosexual men than in brain tissues obtained from a comparison group of 6 presumably heterosexual women. No significant differences in size were found between the brain tissues of the gay men and the women, however.

LeVay's findings are intriguing, but they are preliminary. We do not know, for example, whether the structural differences found by LeVay are innate. Nor should LeVay's findings be taken to mean that biology is destiny. As Richard Nakamura, a scientist with the National Institute of Mental Health, commented, "This [LeVay's findings] shouldn't be taken to mean that you're automatically [gay] if you have a structure of one size versus a structure of another size" (Angier, 1991).

Psychological Perspectives

Do family relationships play a role in the origins of sexual orientation? What are the effects of childhood sexual experiences? Psychoanalytic theory and learning theory provide two of the major psychological approaches to understanding the origins of sexual orientation.

Psychoanalytic Views Sigmund Freud, the originator of psychoanalytic theory, believed that children enter the world **polymorphously perverse**. That is, prior to internalizing social inhibitions, children are open to all forms of sexual stimulation. However, through proper resolution of the Oedipus complex, a boy will forsake his incestuous desires for his mother and come to identify with his father. As a result, his erotic attraction to his mother will eventually be transferred, or **displaced**, onto more appropriate *female* partners. A girl, through proper resolution of her Electra complex, will identify with her mother and seek erotic stimulation from men when she becomes sexually mature.

In Freud's view, a gay male or lesbian sexual orientation results from failure to successfully resolve the Oedipus complex by identifying with the parent of the same gender. In men, faulty resolution of the Oedipus complex is most likely to result from the so-called classic pattern of an emotionally "close-binding" mother and a "detached–hostile" father. A boy reared in such a family may come to identify with his mother and even to "transform himself into her" (Freud, 1922/1959, p. 40). He may thus become effeminate and develop sexual interest in men.

Freud believed that the mechanism of unresolved **castration anxiety** plays a role in a gay male sexual orientation. By the time the Oedipus complex takes effect, the boy will have learned from self-stimulation that he can obtain sexual pleasure from his penis. In his youthful fantasies, he associates this pleasure with mental images of his mother. He is also likely to have learned that females do not possess a penis. Somewhere along the line the psychoanalyst theorizes that the boy may also have been warned that his penis will be removed if he plays with himself. From all this, the boy may surmise that females—including his mother—once had penises, but that they were removed.

During the throes of the Oedipus complex, the boy unconsciously comes to fear that his father, his rival in love for the mother, will retaliate by removing the organ that

Polymorphously perverse In psychoanalytic theory, being receptive to all forms of sexual stimulation.

Displacement In psychoanalytic theory, a defence mechanism that allows one to transfer unacceptable wishes or desires onto more appropriate or less threatening objects.

Castration anxiety In psychoanalytic theory, a man's fear that his genitals will be removed. Castration anxiety is an element of the Oedipus complex and is implicated in the directionality of erotic interests.

the boy has come to associate with sexual pleasure. His fear causes him to repress his sexual desire for his mother and to identify with the potential aggressor—his father. The boy thus overcomes his castration anxiety and is headed along the path of adult heterosexuality.

If the Oedipus complex is not successfully resolved, castration anxiety may persist. When sexually mature, the man will not be able to tolerate sex with women. Their lack of a penis will arouse unconscious castration anxiety within himself. According to psychoanalytic theory, the boy may unconsciously associate the vagina with teeth, or other sharp instruments, and be unable to perform sexually with a woman.

The Electra complex in little girls follows a somewhat different course. Freud believed that little girls become envious of boys' penises, since they lack their own. This concept of **penis envy** was one of Freud's most controversial beliefs. In Freud's view, jealousy leads little girls to resent their mothers, whom they blame for their anatomic "deficiency," and to turn from their mothers to their fathers as sexual objects. They now desire to possess the father, because the father's penis provides what they lack. But incestuous desires bring the girl into competition with her mother. Motivated by fear that her mother will withdraw her love if the desires persist, the girl normally represses them and identifies with her mother. She then develops traditional feminine interests and eventually seeks erotic stimulation from men. She supplants her childhood desire for a penis with a desire to marry a man and bear children. The baby, emitted from between her legs, serves as the ultimate penis substitute.

A girl who does not resolve her penis envy in childhood may "manifest homosexuality,… exhibit markedly masculine traits in the conduct of her later life, choose a masculine vocation, and so on" (Freud, 1922/1959, p. 50). The residue of this unresolved complex is continued penis envy, the striving to become a man by acting like a man and seeking sexual satisfaction with women: lesbianism.

In Freud's view, a gay male or lesbian sexual orientation is one result of assuming the gender role normally taken up by the other gender. The gay male is expected to be effeminate; the lesbian, masculine. But, as noted in research into gender-typed behaviour and sexual orientation, this stereotypical view of gay people is far from universal. Nor do the behaviours stereotypical of the other gender found in some adult gay men or women necessarily derive from Oedipal problems. Biological and other psychosocial factors may be involved.

A nagging problem of Freudian theory is that many of its concepts, such as castration anxiety and penis envy, are believed to operate at an unconscious level. As such, they lie beyond the scope of scientific observation and measurement. We cannot learn whether boys experience castration anxiety by asking them, since the theory claims that **repression** will keep such anxieties out of awareness. Nor can we directly learn about penis envy by interviewing girls.

Research on Psychoanalytic Theories of Sexual Orientation

Psychoanalysts—psychotherapists trained in the Freudian tradition—have researched sexual orientation largely through case studies. These studies have been carried out almost exclusively with gay males who were in therapy at the time.

In 1962, psychoanalyst Irving Bieber reported the results of questionnaires filled out by 77 psychiatrists on 106 gay male clients. In 1976, he reported the results of similar surveys of gay men in therapy.

Bieber claimed to find the "classic pattern" among gay males—their orientation was determined by having a dominant, "smothering" mother and a passive, detached father. As the clients described them, the mothers were overprotective, seductive, and jealous of their sons. The fathers were aloof, unaffectionate, and hostile toward them. The father, being detached, may have failed to buffer the close mother–son relationship. The mother's relationship with the father was typically disturbed, and the mother may have substituted a "close-binding" relationship with her son. This classic pattern was believed to result in the boy's developing a fear of sexual contacts with women. Though he would be unconscious of this dynamic, for him, any female partner would represent his mother. Desire for her would stir unconscious fears of retaliation by the father—that is, castration anxiety.

Penis envy In psychoanalytic theory, the girl's wish to have a penis.

Repression The automatic ejection of anxiety-evoking ideas from consciousness.

Bieber's findings may be criticized on several grounds:

1. The study participants were all in analysis, and many wanted to become heterosexual. Thus we cannot generalize the results to well-adjusted gay men.

2. The analysts may have chosen cases that confirmed their theoretical perspectives.

3. No clear evidence exists that gay males either fear or are repulsed by female genitalia.

4. Many heterosexual men have family backgrounds that fit the classic pattern, and the families of many gay men do not fit the pattern.

5. Retrospective accounts of childhood relationships with parents are subject to gaps in memory and distortions.

More recent evidence has brought the issue of familial closeness between gay men and their parents into closer perspective. Richard Pillard and his colleagues (Pillard & Weinrich, 1986; Pillard, 1990) found that gay males described themselves as more distant from their fathers during childhood than did either heterosexual controls or the gay men's own heterosexual brothers. The gay men in their sample also reported greater closeness to their mothers. Still, the father's psychological distance from the son may have reflected the son's alienation from him, not the reverse. That is, the son may have been so attached to his mother, or so uninterested in traditional masculine activities, that he rebuffed paternal attempts to engage him in conventional father–son activities.

In sum, family characteristics may play a role in the development of sexual orientation. However, there is great variation among the families of gay males and lesbians. No single pattern applies in all cases (Isay, 1990). Family dynamics may be one of many factors that shape sexual orientation.

Learning Theories Learning theorists agree with Freud that early experiences play an important role in the development of sexual orientation. They focus on the role of reinforcement of early patterns of sexual behaviour, however, rather than on the resolution of unconscious conflicts. People generally repeat pleasurable activities and discontinue painful ones. Thus, people may learn to engage in sexual activity with people of their own gender if childhood sexual experimentation with them is connected with sexual pleasure.

If sexual motivation is high, as it tends to be during adolescence, and the only outlets are with others of one's own gender, adolescents may experiment sexually with them. If these encounters are pleasurable, and heterosexual experiences are unpleasant, a firmer gay male or lesbian sexual orientation may develop (Gagnon & Simon, 1973). Conversely, pain, anxiety, or social disapproval may be connected with early contacts with people of one's own gender. In such cases, the child may learn to inhibit feelings of attraction to people of his or her own gender and develop a firmer heterosexual orientation.

Although learning may play a role in the development of a gay male or lesbian sexual orientation, most adolescent encounters with people of the same gender, even if pleasurable, do not lead to an adult gay male or lesbian sexual orientation. Many heterosexual people have had adolescent encounters with members of their own gender without being swayed in their adult orientations. Moreover, the overwhelming majority of gay males and lesbians were aware of sexual interest in people of their own gender before they had sexual encounters with them, pleasurable or otherwise (Bell et al., 1981).

Twin Studies. *Twin studies are important in raising "nature versus nurture" issues in research.*

All in all, the origins of sexual orientation remain mysterious and complex. Perhaps sexual orientation springs from multiple origins, including biological and psychosocial factors (Strickland, 1995). Genetic and biochemical factors (such as hormone levels) may affect the prenatal organization of the brain (Money, 1994). These factors may predispose people to a certain sexual orientation. But it may be that early socialization experiences are also involved. The precise effects of these factors have so far eluded researchers.

Adjustment of Gay Males and Lesbians

Answers to Your Questions About Sexual Orientation and Homosexuality
www.apa.org/pubinfo/answers.html
This American Psychiatric Association page answers questions about sexual orientation and states that research has confirmed that homosexuality is not a form of mental illness.

Despite the widespread belief that there is something wrong with gay men and lesbians, evidence has failed to show that they are more emotionally unstable or more subject to psychological disorders (such as anxiety and depression) than other people (Reiss, 1980; Cochrane 2001). Nor have researchers been able to distinguish between gay and heterosexual people on the basis of psychological tests (Reiss, 1980). A gay male or lesbian sexual orientation is no longer itself considered a form of mental illness. In 1973, after heated debate, the American Psychiatric Association voted to drop a gay male or lesbian sexual orientation from its list of mental disorders, which is used as the standard reference throughout much of the world. A diagnostic category remains for people with persistent and marked distress about their sexual orientation (American Psychiatric Association, 1994, p. 538).

Gay men, lesbians, and bisexuals occupy all socioeconomic and vocational levels and follow a variety of lifestyles. Researchers find gay men and lesbians overall to be more highly educated than most Americans (Cronin, 1993). Bell and Weinberg (1978) found variations in adjustment in the gay community that seem to mirror the variations in the heterosexual community. Gay people who lived with partners in stable, intimate relationships—so-called close couples—were about as well adjusted as married people. Older gay people who lived alone and had few sexual contacts were more poorly adjusted. So, too, are many heterosexual people who have similar lifestyles. All in all, differences in adjustment seem more likely to reflect the lifestyle than the sexual orientation.

"Treatment" of Gay Male and Lesbian Sexual Orientations

Despite the judgment of the American Psychiatric Association, some people still view a gay male or a lesbian sexual orientation as an illness.

While the majority of gay men and lesbians reject the belief that sexual orientation is an illness to be "cured," a few gay men and women do express an interest in changing their orientations. Helping professionals have tried to help them do so in a variety of ways. At one time, when it was commonly believed that hormonal imbalances influenced one's sexual orientation, hormone treatments were in vogue. There is no evidence that they were effective.

A few psychotherapists have reported changing the sexual orientations of some individuals. For example, Bieber (1976) claimed that about one in four clients changed his or her sexual orientation through psychoanalytic psychotherapy. But critics charge that these clients were highly motivated to change. Moreover, some of them began therapy as bisexuals. Their change in lifestyle may be attributable to their initial motivation to change and not to the therapy itself.

Masters and Johnson (1979) employed methods used to treat sexual dysfunctions (see Chapter 12) to "reverse" patients' gay male or lesbian sexual orientations. For example, they involved gay males in a graded series of pleasurable activities with women, such as massage and genital stimulation. Masters and Johnson reported a failure rate of 20% for the gay men and 23% for the lesbians they treated in their therapy program. At a five-year follow-up, more than 70% of the clients continued to engage in male–female sexual activity (Schwartz & Masters, 1984). For many reasons, however, these patients do not seem to represent the general gay population:

- Most of them were bisexuals. Only about one in five engaged exclusively in male–male or female–female sexual activities.
- More than half were married.
- They all were motivated to switch their sexual orientations.

Regardless of these people's changes in sexual behaviour, remember that sexual behaviour is not the equivalent of sexual orientation. (It was thus inaccurate for Masters and Johnson to claim that they had reversed an individual's sexual orientation.) That is, many gay people engage in sexual activities with people of the other gender. Nevertheless, they still prefer to have such relationships with people of their own gender.

Green (2003) raises various ethical issues for therapists who practise conversion therapy. He points out that clients need to be informed of the high failure rate of such therapy. As well, there is evidence that some therapeutic interventions exacerbate a client's internalized homophobic feelings, thus promoting self-hatred and depression. Internalized homophobia is correlated with an increased incidence of suicide, substance abuse, and HIV-risk behaviours. Isay (1990), a psychoanalyst, argues that gay men and women often enter therapy because of conflicts that arise from social pressure and prejudice. Such pressures can create problems in the acceptance of one's gay male or lesbian sexual orientation. The role of the therapist, he argues, should be to help unburden the client of conflict and promote a more gratifying life as a gay person.

Gay Male and Lesbian Sexual Behaviour

Generally speaking, gay couples express themselves sexually through as wide a range of activities as heterosexual couples, with the exception of vaginal intercourse. But there are shades of difference between gay and heterosexual couples in sexual techniques.

Gay male couples tend to engage in sexual activities such as kissing, hugging, petting, mutual masturbation, fellatio, and anal intercourse. Laboratory observations of sexual relations between gay males by Masters and Johnson (1979) showed that gay males spent a good deal of time caressing their partners' bodies before approaching the genitals. After hugging and kissing, 31 of 42 gay male couples observed by Masters and Johnson used oral or manual nipple stimulation.

Not all gay males enjoy or practise anal intercourse. Of those who do, most alternate between being the inserter and the insertee. The frequency of anal intercourse among gay males is apparently declining in the face of the AIDS epidemic (Catania et al., 1991; Centers for Disease Control, 1990a; Sonenstein et al., 1989).

Risks of infection and of injury to the rectum or anus are associated with another sexual practice called "fisting." Fisting is the insertion of the fist or hand into the rectum, usually after the bowels have been evacuated with an enema.

Sexual techniques practised by lesbians vary. Lesbian couples report kissing, manual and oral breast stimulation, and manual and oral stimulation of the genitals (Kinsey et al., 1953). Manual genital stimulation is the most common and frequent sexual activity among lesbian couples (Bell & Weinberg, 1978). Most lesbian couples also engage in genital apposition. That is, they position themselves so as to rub their genitals together rhythmically (Kinsey et al., 1953). Like gay males, lesbians spend a good deal of time holding, kissing, and caressing each other's bodies before they approach the breasts and genitals. By contrast, heterosexual males tend to move quickly to stimulate their partners' breasts or start directly with genital stimulation (Masters & Johnson, 1979).

Like heterosexual women, lesbians are less genitally oriented and less fixated on orgasm than men. Lesbians generally begin stimulating their partners with more general genital stimulation rather than direct clitoral stimulation, whereas heterosexual males often begin by stimulating the clitoris (Masters & Johnson, 1979). Nor do lesbian couples generally engage in deep penetration of the vagina with fingers. Rather, they may use more shallow vaginal penetration, focusing stimulation on the vaginal lips and entrance. The emotional components of lovemaking—gentle touching, cuddling, and hugging—are important elements of sexual sharing in lesbian relationships.

Gay Lifestyles

One of the mistakes that lay people (and some researchers) make is to treat gay people as if they were all the same. According to Bell and Weinberg (1978), gay people do not adopt a single, stereotypical lifestyle. That is why the authors termed their report *Homosexualities: A Study of Diversity Among Men and Women*. Variations in sexual expression exist within and across sexual orientations. Descriptions of gay and heterosexual lifestyles must consider individual differences.

Gay men and lesbians in larger urban centres can usually look to gay community structures to provide services and support. These include gay rights organizations and gay-oriented newspapers, magazines, bookstores, housing cooperatives, medical services, and other support services (Gagnon, 1990). The gay community provides a sense of acceptance and belonging that gay people do not typically find in society at large. Gay people still encounter discrimination in the workplace, in housing, and in the military.

Before 1988, openly gay men and women were excluded from serving in the Canadian Forces. They were not allowed to enlist, and any soldier discovered to be gay or lesbian could be dismissed. Personnel were required to inform on fellow service members whom they suspected were homosexual. The passage of the Canadian Charter of Rights and Freedoms, while not specifically mentioning sexual orientation, did bring this exclusionary policy under closer scrutiny, however. In 1992, the restriction on gay men and lesbians serving in the Canadian Forces was lifted. In 1996, sexual orientation was added to the Canadian Human Rights Act as prohibited grounds for discrimination.

Gay rights organizations fight for the rights of gay people to participate fully in society—to teach in public schools, to adopt children, and to live together in sanctioned relationships. Cafés and social clubs provide places where gay men and lesbians can socialize and be open about their sexual orientations. Many organizations provide medical, social, and psychological assistance to gay males who have been afflicted by AIDS.

Not all gay people, however, feel that they are a part of the "gay community" or participate in gay rights organizations. For many, their sexual orientation is a part of their identity, but not a dominant theme that governs their social and political activities.

Lifestyle Differences Between Gay Males and Lesbians

Much of our knowledge of lifestyle patterns among gay males and lesbians comes from research that predates the AIDS epidemic. Researchers in the 1970s found that gay males were more likely than lesbians to engage in casual sex with many partners. Lesbians more often confined their sexual activity to a committed, affectionate relationship (Bell & Weinberg, 1978). Bell and Weinberg reported that 84% of gay males, as compared to about 7% of lesbian women, reported having more than 50 partners in their lifetimes. Seventy-nine percent of gay males in their study, as compared to only 6% of lesbians, reported that more than half of their partners had been strangers.

A survey of gay men and lesbians found that half of gay men (40% to 60%), and about three in four lesbians, were involved in a steady relationship (Peplau & Cochran, 1990). This research indicated that gay males within committed relationships had more permissive attitudes toward extracurricular sexual activity than did lesbians (Blumstein & Schwartz, 1990; Peplau & Cochran, 1990). Research also indicates heterosexual men are more accepting of casual sex than are heterosexual women (Okami & Shackelford, 2001).

Traditionally, the gay bar was an arena for making sexual contacts (Bell & Weinberg, 1978). **Cruising** is the name gay people give to searching for a sex partner, principally for casual sex. One can "cruise," and one can "be cruised." In a 1993 Canadian survey of gay and bisexual men, 57% said they frequent gay bars at least once a week. Only 7% reported going to bathhouses on a weekly basis, while 54% said that they never go to bathhouses (Myers et al., 1993). Recent Canadian research indicates that gay and bisexual men are more likely to engage in risky sexual behaviour, such as unprotected anal sex, with their regular partners than with casual partners (Myers et al., 1999; Piaseczna et al., 2001).

Cruising The name that gay people give to searching for a sex partner.

Applications

Coming Out: Coming to Terms with Being Gay

Because of the backdrop of social condemnation and discrimination, gay males and lesbians in our culture often struggle to come to terms with their sexual orientation. Gay men and lesbians usually speak of the process of accepting their sexual orientation as "coming out" or as "coming out of the closet." Coming out is a two-pronged process: coming out to oneself (recognizing one's gay male or lesbian sexual orientation) and coming out to others (declaring one's orientation to the world). Coming out can create a sense of pride in one's sexual orientation and foster the ability to form emotionally and sexually satisfying relationships with gay male or lesbian partners.

Coming Out to Oneself

Many gay people have a difficult time coming to recognize, let alone accept, their sexual orientation. Some have even considered or attempted suicide because of problems in self-acceptance:

> It (suicidal thinking) was because of my homosexuality. I was completely depressed that my homosexuality was leading me nowhere. My life seemed to be going around in a circle. I was still fighting against recognition of my homosexuality. I knew what I was but I didn't want to be.
>
> [I had] the feeling that homosexuality was a hopeless existence. I felt there was no future in it, that I was doomed to be alone. And from my Catholic background, I felt that homosexuality was very evil.
>
> (Bell & Weinberg, 1978, p. 202)

Consider the experience of a New Zealand gay adolescent who was subjected to merciless taunting until his parents pulled him out of school. "He threw a ball like a girl does," said a hot-line worker (cited in Shenon, 1995), "and the hassling just wouldn't stop. He was hassled non-stop from the day he got to that school until the day he left."

"You're judged constantly on your maleness," adds a Roman Catholic priest in New Zealand (cited in Shenon, 1995). "It can be a very intolerant country. You must worship rugby and beer. And if you don't, God help you. I think we've just been dreadful about this macho-ness."

For some people, coming to recognize and accept a gay male or lesbian sexual orientation involves gradually stripping away layers of denial. For others it may be a sudden awakening. Long-standing sexual interest in members of one's own gender may rush into focus on a particular person, as happened with a graduate student named David:

> In college [David's] closest friend was gay. Although this friend had wanted to have sex with David and the attraction was mutual, David still could not associate this attraction with a sexuality that was not acceptable to him. In his first year of graduate school, when he was about 23, he fell in love and then suddenly and with a great sense of relief recognized and acknowledged to himself that he was homosexual. He then had sex for the first time and has subsequently been... open about his sexuality.
>
> (Isay, 1990, p. 295)

Recognition of a gay sexual orientation may be only the first step in a lifelong process of sexual identity formation. Acceptance of being gay becomes part of one's self-definition (Isay, 1990). The term *gay,* or *homosexual, identity* refers to the subjective or psychological sense of being gay.

Some gay men and lesbians who have not yet come to recognize or accept their gay sexual orientation get married to a person of the other gender. For some, marriage is a means of testing feelings toward people of the other gender, and also follows from a desire for children and a family life. For others, marriage represents an attempt to conceal or overcome their sexual orientation (Buxton, 1994; Gabriel, 1995). But such marriages tend to be unhappy and short-

lived. They may be strained by one partner's concealing her or his gay sexual orientation. Alternatively, they may buckle from the open acknowledgment of being gay. Virtually all such marriages in Bell and Weinberg's study eventually ended in separation or divorce.

In the 1990s, many couples had a gay or lesbian spouse. In some cases, gay men and lesbians who had conformed to social pressures by getting married came out of the closet and sometimes left home (Buxton, 1994; Gabriel, 1995).

Coming Out to Others

There are different patterns of coming out to others. Coming out occasionally means an open declaration to the world. More often a person may inform only one or a few select people. The person might tell friends but not family members.

Many gay men and lesbians remain reluctant to declare their sexual orientation, even to friends and family. Disclosure is fraught with the risk of loss of jobs, friendships, and social standing (Padesky, 1988). A social worker who counsels lesbians described some fears of coming out to others expressed by her clients:

> Will I lose my job, will I lose my house, will I lose my children, will I be attacked? I've seen people lose a job. Even if you don't lose it, you become marginal, excluded either actively or through uncomfortable vibes.
>
> (Cited in Barrett, 1990, p. 470)

Gay men and lesbians often anticipate negative reactions from informing family members, including denial, anger, and rejection. Family members and loved ones may refuse to hear or be unwilling to accept reality. Other families are more accepting. They may in fact have had suspicions and prepared themselves for such news. Then, too, many families are initially rejecting but often eventually come to at least grudging acceptance that their child is gay.

Research also shows that extracurricular sexual activity continues to be commonplace among gay male couples. One study surveyed 943 gay males and 1510 married heterosexual males who had been living with a partner for two to ten years. Four of five

(79%) of the gay males reported sex with another partner during the preceding year, as compared to only 11% of the heterosexual males (Blumstein & Schwartz, 1990). Among couples who had been together for longer than 10 years, 94% of gay men reported extracurricular activity at some time during their primary relationships.

Variations in Gay Lifestyles

Bell and Weinberg (1978) found that about three out of four gay couples they studied could be classified according to one of five lifestyles: close couples, open couples, functionals, dysfunctionals, and asexuals. **Close couples** strongly resembled married couples. They evidenced deep emotional commitment and few outside sexual relationships. Almost three times as many lesbians (28%) as gay males (10%) lived in such committed, intimate relationships. Gay people living in close relationships showed fewer social and psychological problems than those with any other lifestyle.

Partners in **open couples** lived together but engaged in clandestine affairs. Gay people in open couples were not as well adjusted as those in close couples. Nevertheless, their overall adjustment was similar to that of heterosexual people. Still other gay people lived alone and had sexual contacts with numerous partners—a kind of "swinging singles" gay lifestyle. Some of those who lived alone, **functionals**, appeared to have adapted well to their swinging lifestyle and were sociable and well adjusted. Others, called **dysfunctionals**, had sexual, social, or psychological problems. Dysfunctionals were often anxious, unhappy, and found it difficult to form intimate relationships. **Asexuals** also lived alone but were distinguished by having few sexual contacts. Asexuals tended to be older than gay people in the other groups. Although they did not have the adjustment problems of dysfunctionals, they too did not form intimate relationships. Despite being largely asexual in terms of their behaviour, their sexual orientation was clearly gay.

The Bell and Weinberg study described diversity of lifestyles in the gay community in the 1970s, before the AIDS epidemic struck. Although such lifestyles continue today to a certain extent, the AIDS epidemic has inhibited promiscuous sex within the gay community. The spectre of AIDS has had a more profound effect on the lifestyles and sexual practices of gay males than on any other group in society.

Close couples Bell and Weinberg's term for gay couples whose relationships resemble marriage in their depth of commitment and exclusiveness.

Open couples Bell and Weinberg's term for gay couples who live together but engage in secret affairs.

Functionals Bell and Weinberg's term for gay people who live alone, have adapted well to a swinging lifestyle, and are sociable and well adjusted.

Dysfunctionals Bell and Weinberg's term for gay people who live alone and have sexual, social, or psychological problems.

Asexuals Bell and Weinberg's term for gay people who live alone and have few sexual contacts.

Summing Up

Coming to Terms with Terms

Sexual orientation describes the directionality of one's sexual and romantic interests—toward members of the same gender, members of the other gender, or both. Gay male and lesbian sexual orientations denote sexual and romantic interest in members of one's own gender. **Kinsey** and his colleagues found evidence of degrees of homosexuality and heterosexuality, with bisexuality representing a midpoint between the two. Heterosexuality and homosexuality may, however, be separate dimensions rather than polar opposites. **Bisexual** people are attracted to both males and females. Many have a somewhat stronger attraction to one gender than to the other, yet they remain bisexual.

Perspectives on Gay Male and Lesbian Sexual Orientations

Historical and cross-cultural perspectives: Throughout much of Western history, gay people have been deemed sinful and criminal. But male–male sexual behaviour is practised by at least some members of many preliterate societies.

Contemporary attitudes: Many people in our society view gay people negatively. During the past generation, gay males and lesbians have organized effective political groups to fight discrimination and overturn laws that have traditionally targeted them. Recent polls in Canada show that a majority of the population support gay marriage and that younger Canadians are more accepting of gay men and lesbians than older Canadians.

Biological perspectives: Evidence of a genetic contribution to sexual orientation is accumulating. Research has failed to connect sexual orientation with differences in current (adult) levels of sex hormones. Prenatal sex hormones may, however, play a role in determining sexual orientation in humans.

Psychological perspectives: Psychoanalytic theory connects sexual orientation with unconscious castration anxiety and improper resolution of the Oedipus complex. Learning theorists focus on the role of reinforcement of early patterns of sexual behaviour.

Adjustment of Gay Males and Lesbians

Evidence has failed to show that gay males, lesbians, and bisexuals are more emotionally unstable or more subject to psychiatric disorders than heterosexual people are.

Gay Male and Lesbian Sexual Behaviour

Gay people generally express themselves sexually through as wide a range of activities as heterosexual people do, with the exception of vaginal intercourse.

Gay Lifestyles

Gay people do not adopt a single, stereotypical lifestyle. Gay males are more likely than lesbians to engage in casual sex with many partners. Lesbians more often confine sexual activity to a committed, affectionate relationship. Many gay males have changed their sexual behaviour to prevent contracting or spreading AIDS. The majority of gay people studied by Bell and Weinberg could be classified as representing one of five lifestyles: close couples, open couples, functionals, dysfunctionals, and asexuals.

Chapter Quiz

1. What is the usual relationship between sexual orientation and gender identity?
   (a) Bisexuals have a confused gender identity.
   (b) Gender identity develops later than usual among gay males and lesbians.
   (c) There is no research on the relationship between sexual orientation and gender identity.
   (d) Gay people have a gender identity that is consistent with their anatomic gender.

2. In a survey of male readers of *Playboy* magazine, of those who had sexual experiences with both men and women in adulthood, _____ reported themselves to be heterosexual rather than bisexual.
   (a) none
   (b) one-third

   (c) one-half
   (d) more than two-thirds

3. Kinsey and his colleagues conceived a _____-point "heterosexual–homosexual continuum."
   (a) 2
   (b) 5
   (c) 7
   (d) 10

4. The term *sodomy* most commonly refers to
   (a) anal intercourse.
   (b) masturbation.
   (c) oral–anal sexual activity.
   (d) sexual activity with three or more partners.

5. Why do young Sambian males perform fellatio on older males?
   (a) They have Dominican Republic syndrome and spend their early years as females.
   (b) They are attempting to achieve the fierce manhood of the headhunter.
   (c) Sexual orientation changes frequently during childhood and adolescence.
   (d) They are paid to do so as part of a religious ritual.

6. Research conducted by Henry Adams and his colleagues (1996) suggests that many men may be homophobic because
   (a) they drink (alcohol) excessively.
   (b) they have sexual interest in other men but are unaware of it.
   (c) of the AIDS epidemic.
   (d) the Judeo-Christian tradition frowns on male–male sexual behaviour.

7. Which of the following statements about genetics and sexual orientation is most accurate?
   (a) A gay male orientation is not found among MZ and DZ twins.
   (b) The concordance rate for a gay male orientation is equal among MZ and DZ twins.
   (c) The concordance rate for a gay male orientation is higher among MZ than DZ twins.
   (d) The concordance rate for a gay male orientation is higher among DZ than MZ twins.

8. Simon LeVay conducted research on sexual orientation through
   (a) the survey method.
   (b) autopsies of the brains of people who died from AIDS.
   (c) studies of the genetic makeup of heterosexuals and gay people.
   (d) cross-cultural research.

9. According to _____, sexual orientation in males is connected with the resolution of the Oedipus complex.
   (a) Michael Storms
   (b) Alfred Kinsey
   (c) Alan Bell
   (d) Sigmund Freud

10. Which of the following statements about gender and sexual orientation appears to be best supported by research reported in the text?
   (a) Lesbians are more likely than gay males to have many sex partners.
   (b) Gay males are more likely than lesbians to have many sex partners.
   (c) Heterosexual males are more likely than gay males to have many sex partners.
   (d) Heterosexual females are more likely than lesbians to have many sex partners.

Chapter 9

Conception, Pregnancy, and Childbirth

Did You Know That...

• Fertilization normally occurs in a fallopian tube, not the uterus?

• Prolonged athletic activity can decrease fertility in the male?

• A human embryo can be removed from one woman and implanted in the uterus of another?

• Morning sickness can actually occur throughout the day?

• In most cases, sexual intercourse is safe throughout the course of pregnancy?

• For the first week following conception, a fertilized egg cell is not attached to its mother's body?

• The placenta is unique in that it develops from material supplied by both mother and embryo?

• The majority of babies born to mothers who are infected with HIV do not become infected themselves?

• Most women who have had caesarean deliveries can subsequently have vaginal deliveries?

• More than 70% of Canadian women breast-feed their babies?

Conception is the union of a sperm cell and an ovum. On one hand, conception is the beginning of a new human life. Conception is also the end of a fantastic voyage, however, in which a viable ovum, one of only several hundred that will mature and ripen during a woman's lifetime, unites with one of several hundred *million* sperm produced by the man in the average ejaculate.

Ova carry X sex chromosomes. Sperm carry either X or Y sex chromosomes. Girls are conceived from the union of an ovum and an X-bearing sperm, boys from the union of an ovum and a Y-bearing sperm.

The 200 to 400 million sperm in an average ejaculate may seem excessive, since only one can fertilize an egg. Only 1 in 1000, however, will ever arrive in the vicinity of an ovum. Millions deposited in the vagina simply flow out of the woman's body because of gravity, unless she remains lying down for quite some time. Normal vaginal acidity kills many more. Many surviving sperm swim against the current of fluid coming from the cervix, through the os and into the uterus. Surviving sperm may reach the fallopian tubes 60 to 90 minutes after ejaculation. About half the sperm end up in the wrong tube—that is, the one not containing the egg. Perhaps some 2000 sperm find their way into the right tube. Fewer still manage to swim the final 5 cm against the currents generated by the cilia that line the tube.

Fertilization normally occurs in a fallopian tube. (Figure 9.1 shows sperm swarming around an egg in a fallopian tube.) Ova are surrounded by a gelatinous layer called the **zona pellucida**. Sperm that have completed their journey secrete the enzyme **hyaluronidase**, which briefly thins the zona pellucida, enabling one sperm to penetrate. Once a sperm has entered, the zona pellucida thickens, locking other sperm out. The corresponding chromosomes in the sperm and ovum line up opposite each other. Conception occurs as the chromosomes from the sperm and ovum combine to form 23 new pairs, which carry a unique set of genetic instructions.

Figure 9.1. Human Sperm Swarming Around an Ovum in a Fallopian Tube.

Fertilization normally occurs in a fallopian tube, not in the uterus.

Zona pellucida A gelatinous layer that surrounds an ovum. (From roots meaning "zone that light can shine through.")

Hyaluronidase An enzyme that briefly thins the zona pellucida, enabling one sperm to penetrate. (From roots meaning "substance that breaks down a glasslike fluid.")

Infertility Inability to conceive a child.

Infertility and Ways of Becoming Parents

The term **infertility** is usually not applied until the failure to conceive has persisted for more than a year. Infertility concerns many Canadians. Because the incidence of infertility increases with age, it is partly the result of a rise in couples who postpone childbearing until their 30s and 40s (Sheehy, 1995). All in all, about 15% of North American couples have fertility problems (Howards, 1995). However, about half of them

Applications

Optimizing the Chances of Conception

Some couples may wish to optimize their chances of conceiving during a particular month so that birth occurs at a desired time. Others may have difficulty conceiving and wish to maximize their chances for a few months before consulting a fertility specialist. Some fairly simple procedures can dramatically increase the chances of conceiving for couples without serious fertility problems.

The ovum can be fertilized for about 4 to 20 hours after ovulation. Sperm are most active within 48 hours after ejaculation. So one way of optimizing the chances of conception is to engage in coitus within a few hours of ovulation. There are a number of ways to predict ovulation.

Using the Basal Body Temperature Chart

Few women have perfectly regular cycles, so they can only guess when they are ovulating. In fact, a British study of 221 women found that ovulation could occur as early as day 8 and as late as day 60 in the menstrual cycle (Wilcox, et al., 2000). A basal body temperature (BBT) chart (see Figure 9.2) may help provide a more reliable estimate.

Body temperature is fairly even before ovulation, and early morning body temperature is generally below 37 degrees Celsius. But just prior to ovulation, basal temperature dips. On the day following ovulation, temperature tends to rise by about 0.2 to 0.5 degrees and to remain higher until menstruation. In using the BBT method, a women attempts to detect these temperature changes by tracking her temperature just after awakening each morning but before rising from bed. The couple record the woman's temperature and the day of the cycle (as well as the day of the month)

and indicate whether they have engaged in coitus. With regular charting for six months, the woman may learn to predict the day of ovulation more accurately—assuming that her cycles are fairly regular.

Analyzing Urine for Luteinizing Hormone

Over-the-counter kits are more accurate than the BBT method. They predict ovulation by analyzing the woman's urine for the surge in luteinizing hormone (LH) that precedes ovulation.

Tracking Vaginal Mucus

Women can track the thickness of their vaginal mucus during the phases of the menstrual cycle by rolling it between their fingers and noting changes in texture. The mucus is thick, white, and cloudy during most phases of the cycle. It becomes thin, slippery, and clear for a few

days preceding ovulation. A day or so after ovulation the mucus again thickens and becomes opaque.

Additional Considerations

Coitus in the male-superior position allows sperm to be deposited deeper in the vagina and minimizes leakage of sperm out of the vagina due to gravity. Women may improve their chances of conceiving by lying on their backs and drawing their knees close to their breasts following ejaculation. This position makes gravity work for, rather than against, conception. Women may also lie still for about 30 to 60 minutes following ejaculation.

The man should penetrate the woman as deeply as possible just prior to ejaculation, hold still during ejaculation, and then withdraw slowly in a straight line to avoid dispersing the pool of semen.

Figure 9.2. A Basal Body Temperature (BBT) Chart.
Body temperature dips slightly just prior to ovulation, rises about 0.2 to 0.5 of a degree following ovulation, and remains elevated through the course of the cycle. Part (a) represents a cycle in which a sustained elevation in temperature occurred following ovulation on day 15. Part (b) shows no sustained temperature rise, which is indicative of an absence of ovulation in this cycle.
Source: Adapted from Kolodny, R.C., Masters, W.H., and Johnson, V.E. (1979). *Textbook of Sexual Medicine.*

eventually succeed in conceiving a child (Jones & Toner, 1993). Many treatment options are available, ranging from drugs to stimulate ovulation to newer reproductive technologies, such as in vitro fertilization.

Male Fertility Problems

Although most concerns about fertility have traditionally centred on women, the problem lies with the man in about 30% of cases (Howards, 1995). In about 20% of cases, problems are found in both partners (Hatcher et al., 1990; Howards, 1995).

Fertility problems in the male may be due to a number of different factors, including

1. Low sperm count
2. Irregularly shaped sperm—for example, malformed heads or tails
3. Low sperm **motility**
4. Chronic diseases such as diabetes, as well as infectious diseases such as sexually transmitted infections
5. Injury to the testes
6. An **autoimmune response**, in which antibodies produced by the man deactivate his own sperm
7. A pituitary imbalance and/or thyroid disease

> **Motility** Self-propulsion. A measure of the viability of sperm cells.
>
> **Autoimmune response** The production of antibodies that attack naturally occurring substances that are (incorrectly) recognized as being foreign or harmful.

Problems in producing normal, abundant sperm may be caused by genetic factors, advanced age, hormonal problems, diabetes, injuries to the testes, varicose veins in the scrotum, drugs (alcohol, narcotics, marijuana, tobacco), antihypertensive medications, environmental toxins, excess heat, and emotional stress.

Low sperm count is the most common problem. Sperm counts of 40 million to 150 million sperm per millilitre of semen are considered normal. A count of fewer than 20 million is generally regarded as low. Sperm production may be low among men with undescended testes that were not surgically corrected prior to puberty. Frequent ejaculation can reduce sperm counts. Sperm production may also be impaired in men whose testicles are consistently .5 to 1 degree above the typical scrotal temperature of 34.5 to 35 degrees Celsius (Leary, 1990). Some men may encounter temporary fertility problems from prolonged athletic activity, use of electric blankets, wearing tight-fitting underwear, or even long, hot baths. In such cases the problem can be readily corrected. Male runners with fertility problems are often counselled to take time off to increase their sperm counts.

Infertility Awareness Association of Canada **www.iaac.ca/** This association works for choices in and access to treatment for those with infertility concerns, through awareness, support, and education.

Sometimes the sperm count is adequate, but prostate, hormonal, or other factors deprive sperm of motility or deform them. Motility can also be hampered by scar tissue from infections. Scarring may prevent sperm from passing through parts of the male reproductive system, such as the vas deferens. To be considered normal, sperm must be able to swim for at least two hours following coitus, and most (60% or more) must be normal in shape.

Sperm counts have been increased by surgical repair of the varicose veins in the scrotum. Microsurgery can open blocked passageways that prevent the outflow of sperm (Howards, 1995). Most men whose infertility is due to higher-than-normal scrotal temperatures show increased sperm count and quality with the wearing of cooling undergarments (Leary, 1990; Silber, 1991).

Artificial Insemination The sperm of men with low sperm counts can be collected and quick-frozen. The sperm from multiple ejaculations can then be injected into a woman's uterus at the time of ovulation. This is one kind of **artificial insemination**. The sperm of men with low sperm motility can also be injected into their partners' uteruses, so that the sperm begin their journey closer to their destination. Sperm from a donor can be used to artificially inseminate a woman whose partner is infertile. The child then bears the genes of one of the parents, the mother. A donor can be chosen who resembles the man in physical traits and ethnic background.

> **Artificial insemination** The introduction of sperm into the reproductive tract through means other than sexual intercourse.

In 2003, Parliament passed legislation to regulate artificial insemination and other aspects of assisted human reproduction. Bill C-13, among other things, created a sperm donor databank to provide people conceived by artificial insemination with access to medical information about their donors.

Female Fertility Problems

Major causes of infertility in women include the following:

1. Irregular ovulation, including failure to ovulate
2. Obstructions or malfunctions of the reproductive tract
3. Endometriosis
4. Polycystic ovary syndrome (PCOS)
5. Declining hormone levels that occur with aging and may prevent the ovum from becoming fertilized or remaining implanted in the uterus

Ten to 15 percent of female infertility problems stem from failure to ovulate. Many factors can play a role in failure to ovulate, including hormonal irregularities, malnutrition, genetic factors, stress, and disease. Failure to ovulate may occur in response to extreme dieting, as in the case of the eating disorder anorexia nervosa.

Ovulation may often be induced by the use of fertility drugs such as clomiphene (Clomid). Clomiphene stimulates the pituitary gland to secrete FSH and LH, which in turn stimulate maturation of ova. Clomiphene leads to conception in the majority of cases of infertility that are due *solely* to irregular or absent ovulation (Reinisch, 1990). But since infertility can have multiple causes, only about 50% of women who use clomiphene become pregnant. Another fertility drug, Pergonal, contains a high concentration of FSH, which directly stimulates maturation of ovarian follicles. Like clomiphene, Pergonal has high success rates with women whose infertility is due to lack of ovulation. Clomiphene and Pergonal have been linked to multiple births, including quadruplets and even quintuplets.

Local infections that scar the fallopian tubes and other organs impede the passage of sperm or ova. Such infections include pelvic inflammatory disease—an inflammation of the woman's internal reproductive tract that can be caused by various infectious agents, such as the bacteria responsible for gonorrhea and chlamydia (see Chapter 13).

In **endometriosis**, cells break away from the uterine lining (the endometrium) and become implanted and grow elsewhere. When they grow on the surface of the ovaries or fallopian tubes, they may block the passage of ova or impair conception. About one case in six of female sterility is believed to be due to endometriosis. Hormone treatments and surgery sometimes reduce the blockage to the point that women can conceive. A physician may suspect endometriosis during a pelvic exam, but it is diagnosed with certainty by **laparoscopy**. A long, narrow tube is inserted through an incision in the navel, permitting the physician to inspect the organs in the pelvic cavity visually. The incision is practically undetectable.

Polycystic ovary syndrome (PCOS) is one of the leading causes of infertility in women. The exact causes of PCOS are unknown, but it is often hereditary. Women with PCOS may have infrequent or absent menstrual periods, ovulate infrequently or not at all, and have increased growth of facial and body hair and obesity. Treatments include hormonal therapies, including oral contraceptives and anti-androgen drugs, drugs to lower insulin levels, surgical removal of part of the ovary and, if a woman is having difficulty becoming pregnant, fertility drugs.

Several new methods help many couples with problems, such as blocked fallopian tubes, bear children.

In Vitro Fertilization
In the method of **in vitro fertilization** (IVF), conception takes place in a laboratory dish (not a test tube). Fertility drugs may be used to ripen a number of ova. Ripe ova are then surgically removed from an ovary and placed in a laboratory dish along with the father's sperm. The fertilized egg is then placed in the mother's uterus, where it must become implanted to develop to term.

GIFT
In **gamete intrafallopian transfer**, or GIFT, sperm and ova are inserted together into a fallopian tube for fertilization. Unlike in vitro fertilization, conception occurs in a fallopian tube rather than a laboratory dish.

Endometriosis A condition caused by the growth of endometrial tissue in the abdominal cavity or elsewhere outside the uterus. Characterized by menstrual pain, it may cause infertility.

Laparoscopy A medical procedure in which a long, narrow tube (laparoscope) is inserted through an incision in the navel, permitting visual inspection of organs in the pelvic cavity. (From the Greek *lapara*, meaning "flank.")

Polycystic ovary syndrome (PCOS) A condition whose exact causes are unknown. Characterized by infrequent or absent ovulation and menstrual periods, increased growth of facial and body hair, and obesity, it may cause infertility.

Polycystic Ovary Syndrome Health Centre
www.womenshealthmatters.ca/centres/pelvic_health/PCOS/
Information on PCOS is available at this Canadian website.

In vitro fertilization A method of conception in which mature ova are surgically removed from an ovary and placed in a laboratory dish along with sperm.

Gamete intrafallopian transfer (GIFT) A method of conception in which mature sperm and ova are inserted into a fallopian tube to encourage conception.

ZIFT **ZIFT (zygote intrafallopian transfer)** involves a combination of IVF and GIFT. Sperm and ova are combined in a laboratory dish. Following fertilization, the **zygote** is placed in the mother's fallopian tube to begin its journey to the uterus for implantation. ZIFT has an advantage over GIFT in that the fertility specialists can ascertain that fertilization has occurred before insertion is performed.

Donor IVF **Donor IVF** is a variation of the IVF procedure in which the ovum is taken from another woman, fertilized, and then injected into the uterus or fallopian tube of the intended mother. The procedure is used in cases in which the intended mother does not produce ova.

Embryonic Transfer A similar method for women who do not produce ova of their own is **embryonic transfer**. In this method a woman volunteer is artificially inseminated by the male partner of the infertile woman. Five days later the embryo is removed from the volunteer and inserted within the uterus of the mother-to-be.

In vitro and transfer methods are costly. Success with in vitro fertilization drops from nearly 30% in women in their mid-20s to 10% to 15% in women in their late 30s (Toner et al., 1991). As success remains elusive in many cases, frustration and lack of hope often lead couples to consider dropping out of infertility treatment programs (Blenner, 1992).

Intracytoplasmic Injection **Intracytoplasmic injection** has been used when the man has too few sperm for IVF, or when IVF fails (Howards, 1995). In this method, sperm is injected directly into an ovum. To date, the method has resulted in pregnancy in about 35% of cases (Van Steirteghem et al., 1993).

Surrogate Motherhood A **surrogate mother** is artificially inseminated by the partner of the infertile woman and carries the baby to term. The surrogate may sign a contract to turn the baby over to the infertile couple. Such contracts are illegal in Canada, however, so surrogate mothers cannot be compelled to hand over the baby. Bill C-13 also made it illegal to pay a woman to be a surrogate mother.

Adoption

Adoption is yet another way for people to become parents. Despite the occasional conflicts in which adoptive parents are pitted against biological parents who change their minds about giving their children up for adoption, most adoptions result in the formation of loving new families. Many Canadians choose to adopt infants from other countries, infants with special needs, or older children.

Pregnancy

In this section we examine biological and psychological aspects of pregnancy: signs of pregnancy, prenatal development, complications, effects of drugs and sex, and the psychological experiences of pregnant women and fathers.

Early Signs of Pregnancy

For many women the first sign of pregnancy is missing a period. But some women have irregular menstrual cycles or miss a period because of stress. Missing a period is thus not a fully reliable indicator. Some women also experience cyclic bleeding or spotting during pregnancy, although the blood flow is usually lighter than normal. If a woman's basal body temperature remains high for about three weeks after ovulation, there is reason to suspect pregnancy even if she spots two weeks after ovulation.

Pregnancy Tests

Pregnancy tests rely on the fact that women produce **human chorionic gonadotropin** (HCG) shortly after conception. Tests can detect HCG in the urine as early as the third

Zygote intrafallopian transfer (ZIFT) A method of conception in which an ovum is fertilized in a laboratory dish and then placed in a fallopian tube.

Zygote A fertilized ovum (egg cell).

Donor IVF A variation of in vitro fertilization in which the ovum is taken from one woman, fertilized, and then injected into the uterus or fallopian tube of another woman.

Embryonic transfer A method of conception in which a woman volunteer is artificially inseminated by the male partner of the intended mother, after which the embryo is removed from the volunteer and inserted within the uterus of the intended mother.

Intracytoplasmic injection A method of conception in which sperm is injected directly into an ovum.

Surrogate mother A woman who is impregnated through artificial insemination with the sperm of a prospective father, carries the embryo and fetus to term, and then gives the child to the prospective parents.

Human chorionic gonadotropin A hormone produced by women shortly after conception, which stimulates the corpus luteum to continue to produce progesterone. The presence of HCG in a woman's urine indicates that she is pregnant.

week of pregnancy. A blood test can detect HCG in the woman's blood as early as the eighth day of pregnancy, about five days preceding her expected period.

Over-the-counter home pregnancy tests are also available. They too test the woman's urine for HCG and are intended to be used as early as one day after a missed period. Laboratory-based tests are considered 98% or 99% accurate. Home-based tests performed by lay people are somewhat less accurate. Women are advised to consult their physician if they suspect that they are pregnant or wish to confirm a home pregnancy test result.

About a month after a woman misses her period, a health professional may be able to confirm pregnancy by pelvic exam. Women who are pregnant usually show **Hegar's sign**. Hegar's sign is softness of a section of the uterus between the uterine body and the cervix, which may be palpated (felt) by the woman's physician by placing a hand on the abdomen and two fingers in the vagina.

Early Effects of Pregnancy

Just a few days after conception, a woman may note tenderness of the breasts. Hormonal stimulation of the mammary glands may make the breasts more sensitive and cause sensations of tingling and fullness.

Morning sickness, which may actually occur throughout the day, refers to the nausea, food aversions, and vomiting experienced during pregnancy. About half of all pregnant women experience some degree of morning sickness during the first few months of pregnancy (Thompson, 1993). In some cases, morning sickness is so severe that the woman cannot eat regularly and must be hospitalized to ensure that she and the fetus receive adequate nutrition. Morning sickness usually subsides by about the twelfth week of pregnancy. Pregnant women may also experience greater-than-normal fatigue during the early weeks, so that they sleep longer and fall asleep more readily than usual. Frequent urination, which may also be experienced, is caused by pressure from the swelling uterus on the bladder.

Miscarriage

Miscarriages have many causes, including chromosomal defects in the fetus and abnormalities of the placenta and uterus. About three in four miscarriages occur in the first 16 weeks of pregnancy, and the great majority of these occur in the first seven weeks. Some miscarriages occur so early that the woman is not aware that she was pregnant. In most cases women who miscarry can carry subsequent pregnancies to term.

Sex During Pregnancy

Most health professionals concur that coitus is safe throughout the course of pregnancy until the start of labour, provided that the pregnancy is developing normally and the woman has no history of miscarriages. Women who experience bleeding or cramps during pregnancy may be advised by their obstetricians not to engage in coitus (Samuels & Samuels, 1986).

Many women show a decline in sexual interest and activity during the first trimester because of fatigue, nausea, or misguided concerns that coitus will harm the embryo or fetus. Also during the first trimester, vasocongestion may cause tenderness of the breasts, discouraging fondling and sucking. Researchers in Israel reported a gradual decline in sexual interest and frequency of intercourse and orgasm during pregnancy among a sample of 219 women. The greatest decline occurred during the third trimester (Hart et al., 1991). Pain during intercourse is also commonly reported, especially in the third trimester (Ulbrich et al., 1990).

As the woman's abdominal region swells, the popular male-superior position becomes unwieldy. The female-superior, lateral-entry, and rear-entry positions are common alternatives. Of course, manual and oral sex can continue as usual.

Hegar's sign Softness of a section of the uterus between the uterine body and the cervix, which indicates that a woman is pregnant.

Morning sickness Symptoms of pregnancy, including nausea, aversions to specific foods, and vomiting.

Miscarriage A spontaneous abortion.

Some women are concerned that the uterine contractions of orgasm may dislodge an embryo. Such concerns are usually unfounded, unless the woman has a history of miscarriage or is presently at risk of miscarriage. Women may also be concerned that orgasmic contractions during the final month may induce labour. Evidence on the issue is mixed, however. Women and their partners are advised to discuss their concerns with their obstetricians.

Psychological Changes During Pregnancy

A woman's psychological response to pregnancy reflects her desire to be pregnant, her physical changes, and her attitudes toward these changes. Women with the financial, social, and psychological resources to meet the needs of pregnancy and child rearing may welcome pregnancy. Other women may question their ability to handle their pregnancies and childbirth. Or they may fear that pregnancy will interfere with their careers or their mate's feelings about them. In general, women who want to have a baby are better adjusted during their pregnancies.

The first trimester may be difficult for women who are ambivalent about pregnancy. At that stage symptoms like morning sickness are most pronounced, and women must come to terms with being pregnant. The second trimester is generally less tempestuous.

Morning sickness and other symptoms have largely vanished. It is not yet difficult to move about, and the woman need not yet face the delivery. Women first note fetal movement during the second trimester, and for many the experience is stirring:

> I was lying on my stomach and felt—something, like someone lightly touching my deep insides. Then I just sat very still and... felt the hugeness of having something living growing in me. Then I said, No, it's not possible, it's too early yet, and then I started to cry.... That one moment was my first body awareness of another living thing inside me.

(BOSTON WOMEN'S HEALTH COLLECTIVE, 1992)

During the third trimester it is normal, especially for first-time mothers, to worry about the mechanics of delivery and whether the child will be normal. The woman becomes increasingly heavy and literally "bent out of shape." It may become difficult to get up from a chair or out of bed. She must sit farther from the steering wheel when driving. Muscle tension from supporting the extra weight in her abdomen may cause backaches. She may feel impatient in the days and weeks just prior to delivery.

Men, like women, respond to pregnancy according to the degree to which they want the child. Many men are proud and look forward to the child with great anticipation. In such cases, pregnancy may bring the couple closer together. But fathers who are financially or emotionally unprepared may consider the pregnancy a trap. Now and then an expectant father experiences some signs of pregnancy, including morning sickness and vomiting. This reaction is termed a **sympathetic pregnancy.**

Sympathetic pregnancy
The experiencing of a number of signs of pregnancy by the father.

Prenatal Development

We can date pregnancy from the onset of the last menstrual cycle before conception, which makes the normal gestation period 280 days. We can also date pregnancy from the date at which fertilization was assumed to have taken place, which normally corresponds to two weeks after the beginning of the woman's last menstrual cycle. In this case, the normal gestation period is 266 days.

Once pregnancy has been confirmed, the delivery date may be calculated by *Nagele's rule:*

- Note the date of the first day of the last menstrual period.
- Add seven days.
- Subtract three months.
- Add one year.

For example, if the last period began on November 12, 2004, adding seven days yields November 19, 2004. Then subtracting three months yields August 19, 2004. Adding one year gives a "due date" of August 19, 2005. Few babies are born exactly when they are due, but the great majority are delivered during a ten-day period that spans the date.

Shortly following conception, the single cell that results from the union of sperm and egg begins to multiply—becoming two cells, then four, then eight, and so on. During the weeks and months that follow, tissues, structures, and organs begin to form, and the fetus gradually takes on the shape of a human being. By the time the fetus is born, it consists of hundreds of billions of cells—more cells than there are stars in the Milky Way galaxy. Prenatal development can be divided into three periods: the *germinal stage*, which corresponds to about the first two weeks, the *embryonic stage*, which coincides with the first two months, and the *fetal stage*. We also commonly speak of prenatal development in terms of three trimesters of three months each.

The Germinal Stage

Germinal stage The period of prenatal development prior to implantation in the uterus.

Period of the ovum Germinal stage.

Blastocyst A stage within the germinal stage of prenatal development, in which the embryo is a sphere of cells surrounding a cavity of fluid.

Embryonic stage The stage of prenatal development that lasts from implantation through the eighth week and is characterized by the differentiation of the major organ systems.

Within 36 hours after conception, the zygote divides into two cells. It then divides repeatedly, becoming 32 cells within another 36 hours as it continues its journey to the uterus. It takes the zygote perhaps three or four days to reach the uterus. This mass of dividing cells then wanders about the uterus for perhaps another three or four days before it begins to become implanted in the uterine wall. The process of implantation takes about another week. This period from conception to implantation is termed the **germinal stage**, or the **period of the ovum** (see Figure 9.3).

Several days into the germinal stage, the cell mass takes the form of a fluid-filled ball of cells, which is called a **blastocyst**. Already some cell differentiation has begun. Cells begin to separate into groups that will eventually become different structures.

Implantation may be accompanied by some bleeding, which results from the usual rupturing of some small blood vessels that line the uterus. Bleeding can also be a sign of a miscarriage—though most women who experience implantation bleeding do not miscarry but go on to have normal pregnancies and deliver healthy babies.

The Embryonic Stage

The period from implantation to about the eighth week of development is called the **embryonic stage**. The major organ systems of the body begin to differentiate during this stage.

Figure 9.3. The Ovarian Cycle, Conception, and the Early Days of the Germinal Stage.

The zygote first divides about 36 hours after conception. Continuing division creates the hollow sphere of cells termed the blastocyst. The blastocyst normally becomes implanted in the wall of the uterus.

Prenatal Development. The rates of human growth and development are most dramatic prior to birth. Within a few months, a human fetus advances from less than a gram to several kilograms, and from one cell to billions of cells.

Development of the embryo follows two trends—**cephalocaudal** and **proximodistal**. The apparently oversized heads depicted in Figure 9.4 represent embryos and fetuses at various stages of prenatal development. Growth of the head (the cephalic region) takes precedence over the growth of the lower parts of the body. You can also think of the body as containing a central axis that coincides with the spinal cord. The growth of the organ systems that lie close to this axis (that is, proximal to the axis) takes precedence over the growth of those that lie farther away toward the extremities (that is, distal to the axis). Relatively early maturation of the brain and organ systems that lie near the central axis allows these organs to facilitate further development of the embryo and fetus.

During the third week of development, the head and blood vessels begin to form. By the fourth week, a primitive heart begins to beat and pump blood in an embryo that measures less than half a centimetre in length. The heart will normally continue to beat without rest for every minute of every day for the better part of a century. By the end of the first month of development we can see the beginnings of the arms and legs—"arm buds" and "leg buds." The mouth, eyes, ears, and nose begin to take shape. The brain and other parts of the nervous system begin to develop.

The arms and legs develop in accordance with the proximodistal principle. First the upper arms and legs develop, then the forearms and lower legs. Then the hands and feet form, followed by webbed fingers and toes by about six to eight weeks into development. The webbing is gone by the end of the second month. By this time the head has become rounded, and the limbs have elongated and separated. Facial features are visible. All this has occurred in an embryo that is about 2 cm long and weighs about 1 gram.

The Amniotic Sac

The embryo—and later on, the fetus—develops within a protective environment in the mother's uterus called the **amniotic sac**, which is surrounded by a clear membrane. The embryo and fetus are suspended within the sac in **amniotic**

Cephalocaudal From the head downward. (From Latin roots meaning "head" and "tail.")

Proximodistal From the central axis of the body outward. (From Latin roots meaning "near" and "far.")

Amniotic sac The sac containing the fetus.

Figure 9.4. Human Embryos and Fetuses.

Development is cephalocaudal and proximodistal. Growth of the head takes precedence over the growth of the lower parts of the body.

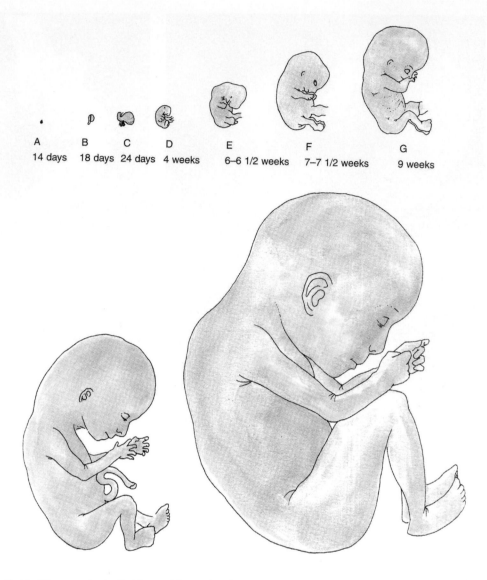

A	B	C	D	E	F	G
14 days	18 days	24 days	4 weeks	6–6 1/2 weeks	7–7 1/2 weeks	9 weeks

Amniotic fluid Fluid within the amniotic sac that suspends and protects the fetus.

Placenta An organ connected to the fetus by the umbilical cord. The placenta serves as a relay station between mother and fetus, allowing the exchange of nutrients and wastes.

Umbilical cord A tube that connects the fetus to the placenta.

fluid. The amniotic fluid acts like a shock absorber. It cushions the embryo from damage that might result from the mother's movements. The fluid also helps maintain a steady temperature.

The Placenta Nutrients and waste products are exchanged between mother and embryo (or fetus) through a mass of tissue called the **placenta**. The placenta is unique in origin. It develops from material supplied by both mother and embryo. Toward the end of the first trimester, it becomes a flattish, round organ about 18 cm in diameter and 2–3 cm thick—larger than the fetus itself. The fetus is connected to the placenta by the **umbilical cord**. The mother is connected to the placenta by the system of blood vessels in the uterine wall. The umbilical cord develops about five weeks after conception and reaches 50 cm in length. It contains two arteries through which maternal nutrients reach the embryo. A vein transports waste products back to the mother.

The circulatory systems of mother and embryo do not mix. A membrane in the placenta permits only certain substances to pass through, such as oxygen (from the mother to the fetus); carbon dioxide and other wastes (from the embryo or fetus to the mother, to be eliminated by the mother's lungs and kidneys); nutrients; some microscopic disease-causing organisms; and some drugs, including ASA (Aspirin), narcotics, alcohol, and tranquillizers.

The placenta is also an endocrine gland. It secretes hormones that preserve the pregnancy, stimulate the uterine contractions that induce childbirth, and help prepare the breasts for breast-feeding. The placenta itself secretes increasing amounts of estrogen and progesterone. The placenta passes from the woman's body after delivery. For this reason it is also called the "afterbirth."

The Fetal Stage

The fetal stage begins by the ninth week and continues until birth. By about the ninth or tenth week, the fetus begins to respond to the outside world by turning in the direction of external stimulation. By the end of the first trimester, the major organ systems, the fingers and toes, and the external genitals have been formed. The gender of the fetus can be determined visually. The eyes have become clearly distinguishable.

During the second trimester the fetus increases dramatically in size, and its organ systems continue to mature. The brain now contributes to the regulation of basic body functions. The fetus increases in weight from 20 *grams* to a *kilogram* and grows from about 10 to 35 cm in length. Soft, downy hair grows above the eyes and on the scalp. The skin turns ruddy because of blood vessels that show through the surface. (During the third trimester, layers of fat beneath the skin will give the red colour a pinkish hue in light-skinned babies.) By the middle of the fourth month, the mother can usually feel the first fetal movements. By the end of the second trimester, the fetus moves its limbs so vigorously that the mother may complain of being kicked—often at 4:00 A.M. It opens and shuts its eyes, sucks its thumb, alternates between periods of wakefulness and sleep, and perceives lights and sounds. The fetus also does somersaults, which the mother will definitely feel. Fortunately, the umbilical cord will not break or strangle the fetus, no matter what acrobatic feats the fetus performs.

Near the end of the second trimester the fetus approaches the **age of viability**. Still, only a minority of babies born at this time who weigh less than 1 kg will survive—even with intense medical efforts.

During the third trimester, the organ systems continue to mature and enlarge. The heart and lungs become increasingly capable of maintaining independent life. Typically, during the seventh month the fetus turns upside down in the uterus so that it will be headfirst, or in a **cephalic presentation**, for delivery. But some fetuses do not turn during this month. If such a fetus is born prematurely it can have either a **breech presentation** (bottom or feet first) or a shoulder-first presentation, which can complicate problems of prematurity. The closer to term (the full nine months) the baby is born, the more likely it is that the presentation will be cephalic. If birth occurs at the end of the eighth month, the odds are overwhelmingly in favour of survival.

During the final months of pregnancy, the mother may become concerned that the fetus seems to be less active than before. Most of the time the change in activity level is normal. The fetus has grown so large that it is cramped, and its movements are restricted.

Environmental Influences on Prenatal Development

Environmental factors that affect prenatal development include the mother's diet, maternal diseases and disorders, and the mother's use of drugs.

The Mother's Diet It is a common misconception that the fetus will take what it needs from its mother. Actually, malnutrition in the mother can adversely affect fetal development. Maternal malnutrition during the third trimester, when the fetus normally makes sharp gains in weight, is linked to low birthweight and increased infant mortality. Pregnant women who are well nourished are more likely to deliver babies of average or above average size. Their infants are also less likely to develop colds and serious respiratory disorders.

A woman can expect to gain at least 9 kg during pregnancy because of the growth of the placenta, amniotic fluid, and the fetus itself. Most women will gain about 11 or 12 kg (Thompson, 1993). Overweight women may gain less. Slender women may gain 14 kg. Regular weight gains are most desirable, about 250 grams a week during the first half of pregnancy and about 500 grams a week during the second half.

Age of viability The age at which a fetus can sustain independent life.

Cephalic presentation Emergence of the baby head-first from the womb.

Breech presentation Emergence of the baby bottom or feet first from the womb.

Health Canada: Nutrition for a Healthy Pregnancy www.hc-sc.gc.ca/hppb/ nutrition/pube/pregnancy/ index.html This document contains national nutrition guidelines for women of childbearing age.

Teratogens Environmental influences or agents that can damage an embryo or fetus. (From the Greek *teras,* meaning "monster.")

Critical period of vulnerability A period of time during which an embryo or fetus is vulnerable to the effects of a teratogen.

Maternal Diseases and Disorders Environmental influences or agents that can harm the embryo or fetus are called **teratogens**. These include drugs taken by the mother, such as alcohol and even ASA, as well as substances produced by the mother's body, such as Rh-positive antibodies. Other teratogens include the metals lead and mercury, radiation, and certain viruses and bacteria. Although many disease-causing organisms cannot pass through the placenta to infect the embryo or fetus, some extremely small organisms, such as those causing syphilis, measles, mumps, and chicken pox, can. Some disorders such as toxemia are not transmitted to the embryo or fetus but can adversely affect the environment in which it develops.

Critical Periods of Vulnerability The times at which exposure to particular teratogens can cause the greatest harm are termed **critical periods of vulnerability**. Critical periods correspond to the times at which the structures most affected by the teratogens are developing (see Figure 9.5). The heart, for example, develops rapidly from the third to the fifth week following conception. It may be most vulnerable to certain teratogens at this time. The arms and legs, which develop later, are most vulnerable from the fourth through the eighth week of development. Since the major organ systems differentiate during the embryonic stage, the embryo is most vulnerable to the effects of teratogens during this stage.

Let us now consider some of the most damaging effects of specific maternal diseases and disorders.

Rubella A viral infection that can cause mental retardation and heart disease in an embryo. Also called *German measles.*

Rubella (German Measles) **Rubella** is a viral infection. Women who contract rubella during the first month or two of pregnancy, when rapid differentiation of major organ systems is taking place, may bear children who are deaf or who develop mental retardation, heart disease, or cataracts. Risk of these defects declines as pregnancy progresses.

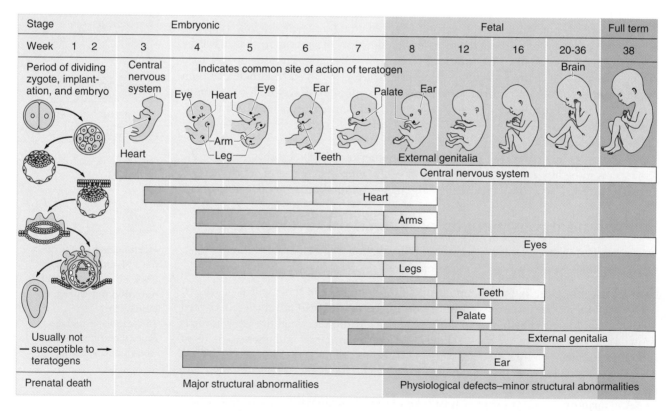

Figure 9.5. Critical Periods in Prenatal Development.

The developing embryo is most vulnerable to teratogens when the organ systems are taking shape. The periods of greatest vulnerability of organ systems are shown in grey. Periods of lesser vulnerability are shown in yellow.

Source: Rathus, S. A. (1988). *Understanding Child Development.* Copyright © 1988 by Holt, Rinehart, & Winston, Inc. Reprinted with permission.

Most Canadian women have either had rubella as children or have been vaccinated against it. Women who do not know whether they have had rubella may be tested; if they are not immune, they can be vaccinated *prior to pregnancy*. Inoculation during pregnancy is considered risky because the vaccine causes a mild case of the disease in the mother, which can affect the embryo or fetus. Increased awareness of the dangers of rubella during pregnancy, and of the preventive effects of inoculation, has led to a decline in the number of children born with defects caused by rubella.

Sexually Transmitted Infections Maternal **syphilis** may cause miscarriage or **stillbirth**, or be passed along to the child in the form of congenital syphilis. Congenital syphilis can impair vision and hearing, damage the liver, or deform the bones and teeth.

Routine blood tests early in pregnancy can diagnose syphilis and other problems. Because the bacteria that cause syphilis do not readily cross the placental membrane during the first months of pregnancy, the fetus will probably not contract syphilis if an infected mother is treated successfully with antibiotics before the fourth month of pregnancy.

Acquired immunodeficiency syndrome (AIDS) is caused by the human immunodeficiency virus (HIV). HIV is blood-borne and is sometimes transmitted through the placenta to infect the fetus. The rupturing of blood vessels in mother and baby during childbirth provides another opportunity for transmission of HIV (Peckham & Gibb, 1995). However, the majority of babies born to mothers who are infected with HIV do *not* become infected themselves. Chapter 13 describes measures that can be taken to minimize the probability of transmission. HIV can also be transmitted to children by breast-feeding.

Toxemia **Toxemia** is a life-threatening condition characterized by high blood pressure that may afflict women late in the second or early in the third trimester of pregnancy. The first stage is termed *preeclampsia*. It is diagnosed by protein in the urine, swelling from fluid retention, and high blood pressure, and may be relatively mild. As preeclampsia worsens, the mother may have headaches and visual problems from the raised blood pressure, along with abdominal pain. If left untreated, the disease may progress to the final stage, termed *eclampsia*. Eclampsia can lead to maternal or fetal death. Babies born to women with toxemia are often undersized or premature.

Toxemia appears to be linked to malnutrition. Ironically, undernourished women may gain weight rapidly through fluid retention, but their swollen appearance may discourage them from eating. Pregnant women who gain weight rapidly but have not increased their food intake should consult their obstetricians.

Ectopic Pregnancy

In an **ectopic pregnancy**, the fertilized ovum implants itself someplace other than the uterus. Most ectopic pregnancies occur in a fallopian tube ("tubal pregnancies") when the ovum is prevented from moving into the uterus because of obstructions caused by infections. If ectopic pregnancies do not abort spontaneously, they must be removed by surgery or use of medicines such as methotrexate (Hausknecht, 1995), since the fetus cannot develop to term. Delay in removal may cause hemorrhaging and the death of the mother. A woman with a tubal pregnancy will not menstruate, but may notice spotty bleeding and abdominal pain.

Rh Incompatibility

In **Rh incompatibility**, antibodies produced by the mother are transmitted to a fetus or newborn infant. Rh is a blood protein found in some people's red blood cells. Rh incompatibility occurs when a woman who does not have this blood factor, and is thus *Rh-negative*, is carrying an *Rh-positive* fetus, which can happen if the father is Rh-positive. The negative–positive combination is found in about 10% of North American couples. However, it becomes a problem only in a minority of the resulting pregnancies. In such cases the mother's antibodies attack the red blood cells of the fetus, which can cause brain damage or death. Rh incompatibility does not usually adversely affect a first child because women will usually not yet have formed antibodies to the Rh factor.

Since mother and fetus have separate circulatory systems, it is unlikely that Rh-positive fetal red blood cells will enter the Rh-negative mother's body. The probability of an exchange of blood increases during childbirth, however, especially when the placenta becomes detached from the uterine wall. If an exchange of blood occurs, the

Syphilis A sexually transmitted infection caused by a bacterium.

Stillbirth The birth of a dead fetus.

Acquired immunodeficiency syndrome (AIDS) A sexually transmitted infection that destroys white blood cells in the immune system, leaving the body vulnerable to various "opportunistic" diseases.

Toxemia A life-threatening condition that is characterized by high blood pressure.

Ectopic pregnancy A pregnancy in which the fertilized ovum becomes implanted outside the uterus, usually in the fallopian tube. (*Ectopic* derives from Greek roots meaning "out of place.")

Rh incompatibility A condition in which antibodies produced by a pregnant woman are transmitted to the fetus and may cause brain damage or death.

mother will then produce antibodies to the baby's Rh-positive blood. In a subsequent pregnancy, the mother's antibodies may enter the fetal bloodstream and destroy red blood cells (a condition called *fetal erythroblastosis*), which can result in anemia, mental deficiency, or even the death of the fetus or newborn infant.

Blood-typing of pregnant women significantly decreases the threat of erythroblastosis. If an Rh-negative mother is injected with the vaccine Rhogam within 72 hours after delivery of an Rh-positive baby, she will not develop the dangerous antibodies and thus will not pass them on to the fetus in a subsequent pregnancy. A fetus or newborn child at risk for erythroblastosis may also receive a preventive blood transfusion, in order to remove the mother's Rh-positive antibodies from its blood.

Drugs Taken by the Mother (and the Father) Some widely used drugs, including
nonprescription drugs like ASA, are linked with birth abnormalities. In the 1960s the drug thalidomide was marketed to pregnant women as a presumably safe treatment for nausea and insomnia. However, the drug caused birth deformities, including stunted or missing limbs. Maternal use of illegal drugs such as cocaine and marijuana may also place the fetus at risk.

Paternal use of certain drugs may also endanger the fetus. One question is whether drugs alter the genetic material in the father's sperm. The use of certain substances by those who come into contact with a pregnant woman can also harm the fetus. For example, the mother's inhalation of second-hand tobacco or marijuana smoke can hurt the fetus.

Several antibiotics may harm a fetus, especially if they are taken during certain periods of fetal development. Tetracycline may yellow the teeth and deform the bones. Other antibiotics have been implicated in deafness and jaundice.

Acne drugs can cause physical and mental handicaps in the children of women who use them during pregnancy (Mills, 1995). Antihistamines, used commonly for allergies, may deform the fetus.

If you are pregnant, or suspect that you are, it is advisable to consult your physician before taking any and all drugs, not just prescription drugs. Your physician can usually direct you to a safe and effective substitute for a drug that could harm a fetus.

Hormones The hormones progestin and DES have sometimes been used to help women at risk of miscarriage maintain their pregnancies. When taken at about the time that sex organs differentiate, progestin—which is similar in composition to male sex hormones—can masculinize the external sex organs of embryos with female (XX) sex chromosomal structures. Progestin taken during the first trimester has also been linked to increased levels of aggressive behaviour during childhood.

DES Diethylstilbestrol: an estrogen that was once given to women at risk for miscarriage to help maintain pregnancy.

DES (short for *diethylstilbestrol*), a powerful estrogen, was given to many women at risk for miscarriage from the 1940s through the 1960s to help maintain their pregnancies. DES is suspected of causing cervical and testicular cancer in some of the children whose mothers used it when pregnant. Other problems have been reported as well. Daughters whose mothers used DES during their pregnancies have a higher-than-expected rate of miscarriages and premature deliveries. It was once suspected that men who were exposed prenatally to DES had higher than expected rates of infertility. However, research reveals no connection between in utero exposure to DES and male infertility (Wilcox et al., 1995).

Vitamins Many pregnant women are prescribed daily doses of multivitamins to maintain their own health and to promote the development of a healthy pregnancy. "Too much of a good thing" may be hazardous, however. High doses of vitamins such as A, B6, D, and K have been linked to birth defects. Vitamin A excesses have been linked with cleft palate and eye damage, whereas excesses of vitamin D are linked to mental retardation.

Narcotics Narcotics such as heroin and methadone can readily pass from mother to fetus through the placental membrane. Narcotics are addictive. Fetuses of mothers who use them regularly during their pregnancies can become addicted in utero. At birth, such babies may undergo withdrawal and show muscle tension and agitation. Women who use narcotics are advised to notify their obstetricians so that measures can be taken to aid the infant prior to and following delivery.

Tranquillizers and Sedatives The tranquilizers Librium and Valium cross the placental membrane and may cause birth defects such as a cleft lip. Sedatives, such as the barbiturate phenobarbital, are suspected of decreasing testosterone production and causing reproductive problems in the sons of women who use them during pregnancy.

Hallucinogens Use of hallucinogenic drugs such as marijuana and LSD during pregnancy has been linked to chromosomal damage in fetuses (National Academy of Sciences, 1982). The active ingredient in marijuana, THC, readily crosses the placenta, as does LSD. Use of marijuana can lead to decreased androgen production in male fetuses, which can interfere with the process of sexual differentiation. Research provides evidence that preschoolers whose mothers used marijuana during their pregnancies suffered more neurological and visual problems than did children of nonusers (Fried, 1986).

Alcohol Mothers who drink heavily during pregnancy expose the fetus to greater risk of birth defects, infant mortality, sensory and motor problems, and mental retardation (Barr et al., 1990; Coles, 1994). Nearly 40% of children whose mothers drank heavily during pregnancy develop **fetal alcohol syndrome** (FAS). FAS is a cluster of symptoms typified by developmental lags and characteristic facial features, such as an underdeveloped upper jaw, flattened nose, and widely spaced eyes. Infants with FAS are often smaller than average and have smaller than average brains. They may be mentally retarded, lack coordination, and have deformed limbs and heart problems.

Although research suggests that light drinking is unlikely to harm the fetus in most cases (Jacobson & Jacobson, 1994), FAS has been found even among the children of mothers who drank only two ounces of alcohol a day during the first trimester (Astley et al., 1992). Moreover, individual sensitivities to alcohol may vary widely (Jacobson & Jacobson, 1994). The critical period for the development of the facial features associated with FAS seems to be the first two months of prenatal development, when the head is taking shape (Coles, 1994).

Cigarette Smoking Maternal smoking increases the risk of miscarriage and complications during pregnancy such as premature rupturing of the amniotic sac, stillbirth, premature birth, low birthweight, and early infant mortality (English & Eskenazi, 1992; Floyd et al., 1993; USDHHS, 1992). Women who smoke less than a pack a day stand a higher risk of pregnancy and birth complications than do nonsmokers (Floyd et al., 1993; Mayer et al., 1990). The health risks generally increase with the amount smoked.

Maternal smoking may also impair intellectual development. In one study, women who smoked during pregnancy were 50% more likely than nonsmokers to have children whose intelligence test scores placed them in the mentally retarded range (that is, beneath an IQ score of 70) when the children were 10 years old (Drews et al., 1996).

Low birthweight is the most common risk factor for infant disease and mortality (USDHHS, 1992). Maternal smoking during pregnancy more than doubles the risk of low birthweight (Mayer et al., 1990). The combination of smoking and drinking alcohol places the child at greater risk of low birthweight than either practice alone (Day & Richardson, 1994). As many as one in four cases of low birthweight could be prevented if mothers-to-be quit smoking during pregnancy (USDHHS, 1990). The earlier the pregnant smoker quits, the better for the baby (and herself!). Simply cutting down on smoking during pregnancy may not offer much protection in preventing low birthweight (USDHHS, 1990).

Maternal smoking also has important acute effects on fetal heart rate (Graca et al., 1991) and increases the risk of sudden infant death syndrome (SIDS) (Feng, 1993; Haglund & Cnattingius, 1990; Malloy et al., 1992; Schoendorf & Kiely, 1992; Zhang & Fried, 1992). Maternal smoking has also been linked to reduced lung function in newborns (Hanrahan et al., 1992) and asthma in childhood (Martinez et al., 1992). Evidence

Fetal alcohol syndrome A cluster of symptoms caused by maternal drinking, in which the child shows developmental lags and characteristic facial features such as an underdeveloped upper jaw, flattened nose, and widely spaced eyes.

Canadian Perinatal Surveillance System: Alcohol and Pregnancy www.hc-sc.gc.ca/hpb/lcdc/brch/factshts/alcprg_e.html This fact sheet presents information on the relationship between alcohol consumption and pregnancy and on the prevalence of FAS in some Canadian subpopulations.

Smoking. *Maternal smoking during pregnancy increases the risk of miscarriage and complications during childbirth. It doubles the risk of low birthweight and may impair the child's intellectual development.*

Down syndrome A chromosomal abnormality that leads to mental retardation, caused by an extra chromosome on the 21st pair.

also points to reduced attention spans, hyperactivity, and lower IQs and achievement test scores in children exposed to maternal smoking during and following pregnancy (Barr et al., 1990).

Smoking by the father (or other household members) may be dangerous to a fetus because secondary smoke (smoke exhaled by the smoker or emitted from the tip of a lit cigarette) may be absorbed by the mother and passed along to the fetus. Passive exposure to second-hand smoke during infancy is also linked to increased risk of SIDS (Schoendorf & Kiely, 1992).

Other Agents X-rays increase the risk of malformed organs in the fetus, especially within a month and a half following conception. (Ultrasound has not been shown to harm the embryo or fetus.)

Chromosomal and Genetic Abnormalities

Not all of us have the normal complement of chromosomes. Some of us have genes that threaten our health or our existence (see Table 9.1).

Down Syndrome Children with **Down syndrome** have characteristic round faces; wide, flat noses; and protruding tongues. They often suffer from respiratory problems and heart malformations, problems that tend to claim their lives by middle age—the prime of life when most of us are reaching our vocational heights. People with Down syndrome are also moderately mentally retarded, but they usually can learn to read and write. With a little help from family and social agencies, they may hold jobs and lead largely independent lives.

The risk of a child's having Down syndrome increases with the mother's age (see Table 9.2). Down syndrome is usually caused by an extra chromosome on the 21st pair. In about 95% of cases, Down syndrome is transmitted by the mother (Antonarakas et al., 1991). The inner corners of the eyes of people with the syndrome have a downward-sloping crease of skin that gives them a superficial likeness to Asians. This is why the syndrome was once dubbed *mongolism*, a label that has since been rejected because of its racist overtones.

TABLE 9.1 Some chromosomal and genetic abnormalities

Cystic fibrosis	A genetic disease in which the pancreas and lungs become clogged with mucus, which impairs the processes of respiration and digestion.
Down syndrome	A condition characterized by a third chromosome on the 21st pair. The child with Down syndrome has a characteristic fold of skin over the eye and mental retardation. The risk of a child's exhibiting the syndrome increases as parents increase in age.
Hemophilia	A sex-linked disorder in which the blood fails to clot properly.
Huntington's chorea	A fatal neurological disorder whose onset occurs in middle adulthood.
Neural-tube defects	Disorders of the brain or spine, such as *anencephaly*, in which part of the brain is missing, and *spina bifida,* in which part of the spine is exposed or missing. Anencephaly is fatal shortly after birth, but individuals with spina bifida may live into adulthood, albeit with severe handicaps.
Phenylketonuria	A disorder in which children cannot metabolize phenylalanine, which builds up in the form of phenylpyruvic acid and causes mental retardation. The disorder can be diagnosed at birth and controlled by diet.
Retinoblastoma	A form of blindness caused by a dominant gene.
Sickle cell anemia	A blood disorder that mostly afflicts blacks, in which deformed blood cells obstruct small blood vessels, decreasing their capacity to carry oxygen and heightening the risk of occasionally fatal infections.
Tay-Sachs disease	A fatal neurological disorder that primarily afflicts Jews of European origin.

Source: Etaugh & Rathus (1995).

Age of Mother	Probability of Down Syndrome
30	1/885
31	1/826
32	1/725
33	1/592
34	1/465
35*	1/365
36	1/287
37	1/225
38	1/176
39	1/139
40	1/109
41	1/85
42	1/67
43	1/53
44	1/41
45	1/32
46	1/25
47	1/20
48	1/16
49	1/11

TABLE 9.2 Risk of giving birth to an infant with Down syndrome, according to age of the mother

*Age at which testing for Down syndrome is usually first recommended.

Source: Adapted from Samuels & Samuels, 1986, p. 240. Reprinted with permission.

Sickle Cell Anemia and Tay-Sachs Disease Sickle cell anemia and Tay-Sachs disease are genetic disorders that are most likely to afflict certain racial and ethnic groups. Sickle cell anemia is most prevalent among blacks. One of every 375 North American blacks is affected by the disease, and 8% are carriers of the sickle cell trait (Leary, 1993). In sickle cell anemia, the red blood cells assume a sickle shape—hence the name—and they form clumps that obstruct narrow blood vessels and diminish the supply of oxygen. As a result, victims can suffer problems ranging from swollen, painful joints to potentially lethal problems such as pneumonia and heart and kidney failure. Infections are a leading cause of death among those with the disease (Leary, 1993).

Tay-Sachs disease is a fatal neurological disease of young children. Only 1 in 100 000 people in the general population is affected, but among Jews of Eastern European background the figure rises steeply to 1 in 3600 (Hubbard & Wald, 1993). The disease is characterized by degeneration of the central nervous system and gives rise to retardation, loss of muscle control and paralysis, blindness, and deafness. Victims seldom live beyond the age of 5. Testing is available to identify people who carry the gene.

Sex-Linked Genetic Abnormalities Some genetic defects, such as hemophilia, are sex linked, in that they are carried only on the X sex chromosome. They are transmitted from generation to generation as **recessive traits**. Females, each of whom has two X sex chromosomes, are less likely than males to be afflicted by sex-linked disorders, because the genes that carry the disorder would have to be present on both of their sex chromosomes for the disorder to be expressed. Sex-linked disorders are more likely to afflict sons of female carriers because they have only one X sex chromosome, which they inherit from their mothers. England's Queen Victoria was a hemophilia carrier and transmitted the condition to several of her children, who in turn carried it into several ruling houses of Europe. For this reason hemophilia has been dubbed the "royal disease."

Recessive trait A trait that is not expressed when the gene or genes involved have been paired with dominant genes. Recessive traits are transmitted to future generations, however, and are expressed if they are paired with other recessive genes.

Applications

Averting Chromosomal and Genetic Abnormalities

Based upon information about a couple's medical background and family history of genetic defects, genetic counsellors help couples appraise the risks of passing along genetic defects to their children. Some couples facing a high risk of passing along genetic defects to their children decide to adopt. Other couples may decide to have an abortion if the fetus is determined to have certain abnormalities.

Various medical procedures are used to detect the presence of these disorders in the fetus. **Amniocentesis** is usually performed about four months into pregnancy but is sometimes done earlier. Fluid is drawn from the amniotic sac (or "bag of waters") with a syringe. Fetal cells in the fluid are grown in a culture and examined under a microscope for the presence of biochemical and chromosomal abnormalities. *Chorionic villus sampling* (CVS) is performed several

weeks earlier. A narrow tube is used to snip off material from the chorion, which is a membrane that contains the amniotic sac and fetus. The material is analyzed. CVS is somewhat riskier than amniocentesis, so most obstetricians prefer to use the latter. The tests detect Down syndrome, sickle cell anemia, Tay-Sachs disease, spina bifida, muscular dystrophy, Rh incompatibility, and other conditions. The tests also identify the gender of the fetus.

In ultrasound, high-pitched sound waves are bounced off the fetus, like radar, revealing a picture of the fetus on a TV monitor and allowing the obstetrician to detect certain abnormalities. Obstetricians also use ultrasound to locate the fetus during amniocentesis in order to lower the probability of injuring it with the syringe.

Parental blood tests can suggest the presence of problems such as sickle cell anemia, Tay-Sachs disease, and neural-tube defects. Still other tests examine fetal DNA and can indicate the presence of Huntington's chorea, cystic fibrosis, and other disorders.

Amniocentesis. In this form of prenatal testing, cells sloughed off by the fetus into amniotic fluid are withdrawn by a syringe and examined for genetic and chromosomal abnormalities.

Amniocentesis A procedure for drawing off and examining fetal cells in the amniotic fluid to determine the presence of various disorders in the fetus.

Braxton-Hicks contractions So-called false labour contractions that are relatively painless.

Prostaglandins Hormones that cause muscle fibres in the uterine wall to contract, as during labour.

Childbirth

Early in the ninth month of pregnancy, the fetus's head settles in the pelvis. This shift is called "dropping" or "lightening." The woman may actually feel lighter because of lessened pressure on the diaphragm. About a day or so before the beginning of labour, the woman may notice blood in her vaginal secretions because fetal pressure on the pelvis may rupture superficial blood vessels in the birth canal. Tissue that had plugged the cervix, possibly preventing entry of infectious agents from the vagina, becomes dislodged. There is a resultant discharge of bloody mucus. At about this time one woman in ten also has a rush of warm "water" from the vagina. The "water" is amniotic fluid, and it means that the amniotic sac has burst. Labour usually begins within a day after rupture of the amniotic sac. For most women the amniotic sac does not burst until the end of the first stage of childbirth. Other signs of impending labour include indigestion, diarrhea, abdominal cramps, and an ache in the small of the back. Labour begins with the onset of regular uterine contractions.

The first uterine contractions are relatively painless and are called **Braxton-Hicks contractions**, or "false" labour contractions. They are false because they do not widen the cervix or advance the baby through the birth canal. They tend to increase in frequency but are less regular than labour contractions. "Real" contractions, by contrast, become more intense when the woman moves around or walks.

The initiation of labour may involve the secretion of hormones by the fetal adrenal and pituitary glands that stimulate the placenta and mother's uterus to secrete **prostaglandins**. Prostaglandins stimulate the uterine musculature to contract. It would make sense for the fetus to have a mechanism for signalling the mother that it is mature enough to sustain independent life. The mechanisms that initiate and maintain labour are not fully understood, however. Later in labour the pituitary gland releases **oxytocin**, a hormone that stimulates contractions strong enough to expel the baby.

The Stages of Childbirth

Childbirth begins with the onset of labour and progresses through three stages.

The First Stage In the first stage, uterine contractions **efface** and **dilate** the cervix to about 10 cm in diameter, so that the baby may pass through. Stretching of the cervix causes most of the discomfort of childbirth. A woman may experience little or no pain if her cervix dilates easily and quickly. The first stage may last from a couple of hours to more than a day. Twelve to twenty-four hours of labour is considered about average for a first pregnancy. In later pregnancies labour takes about half this time.

The initial contractions are usually mild and spaced widely, at intervals of 10 to 20 minutes. They may last 20 to 40 seconds. As time passes, contractions become more frequent, longer, stronger, and more regular.

Transition is the process that occurs when the cervix becomes nearly fully dilated and the baby's head begins to move into the vagina, or birth canal. Contractions usually come quickly during transition. Transition usually lasts about 30 minutes or less and is often accompanied by feelings of nausea, chills, and intense pain.

Oxytocin A pituitary hormone that stimulates uterine contractions in labour and the ejection of milk during nursing.

Efface To become thin.

Dilate To open or widen.

Transition The process during which the cervix becomes nearly fully dilated and the head of the fetus begins to move into the birth canal.

1. The second stage of labour begins

2. Further descent and rotation

3. The crowning of the head

4. Anterior shoulder delivered

5. Posterior shoulder delivered

6. The third stage of labour begins with separation of the placenta from the uterine wall

Figure 9.6. The Stages of Childbirth.

In the first stage, uterine contractions efface and dilate the cervix to about 10 cm so that the baby may pass. The second stage begins with movement of the baby into the birth canal and ends with birth of the baby. During the third stage the placenta separates from the uterine wall and is expelled through the birth canal.

The Second Stage The second stage of childbirth follows transition and begins when the cervix has become fully dilated and the baby begins to move into the vagina and first appears at the opening of the birth canal (see Figure 9.6). The woman may be taken to a delivery room for the second stage of childbirth. The second stage is shorter than the first stage. It lasts from a few minutes to a few hours and ends with the birth of the baby.

Each contraction of the second stage propels the baby farther along the birth canal (vagina). When the baby's head becomes visible at the vaginal opening, it is said to have crowned. The baby typically emerges fully a few minutes after crowning.

An **episiotomy** may be performed on the mother when the baby's head has crowned to enlarge the vaginal opening and prevent it from tearing if the baby's head emerges too quickly. Episiotomies are controversial, however. The incision can be painful in itself and cause discomfort and itching as it heals. In some cases the discomfort interferes with coitus for months. Many obstetricians no longer perform episiotomies routinely. However, most health professionals concur that an episiotomy is preferable to the random tearing that can occur if the tissues of the **perineum** become extremely effaced.

With or without an episiotomy, the baby's passageway to the external world is a tight fit at best. As a result, the baby's facial features and the shape of its head may be temporarily distended. The baby may look as if it has been through a prizefight. Its head may be elongated, its nose flattened, and its ears bent. Although parents may be concerned about whether the baby's features will assume a more typical shape, they almost always do.

The Third Stage The third, or placental, stage of childbirth may last from a few minutes to an hour or more. During this stage, the placenta is expelled. Detachment of the placenta from the uterine wall may cause some bleeding. The uterus begins the process of contracting to a smaller size. The attending physician sews up the episiotomy or any tears in the perineum.

Episiotomy A surgical incision in the perineum that may be made during childbirth to protect the vagina from tearing. (From Greek roots *epision*, meaning "pubic region," and *tome*, meaning "cutting.")

Perineum The skin and underlying tissue that lie between the vaginal opening and the anus. (From the Greek roots meaning "around" and "to empty out.")

Coming into the World. *Childbirth progresses through three stages. In the first stage, uterine contractions efface and dilate the cervix so that the baby may pass through. The second stage lasts from a few minutes to a few hours and ends with the birth of the baby. During the third stage the placenta is expelled.*

In the New World As the baby's head emerges, mucus is cleared from its mouth by means of suction aspiration to prevent the breathing passageway from being obstructed. Aspiration is often repeated once the baby is fully delivered. (Newly delivered babies are no longer routinely held upside down to help expel mucus. Nor is the baby slapped on the buttocks to stimulate breathing, as in old films.)

Once the baby is breathing adequately, the umbilical cord is clamped and severed about 6 cm from the baby's body. The stump of the umbilical cord dries and falls off in its own time, usually in seven to ten days.

While the mother is in the third stage of labour, the nurse may perform procedures on the baby, such as placing drops of silver nitrate or an antibiotic ointment into the eyes to prevent bacterial infections. Typically the baby is also footprinted and (if the birth has taken place in a hospital) given an identification bracelet. Since neonates do not manufacture vitamin K on their own, the baby may also receive an injection of the vitamin to ensure that her or his blood will clot normally in case of bleeding.

Methods of Childbirth

Until the twentieth century, childbirth was usually an event that happened at home and involved the mother, a midwife, family, and friends. These days women in Canada and the United States typically give birth in hospitals, attended by obstetricians who use surgical instruments and anaesthetics to protect mothers and children from infection, complications, and pain. Medical procedures save lives but also make childbearing more impersonal. Social critics argue that these procedures have "medicalized" a natural process. They have usurped control over women's bodies and, through the use of drugs, denied many women the experience of giving birth.

Anaesthetized Childbirth

In sorrow thou shalt bring forth children.
(GENESIS 3:16)

The Bible suggests that the ancients saw suffering as a woman's lot. But during the past two centuries, science and medicine have led to the expectation that women should experience minimal discomfort during childbirth. Today some anaesthesia is used to minimize or eliminate pain in most North American deliveries.

Occasionally, women receive **general anaesthesia**, which induces unconsciousness. The drug sodium pentothal, a barbiturate, induces general anaesthesia when it is injected into a vein. Barbiturates may also be taken orally to reduce anxiety while the woman remains awake. Women may also receive tranquillizers like Valium or narcotics like Demerol to help them relax and to blunt pain without inducing sleep.

Anaesthetic drugs, as well as tranquillizers and narcotics, decrease the strength of uterine contractions during delivery. They may thus delay the process of cervical dilation and prolong labour. They also weaken the woman's ability to push the baby through the birth canal. Because they cross the placental membrane, they also lower the newborn's overall responsiveness.

Much more common are regional or **local anaesthetics**, which block pain in parts of the body without generally depressing the mother's alertness or putting her to sleep. In a *pudendal block*, the external genitals are numbed by local injection. In an *epidural block* or a *spinal block*, an anaesthetic is injected into the spinal canal, which temporarily numbs the mother's body below the waist. To prevent injury, the needles used for these injections do not come into contact with the spinal cord itself. Although local anaesthesia decreases the responsiveness of the newborn baby, there is little evidence that medicated childbirth has serious, long-term consequences on children (Ganitsch, 1992).

Natural Childbirth Partly as a reaction against the use of anaesthetics, English obstetrician Grantly Dick-Read endorsed **natural childbirth** in his 1944 book *Childbirth Without Fear*. Dick-Read argued that women's labour pains were heightened by their fear of the unknown and resultant muscle tensions. Many of Dick-Read's contributions

General anaesthesia The use of drugs to put people to sleep and eliminate pain, as during childbirth.

Local anaesthesia Anaesthesia that eliminates pain in a specific area of the body, as during childbirth.

Natural childbirth A method of childbirth in which women use no anaesthesia but are given other strategies for coping with discomfort and are educated about childbirth.

came to be regarded as accepted practice in modern childbirth procedures, such as the emphasis on informing women about the biological aspects of reproduction and childbirth, the encouragement of physical fitness, and the teaching of relaxation and breathing exercises.

Prepared Childbirth: The Lamaze Method The French obstetrician Fernand Lamaze visited the Soviet Union in 1951 and found that many Russian women bore babies without anaesthetics and without reporting a great deal of pain. Lamaze returned to western Europe with some of the techniques the women used, and they are now usually termed the **Lamaze method**, or *prepared childbirth*. Lamaze (1981) argued that women can learn to conserve energy during childbirth and reduce the pain of uterine contractions by associating the contractions with other responses, such as thinking of pleasant mental images such as beach scenes, or engaging in breathing and relaxation exercises.

A pregnant woman typically attends Lamaze classes with a "coach"—usually the father—who will aid her in the delivery room by timing contractions, offering emotional support, and coaching her in the breathing and relaxation exercises. The woman and her partner also receive more general information about childbirth. The father is integrated into the process, and many couples report that their marriages are strengthened as a result.

The Lamaze method is flexible concerning the use of anaesthetics. Many women report some pain during delivery and obtain anaesthetics. However, the Lamaze method appears to enhance women's self-esteem by helping them gain a greater sense of control over the delivery process.

Caesarean Section In a **caesarean section**, the baby is delivered through surgery rather than naturally through the vagina. The word *section* is derived from the Latin for "to cut." In a caesarean section (*C-section* for short) the woman is anesthetized, and incisions are made in the abdomen and uterus so that the surgeon can remove the baby. The incisions are then sewn up and the mother can begin walking, often on the same day, although generally with some discomfort for a while.

C-sections are most likely to be advised when normal delivery is difficult or threatening to the health of the mother or child. Vaginal deliveries can become difficult if the baby is large or the mother's pelvis is small or misshapen, or if the mother is overly tired or weakened. Herpes and HIV infections in the birth canal can be bypassed by C-section. C-sections are also likely to be performed if the baby presents for delivery in the breech position (feet downward) or the **transverse position** (lying crosswise), or if the baby is in distress.

Use of the C-section mushroomed in the 1980s. In 1988, it stood at an all-time high of 19.6 per 100 deliveries. Compare this figure to about 1 in 10 births in 1975. The rate declined to approximately 17.6 per 100 in 1992, but then began to increase again. In 2002, the overall Canadian rate was 18.7 C-sections per 100 deliveries (Canadian Institute for Health Information, 2000). The increased rate of C-sections reflects advances in medical technology (such as the use of fetal monitors, which allow doctors to detect fetal distress) and simply the current medical practice patterns (DiMatteo et al., 1996). Critics claim that many C-sections are unnecessary and reflect overly aggressive medical practices. The World Health Organization has set a target of 15 caesarean sections per 100 deliveries as medically appropriate.

Medical opinion once held that after a woman had a C-section, subsequent deliveries also had to be performed by C-section. Otherwise, uterine scars might rupture during labour. However, research has shown that rupture is rare. In one study, only 10 of 3249 women who chose to try vaginal delivery after a previous C-section had a uterine rupture (McMahon et al., 1996). Moreover, there were no maternal deaths.

Birth Problems

Most deliveries are uncomplicated, or "unremarkable" in the medical sense—although childbirth is the most remarkable experience of many parents' lives. Problems can and

Lamaze method A childbirth method in which women learn about childbirth, learn to relax and to breathe in patterns that conserve energy and lessen pain, and have a coach (usually the father) present at childbirth. Also termed *prepared childbirth*.

Caesarean section (C-section) A method of childbirth in which the fetus is delivered through a surgical incision in the abdomen.

Transverse position A crosswise birth position.

do occur, however. Some of the most common birth problems are anoxia and the birth of preterm and low-birthweight babies.

Anoxia

Prenatal **anoxia** can cause various problems in the neonate and affect later development. It leads to complications such as brain damage and mental retardation. Prolonged anoxia during delivery can also result in cerebral palsy and possibly death.

    The baby is supplied with oxygen through the umbilical cord. Passage through the birth canal squeezes the umbilical cord. Temporary squeezing, like holding one's breath for a moment, is unlikely to cause problems. (In fact, slight oxygen deprivation at birth is not unusual because the transition from receiving oxygen through the umbilical cord to breathing on its own may not happen immediately after the baby emerges.) However, if constriction of the cord is prolonged, anoxia can result. Prolonged constriction is more likely to occur with a breech presentation, because the baby's head presses the umbilical cord against the birth canal during delivery. Fetal monitoring can help detect anoxia early, however, before damage occurs. A C-section can be performed if the fetus appears to be in distress.

Anoxia Oxygen deprivation.

Preterm and Low-Birthweight Children

A neonate is considered to be premature, or **preterm**, if it is born before 37 weeks of gestation. The normal period of gestation is 40 weeks. Prematurity is generally linked with low birthweight, since the fetus normally makes dramatic gains in weight during the last weeks of pregnancy. Regardless of the length of its gestation period, a newborn baby is considered to have a low birthweight if it weighs less than 2500 grams.

    Preterm or low-birthweight babies face a heightened risk of infant mortality (Singh & Yu, 1995). A birthweight of 1500 grams is considered to be the cutoff with respect to the likelihood of mortality.

    Preterm babies are relatively thin because they have not yet formed the layer of fat that accounts for the round, robust appearance of most full-term babies. Their muscles are immature, which weakens their sucking and breathing reflexes. Also, in the last weeks of pregnancy, fetuses secrete **surfactants** that prevent the walls of their airways from sticking together. Muscle weakness and incomplete lining of the airways with surfactants can cause a cluster of problems known as **respiratory distress syndrome**, which is responsible for many neonatal deaths. Preterm babies may also suffer from underdeveloped immune systems, which leave them more vulnerable to infections.

    Preterm infants usually remain in the hospital for a time. There they can be monitored and placed in incubators that provide a temperature-controlled environment and offer some protection from disease. If necessary, they may also receive oxygen.

Preterm Born prior to 37 weeks of gestation.

Surfactants Substances that prevent the walls of the airways from sticking together.

Respiratory distress syndrome A cluster of breathing problems, including weak and irregular breathing, to which preterm babies are especially vulnerable.

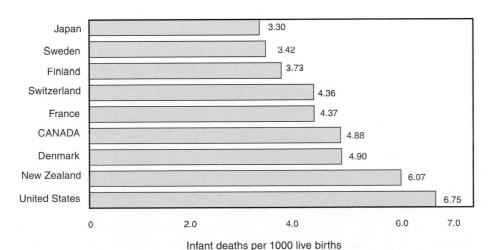

Figure 9.7. Infant Mortality Rates, Selected Countries, 2003.

Infant mortality rates have significantly declined in major industrialized countries.

Source: CIA, 2003.

Infant mortality Usually defined as the number of deaths of babies under one year of age in a given year per live births in the same year

Canadian Perinatal Surveillance System: Infant Mortality
www.hc-sc.gc.ca/hpb/lcdc/brch/factshts/mort_e.html
This fact sheet examines trends in Canadian infant mortality, explores differences within Canada, and compares Canadian rates to those of other countries.

Infant Mortality in Canada and Worldwide

During the last 100 years, **infant mortality** decreased significantly worldwide, especially in developed countries. Canada has had one of the most dramatic declines in infant mortality—from 27.3 per 1000 in 1960 to 4.88 per 1000 in 2003 (Health Canada, 1998a; CIA, 2003). Due to differences in reporting methods, it is difficult to make comparisons between countries. As shown in Figure 9.7, of the major industrialized countries, Japan has the lowest infant mortality rate (3.30 per 1000) and the United States has the highest (6.75 per 1000).

Provincial differences in infant mortality rates must be interpreted with caution, as there can be considerable variation from year to year. In 1999, Yukon and British Columbia had the lowest infant mortality rates and Nunavut and the Northwest Territories had the highest (see Figure 9.8).

In urban areas, infant mortality varies inversely with income. As shown in Figure 9.9, infant mortality is higher among people with lower incomes. In 1996, the infant mortality rate among the 20% of the population with the highest incomes was 3.9 per 1000 births; among the 20% of the population with the lowest incomes, the infant mortality rate was 6.5 per 1000.

A World of Diversity

Infant and Child Mortality Among Native Peoples

Native infant mortality rates averaged 13.8 per 1000 live births between 1986 and 1990. In comparison, infant mortality among all other Canadian babies was 7.3 per 1000 live births. On a positive note, infant mortality has decreased within Native populations over the last quarter of [the twentieth] century. In 1960, the figures were alarmingly high with 82 per 1000 live births. In 1986, this figure decreased to 17.2 per 1000 live births and continues to decline. However, the most recent figures indicate that Native babies still have almost twice the chance of dying as newborns, compared with the rest of the Canadian population. Infant deaths are primarily the result of infectious diseases, respiratory illnesses, sudden infant death syndrome (SIDS), and injuries.

A number of socioeconomic factors—for example, depression, alcoholism, and lack of employment opportunities—and other health factors contribute to this problem. Native living conditions remain below the national average. If a newborn is returned to a reserve, he or she has a greater chance of being raised in a poorly made reserve house, with little or no heat, inferior bathroom facilities (many northern Natives still use outdoor toilets), etc. In addition, many northern Native communities are far from medical facilities. When infants from these reserves become ill, by the time they are taken to the nearest hospital, their situations have become critical. Another factor contributing to the poor health of some children is the lack of parenting skills of a number of Native mothers and fathers. This can be linked to the residential schools where the grandparents and parents of today as children were not raised in an environment that enabled them to observe parenting skills and behaviours first hand.

The high rate of adolescent pregnancies among Native mothers may also be related to infant ill health and mortality rates. Native mothers on-reserve tend to be younger than the average Canadian mother. Nine percent of Native mothers, as opposed to 1 percent of non-Native mothers, are under the age of 18. The maturity, knowledge, and personal supports that each young mother possesses contribute to her overall ability to raise her child in a healthy and happy environment.

Native communities are working to combat these problems by providing parenting classes and other programs to support parents and their children. For example, in prenatal classes, mothers-to-be learn about the effects of smoking, alcohol drinking, and caffeine consumption, and how these factors may affect fetal growth and birthweight. In addition, Native health services promote the positive effects of breast-feeding. In 1998, a survey conducted for the national Database on Breastfeeding Among Indian and Inuit Women found that 60.7 percent of infants were breast-fed at birth, and the rate dropped to 31.1 percent by the time the infants were 6 months old. Breast-feeding rates were the lowest among the mothers younger than 18 (MacMillan, 1996a). Further efforts are being made to promote better health and care of Native children of all ages by Native services both on- and off-reserve.

Source: Excerpt from Pam Williamson, *First Nations People.* © 1999 Emond Montgomery Publications Limited, pp. 180–81. By permission.

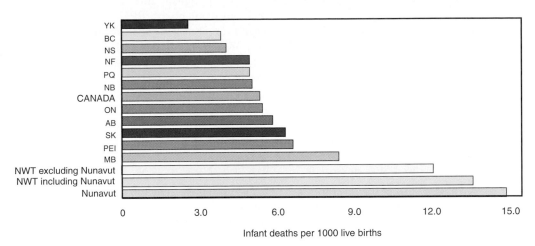

Figure 9.8. Infant Mortality Rates in Canadian Provinces and Territories, 1999.

Within Canada, Nunavut and the Northwest Territories have the highest infant mortality rates and Yukon and British Columbia have the lowest.
Source: Statistics Canada, 2004. Adapted from the Statistics Canada website **www.statcan.ca/english/Pgdb/health21a.htm.**

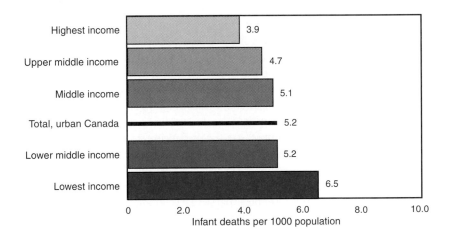

Figure 9.9. Infant Mortality Rates in Urban Canada, 1996.

Infant mortality rises as income falls.
Source: Wilkins, R., et al. (2000). The changing health status of children in Canada. Isuma 2000; 1(2): 58–63. By permission.

The Postpartum Period

The weeks following delivery are called the **postpartum** period. The first few days postpartum are frequently happy ones. The long wait is over, as are the discomforts of childbirth. A sizable number of women, however, experience feelings of depression, in the days and sometimes weeks and months following childbirth.

Postpartum Following birth.

Maternal Depression

During the days or weeks following the delivery of their babies, anywhere from 50% to 80% of new mothers experience periods of sadness, tearfulness, and irritability that are commonly called the "postpartum blues," the "maternity blues," or the "baby blues" (Harding, 1989). The baby blues usually last about 48 hours and are generally believed to be a normal response to hormonal and psychological changes that attend childbirth (Harding, 1989; Samuels & Samuels, 1986).

Some mothers experience more persistent and severe mood changes, called **postpartum depression** (PPD) (Whiffen, 1992). PPD may last a year or even longer. PPD can involve extreme sadness or despair, apathy, changes in appetite and sleep patterns, low self-esteem, and difficulty concentrating. Some researchers (e.g., Gitlin & Pasnau, 1989) estimate that PPD affects up to 15% of new mothers.

Postpartum depression Persistent and severe mood changes during the postpartum period, involving feelings of despair and apathy and characterized by changes in appetite and sleep, low self-esteem, and difficulty in concentrating.

PPD may reflect a combination of physiological and psychological factors. Hormonal changes may play a role in PPD, but women with PPD are more likely than those with the "maternity blues" to have been susceptible to depression before and during their pregnancies (O'Hara et al., 1984). Psychosocial factors such as stress, a troubled marriage, or the need to adjust to an unwanted or sick baby may all increase a woman's susceptibility to PPD (Gitlin & Pasnau, 1989; O'Hara et al., 1984, 1991). Adjusting to a new baby imposes inevitable changes on parents, and change is usually stressful in itself. Depression is likely to be prolonged in women who feel helpless in meeting the demands they face (Cutrona, 1983). First-time mothers, single mothers, and mothers who lack social support from their partners or family members face the greatest risk of PPD (Gitlin & Pasnau, 1989).

New fathers may also have bouts of depression. New mothers are not the only ones who must adjust to the responsibilities of parenthood. Fathers too may feel overwhelmed or unable to cope. Perhaps more fathers might experience the "paternity blues" but for the fact that mothers generally shoulder the lion's share of child-rearing chores.

Breast-Feeding Versus Bottle-Feeding

A Multicultural Perspective on Breastfeeding in Canada www.hc-sc.gc.ca/dca-dea/prenatal/nutrition_e.html
This document provides a summary of various beliefs and practices underlying breast-feeding and related infant practices in Canada.

Prolactin A pituitary hormone that stimulates production of milk.

Lactation Production of milk by the mammary glands.

The majority of Canadian women breast-feed their babies, at least to start. More than 70% of women breast-feed their babies for at least the first three months. Younger mothers, single mothers, mothers with only a high school education, and those living in the Atlantic provinces and Quebec are less likely to breast-feed than those who are older, married, more highly educated, and living in Western Canada or Ontario. The most common reason given by mothers for breast-feeding is that it is best for the infant. Women who discontinue breast-feeding early (less than three months of age) generally do so because they feel they have insufficient milk. For those who breast-feed longer than three months, returning to work is the most common reason for discontinuing (Health Canada, 1998c).

Long-term comparisons of breast-fed and bottle-fed children show few, if any, significant differences. Breast-feeding does, however, reduce the general risk of infections to the baby by transmitting the mother's antibodies to the baby. Breast-feeding also reduces the incidence of allergies in babies, particularly in allergy-prone infants.

The hormones prolactin and oxytocin are involved in breast-feeding. **Prolactin** stimulates production of milk, or **lactation**, two to three days after delivery. Oxytocin causes the breasts to eject milk and is secreted in response to suckling. When an infant is weaned, secretion of prolactin and oxytocin is discontinued, and lactation comes to an end.

Uterine contractions that occur during breast-feeding help return the uterus to its typical size. Breast-feeding also delays resumption of normal menstrual cycles. Breast-feeding is not a perfectly reliable birth-control method, however. (But nursing women are advised not to use birth-control pills, since the hormone content of the pills is passed to the infant through the milk.)

Should a woman breast-feed her baby? Although breast-feeding has benefits for both mother and infant, each woman must weigh these benefits against any difficulties breast-feeding may pose for her. These include assuming the sole responsibility for nighttime feedings, the physical demands of producing and expelling milk, a tendency to soreness in the breasts, and the inconvenience of being continually available to meet the infant's feeding needs. Women should breast-feed because they want to, not because they feel they must.

Resumption of Sexual Activity

The resumption of coitus depends on a couple's level of sexual interest, the healing of episiotomies or other injuries, fatigue, the recommendations of physicians, and, of course, tradition. Obstetricians usually advise a six-week waiting period for safety and comfort.

Women will typically prefer to delay coitus until it becomes physically comfortable, generally when the episiotomy or other lacerations have healed and the lochia has ended. This may take several weeks. Women who breast-feed may also find they have less vaginal lubrication, which can cause some discomfort during coitus. K-Y jelly or other lubricants may help in such cases.

The return of sexual interest and resumption of sexual activity may take longer for some couples than for others. Sexual interest depends more on psychological than on physical factors. Many couples encounter declining sexual interest and activity in the first year following childbirth, generally because child care can sap energy and limit free time. Generally speaking, couples whose sexual relationships were satisfying before the baby arrived tend to show greater sexual interest and to resume sexual activity earlier than those who had less satisfying relationships beforehand. (No surprise.)

Summing Up

Conception is the union of a sperm cell and an ovum. Fertilization usually takes place in a fallopian tube. Conception is most likely to happen if a couple times intercourse with ovulation. Ovulation can be predicted by measuring a woman's basal body temperature, tracking the thickness of vaginal mucus, or analyzing her urine for luteinizing hormone.

Infertility and Alternative Ways of Becoming Parents

Male fertility problems include low sperm count, irregularly shaped sperm, low sperm motility, certain chronic or infectious diseases, trauma to the testes, an autoimmune response to sperm, pituitary imbalances, and thyroid disease. The major causes of **female infertility** include irregular ovulation, obstructions or malfunctions of the reproductive tract, endometriosis, and polycystic ovarian syndrome. Failure to ovulate may be overcome by the use of fertility drugs. Other methods used to overcome female infertility include in vitro fertilization, GIFT, ZIFT, donor IVF, and embryonic transfer. Surrogate motherhood is illegal in Canada.

Pregnancy

Early signs include a missed menstrual period, the presence of HCG in the blood or urine, and Hegar's sign. **Early effects of pregnancy** include breast tenderness and morning sickness (which can last all day). **Sex during pregnancy** is generally safe. **Miscarriages** or **spontaneous abortions** have many causes, including chromosomal defects in the fetus and abnormalities of the placenta or uterus. A woman's psychological response to pregnancy reflects her desire to be pregnant, the physical changes in her body, and her reaction to these changes. Men also respond to pregnancy according to the degree to which they want the child.

Prenatal Development

Prenatal development occurs in stages. The **germinal stage** is the period from conception to implantation. The **embryonic stage** begins with implantation and extends to about the eighth week of development. It is characterized by the development of the major organ systems. The **fetal stage** begins by the ninth week and ends with the birth of the baby. This stage is characterized by continued maturation of the fetus's organ systems and dramatic increases in size. A number of **environmental factors** can influence prenatal development. These include the mother's diet, maternal diseases and disorders, and drug use. Maternal malnutrition has been linked to low birthweight and increased infant mortality. Exposure to harmful substances can cause great harm during critical periods of vulnerability. **Chromosomal and genetic abnormalities** can lead to cystic fibrosis, Down syndrome, hemophilia, Huntington's chorea, neural tube defects, PKU, retinoblastoma, sickle cell anemia, and Tay-Sachs disease. Parental blood tests, amniocentesis, and ultrasound all allow parents to learn whether their children have or are at risk for many such disorders.

Childbirth

Childbirth occurs in stages. In the first stage, uterine contractions efface (thin out) and dilate the cervix so that the baby may pass through. This stage may last from a couple of hours to more than a day. The second stage lasts from a few minutes to a few hours and ends with the birth of the baby. The placenta is expelled in the third stage. **Methods of childbirth** include the use of anaesthesia or psychological preparation to cope with pain. Caesarean sections are necessary for some difficult births, but critics claim that many are unnecessary.

Birth Problems

Some babies have problems at birth due to **anoxia** (lack of oxygen), which can cause brain damage. **Preterm** and **low birthweight** babies have an increased risk of infant mortality. **Infant mortality** has decreased both worldwide and in Canada, but is higher among Native people and lower-income groups.

The Postpartum Period

Transient mood changes following childbirth are common in new mothers. Women with **postpartum depression** experience lingering depression following childbirth. **Breast-feeding** is connected to fewer infections and allergic reactions than bottle-feeding, although there are few long-term differences between the feeding methods.

Chapter Quiz

1. The enzyme hyaluronidase
   (a) stimulates production of milk.
   (b) passes through the placenta.
   (c) stimulates contractions of labour.
   (d) thins the zona pellucida.

2. The most common cause of male infertility is
   (a) low sperm motility.
   (b) low sperm count.
   (c) injury to the testes.
   (d) higher-than-normal scrotal temperature.

3. The presence of human chorionic gonadotropin is assessed to determine
   (a) blocked fallopian tubes.
   (b) sickle-cell anemia.
   (c) pregnancy.
   (d) Down syndrome.

4. If we date pregnancy from the onset of the last menstrual cycle before conception, the normal gestation period is _____ days.
   (a) 266
   (b) 272
   (c) 280
   (d) 288

5. In the method of _____, an ovum is fertilized in a laboratory dish and then placed in a fallopian tube.
   (a) ZIFT
   (b) GIFT
   (c) embryonic transfer
   (d) intracytoplasmic injection

6. The umbilical cord contains
   (a) one artery and one vein.
   (b) two arteries and two veins.
   (c) two arteries and one vein.
   (d) one artery and two veins.

7. A breech presentation is
   (a) bottom or feet first.
   (b) head first.
   (c) sideways.
   (d) shoulder first.

8. Preeclampsia is a stage of
   (a) sickle-cell anemia.
   (b) Tay-Sachs disease.
   (c) rubella.
   (d) toxemia.

9. The critical period for the development of the facial features associated with FAS seems to be the first _____ of prenatal development.
   (a) week
   (b) two weeks
   (c) month
   (d) two months

10. The pudendal block is an example of
    (a) general anaesthesia.
    (b) local anaesthesia.
    (c) use of a tranquillizer.
    (d) use of a narcotic.

Chapter 10

Contraception and Abortion

OUTLINE

Did You Know That...

• Most contraceptives provide little or no protection against sexually transmitted infections?

• Oral contraceptives fool the brain into acting as though the woman is already pregnant so that no additional ova mature or are released?

• Many birth-control pills have healthful side effects? For example, the combination pill reduces the risks of ovarian and endometrial cancer.

• There is a contraceptive pill that can be taken up to 72 hours after intercourse?

• Many sterilization operations can be surgically reversed?

• Testosterone can be used as a male contraceptive device?

• The majority of abortions performed in Canada take place in the first trimester of pregnancy?

Methods of birth control include contraception and abortion. Contraception refers to techniques that prevent conception. Abortion refers to the termination of a pregnancy before the embryo or fetus is capable of surviving outside the womb.

A Brief History of Birth Control in Canada

The Hall of Contraception
http://desires.com/1.6/Sex/
Museum/museum1.html
This site describes in words and photographs the collections in the History of Contraception Museum in Toronto.

In 1882 it became a crime to sell or advertise birth control in Canada. Even though doctors knew that it was dangerous for women to have many pregnancies closely spaced, they were often reluctant to provide information about birth control.

With the Great Depression, more emphasis was put on limiting family size, especially for the poor. Doctors began to provide birth control information to their patients, and the Parents' Information Bureau was established in Kitchener, Ontario, to provide birth control to poor women. This organization sent nurses into people's homes, mainly in Ontario and western Canada. However, birth control was available only for married women wanting to limit family size. Single women generally could not obtain birth control. By the late 1950s condoms were available in many drugstores, but they could only be sold legally "for the prevention of contagious disease."

The sexual revolution of the 1960s brought about major changes in attitudes about sexuality, sexual expression, and birth control. The contraceptive pill became available in Canada around 1965, although it had to be prescribed for therapeutic purposes, such as the regulation of the menstrual cycle.

In 1961 a Toronto druggist was fined for selling condoms. Barbara and George Cadbury were so shocked by this that they set up Planned Parenthood of Toronto. Lobbying efforts by this and other groups eventually resulted in the legalization of contraception in 1969.

Methods of Contraception

The Birth Control Pill
http://archives.cbc.ca/IDD-
1-69-572/life_society/pill/
This website offers multimedia footage from the CBC's archives on the history of the pill in Canada.

There are many methods of contraception, including oral contraceptives (the pill), the birth control patch, contraceptive injections, intrauterine devices (IUDs), diaphragms, cervical caps, spermicides, condoms, douching, withdrawal (coitus interruptus), timing of ovulation (rhythm method), and some devices under development.

Oral Contraceptives ("the Pill")

Oral contraceptive A contraceptive, consisting of female sex hormones, which is taken by mouth.

An **oral contraceptive** is commonly referred to as a birth-control pill, or simply "the pill." However, there are many kinds of birth-control pills that vary in the type and dosages of hormones they contain. Birth-control pills fall into two major categories: combination pills and minipills.

Combination pills contain a combination of synthetic forms of the hormones estrogen and progesterone (progestin). *Multiphasic* combination pills, the pills usually prescribed today, vary the dosage of these hormones across the menstrual cycle to reduce the overall dosages to which the woman is exposed and thus reduce possible side effects. The **minipill**, less commonly used, contains synthetic progesterone (progestin) only.

Available only by prescription, oral contraceptives are used by 28% of women in Canada (Fisher et al., 1999). Birth-control pills are the most popular forms of contraception among women under 30 (Martin & Wu, 2000).

How They Work Women cannot conceive when they are already pregnant because high levels of estrogen and progesterone suppress maturation of egg follicles and ovulation. The birth control pill fools the brain into acting as though the woman is already pregnant, so that no additional ova mature or are released. If ovulation does not take place, a woman cannot become pregnant.

The estrogen in the combination pill inhibits FSH production, so follicles do not mature. The progesterone (progestin) inhibits the pituitary's secretion of LH, which would otherwise lead to ovulation. The woman continues to have menstrual periods, but there is no unfertilized ovum to be sloughed off in the menstrual flow.

The pill is taken for 21 days of the typical 28-day cycle. Then, for 7 days, the woman takes either no pill at all or an inert placebo pill to maintain the habit of taking a pill a day. The sudden drop in hormone levels causes the endometrium to disintegrate and menstruation to follow three or four days after the last pill has been taken. Then the cycle is repeated.

The progestin in the combination pill also increases the thickness and acidity of the cervical mucus. The mucus thus becomes a more resistant barrier to sperm. Also, the progestin inhibits development of the endometrium. Therefore, even if an egg were somehow to mature and be released into a fallopian tube, sperm would not be likely to reach it. Even if sperm were to fertilize an egg, the failure of the endometrium to develop would mean that the fertilized ovum could not become implanted in the uterus. Progestin may also impede the progress of ova through the fallopian tubes and make it more difficult for sperm to penetrate ova.

The minipill contains progestin but no estrogen. Minipills are taken daily through the menstrual cycle, even during menstruation. They thicken the cervical mucus, presenting a barrier to sperm and reducing its motility, and render the inner lining of the uterus less receptive to a fertilized egg. Thus, even if the woman does conceive, the fertilized egg will pass from the body rather than becoming implanted in the uterine wall. Since it contains no estrogen, the minipill does not usually prevent ovulation. The combination pill, by contrast, prevents ovulation. Since ovulation may occur and fertilization is possible (though not likely) in women who use the minipill, some people see use of the minipill as an early abortion method.

Effectiveness The failure rate of the birth-control pill associated with perfect use is very low—0.5% or less, depending on the type of pill (see Table 10.1). The failure rate increases to 3% in typical use. Failures can occur when women forget to take the pill for two days or more, when they do not use backup methods when they first go on the pill, and when they switch from one brand to another. Forgetting to take the pill for even one day may alter the woman's hormonal balance, allowing ovulation—and fertilization—to occur.

Reversibility Use of oral contraceptives may temporarily reduce fertility after they are discontinued but is not associated with permanent infertility (Mishell, 1989). Nine of ten women begin ovulating regularly within three months of suspending use (Reinisch, 1990). When a woman appears not to be ovulating after going off the pill, a drug like clomiphene is often used to induce ovulation.

Advantages and Disadvantages Oral contraception, used properly, is nearly 100% effective. It does not interfere with sexual spontaneity or diminish sexual sensations.

Birth-control pills may also have some healthful side effects. They appear to reduce the risk of pelvic inflammatory disease (PID), benign ovarian cysts, and fibrocystic

Combination pill A birth-control pill that contains synthetic estrogen and progesterone.

Minipill A birth-control pill that contains synthetic progesterone but no estrogen.

Planned Parenthood Federation of Canada
www.ppfc.ca/
The Planned Parenthood Federation provides services, information, and counselling on sexual and reproductive health.

Oral Contraceptives. *Birth-control pills are the most popular forms of contraception among women under 30.*

The pill may also have psychological effects. Some users report depression or irritability. Switching brands or altering doses may help.

Progestin fosters male secondary sex characteristics, so women who take the mini-pill may develop acne, facial hair, thinning of scalp hair, reduction in breast size, vaginal dryness, and missed or shorter periods. Irregular or so-called breakthrough bleeding between menstrual periods is a common side effect of the minipill (Reinisch, 1990). Irregular bleeding should be brought to the attention of a health professional.

Because they can produce vaginal dryness, minipills can hinder vaginal lubrication during intercourse, decreasing sexual sensations and rendering sex painful.

Researchers have also examined suspected links between the use of the pill and certain forms of cancer, especially breast cancer, since breast cancer is sensitive to hormonal changes. The evidence linking use of the pill with increased risk of cervical cancer is mixed, with some studies showing such a link and others showing none (Hatcher et al., 1994). However, a recent study of more than 9000 women found no association between oral contraceptive use and the incidence of breast cancer (Marchbanks et al., 2002). Women who begin to use the pill, regardless of their age or risk status, should pay attention to changes in their physical condition, have regular checkups, and promptly report any physical complaints or unusual symptoms to their physicians.

"Morning-After" Pills The so-called morning-after pill, or postcoital contraceptive, actually refers to several types of pills that have high doses of estrogen and progestin. Since they are not taken regularly, they do not prevent ovulation from occurring. Instead, they stop fertilization from taking place or prevent the fertilized egg from implanting itself in the uterus (Hoffman, 1993). In that respect, then, some people consider them an early abortion technique. Morning-after pills are most effective when taken within 72 hours after ovulation. Women who wait to see whether they have missed a period are no longer candidates for the morning-after pill.

Morning-after pills have a higher hormone content than most birth-control pills. For this reason, nausea is a common side effect (Hatcher et al., 1994). Because of the strength of the dosage, the morning-after pill is not recommended as a regular form of birth control. We also know little about possible long-term health complications. Morning-after pills are one-time forms of "emergency" protection (Hatcher et al., 1994). The morning-after pill was approved for sale in Canada in November 1999. One emergency contraceptive (Plan B) is available in British Columbia and Quebec without a prescription.

Intrauterine Devices (IUDs)

Intrauterine device
A small object that is inserted into the uterus and left in place to prevent conception. Abbreviated *IUD*.

Camel drivers setting out on long desert journeys placed round stones in the uteruses of female camels to prevent them from becoming pregnant and lost to service. The stones may have acted as primitive **intrauterine devices** (IUDs). IUDs are small objects of various shapes that are inserted into the uterus. IUDs have been used by humans since the time of ancient Greece. Today, they are inserted into the uterus by a physician or nurse practitioner and usually left in place for a year or more. Fine plastic threads or strings hang down from the IUD into the vagina, so that the woman can check to see that it remains in place.

IUDs are used by about 1% of Canadian women (Fisher et al., 1999), and more than 80 million women around the world (Altman, 1991). Married women are more likely to use the IUD than single women (Fisher et al., 1999).

The only copper IUD currently available in Canada, the Nova-T, is a T-shaped copper-based device (see Figure 10.1). The Nova-T can be left in place for seven years (Montreal Health Press, 1999), unless the woman is allergic to copper (Hatcher et al., 1994). A progestin-releasing device, Mirena, can be left in place for five years (Health Canada, 2001).

How It Works We do not know exactly how IUDs work. A foreign body, such as the IUD, apparently irritates the uterine lining. This irritation gives rise to mild inflammation and the production of antibodies that may be toxic to sperm or to fertilized ova and/or may prevent fertilized eggs from becoming implanted. Inflammation may also impair proliferation of the endometrium—another impediment to implantation. Action on fertilized ova may be considered to constitute an early abortion. Since IUDs may not prevent fertilization, people who oppose abortion, regardless of how soon it occurs after conception, also oppose the IUD.

Effectiveness The failure rate associated with typical use of the IUD is less than 1% (see Table 10.1). Most failures occur within three months of insertion, often because the device shifts position or is expelled.

The IUD may irritate the muscular layer of the uterine wall, causing contractions that expel it through the vagina. The device is most likely to be expelled during menstruation, so users are advised to check their sanitary napkins or tampons before discarding them. Women who use IUDs are advised to check the string several times a month to ensure that the IUD is in place. Spontaneous expulsions occur in 2% to 10% of users within the first year of use (Hatcher et al., 1994). Some family-planning clinics advise women to supplement their use of IUDs with other devices for the first three months, when the risks of a shift in position or expulsion are greatest.

Reversibility IUDs may be removed readily by professionals. Nine out of ten former IUD users who wish to do so become pregnant within a year (Reinisch, 1990).

Advantages and Disadvantages The IUD has three major advantages: (1) it is highly effective; (2) it does not diminish sexual spontaneity or sexual sensations; and (3) once in place, the woman need not do anything more to prevent pregnancy (other than check that it remains in place).

The IUD also does not interfere with the woman's normal hormonal production. Users continue to produce pituitary hormones that stimulate ovarian follicles to mature and rupture, thereby releasing mature ova and producing female sex hormones.

If IUDs are so effective and relatively "maintenance free," why are they not more popular? One reason is that insertion can be painful. Another reason is side effects. The most common side effects are excessive menstrual cramping, irregular bleeding (spotting) between periods, and heavier than usual menstrual bleeding (Reinisch, 1990). A more serious concern is the possible risk of pelvic inflammatory disease (PID), a serious disease that can become life threatening if left untreated (Hatcher et al., 1994).

PID can scar the fallopian tubes, causing infertility. Women with pelvic infections should not use an IUD (Hatcher et al., 1994).

Another risk in using an IUD is that the device may perforate (tear) the uterine or cervical walls, which can cause bleeding, pain, and adhesions and become life threatening. Perforations are usually caused by improper insertion and occur in perhaps 1 case in 1000 (Reinisch, 1990). IUD users are also at greater risk for ectopic pregnancies and for miscarriage.

Despite the fact that the IUD irritates uterine tissues, there is no evidence that IUD users run a greater risk of cancer. Long-term data on the health effects of IUD use are limited, however.

Another drawback to the IUD is its cost. Although the insertion of the IUD is covered by provincial health insurance plans, women must purchase the device, either from their health care provider or from a pharmacy, with a prescription. Costs can range from $35 to upwards of $100. Potential expulsion of the IUD presents yet another disadvantage. Moreover, the IUD, like the pill, offers no protection against STIs. Finally, like the pill, IUDs place the burden of contraception entirely on the woman.

The Diaphragm

Diaphragms were once used by many couples who practised birth control. When invented in 1882, they were a breakthrough. Their popularity declined only in the 1960s

Figure 10.1. Nova-T.

The Nova-T is a T-shaped copper-based device which can be left in place for seven years.

Diaphragm A shallow rubber cup or dome, fitted to the contour of a woman's vagina, that is coated with a spermicide and inserted prior to coitus to prevent conception.

Figure 10.2. A Diaphragm.

The diaphragm is a shallow cup or dome made of latex. Diaphragms must be fitted to the contour of the vagina by a health professional. The diaphragm forms a barrier to sperm but should be used in conjunction with a spermicidal cream or jelly.

with the advent of the pill and the IUD. Between 1984 and 1995, diaphragm use by Canadian women dropped dramatically (Martin & Wu, 2000). Currently, fewer than 1% of Canadian women use a diaphragm.

The diaphragm is a shallow cup or dome made of thin latex rubber (see Figure 10.2). The rim is a flexible metal ring covered with rubber. Diaphragms come in different sizes, to allow a precise fit.

Diaphragms are available by prescription and must be fitted to the contour of the vagina by a health professional. Several sizes and types of diaphragms may be tried during a fitting. Women practise insertion in a health professional's office so they can be guided as needed.

How It Works The diaphragm is inserted and removed by the woman, much like a tampon. It is akin to a condom in that it forms a barrier against sperm when placed snugly over the cervical opening. Yet it is unreliable as a barrier alone. Thus, the diaphragm should be used in conjunction with a spermicidal cream or jelly. The diaphragm's main function is to keep the spermicide in place.

How It Is Used The diaphragm should be inserted no more than two hours before coitus, since the spermicides that are used may begin to lose effectiveness beyond this time. Some health professionals, however, suggest that the diaphragm may be inserted up to six hours preceding intercourse. (It seems reasonable to err on the side of caution and assume that there is a two-hour time limit.) The woman or her partner places a tablespoonful of spermicidal cream or jelly on the inside of the cup and spreads it inside the rim. (Cream spread outside the rim might cause the diaphragm to slip.) The woman opens the inner lips of the vagina with one hand and folds the diaphragm with the other by squeezing the ring. She inserts the diaphragm against the cervix, with the inner side facing upward (see Figure 10.3). Her partner can help insert the diaphragm, but the woman is advised to check its placement. Some women prefer a plastic insertion device, but most find it easier to insert the diaphragm without it. The diaphragm should be left in place at least six hours after intercourse to allow the spermicide to kill any remaining sperm in the vagina, and additional spermicidal cream or foam should be used for subsequent acts of intercourse (Hatcher et al., 1994). It should not be left in place for longer than 24 hours, to guard against toxic shock syndrome.

After use, the diaphragm should be washed with mild soap and warm water and stored in a dry, cool place. When cared for properly, a diaphragm can last about two years. Women may need to be refitted after pregnancy or a change in weight of about 5 kilograms or more.

Effectiveness If used consistently and correctly, the failure rate of the diaphragm is estimated to be 6% during the first year of use (see Table 10.1). In typical use, however, the failure rate is believed to be three times as high—18%. Some women become pregnant because they do not use the diaphragm during every coital experience. Others

Figure 10.3. Insertion and Checking of the Diaphragm.

Women are instructed in insertion of the diaphragm by a health professional. A woman and her partner may find joint insertion an erotic experience.

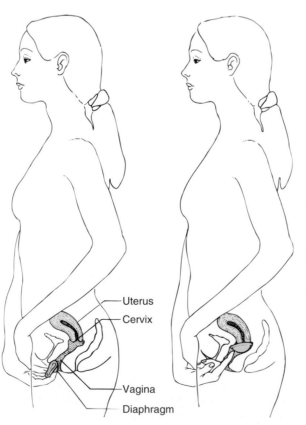

may insert it too early or not leave it in long enough. The diaphragm may not fit well, or it may slip—especially if the couple is acrobatic. A diaphragm may develop tiny holes or cracks. Women are advised to inspect the diaphragm for signs of wear and consult their health professionals when in doubt. Effectiveness is also seriously compromised when the diaphragm is not used along with a correctly applied spermicide (Trussell et al., 1993).

Reversibility The effects of the diaphragm are fully reversible. In order to become pregnant, the woman simply stops using it. The diaphragm has not been shown to influence subsequent fertility.

Advantages and Disadvantages The major advantage of the diaphragm is that when used correctly it is a safe and effective means of birth control and does not alter the woman's hormone production or reproductive cycle. The diaphragm can be used as needed, whereas the pill must be used daily and the IUD remains in place whether or not the woman engages in coitus. Another advantage is the virtual absence of side effects. The few women who are allergic to the rubber in the diaphragm can switch to a plastic model.

The major disadvantage is the high pregnancy rate associated with typical use. Nearly 1 in 5 users (18%) of the diaphragm combined with spermicidal cream or jelly becomes pregnant during the first year of use (Hatcher et al., 1994). Another disadvantage is the need to insert the diaphragm prior to intercourse, which the couple may find disruptive. As well, the woman's partner may find the taste of the spermicides used in conjunction with the diaphragm to be unpleasant during oral sex. The pressure exerted by the diaphragm against the vaginal and cervical walls may also irritate the urinary tract and cause urinary or even vaginal infections. Switching to a different size diaphragm or one with a different type of rim may help alleviate this problem. About 1 woman or man in 20 may develop allergies to the particular spermicide that is used, which can lead to irritation of the genitals. This problem may also be alleviated by switching to another brand.

Spermicides

Spermicides are chemical agents that kill sperm. They come in different forms, including jellies and creams, suppositories, aerosol foam, film, and gels. Spermicides should be left in place in the vagina (no douching) for at least 6–8 hours after coitus (Hatcher et al., 1994).

Spermicidal jellies, creams, foam, and suppositories should be used no more than 60 minutes preceding coitus for maximum effectiveness (Hatcher et al., 1994). Spermicidal jellies and creams come in tubes with plastic applicators that introduce the spermicide into the vagina (see Figure 10.4). Spermicidal foam is a fluffy white cream with the consistency of shaving cream. It is contained in a pressurized can and is introduced with a plastic applicator in much the same way as spermicidal jellies and creams.

Vaginal suppositories are inserted into the upper vagina, near the cervix, where they release spermicide as they dissolve. Unlike spermicidal jellies, creams, and foam, which

Uterus
Cervix
Foam applicator
Foam
Vagina

Figure 10.4.
The Application of Spermicides.

Spermicidal jellies and creams come in tubes with plastic applicators. Spermicidal foam comes in a pressurized can and is applied with a plastic applicator.

are effective immediately, suppositories must be inserted at least 10 to 15 minutes before coitus so that they have sufficient time to dissolve (Hatcher et al., 1994).

Spermicidal film consists of thin, 5-cm-square sheets that are saturated with spermicide. When placed in the vagina, they dissolve into a gel and release the spermicide. The spermicidal film should be inserted at least five minutes before intercourse to allow it time to melt and disperse the spermicide (Hatcher et al., 1994). It remains effective for upwards of one hour (Hatcher et al., 1994). One disadvantage of the film is a tendency to adhere to the fingertips, which makes it difficult to insert correctly.

How They Work Spermicides coat the cervical opening, blocking the passage of sperm and killing sperm by chemical action.

Effectiveness In typical use, the first-year failure rate of spermicides used alone is 21 pregnancies per year per 100 users (Hatcher et al., 1994; Reinisch, 1990). When used correctly and consistently, the failure rate is estimated to drop to about 6 pregnancies per 100 users in the first year. All forms of spermicide are more effective when they are combined with other forms of contraception, such as the condom.

Reversibility Spermicides have not been linked with any changes in reproductive potential. Couples who wish to become pregnant simply stop using them.

Advantages and Disadvantages The major advantages of spermicides are that they do not alter the woman's natural biological processes and are applied only as needed. Unlike a diaphragm, they do not require a doctor's prescription or a fitting. They can be bought in virtually any drugstore, and the average cost per use of the foam variety is modest—about 50 cents.

The major disadvantage is the high failure rate among typical users. Foam often fails when the can is not shaken enough, when too little is used, when it is not applied deeply enough within the vagina, or when it is used after coitus has begun.

Spermicides are generally free of side effects but may cause vaginal or penile irritation. Irritation is sometimes alleviated by changing brands. Some partners find the taste of spermicides unpleasant. (Couples can engage in oral sex before applying spermicides.)

For a number of years, it was believed that spermicides containing nonoxynol-9 could provide some protection against organisms that cause STIs, including HIV, and genital herpes. However, recent research suggests that this is not the case. In fact, because it can cause lesions in the vagina, nonoxynol-9 may facilitate the transmission of HIV (Health Canada, 2003p). Most condom manufacturers have discontinued condoms coated with nonoxynol-9. Spermicides may pose a danger to an embryo, so women who suspect they are pregnant are advised to suspend use until they find out for certain.

The Cervical Cap

The cervical cap, like the diaphragm, is a dome-shaped rubber cup. It comes in different sizes and must be fitted by a health professional. It is smaller than the diaphragm, however—about the size of a thimble—and is meant to fit snugly over the cervical opening.

How It Is Used Like the diaphragm, the cap is intended to be used with a spermicide applied inside it (Hatcher et al., 1994). When inserting it, the woman (or her partner) fills the cap about a third full of spermicide. Then, squeezing the edges together, the woman inserts the cap high in the vagina, so that it presses firmly against the cervix. The woman can test the fit by running a finger around the cap to ensure that the cervical opening is covered. It should be left in place for at least eight hours after intercourse. The cap provides continuous protection for up to 48 hours without the need for additional spermicide. To reduce the risk of toxic shock syndrome, the cap should not be left in place longer than 48 hours.

How It Works Like the diaphragm, the cervical cap forms a barrier and also holds spermicide in place against the cervix. It prevents sperm from passing into the uterus and fallopian tubes and kills sperm by chemical action.

Effectiveness The failure rate in typical use is high, with estimates ranging from 18% in women who have not borne children to 36% in women who have (Hatcher et al., 1994). Failures may be attributed, at least in part, to the cap's becoming dislodged and to changes in the cervix during the menstrual cycle, which can cause the cap to fit less snugly over the cervix.

Reversibility There is no evidence that the cervical cap affects fertility.

Advantages and Disadvantages Like the diaphragm, the cap is a mechanical device that does not affect the woman's hormonal production or reproductive cycle. The cap may be especially suited to women who cannot support a diaphragm because of lack of vaginal muscle tone. Because of concern that the cap may irritate cervical tissue, however, Mishell (1989) recommends that repeat Pap tests be performed with users.

Some women find the cap uncomfortable. The cap can also become dislodged during sexual activity or lose its fit as the cervix changes over the menstrual cycle. Reported side effects include urinary tract infections and allergic reactions or sensitivities to the rubber or spermicide.

The effectiveness of the cervical cap is considerably greater among women who have not given birth (Trussell et al., 1993). Women who have given birth may wish to consult their gynecologists concerning the suitability of the cap.

Condoms

Condoms are also called "rubbers," "safes," **prophylactics** (because latex condoms protect against STIs), and "skins" (referring to those that are made from lamb intestines). Condoms lost popularity with the advent of the pill and the IUD. They are less effective than the pill or IUD, may disrupt sexual spontaneity, and can decrease coital sensations because they prevent the penis from actually touching the vaginal wall.

Condoms have made a comeback, however, because those made of latex rubber can help prevent the spread of the AIDS virus (the human immunodeficiency virus [HIV]) and other STIs and, to a lesser extent, because of concerns about side effects of the pill and the IUD. Condoms are used by 44% of Canadian women who use contraception. Unmarried women are more likely to report using condoms than are married women. Overall, 21% of Canadian women use condoms (Fisher et al., 1999).

Condom advertisements have appeared in mainstream media, including magazines such as *People* and *Cosmopolitan*, and on major TV networks. In a TV commercial, a man and a woman are shown hurriedly undressing. The man tells the woman that he forgot to bring a condom with him. She then tells him that he'd best forget it (making love, that is). Whether these media campaigns will increase condom usage remains to be seen.

The renewed popularity of condoms has also been spurred by the increased assertiveness of contemporary women. They make the point (which should be obvious, but all too often is not) that contraception is as much the man's responsibility as the woman's. Condoms alter the psychological aspect of sexual relations. By using a condom the man assumes much of the responsibility for contraception. Condoms are the only contraceptive device worn by men, and the only readily reversible method of contraception that is available to men. Condoms are inexpensive and can be obtained without prescription from pharmacies, clinics, and even from vending machines in some high school, college, and university washrooms.

Some condoms are made of latex rubber. Thinner, more expensive condoms ("skins") are made from the intestinal membranes of lambs. The latter allow greater sexual sensation but do not protect as well against STIs. Only latex condoms are effective against the tiny AIDS virus. Condoms made of animal intestines have pores large enough to permit the AIDS virus and other viruses, such as the one that causes hepatitis B, to slip through (Consumer's Union, 1995). A few condoms are made from other

Condom A sheath made of animal membrane or latex that covers the penis during coitus and serves as a barrier to sperm following ejaculation.

Prophylactic An agent that protects against disease.

Figure 10.5. Condoms.

Some condoms are plain-tipped, whereas others have nipples or reservoirs that catch semen and may help prevent the condom from bursting during ejaculation. Latex condoms form effective barriers to the tiny AIDS virus.

materials, such as plastic (polyurethane). Questions remain about the effectiveness of polyurethane condoms (Consumer's Union, 1995). Some condoms have plain ends. Others have nipples or reservoirs (see Figure 10.5) that catch semen and may help prevent the condom from bursting during ejaculation.

How It Works

A condom is a cylindrical sheath that serves as a barrier, preventing the passage of sperm and disease-carrying microorganisms from the man to his partner. It also helps prevent infected vaginal fluids (and micro-organisms) from entering the man's urethral opening or from penetrating through small cracks in the skin of the penis.

How It Is Used

The condom is rolled onto the penis once erection is achieved and before any contact between the penis and the vagina (see Figure 10.6). If the condom is not used until moments before the point of ejaculation, sperm-carrying fluid from the Cowper's glands or from preorgasmic spasms may already have passed into the vagina. Nor does the condom afford protection against STIs if it is fitted after penetration.

Condoms sometimes fall off or break. Between 1% and 2% of condoms break or fall off during intercourse or when withdrawing the penis afterward (Cates & Stone, 1992a; Trussell et al., 1992). Condoms also sometimes slip down the shaft of the penis without falling off. The following guidelines[1] will help couples use condoms effectively:

Figure 10.6. Applying a Condom.

First the rolled-up condom is placed on the head of the penis, and then it is rolled down the shaft of the penis. If a condom without a reservoir tip is used, a 1-cm space should be left at the tip for the ejaculate to accumulate.

- Use a condom each and every time you have intercourse. Inexperienced users should also practise putting on a condom before they have the occasion to use one with a partner.

- Handle the condom carefully, making sure not to damage it with your fingernails, teeth, or sharp objects.

- Place the condom on the erect penis before it touches the vulva.

- Uncircumcised men should pull back the foreskin before putting on the condom.

- If you use a spermicide, place some inside the tip of the condom before placing the condom on the penis. You may also wish to use additional spermicide applied by an applicator inside the vagina to provide extra protection, especially in the event of breakage of the condom.

- Do not pull the condom tightly against the tip of the penis.

- For a condom without a reservoir tip, leave a small empty space—about a centimetre—at the end of the condom to hold semen, yet do not allow any air to be trapped at the tip. Some condoms come equipped with a reservoir (nipple) tip that will hold semen.

- Unroll the condom all the way to the bottom of the penis.

- Ensure that adequate vaginal lubrication during intercourse is present, possibly using lubricants if necessary. But use only water-based lubricants such as contraceptive jelly or K-Y jelly. Never use an oil-based lubricant that can weaken the latex material, such as petroleum jelly (Vaseline), cold cream, baby oil or lotion, mineral oil, massage oil, vegetable oil, Crisco, hand or body lotions, and most skin creams. Do not use saliva as a lubricant because it may contain infectious organisms, such as viruses.

- If the condom breaks during intercourse, withdraw the penis immediately, put on a new condom, and use more spermicide.

- After ejaculation, carefully withdraw the penis while it is still erect.

- Hold the rim of the condom firmly against the base of the penis as the penis is withdrawn, to prevent the condom from slipping off.

- Remove the condom carefully from the penis, making sure that semen doesn't leak out.

---

[1] Adapted from the Centers for Disease Control pamphlet "Condoms and Sexually Transmitted Disease... Especially AIDS" (HHS Publication FDA 90-4329) and other sources.

- Check the removed condom for tears or cracks. If any are found, immediately apply a spermicide containing nonoxynol-9 directly to the penis and within the vagina. Wrap the used condom in a tissue, and discard it in the garbage. Do not flush it down the toilet, as condoms may cause problems in the sewers. Wash your hands thoroughly with soap and water.

Here are some things you should never do with a condom:

- Never use teeth, scissors, or sharp fingernails to open a package of condoms. Open the condom package carefully to avoid tearing or puncturing the condom.

- Never test a condom by inflating it or stretching it.

- Never use a condom after its expiration date.

- Never use a condom that is sticky, gummy, discoloured, brittle, or otherwise appears damaged or shows signs of deterioration.

- Never use a condom if the sealed packet containing the condom is damaged, cracked, or brittle, as the condom itself may be damaged or defective.

- Do not open the sealed packet until you are ready to use the condom. A condom contained in a packet that has been opened can become dry and brittle within a few hours, causing it to tear more easily. The box that contains the condom packets, however, may be opened at any time.

- Never use the same condom twice. Use a new condom if you switch the site of intercourse, such as from the vagina to the anus, or from the anus to the mouth, during a single sexual act.

- Never carry a condom in your pants pocket or in a wallet held in your pants pocket, where it might be exposed to body heat. If you want to carry a condom with you, place it in a loose jacket pocket or purse.

- Do not carry a condom for any length of time in a pocket or a car's glove compartment, where it may be exposed to heat.

- Never buy condoms from vending machines that are exposed to extreme heat or placed in direct sunlight.

Effectiveness In typical use, the failure rate of the male condom is estimated at 12% (see Table 10.1). That is, 12 out of 100 women whose partners rely on condoms alone for contraception can expect to become pregnant during the first year of use. This rate can be reduced to perhaps 2% or 3% if the condom is used correctly and combined with the use of a spermicide (Hatcher et al., 1994; Reinisch, 1990). The effectiveness of a condom and spermicide combined rivals that of the birth-control pill when used correctly and consistently.

Reversibility The condom is simply a mechanical barrier to sperm and does not compromise fertility. Therefore, a couple who wish to conceive a child simply discontinue its use.

Advantages and Disadvantages Condoms have the advantage of being readily available. They can be purchased without prescription. They require no fitting and can remain in sealed packages until needed. They are readily discarded after use. They provide protection against various STI-causing organisms. The combination of condoms and spermicides increases contraceptive effectiveness and may increase protection against some STI-causing organisms, although the spermicide nonoxynol-9 may facilitate transmission of HIV. Condoms do not affect production of hormones, ova, or sperm. Women whose partners use condoms ovulate normally. Men who use them produce sperm and ejaculate normally. The use of a lubricated condom may make insertion of the penis in the vagina more comfortable for the woman. With all these advantages, why are condoms not more popular?

One disadvantage of the condom is that it may render sex less spontaneous. The couple must interrupt lovemaking to apply the condom. Condoms may also lessen sexual sensations, especially for the man. Latex condoms do so more than animal membrane sheaths. Condoms also sometimes slip off or tear, allowing sperm to leak through.

On the other hand, condoms are almost entirely free of side effects (an advantage reported by 70% of female respondents to a *Consumer Reports* survey). They offer protection against STIs that is unparalleled among contraceptive devices. They can also be used without prior medical consultation. Both partners can share putting on the condom, which makes it an erotic part of their lovemaking, not an intrusion. The use of textured or ultrathin condoms may increase sensitivity, especially for the male. Thus many couples find that advantages outweigh disadvantages. Sex in the age of AIDS has given condoms a new respectability, even a certain trendiness. Notice, for example, the new "designer colours," flavours, and styles on display at your local pharmacy. Advertisers now also target women in their ads, suggesting that women, like men, can come prepared with condoms.

It is tempting to claim that the condom has a perfect safety record and no side effects. Let us settle for "close to perfect." Some people may have allergic reactions to the spermicides with which some lubricated condoms are coated or that the woman may apply. In such cases the couple may need to use a condom without a spermicidal lubricant or stop using supplemental spermicides. Some people are allergic to latex.

It is quite reasonable for a woman to make condom use a condition for engaging in sex. STIs such as gonorrhea and chlamydia (see Chapter 13) do far more damage to a woman's reproductive tract than to a man's. Condoms can help protect women from vaginitis, pelvic inflammatory disease (PID), infections that can harm a fetus or cause infertility, and most important, AIDS.

Douching

Douche Application of a jet of liquid to the vagina as a rinse.

Many couples believe that if a woman **douches** shortly after coitus, she will not become pregnant. Women who douche for contraceptive purposes often use syringes to flush the vagina with water or a spermicidal agent. The water is intended to wash sperm out; the spermicides, to kill them. Douching is ineffective, however, because large numbers of sperm move beyond the range of the douche seconds after ejaculation. In fact, squirting a liquid into the vagina may even propel sperm *toward* the uterus. Douching, at best, has a failure rate among typical users of 40% (Reinisch, 1990), too high to be considered reliable.

Regular douching may also alter the natural chemistry of the vagina, increasing the risk of vaginal infection. In short, douching is a "non-method" of contraception.

Withdrawal (Coitus Interruptus)

Coitus interruptus The practice of withdrawing the penis prior to ejaculation during sexual intercourse.

Withdrawal (**coitus interruptus**) means that the man removes his penis from the vagina before ejaculating. Withdrawal has a first-year failure rate among typical users ranging from 19% to 23% (Hatcher et al., 1994; Reinisch, 1990). There are several reasons for these failures. The man may not withdraw in time. Even if the penis is withdrawn just before ejaculation, some ejaculate may still fall on the vaginal lips, and sperm may find their way to the fallopian tubes. Active sperm may also be present in the pre-ejaculatory secretions of fluid from the Cowper's glands, a discharge of which the man is usually unaware and which he cannot control. These sperm are capable of fertilizing an ovum even if the man withdraws before orgasm. Because of its unreliability and high failure rate, withdrawal, like douching, is also a non-method of contraception.

Fertility Awareness Methods (Rhythm Methods, Periodic Abstinence Methods)

Fertility awareness, or *rhythm*, methods rely on awareness of the fertile segments of the woman's menstrual cycle. Terms such as *natural birth control* or *natural family planning* also refer to these methods. The essence of such methods is that coitus is avoided on days when conception is most likely (hence the "periodic abstinence"). Fertility awareness methods are used by about 2% of Canadian women (Fisher et al., 1999). Women of ages 25 to 44 are more than twice as likely as 15- to 24-year-olds to use rhythm methods. Since the rhythm method does not employ artificial devices, it is acceptable to the Roman Catholic Church.

How They Work A number of methods are used to predict the likelihood of conception. They are the mirror images of the methods that couples use to increase their chances of conceiving (see Chapter 9). Methods for enhancing the chances of conception seek to predict time of ovulation so the couple can arrange to have sperm present in the woman's reproductive tract at about that time. As methods of *birth control*, these methods seek to predict ovulation so that the couple can *abstain* from coitus when the woman is fertile.

The Calendar Method The **calendar method** assumes that ovulation occurs 14 days prior to menstruation. The couple abstains from intercourse during the period that begins three days prior to day 13 (because sperm are unlikely to survive for more than 72 hours in the female reproductive tract) and ends two days after day 15 (because an unfertilized ovum is unlikely to remain receptive to fertilization for longer than 48 hours). The period of abstention thus covers days 10 to 17 of the woman's cycle.

When a woman has regular 28-day cycles, predicting the period of abstention is relatively straightforward. Women with irregular cycles are generally advised to chart their cycles for 10 months to a year to determine their shortest and longest cycles. The first day of menstruation counts as day 1 of the cycle. The last day of the cycle is the day preceding the onset of menstruation.

Consider a woman whose cycles vary from 23 to 33 days. In theory she will ovulate 14 days before menstruation begins. (To be safe she should assume that ovulation will take place anywhere from 13 to 15 days before her period.) Applying the rule of "three days before" and "two days after," she should avoid coitus from day 5 of her cycle, which corresponds to three days before her earliest expected ovulation (computed by subtracting 15 days from the 23 days of her shortest cycle and then subtracting three days), through day 22, which corresponds to two days after her latest expected ovulation (computed by subtracting 13 days from the 33 days of her longest cycle and then adding two days). Another way of determining this period of abstention would be to subtract 18 days from the woman's shortest cycle to determine the start of the "unsafe" period and 11 days from her longest cycle to determine the last "unsafe" day. The woman in the example has irregular cycles. She thus faces an 18-day abstention period each month—quite a burden for a sexually active couple.

Most women who follow the calendar method need to abstain from coitus for at least 10 days during the middle of each cycle (Reinisch, 1990). Moreover, the calendar method cannot ensure that the woman's longest or shortest menstrual cycles will occur during the 10- to 12-month period of baseline tracking. Some women, too, have such irregular cycles that the range of "unsafe" days cannot be predicted reliably even if baseline tracking is extended.

The Basal Body Temperature (BBT) Method In the **basal body temperature (BBT) method**, the woman tracks her body temperature upon awakening each morning to detect the small changes that occur directly before and after ovulation. A woman's basal body temperature sometimes dips slightly just before ovulation and then tends to rise between 0.2 and 0.5 degrees Celsius just before, during, and after ovulation. It remains elevated until the onset of menstruation. (The rise in temperature is caused by the increased production of progesterone by the corpus luteum during the luteal phase of the cycle.) Thermometers that provide finely graded readings, such as electronic thermometers, are best suited for determining these minor changes. A major problem with the BBT method is that it does not indicate the several unsafe preovulatory days during which sperm deposited in the vagina may remain viable. Rather, the BBT method indicates when a woman has ovulated. Thus, many women use the calendar method to predict the number of "safe" days prior to ovulation and the BBT method to determine

Calendar method An abstinence-based method of contraception that relies on prediction of ovulation by tracking menstrual cycles, typically for a 10- to 12-month period, and assuming that ovulation occurs 14 days prior to menstruation.

Basal body temperature (BBT) method A fertility awareness method of contraception that relies on prediction of ovulation by tracking the woman's temperature during the course of the menstrual cycle.

the number of "unsafe" days after. A woman would avoid coitus during the "unsafe" pre-ovulatory period (as determined by the calendar method) and then for three days when her temperature rises and remains elevated. A drawback of the BBT method is that changes in body temperature may also result from factors unrelated to ovulation, such as infections, sleeplessness, or stress. So some women triple-check themselves by also tracking their cervical mucus.

The Cervical Mucus (Ovulation) Method The **ovulation method** tracks changes in the **viscosity** of the cervical mucus. Following menstruation, the vagina feels rather dry. There is also little or no discharge from the cervix. These dry days are relatively safe. Then a mucous discharge appears in the vagina that is first thick and sticky, and white or cloudy in colour. Coitus (or unprotected coitus) should be avoided at the first sign of any mucus. As the cycle progresses, the mucous discharge thins and clears, becoming slippery or stringy, like raw egg white. These are the **peak days**. This mucous discharge, called the *ovulatory mucus*, may be accompanied by a feeling of vaginal lubrication or wetness. Ovulation takes place about a day after the last peak day (about four days after this ovulatory mucus first appears). Then the mucus becomes cloudy and tacky once more. Intercourse may resume four days following the last peak day.

One problem with the mucus method is that some women have difficulty detecting changes in the mucous discharge. Such changes may also result from infections, certain medications, or contraceptive creams, jellies, or foam. Sexual arousal may also induce changes in viscosity.

Ovulation-Prediction Kits Ovulation-prediction kits are more accurate than the BBT method. Kits allow women to test their urine daily for the presence of luteinizing hormone (LH). LH levels surge about 12 to 24 hours prior to ovulation. Some couples use the kits to enhance their chances of conceiving a child by engaging in coitus when ovulation appears imminent. Others use them as a means of birth control to find out when to avoid coitus. When used correctly, ovulation-predicting kits are 95% to 100% accurate (Reinisch, 1990).

Ovulation kits are expensive and require that the woman's urine be tested each morning. Nor do they reveal the full range of the unsafe preovulatory period during which sperm may remain viable in the vagina. A couple might thus choose to use the kits to determine the unsafe period following ovulation, and the calendar method to determine the unsafe period preceding ovulation.

Effectiveness The estimated first-year failure rate in typical use is 20%, which is high but no higher than the use of contraceptive devices such as the cervical cap or the female condom (see Table 10.1). Still, perhaps one in five typical users will become pregnant during the first year of use. (You may have heard the joke "What do you call people who use the rhythm method? Parents!") Fewer failures occur when these methods are applied conscientiously, when a combination of rhythm methods is used, and when the woman's cycles are quite regular. Restricting coitus to the postovulatory period can reduce the pregnancy rate to 1% (Hatcher et al., 1994). The trick is to be able to reliably determine when ovulation occurs. The pregnancy rate can be reduced to practically zero if rhythm methods are used with other forms of birth control, such as the condom or diaphragm.

Advantages and Disadvantages Because they are a natural form of birth control, rhythm methods appeal to many people who, for religious or other reasons, prefer not to use artificial means. Since no devices or chemicals are used, there are no side effects. Nor do they cause any loss of sensation, as condoms do. Nor is there disruption of love-making, as with condoms, diaphragms, or foam, although lovemaking could be said to be quite "disrupted" during the period of abstention. Rhythm methods are inexpensive, except for ovulation-prediction kits. Both partners may share the responsibility for rhythm methods. The man, for example, can take his partner's temperature or assist with the charting. All rhythm methods are fully reversible.

A disadvantage is the fact that the reliability of rhythm methods is low. Rhythm methods may be unsuitable for women with irregular cycles. Women with irregular

Ovulation method A fertility awareness method of contraception that relies on prediction of ovulation by tracking the viscosity of the cervical mucus.

Viscosity Stickiness, consistency.

Peak days The days during the menstrual cycle during which a woman is most likely to be fertile.

cycles who ovulate as early as a week after their menstrual flows can become pregnant even if they engage in unprotected intercourse only when they are menstruating, since some sperm remaining in a woman's reproductive tract may survive for up to eight days and fertilize an ovum that is released at that time (Reinisch, 1990). Moreover, the rhythm method requires abstaining from coitus for several days, or perhaps weeks, each month. Rhythm methods also require that records of the menstrual cycle be kept for many months prior to implementation. Unlike diaphragms, condoms, or spermicides, rhythm methods cannot be used at a moment's notice. Finally, rhythm methods do not offer any protection against STIs.

Sterilization

Many people decide to be sterilized when they plan to have no children or no more children. With the exception of abstinence, sterilization is the most effective form of contraception. Yet the prospect of **sterilization** arouses strong feelings because a person is transformed all at once, and presumably permanently, from someone who might be capable of bearing children to someone who is not. This transformation often involves a profound change in self-concept, especially in men and women who link fertility to their sense of masculinity or femininity.

Sterilization is the most widely used form of birth control among Canadian married couples (Fisher et al., 1999). Sixteen percent of the married respondents in a 1998 national sample of women aged 15 to 44 reported being sterilized; 24% reported having partners who had undergone a vasectomy. Married women were far more likely to rely on a permanent method of contraception (tubal sterilization or vasectomy) than were single women (39% versus 3%) (Fisher et al., 1999). Overall, 23% of Canadian women rely on sterilization.

> **Sterilization** Surgical procedures that render people incapable of reproduction without affecting sexual activity.

1. Location of vas deferens

2. Injection of local anaesthetic

3. Incision over vas deferens

4. Isolation of vas from surrounding tissue

5. Removal of segment of vas; tying of ends

6. Return of vas to position; incision is closed and process is repeated on the other side

Figure 10.7. Vasectomy.

The male sterilization procedure is usually carried out in a doctor's office, using local anaesthesia. Small incisions are made in the scrotum. Each vas deferens is cut, and the ends are tied off or cauterized to prevent sperm from reaching the urethra. Sperm are harmlessly reabsorbed by the body after the operation.

Vasectomy A sterilization procedure in which the vas deferens is severed, preventing sperm from reaching the ejaculatory duct.

Male Sterilization The male sterilization procedure used today is the **vasectomy**. About 14% of men in Canada have had vasectomies. A vasectomy is usually carried out in a doctor's office, under local anaesthesia, in 15 to 20 minutes. Small incisions are made in the scrotum. Each vas is cut, a small segment is removed, and the ends are tied off or cauterized to prevent them from growing back together (see Figure 10.7). Now sperm can no longer reach the urethra. Instead, they are harmlessly reabsorbed by the body.

The man can usually resume sexual relations within a few days. Since some sperm may be present in his reproductive tract for a few weeks, however, he is best advised to use an additional contraceptive method until his ejaculate shows a zero sperm count. Some health professionals recommend that the man have a follow-up sperm count a year after his vasectomy, to ensure that the cut ends of the vas deferens have not grown together—a complication that occurs in about 1% of cases (Reinisch, 1990).

Vasectomy does not diminish sex drive or result in any change in sexual arousal, erectile or ejaculatory ability, or sensations of ejaculation. Male sex hormones and sperm are still produced by the testes. Without a passageway to the urethra, however, sperm are no longer expelled with the ejaculate. Since sperm account for only about 1% of the ejaculate, the volume of the ejaculate is not noticeably different.

Though there are no confirmed long-term health risks of vasectomy (Reinisch, 1990), two recent studies of more than 73 000 men who had undergone vasectomies raise concerns that the procedure may not be as risk-free as people generally believe.

The studies showed that men who had had vasectomies more than 20 years earlier faced a slightly increased risk of prostate cancer (Altman, 1993; Giovannucci et al., 1993a, 1993b). The studies found a correlation between vasectomies and the risk of prostate cancer, but did not establish a causal connection. It is possible that other factors than the vasectomy itself may explain the greater risk faced by vasectomized men. The results also conflict with earlier studies showing either no link between vasectomies and the risk of prostate cancer or even a *lower* risk among vasectomized men. More research is needed to clarify the relationship between vasectomy and prostate cancer. In the meantime, medical experts recommend that men who have had vasectomies get annual checkups for signs of prostate cancer (Altman, 1993).

The vasectomy is nearly 100% effective. Fewer than two pregnancies occur during the first year among 1000 couples in which the man has undergone a vasectomy (see Table 10.1). The few failures stem from sperm remaining in the male's genital tract shortly after the operation, or the growing together of the segments of a vas deferens.

Vasovasotomy The surgical method of reversing vasectomy in which the cut or cauterized ends of the vas deferens are sewn together.

Tubal sterilization The most common method of female sterilization, in which the fallopian tubes are surgically blocked to prevent the meeting of sperm and ova. Also called *tubal ligation.*

Minilaparotomy A kind of tubal sterilization in which a small incision is made in the abdomen to provide access to the fallopian tubes.

Reversibility is simple in concept but not in practice. Thus, vasectomies should be considered permanent. In an operation to reverse a vasectomy, called a **vasovasotomy**, the ends of the vas deferens are sewn together, and in a few days they grow together. Estimates of success at reversal, as measured by subsequent pregnancies, range from 16% to 79% (Hatcher et al., 1994). Some vasectomized men develop antibodies that attack their own sperm. The production of antibodies does not appear to endanger the man's health (Hatcher et al., 1994), but it may contribute to infertility following reconnection (Reinisch, 1990).

Major studies conducted over a 15-year period revealed no deaths due to vasectomy (Reinisch, 1990). Few serious complications of vasectomies have been reported in the medical literature. Minor complications are reported in 4% or 5% of cases, however. They typically involve temporary local inflammation or swelling after the operation. Ice packs and anti-inflammatory drugs, such as aspirin, may help reduce swelling and discomfort. More serious but rarer medical complications include infection of the epididymis (Reinisch, 1990).

Female Sterilization Ten percent of Canadian women aged 15 to 44 have been surgically sterilized (Fisher et al., 1999). **Tubal sterilization**, also called tubal ligation, is the most common method of female sterilization. Tubal sterilization prevents ova and sperm from passing through the fallopian tubes.

The two main surgical procedures for tubal sterilization are *minilaparotomy* and *laparoscopy*. In a **minilaparotomy**, a small incision is made in the abdomen, just above the pubic hairline, to provide access to the fallopian tubes. Each tube is cut and either tied back or clamped with a clip. In a **laparoscopy** (see Figure 10.8), sometimes called "belly button surgery," the fallopian tubes are approached through a small incision in the abdomen just below the navel. The surgeon uses a narrow, lighted viewing instrument called a *laparoscope* to locate the tubes. A small section of each of the tubes is cauterized, cut, or clamped. The woman usually returns to her daily routine in a few days and can resume coitus when it becomes comfortable. In an alternative sterilization procedure, a **culpotomy**, the fallopian tubes are approached through an incision in the back wall of the vagina.

None of these methods disrupts sex drive or sexual response. Surgical sterilization does not induce premature menopause or alter the woman's production of sex hormones. The menstrual cycle is undisturbed. The unfertilized egg is simply reabsorbed by the body, rather than being sloughed off in the menstrual flow.

A **hysterectomy** also results in sterilization. A hysterectomy is a major operation that is commonly performed because of cancer or other diseases of the reproductive tract; it is inappropriate as a method of sterilization. Hysterectomy carries the risks of major surgery and, when the ovaries are removed along with the uterus, it induces an instant "surgical menopause" because the woman no longer produces female sex hormones.

Female sterilization is highly effective in preventing pregnancy, although slightly less effective than male sterilization. Overall, about 1 woman in 200 (0.4%) is likely to become pregnant in the first year following a tubal sterilization (Hatcher et al., 1994), most likely the result of a failed surgical procedure or an undetected pregnancy at the time of the procedure. Like vasectomy, tubal ligation should be considered irreversible. Reversals are successful, as measured by subsequent pregnancies, in 43% to 88% of cases (Hatcher et al., 1994). Reversal is difficult, however.

About 2% to 11% of sterilized women incur medical complications (Reinisch, 1990). The most common complications are abdominal infections, excessive bleeding, inadvertent punctures of nearby organs, and scarring. The use of general anaesthesia (typical in laparoscopies and in some minilaparotomies) poses additional risks, as in any major operation. (Most of the deaths that are attributed to tubal sterilization actually result from the anaesthesia [Reinisch, 1990]. The overall death rate is quite small, however—2 to 5 deaths per 100 000 operations.)

Advantages and Disadvantages of Sterilization

The major advantages of sterilization are effectiveness and permanence. Sterilization is nearly 100% effective. Following surgery the couple need not do anything more to prevent conception. The permanence is also its major drawback, however. People sometimes change their minds about wanting to have children.

Laparoscopy Tubal sterilization by means of a *laparoscope*, which is inserted through a small incision just below the navel and used to cauterize, cut, or clamp the fallopian tubes. Sometimes referred to as "belly button surgery."

Culpotomy A kind of tubal sterilization in which the fallopian tubes are approached through an incision in the back wall of the vagina.

Hysterectomy Surgical removal of the uterus.

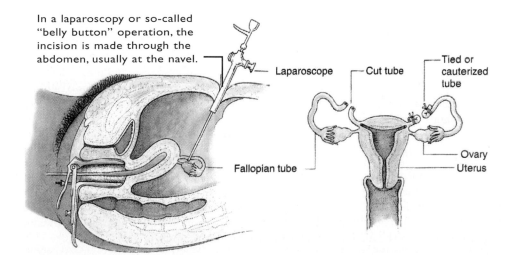

In a laparoscopy or so-called "belly button" operation, the incision is made through the abdomen, usually at the navel.

Laparoscope — Cut tube — Tied or cauterized tube

Fallopian tube

Ovary — Uterus

Figure 10.8. Laparoscopy.

In this method of female sterilization, the surgeon approaches the fallopian tubes through a small incision in the abdomen just below the navel. A narrow instrument called a laparoscope is inserted through the incision, and a small section of each fallopian tube is cauterized, cut, or clamped to prevent ova from joining with sperm.

Sterilization procedures create varying risks of complications following surgery, with women generally incurring greater risks than men. Another disadvantage of sterilization is that it affords no protection against STIs (Cates & Stone, 1992b). People who are sterilized may still wish to use condoms and spermicides for protection against STIs.

Other Devices

A number of other contraceptive devices have recently been introduced or are under development.

Norplant The contraceptive implant Norplant was available in Canada for a few years but in August 2002 was withdrawn from the market by its manufacturer. This method consists of six matchstick-sized silicone tubes that contain progestin and are surgically embedded in a woman's upper arm. Norplant, like the pill, relies on female sex hormones to suppress fertility, but provides continuous contraceptive protection for as long as five years (Hatcher et al., 1994).

The Female Condom The female condom consists of a polyurethane (plastic) sheath that is used to line the vagina during intercourse. It is held in place at each end by a flexible plastic ring. The female condom provides a secure but flexible shield that barricades against sperm but allows the penis to move freely within the vagina during coitus. It can be inserted as long as eight hours preceding intercourse but should be removed immediately afterward (Hatcher et al., 1994). A new one must be used for each act of intercourse.

Like the male condom, the female condom may offer some protection against STIs. Women can use the female condom if their partners refuse to wear a male condom. The female condom (brand name: Reality) was approved in 1996. It appears to be less effective than the male latex condom in preventing pregnancies and transmission of STIs. During test trials, the pregnancy rate was estimated to range between 21% and 26%, but is estimated to be as low as 5% among cautious users (Hatcher et al., 1994). Evidence concerning the effectiveness of the female condom in providing protection against STIs is scarce (Centers for Disease Control, 1993).

Many women also complain that the female condom is bulky and difficult to insert (Stewart, 1992). Still, it is the first barrier method of contraception that women control themselves and that is effective against STIs. Naming the device Reality suggests that it may be used most widely by women faced with the reality of male partners who refuse to use condoms themselves or who fail to use them consistently or properly. The female condom costs several times as much as the male condom.

The Contraceptive Sponge The contraceptive sponge is a soft, disposable device that contains spermicide in gel form and a dispersing agent to ensure that the spermicide covers the vaginal walls. Unlike the diaphragm, the sponge does not need to be fitted. The sponge is inserted into the vagina at least 15 minutes before coitus, and must be left in place for at least six and up to 12 hours after. The sponge is not designed to be re-used, but intercourse may be repeated during this period. The sponge has the additional effect of absorbing seminal fluid. It is odourless and tasteless, and users may find it less drippy than the diaphragm. On the negative side, a small number of women, or their partners, may find the spermicides used irritating. There is also a remote chance of toxic shock syndrome associated with use of the contraceptive sponge. Women who have had toxic shock syndrome must not use this device.

The Vaginal Ring The vaginal ring can be worn in the vagina for three months before replacement. Shaped like a diaphragm, the ring contains either a combination of estrogen and progestin or progestin only. The hormones are slowly released and pass into the bloodstream through the mucosal lining of the vagina. The vaginal ring is a convenient means of receiving a continuous dose of hormones without having to remember to take a pill. Research on the effectiveness of the vaginal ring is underway.

Depo-Provera Depo-Provera (medroxyprogesterone acetate) is a long-acting, synthetic form of progesterone that works as a contraceptive by inhibiting ovulation. The progesterone signals the pituitary gland in the brain to stop producing hormones that would lead to the release of mature ova by the ovaries. Administered by injection once every three months, Depo-Provera is an effective form of contraception, with reported failure rates of less than 1 pregnancy per 100 women during the first year of use (Hatcher et al., 1994). Depo-Provera has been used by more than 30 million women in more than 90 countries worldwide since it was first marketed in 1969. However, approval in Canada was held up because of concerns over side effects, including the risk of breast cancer. A review by researchers finally found the cancer risk to be minimal and Depo-Provera was approved as a contraceptive in 1997. A World Health Organization study of 12 000 women found no links between the drug and the risk of ovarian or cervical cancer (Walt, 1993). Yet the drug may produce side effects such as weight gain, menstrual irregularity, and spotting between periods (Hatcher et al., 1994). Use of Depo-Provera has also been linked to osteoporosis, a condition involving bone loss that can cause bones to become brittle and fracture easily.

Under Development Other methods of contraception are in experimental stages, including sterilization techniques that promise greater reversibility. Also in the experimental stage is a so-called male pill, an oral contraceptive for men. The male sex hormone testosterone has shown promise in reducing sperm production ("Male birth control," 1995). The pituitary gland normally stimulates the testes to produce sperm. Testosterone suppresses the pituitary, in turn suppressing sperm production. Men who have received testosterone injections have shown declines in sperm production. Potential complications include an increased risk of prostate cancer. Testosterone also appears to increase cholesterol levels in the bloodstream, which may heighten the risk of cardiovascular disease.

Another approach was suggested when investigators in China found extremely low birth rates in communities in which cottonseed oil was used in cooking. They extracted a drug from the cotton plant, *gossypol*, which shows promise as a male contraceptive. Chinese studies reveal the drug to be nearly 100% effective in preventing pregnancies. The drug appears to nullify sperm production without affecting hormone levels or the sex drive. However, toxic effects of gossypol have limited its acceptability as a male contraceptive.

Some men are infertile because they produce antibodies that destroy their own sperm. It is also speculated that vasectomy causes some men's bodies to react to their own sperm as foreign substances and produce antibodies. This is an immunological response to sperm. Some researchers have suggested that it may be possible to develop ways to induce the body to produce such antibodies. Ideally this procedure would be reversible.

Applying ultrasound waves to the testes has been shown to produce reversible sterility in laboratory rats, dogs, and monkeys. No one is quite certain how ultrasound works in inducing temporary sterilization. Moreover, its safety has not been demonstrated.

Abortion

An **induced abortion** (in contrast to a *spontaneous abortion*, or miscarriage) is the purposeful termination of a pregnancy. Perhaps more than any other contemporary social issue, induced abortion (hereafter referred to simply as abortion) has divided neighbours and family members into opposing camps.

Thirty-seven million abortions worldwide, including more than 100 000 in Canada, are performed each year (Smolowe, 1993; Statistics Canada, 2003a). In 1995, more than 80% of abortions in Canada occurred during the first trimester (Health Canada 2004). This is when they are safest for the woman and least costly. Most women who have abortions are unmarried.

In 2000, abortion rates across Canada ranged from a low of 11 per 100 live births in Prince Edward Island to over 40 per 100 live births in Quebec (Statistics Canada, 2003a). In part, this is due to differences in accessibility. (See also Table 10.2.)

Frontiers in Nonhormonal Male Contraception: A Call for Research
www.gumption.org/mcip/paper.html
This paper, sponsored by the Male Contraception Information Project, describes the current state of research in two little-known but promising areas of male contraception: vas-based methods and heat methods.

Induced abortion The purposeful termination of a pregnancy before the embryo or fetus is capable of sustaining independent life. (From the Latin *abortio*, meaning "that which is miscarried.")

A World of Diversity

Japan's Abortion Agony: In a Country That Prohibits the Pill, Reality Collides with Religion

Yuka Sugimoto winds her way among thousands of miniature stone statues in a hillside Buddhist temple (WuDunn, 1996). She finds the one she is seeking—the proper *mizuko jizo*—and lingers to ponder the clandestine act that resulted in this.

Buddhists come to the temples to pray for health, wealth, or a wife or husband. Not Ms. Sugimoto. She comes to this ancient temple once a month as a way of making amends to the fetus she aborted two years earlier, when she was an unmarried student.

Japan may be among the richest, most technologically advanced nations in the world, but its abortion rate is one of the highest among the world's industrialized nations. One reason for this is the lack of birth-control alternatives. The government bans the use of the birth-control pill as a contraceptive, and doctors do not encourage the use of sterilization, IUDs, or diaphragms. Nearly 75% of Japanese continue to use condoms and rhythm methods despite their high failure rate.

Over the years Japanese officials defended the ban against the pill by arguing that oral contraceptives are unsafe and would promote promiscuity ("Still no pill for Japan," 1992). In 1992, a review by the Health and Welfare Ministry found birth-control pills to be safe, but decided to uphold the ban because of concerns about

Offerings Made at a Buddhist Temple in Japan by Women Who Have Had Abortions. Japan prohibits women from using the birth-control pill, thereby increasing the incidence of abortion.

AIDS. Though Japan has had relatively few AIDS cases by international standards (fewer than 500 by mid-1991), the health ministry feared that lifting the ban on the pill might discourage condom use and lead to an epidemic of AIDS. Some women in Japan are able to skirt the ban by consulting sympathetic physicians who are willing to prescribe them, presumably to treat gynecological complaints.

In part because of limited contraceptive options, the Japanese use condoms more than any other people in the world. They are widely available in drugstores, supermarkets, and vending machines; embarrassed housewives can buy them from door-to-door saleswomen. Abortion is the widely used backup for failed contraception. And yet, although abortions have now been legal and easily accessible in Japan for over 40 years, women who have them feel stigmatized because abortion is regarded by many Japanese, even those who accept it, as "killing a baby."

The majority of Japanese draw little distinction between a fetus and an infant. According to Samuel Coleman, the author of *Family Planning in Japanese Society,* the reasons lie at least partially in Shinto and Buddhism, Japan's two major religions. Although neither religion promotes active opposition to abortion, Buddhism is based on the ideal of overcoming one's sense of ego. In this context, a woman who aborts wrongly puts her ego before her fetus. Shinto, an ancient religion based on ancestor and nature worship, holds that an aborted fetus can place a curse on the woman who aborts.

Offerings at the Temple

Hiroshi Hihara is a gynecologist in Tokyo. He makes his living on infertility work and abortions, many of them for married women whose method of contraception has failed. Although Hihara is a member of a Buddhist temple, he does not consider himself religious. But he says he is not comfortable with abortion. "Abortion is legal and approved of by the government, and if a patient wants it, I can't turn her down," he says. "She's entitled to it. But I am not happy to do it." And yet, he performs some 200 abortions a year and quietly admits, when asked, that his fees from abortion represent "a large portion of my income."

Caught in this moral and economic trap, he resolves his feelings in a uniquely Japanese way. First, he tells each abortion patient to make an offering after the operation at any of the Buddhist temples selling miniature stone statues, or *mizuko jizo*, which women can buy in memory of an aborted fetus. Thousands of such statues stand on display at temples these days, and although some are for miscarriages and stillborn children, the vast majority are for abortions. Many of the statues are decorated with crocheted hats, plastic bibs, and little pinwheels, all put there by women to keep the soul of the aborted fetus warm and amused.

Debate is going on over whether to legalize the pill and promote other forms of birth control such as the diaphragm. Whether Japanese women will use the pill if legalized is an open question. In a June 1990 survey released by one of Japan's largest newspapers, results showed that fewer than 10% of Japanese women would use it even if it were available.

Source: Fukuyama, F. (1999, June 9). At last, Japan gets the pill. Is this good news? *The New York Times,* p. A29.

The History of Abortion in Canada

In 1967, Justice Minister Pierre Trudeau presented Parliament with a bill that, among other things, legalized homosexuality and contraception in Canada, and allowed for some abortions to be performed legally. This bill, known as the Omnibus Justice Bill, became law in 1969. The bill amended section 251 of the Criminal Code, the section dealing with abortion. A doctor could now perform an abortion in an approved hospital, as long as the hospital's therapeutic abortion committee certified that continuing with a pregnancy would be dangerous to the woman's life or health. A hospital's therapeutic abortion committee consisted of three doctors, none of whom performed abortions. Doctors performing abortions outside of an approved hospital (as in a private clinic or office) or without the approval of a hospital abortion committee were still liable for criminal prosecution.

From the beginning, there were problems with the law. Hospitals were not required to establish therapeutic abortion committees, and many chose not to, even if there were no other hospitals in the area. Women's access to abortion services depended on the availability of a hospital with a therapeutic abortion committee. Some committees took many weeks to approve requests, so that the pregnancy might be too far advanced for the procedure to be performed safely by the time approval was granted. Some committees interpreted the criterion of "dangerous to the mother's life and health" very broadly, essentially rubber-stamping requests, while others were much more conservative. In practice, access to abortion services varied across the country. In general, women in major urban centres had much better access than those in rural areas—similar to the situation that existed before the passage of the law.

In 1973, Dr. Henry Morgentaler, a family physician in Montreal, challenged the government by announcing that he had performed more than 5000 abortions at his clinic. He was arrested and charged with 13 counts of performing an illegal abortion, extending back to 1970. He was tried by a jury and acquitted in November of 1973. In April 1974, after an appeal by the Crown, the Quebec Court of Appeal overturned the acquittal and substituted a guilty verdict. He was sentenced to 18 months in prison, although sentence was stayed while he appealed to the Supreme Court of Canada. The Supreme Court upheld the Quebec Court of Appeal's verdict, and he eventually served

TABLE 10.2 Abortions by Province in Hospitals and Clinics, 1996 to 2000[1]

	1996	1997	1998	1999	2000
Newfoundland and Labrador	812	819	803	834	871
Nova Scotia	2264	2213	2240	2068	2089
New Brunswick	1143	1146	1117	1061	1117
Quebec	28 787	30 224	31 632	30 693	31 185
Ontario[2]	47 024	44 118	42 503	39 969	39 541
Manitoba	3741	3729	3553	3653	3511
Saskatchewan	1810	1802	1779	1706	1761
Alberta	9446	10 594	10 742	10 507	10 780
British Columbia	16 007	16 501	15 459	14 676	14 070
Yukon	169	134	145	112	143
Northwest Territories	253	246	250	256	278
Nunavut[3]	...	...	...	96	108
Total	111 456	111 526	110 223	105 631	105 454

[1]Hospital abortions are not reported by Prince Edward Island. Clinic abortions are not reported by Prince Edward Island, Saskatchewan, the Yukon, the Northwest Territories, and Nunavut.

[2]Caution is recommended when comparing Ontario data from 1999 and after to data before 1999 because of changes in Ontario's data collection methods.

[3]Data for Nunavut include the complete 1999 calendar year.

Source: Statistics Canada, 2003a. Adapted from the Statistics Canada website
www.statcan.ca/english/Pgdb/health40a.htm

10 months in prison, some of it in solitary confinement. In May of that same year, he was tried and acquitted again. Although the Crown again attempted to have the acquittal overturned, the appeal was dismissed. Morgentaler's last trial and acquittal was in March 1975.

In July of 1975, the federal government amended the Criminal Code to prevent any further appeal court from replacing a jury acquittal with a conviction (known as the Morgentaler amendment). The government also established a committee to examine the operation of the abortion law. This committee was known as the Badgley Committee, after its chair, Robin Badgley. In its report to the House of Commons, the Badgley Committee found that the provisions of the abortion law were not being applied equitably across the country.

In 1983 Morgentaler and two other doctors at his Toronto clinic were charged with conspiring to procure a miscarriage. They were acquitted in November 1984. Three weeks later, they were charged again. Early in 1985, Morgentaler was also charged in Winnipeg with the same crime. In October of 1985, the Ontario Court of Appeal set aside the 1984 jury verdict and ordered a new trial. At this point, Morgentaler launched an appeal to the Supreme Court of Canada. On January 28, 1988, the Supreme Court struck down section 251 of the Criminal Code on the grounds that it violated the Charter of Rights and Freedoms.

Since that time, the federal government has twice tried to introduce a new criminal law on abortion. The first bill failed to pass the House of Commons. The second, Bill C43, passed the House of Commons on May 29, 1990, by nine votes, but was defeated by the Senate on January 31, 1991.

It is ironic that the major finding of the 1975 Badgley Committee, that women in Canada did not have equal access to abortion services, still applies today. In general, women in major urban centres and those living in Ontario and Quebec have better access to services, both through hospitals and public and private clinics, than those in rural areas or eastern Canada.

Other Times, Other Voices: No Choice Regardless of their beliefs or feelings about the matter, most students (and some of their instructors) using this book in 2004 have grown up knowing that the option to safely and legally terminate a pregnancy is available to them. But what of Canadian women growing up *before* 1969? What did they do when faced with an unplanned or problematic pregnancy? What were their choices? What secrets did they keep?

To preserve the voices of these women, the Childbirth by Choice Trust collected abortion stories from sixty women, ranging from a Saskatchewan farmer's wife to a socialite (Childbirth by Choice Trust, 1998). In letters and interviews, the women describe their desperation, the lengths they went through to obtain an abortion, and the consequences if there were complications. One woman was threatened with prison if she did not testify against the doctor who performed her abortion. The stories span a 70-year period, from the early 1900s to the 1960s. Amanda lost her mother to an illegal abortion during the Depression. Joanne, pregnant in Montreal in the late 1930s, was sexually assaulted by the doctor who aborted her fetus. She did not report it. Muriel developed a raging infection after her abortion. Fortunately, penicillin had just become available, so she survived. But many women didn't.

Attitudes to Abortion

There are many reasons why women have abortions, including psychological factors as well as external circumstances. Abortion is often motivated by a desire to reduce the risk of physical, economic, psychological, and social disadvantages that the woman perceives for herself and her present and future children should she take the pregnancy to term (Russo et al., 1992).

The national debate over abortion has been played out in recent years against a backdrop of demonstrations, marches, and occasional acts of violence, such as fire-bombings of abortion clinics and even attempted murder. The right-to-life (pro-life) movement asserts that human life begins at conception and thus views abortion as the murder of an unborn child (Sagan & Dryan, 1990). Some in the pro-life movement brook no exception to their opposition to abortion. Others would permit abortion to save the mother's life or when a pregnancy results from rape or incest.

The pro-choice movement contends that abortion is a matter of personal choice and that no one has the right to interfere with a woman's choice to terminate a pregnancy. Pro-choice advocates argue that women should be free to control what happens within their bodies, including pregnancies.

The majority of people in Canada favour freedom of choice in abortion. Over the last 15 years, support for a woman's right to choose has climbed from 53% in 1985 to 66% in 2000. A 2000 Environics poll found that a woman's right to have an abortion was supported by 66% of Canadians, while 26% disagreed. Agreement was higher in Quebec, especially among residents of Montreal, and in Vancouver, and lower in Saskatchewan and Alberta. Men were as supportive as women. Even among groups where disagreement was highest (Canadians over 60, Protestants, and Catholics), the majority supported freedom of choice.

Methods of Abortion

Many abortion methods are in use today.

Vacuum Aspiration **Vacuum aspiration**, or suction curettage, is the safest and most common method of abortion used in Canada. It is relatively painless and simple. It can be done with little or no anaesthesia in a medical office or clinic, but only during the first trimester. Later, thinning of the uterine walls increases the risks of perforation and bleeding.

In the procedure the cervix is usually dilated first by insertion of progressively larger curved metal rods, or "dilators," or by insertion, hours earlier, of a stick of seaweed called *Laminaria digitata*. *Laminaria* expands as it absorbs cervical moisture, providing a gentler means of opening the os. Then an angled tube connected to an aspirator (suction machine) is inserted through the cervix into the uterus. The uterine contents are then evacuated (emptied) by suction (see Figure 10.9). Possible complications include perforation of the uterus, infection, cervical lacerations, and hemorrhaging, but these are rare.

Dilation and Curettage (D&C) The **D&C** was once the customary method of performing abortions. It now accounts for only a small number of abortions. It is usually performed eight to 20 weeks following the last menstrual period (LMP). Once the cervix has been dilated, the uterine contents are scraped from the uterine lining with a blunt scraping tool.

D&C's are carried out in a hospital, usually under general anaesthesia. The scraping increases the chances of hemorrhaging, infection, and perforation. Because of these risks, D&C's have largely been replaced by the vacuum aspiration method. D&C's are still used to treat various gynecological problems, however, such as abnormally heavy menstrual bleeding.

Dilation and Evacuation (D&E) The **D&E** is used most commonly during the second trimester, when vacuum aspiration alone would be too risky. The D&E combines suction and the D&C. First the cervix is dilated. The cervix must also be dilated more fully than with vacuum aspiration to allow for passage of the larger fetus. Then a suction tube is inserted to remove some of the contents of the uterus. But suction alone cannot safely remove all uterine contents. So the remaining contents are removed with forceps. A blunt scraper may also be used to scrape the uterine wall to make sure that the lining has been removed fully. Like the D&C, the D&E is usually performed in the hospital under general anaesthesia. Most women recover quickly and relatively painlessly. In rare instances, however, complications can arise. These include excessive bleeding, infection, and perforation of the uterine lining (Thompson, 1993).

Vacuum aspiration Removal of the uterine contents by suction. An abortion method used early in pregnancy. (From the Latin *aspirare*, meaning "to breathe upon.")

D&C Abbreviation for *dilation and curettage*, an operation in which the cervix is dilated and uterine contents are then gently scraped away.

D&E Abbreviation for *dilation and evacuation*, an abortion method in which the cervix is dilated prior to vacuum aspiration.

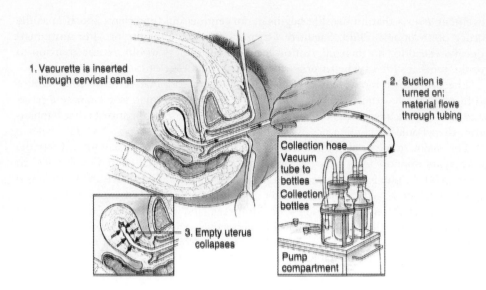

1. Vacurette is inserted
   through cervical canal

2. Suction is
   turned on;
   material flows
   through tubing

Collection hose
Vacuum
tube to
bottles
Collection
bottles

3. Empty uterus
   collapses

Pump
compartment

Intra-amniotic infusion
An abortion method in
which a substance is injected
into the amniotic sac to
induce premature labour.
Also called *instillation*.

Hysterotomy An abortion
method in which the fetus is
removed by caesarean
section.

Inducing Labour by Intra-amniotic Infusion

Second-trimester abortions are some-
times performed by chemically inducing premature labour and delivery. The procedure,
which must be performed in a hospital, is called instillation, or **intra-amniotic infusion**.
It is usually performed when fetal development has progressed beyond the point at
which other methods are deemed safe. A saline (salt) solution or a solution of
prostaglandins (hormones that stimulate uterine contractions during labour) is injected
into the amniotic sac. Prostaglandins may also be administered by vaginal suppository.
Uterine contractions (labour) begin within a few hours after infusion. The fetus and
placenta are expelled from the uterus within the next 24 or 48 hours.

Intra-amniotic infusion accounts for only a small number of abortions. Medical
complications, risks, and costs are greater with this procedure than with other methods
of abortion. Overly rapid labour can tear the cervix, but previous dilation of the cervix
with Laminaria lessens the risk. Perforation, infection, and hemorrhaging are rare if
prostaglandins are used, but about half the recipients experience nausea and vomiting,
diarrhea, or headaches. Saline infusion can cause shock and even death if the solution is
carelessly introduced into the bloodstream.

Hysterotomy

The **hysterotomy** is, in effect, a caesarean section. Incisions are made
in the abdomen and uterus, and the fetus and uterine contents are removed.
Hysterotomy may be performed during the late second trimester, between the 16th and
24th week. It is performed very rarely, usually only when intra-amniotic infusion is not
advised. A hysterotomy is major surgery that must be carried out under general anaesthesia in a hospital. Hysterotomy involves risks of complications both from the anaesthesia and from the surgery itself.

Abortion Drugs

Most early abortions are accomplished by vacuum aspiration, which
is a surgical technique. Although vacuum aspiration is safe enough for the woman, many
women would prefer a drug-induced abortion if it were available (Population Council,
1995).

RU-486 is an abortion pill that has been used in the U.S. but has yet to be approved
in Canada. It contains mifepristone, a chemical that induces early abortion by blocking
the effects of progesterone. Progesterone is the hormone that stimulates proliferation of
the endometrium, allowing implantation of the fertilized ovum and, subsequently,
development of the placenta. The pill was developed in France. Today, nearly half of
French women seeking abortion prefer RU-486 to surgical methods, including vacuum
aspiration.

Supporters of RU-486 argue that it offers a safe, noninvasive substitute for more
costly and unpleasant abortion procedures (Reuter, 1996).

RU-486's availability has been delayed largely because of opposition by pro-life groups (Hausknecht, 1995). Opponents argue that RU-486 makes abortions more accessible and difficult to regulate (Smolowe, 1993). Pro-life groups consider abortion murder, whether induced by surgery or a pill.

As the abortion debate continues, so does research into the use of other drugs. A combination of the cancer drug methotrexate and the ulcer drug misoprostol, for example, can be used to terminate early pregnancy. Methotrexate is toxic to the trophoblastic tissue of the embryo, and misoprostol causes uterine contractions. Hausknecht (1995) reported a pilot study in which an injection of methotrexate followed by a vaginal suppository with misoprostol led to successful abortions in 171 of 178 women. (The remaining seven subsequently underwent aspiration.) Moreover, it would appear that the combination of methotrexate and misoprostol has fewer side effects than RU-486.

Summing Up

Birth-control methods include contraception and induced abortion.

A Brief History of Birth Control in Canada

The provision of contraceptive information and services was illegal in Canada until 1969.

Methods of Contraception

Issues surrounding the choice among methods of contraception involve their convenience, moral acceptability, cost, safety, reversibility, and effectiveness, the sharing of responsibility between the partners, and the protection the methods afford from STIs.

Oral contraceptives include combination pills and minipills. Combination pills contain estrogen and progestin and fool the brain into acting as though the woman is already pregnant, so that no additional ova mature or are released. Minipills contain progestin, thicken the cervical mucus to impede the passage of sperm through the cervix, and render the inner lining of the uterus less receptive to a fertilized egg. Oral contraception is nearly 100% effective. The main drawbacks are side effects and potential health risks. "Morning-after" pills prevent implantation of a fertilized ovum in the uterus.

Intrauterine devices (IUDs) apparently irritate the uterine lining, causing inflammation and the production of antibodies that may be toxic to sperm or fertilized ova and/or may prevent fertilized eggs from becoming implanted. The IUD is highly effective, but there are possible troublesome side effects and the potential for serious health complications.

The **diaphragm** covers the cervix and should be used with a spermicidal cream or jelly. It must be fitted by a health professional. **Spermicides** block the passage of sperm and kill sperm. Their failure rate is high when used alone, but they improve the effectiveness of barrier methods. Like the diaphragm, the **cervical cap** covers the cervix and is most effective when used with a spermicide. **Condoms** are the only contraceptive device worn by men and the only readily reversible method of contraception that is available to men. They are safe and readily available and protect against STIs. **Douching** and **withdrawal (coitus interruptus)** are considered "non-methods" of contraception.

Fertility awareness methods (rhythm methods) rely on awareness of the fertile segments of the woman's menstrual cycle. Rhythm methods include the calendar method, the basal body temperature method, the cervical mucus method, and ovulation kits. They are safe and generally free, but failure rate is high in typical use.

Sterilization methods are highly effective. They should be considered permanent, although they can be reversed in many cases. The *vasectomy* is usually carried out under local anaesthesia in 15 to 20 minutes. Female sterilization methods prevent ova and sperm from passing through the fallopian tubes, and are more complex surgery.

Other devices, none of which are commonly used in Canada, include the female condom, the contraceptive sponge, and Depo-Provera. **Norplant,** which consists of tubes containing progestin that are surgically embedded under the skin of the woman's upper arm, has been withdrawn from the Canadian market. A male pill is in the experimental stage of development.

Abortion

The **history of abortion in Canada** has been contentious. In 1969, the Canadian Parliament modified the Criminal Code to allow abortions to be performed under specific conditions. In 1988, the Supreme Court of Canada struck down restrictions on abortion. In reality, however, abortion services are limited in many parts of Canada.

Attitudes to abortion are often heated. The right-to-life movement considers that human life begins at conception and thus views abortion as murder. The pro-choice movement sees abortion as a woman's personal choice. The majority of Canadians favour freedom of choice. **Methods of abortion** in use today include vacuum aspiration (the safest and most common method), dilation and curettage (D&C), dilation and evacuation (D&E), induction of labour by intra-amniotic infusion, hysterotomy, and abortion drugs, which are not yet available in Canada.

Chapter Quiz

1. Birth-control pills appear to reduce the risk of
   (a) pelvic inflammatory disease.
   (b) sexually transmitted diseases.
   (c) blood clots.
   (d) nausea and vomiting.

2. Which of the following is termed a "non-method" of birth control in the text?
   (a) Sterilization.
   (b) Abortion.
   (c) Withdrawal.
   (d) Fertility awareness techniques.

3. Which of the following is the most effective method of birth control?
   (a) The female condom.
   (b) Oral contraceptives.
   (c) The diaphragm (without spermicide).
   (d) Douching.

4. Which of the following methods of birth control has the most side effects?
   (a) The intrauterine device (IUD).
   (b) The male condom.
   (c) The diaphragm (with or without spermicide).
   (d) Abstinence.

5. Which of the following methods of birth control is acceptable to the Roman Catholic Church?
   (a) Abortion during the first trimester.
   (b) Oral contraceptives.
   (c) The intrauterine device.
   (d) Fertility awareness techniques.

6. Which of the following is least likely to be reversible?
   (a) The intrauterine device.
   (b) Fertility awareness techniques.
   (c) Tubal ligation.
   (d) Oral contraceptives.

7. Which of the following is most likely to make the woman feel nauseous?
   (a) The intrauterine device.
   (b) The morning-after pill.
   (c) The cervical cap.
   (d) The minilaparotomy.

8. The male sterilization procedure used today is the
   (a) vasovasotomy.
   (b) vasectomy.
   (c) laparoscopy.
   (d) culpotomy.

9. Which of the following is true of attitudes toward abortion in Canada?
   (a) The majority of people favour freedom of choice in abortion.
   (b) The majority of people favour abortion for women who cannot financially afford children.
   (c) The majority of Roman Catholics are opposed to abortion under any circumstances.
   (d) A minority of Canadians over 60, Protestants, and Catholics favour freedom of choice.

10. The most common method of abortion practised in Canada today is
    (a) the D&C.
    (b) the D&E.
    (c) vacuum aspiration.
    (d) ectopic pregnancy.

Chapter 11

Sexuality Across the Life Span

Did You Know That...

- Many boys are born with erections?
- Nocturnal emissions in boys are not necessarily accompanied by "wet dreams"?
- The teen pregnancy rate in Canada is half that of the U.S.?
- Singlehood (forgive the word) has become a more common lifestyle over the past few decades?
- More than half of young Canadian adults cohabit before getting married?
- Cohabitation is more common in Quebec than in any other province?
- Most of today's sophisticated young people condemn extramarital affairs?
- Many people who are paralyzed due to spinal-cord injuries can become sexually aroused and engage in sexual intercourse?

This chapter chronicles sexual behaviour across the life span. Within children's personal and social experiences lie the seeds of later sexual competence and self-esteem—or the seeds of incompetence, guilt, and shame. Sexuality remains an integral, potentially joyful part of our lives from childhood through advanced age.

Childhood

Infancy (Birth to Two Years)

Boys are often born with erections. Many sexual reflexes are present even before we are born. For example, fetuses also have erections. Fetuses suck their fingers. The sucking reflex allows babies to gain nourishment, which is necessary for survival. But as Sigmund Freud hypothesized, infants also seem to reap sensual pleasure from sucking fingers, pacifiers, nipples, or whatever else fits into the mouth. This is not surprising, given the sensitivity of the mouth's mucosal lining.

Stimulation of the genitals in infancy may also produce sensations of pleasure. Parents who touch their infants' genitals while changing or washing them may discover the infants smiling or becoming excited. Infants discover the pleasure of self-stimulation (masturbation) for themselves when they gain the capacity to manipulate their genitals with their hands.

Signs of sexual arousal in infant girls, such as vaginal lubrication, are less readily detected. Yet evidence of lubrication and genital swelling has been reported (Martinson, 1976).

Do not interpret children's responses according to adult concepts of sexuality, however. Lubrication and erection are reflexes, not necessarily signals of interest in sex. Infants have the biological capacity for these reflexes, but we cannot say what, if anything, the reflexes mean to them.

Kinsey and his colleagues (1953) noted that baby boys show behaviours that resemble adult orgasm by as early as five months; baby girls, as early as four months. Orgasmic responses in boys are similar to those in men—but without ejaculation. Ejaculation occurs only after puberty.

Masturbation is typical for infants and young children and tends to start between six and 12 months. At early ages children usually masturbate by rubbing the genitals against a soft object, such as a towel, bedding, or a doll. As the child matures and becomes capable of more coordinated hand movements, direct manual stimulation of the genitals often becomes preferred.

Masturbation to orgasm is rare until the second year, however (Reinisch, 1990). Some children begin masturbating to orgasm later. Some never do. All in all, however, an orgasmic response from masturbation is common among children, as it is among adults (Reinisch, 1990).

Children typically do not engage in genital play with others until about the age of two. Then, as an expression of their curiosity about their environment and other people, they may investigate other children's genitals, or hug, cuddle, kiss, or climb on top of them. Rough-and-tumble play, including touching the genitals, is common among children.

Early Childhood (Three to Eight Years)

In early childhood many children masturbate and engage in sexual play with other children. Because of the difficulties in conducting research, statistics concerning the incidence of masturbation in children are largely speculative. Parents may not wish to respond to questions concerning the sexual conduct of their children. Or if they do, they may have a tendency to present their children as little "gentlemen" and "ladies" and underreport their sexual activity. If we are asked to look back as adults, our memories may be less than accurate. We can only conclude that some children masturbate, and others do not.

Three- and four-year-olds commonly express affection through kissing. Curiosity about the genitals may also occur by this stage. Sex games like "show" and "playing doctor" may begin earlier but become common between the ages of six and ten (Reinisch, 1990). Much of this sexual activity takes place in same-gender groups, although mixed-gender sex games are not uncommon. Children may exhibit their genitals to each other, touch each other's genitals, or even masturbate together.

Same-gender sexual play in childhood does not presage adult sexual orientation (Reinisch, 1990). It may, in fact, be more common than male–female play. It typically involves handling the other child's genitals, although it may include oral or anal contact. It may also include an outdoor variation of the game of "show" in which boys urinate together and see who can reach farthest or attain the highest trajectory.

Preadolescence (Nine to Thirteen Years)

During preadolescence children typically form relationships with a close "best friend" that enable them to share secrets and confidences. The friends are usually peers of the same gender. Preadolescents also tend to socialize with larger networks of friends in gender-segregated groups. At this stage boys are likely to think that girls are "dorks." To girls at this stage, "dork" is too good a word to apply to most boys.

Childhood Sexuality?
Children are naturally inquisitive about sexual behaviour and anatomy.

Preadolescents grow increasingly preoccupied with and self-conscious about their bodies. Their peers pressure preadolescents to conform to dress codes, standards of "correct" slang, and group standards concerning sex and drugs. Peer disapproval can be an intense punishment.

Sexual urges are experienced by many preadolescents, but they may not emerge until adolescence. Sigmund Freud theorized that sexual impulses are hidden, or latent, during preadolescence, but many preadolescents are quite active sexually during the so-called latency period.

A World of Diversity

Cross-Cultural Perspectives on Childhood Sexuality

Though we are born with the capacity for sexual response, our expression of sexuality largely reflects the culture in which we are reared. Every culture encourages people to conform to socially acceptable behaviour. Most people in a given culture develop similar behaviour patterns and attitudes.

Cultures vary in their attitudes and practices concerning human sexuality—in particular, childhood and adolescent sexuality. Some may be characterized as sexually permissive, others as sexually restrictive. Broude and Greene (1976) analyzed attitudes toward, and frequency of, premarital sex among 114 of the world's societies. Most societies (55%) either disapproved of or disallowed premarital sex among females. About one in four societies (24%) permitted girls to engage in premarital sex. Another 21% tolerated discreet premarital sex for females. Despite societal prohibitions, premarital sex among females was common or universal in two-thirds of the societies sampled. Female premarital sex was uncommon or absent in the other third. Premarital sex among males was even more common. Among 107 societies in their cross-cultural sample, male

premarital sex was universal or typical in 78%. It was atypical in the other 22%.

Sexually Permissive Societies

Ford and Beach (1951) noted that when masturbation was permitted in a society, children progressed from occasional genital touching to more purposeful masturbation by about six to eight years of age. Sexually permissive cultures also permitted sexual expression among peers. Among the Seniang people of Oceania, boys and girls publicly simulated coitus without fear of reproach by adults (Ford & Beach, 1951). The Lesu of Oceania believed that it is normal for children to imitate coital positions. The Chewu people of Africa believed that childhood sexual experimentation is necessary for adult fertility.

The Lecha people of the Himalayas believed that girls do not attain physical maturity unless they engage in early sexual intercourse. During early childhood, Lecha children engaged in mutual masturbation and attempted copulation. Girls began to engage in regular sexual intercourse by age 11 or 12. Among the Trobrianders of the South Pacific, girls were usually initiated into sexual intercourse by six or eight years of age, boys by age 10 or 12. Among the Muria Gond of India, boys and girls as young as 10 lived together in dormitories and spent their evenings dancing, singing,

and pairing off for sex.

Societies that permit sex play among children also tend to encourage open discussions of sex and to allow children to observe sexual behaviour among adults. Among the Turkese of the South Pacific, children learned about sex by observing and asking adults. Lesu children, too, would observe adults, but there was at least one taboo. They were not to watch their own mothers.

Sexually Restrictive Societies

Ford and Beach (1951) found that only a minority of preliterate societies were sexually restrictive. The Apinaye people of South America warned their children not to masturbate and thrashed them if they were suspected of doing so. The Kwoma of New Guinea warned boys never to touch their genitals, even when urinating. They risked having their penises beaten with a stick if they touched them.

Sexually restrictive societies discourage masturbation and sex play among children. Children who disobey are punished. Such societies also tend to be closed-lipped about sex. Parents try to keep their children ignorant about reproduction. Premarital sex and watching adults engage in sex are also restricted.

Many societies hold to a sexual double standard by which boys are allowed greater sexual freedom than girls.

Kinsey and his colleagues (1948, 1953) reported that masturbation is the primary means of achieving orgasm during preadolescence for both genders. They found that 45% of males and 15% of females masturbated by age 13.

Preadolescent sex play often involves mutual display of the genitals, with or without touching. Such sexual experiences are quite common and do not appear to impair future sexual adjustment (Leitenberg et al., 1989).

Although preadolescents tend to socialize in same-gender groups, interest in the other gender among heterosexuals tends to gradually increase as they approach puberty. Group dating and mixed-gender parties often provide preadolescents with their first exposure to heterosexual activities. Couples may not begin to pair off until early or midadolescence.

Much preadolescent sexual behaviour among members of the same gender is simply exploration. As with younger children, experiences with children of the same gender during preadolescence may be more common than heterosexual experiences (Leitenberg et al., 1989). These activities are usually limited to touching each other's genitals or mutual masturbation. Since preadolescents generally socialize within their genders, it is not surprising that their sexual explorations may also be within their genders. Most same-gender sexual experiences involve single episodes or short-lived relationships and are not signs of a budding gay orientation.

Sex Education and Miseducation

School-based sex-education programs are an excellent means of providing sexuality education to young people. These programs are found across Canada, although the extent and quality of the programs vary considerably (Barrett, 1994). Today, school-based programs are one of the main sources of sexuality information for Canadian teens (McKay & Holowaty, 1997).

The majority of parents support school-based sexuality education (McKay et al., 1998). They feel that adolescents should be taught about STI prevention (95%), abstinence (94%), and love (89%). Fewer parents supported including information about birth control (76%), abortion (78%), and sexual assault (64%). Very few parents supported the inclusion of these topics in sexuality education aimed at younger children (McKay et al., 1998).

Sex education in the schools, especially about value-laden topics, remains a source of controversy. Some people argue that sex education ought to be left to parents and religious authorities. But the data suggest that the real alternatives to the schools are peers and the corner newsstand, which sells more copies of "adult" magazines than of textbooks. Many parents are also concerned that teaching subjects such as sexual techniques and contraception encourages sexual experimentation. However, research has demonstrated that sex education does not lead to earlier sexual experimentation (Grunseit et al., 1997; Kirby, 2000).

School programs may not offer information about contraception and other sensitive topics until the upper grades of high school. Sexual experimentation often begins earlier, however. Most sexually active teens in Coles and Stokes's (1985) sample began engaging in intercourse by age 15. Fifty percent of the sexually active teenage boys and 18% of the sexually active teenage girls began by age 13. Canadian data indicate that half of young people have not begun sexual intercourse by the age of 17. According to statistics from the National Longitudinal Survey of Children and Youth, less than 2% of Canadian adolescents have intercourse before 14 years of age. Canadian youth tend to initiate sexual intercourse at a slightly later age than youth in the United States, France, or Great Britain (Maticka-Tyndale, 2001). Accurate information in preadolescence might prevent various sexual mishaps (Coles & Stokes, 1985). Many teens, for example, erroneously believe that a female cannot get pregnant from her first coital experience. Others believe that douching protects them from sexually transmitted infections (STIs) or unwanted pregnancies.

Effective sex-education programs focus on providing students with accurate, relevant information and the behavioural skills they need to use this information in their daily lives (Fisher & Fisher, 1998).

Canadian Guidelines for Sexual Health Education
www.hc-sc.gc.ca/
pphb-dgspsp/publicat/
cgshe-ldnemss/index.html
The guidelines from Health Canada are intended to assist those individuals, professionals, and agencies working in the area of health promotion.

Adolescence

Adolescence is bounded by the advent of puberty at the lower end and the capacity to take on adult responsibilities at the upper end. In our society adolescents are, as the saying goes, neither fish nor fowl—neither children nor adults. Adolescents may be able to reproduce and be taller than their parents, but they may not be allowed to get driver's licences or attend restricted films. They are prevented from working long hours and must usually stay in school until age 16. They cannot marry until they reach the "age of consent." The message is clear: Adults see adolescents as impulsive, and they must be restricted for their own good. Given these restrictions, a sex drive heightened by surges of sex hormones, and media inundation with sexual themes, it is not surprising that many adolescents are in conflict with their families about "going around" with certain friends, sex, and using the family car.

Applications

Talking to Your Children About Sex

"Daddy, where do babies come from?" "What are you asking me for? Go ask your mother."

Most children do not find it easy to talk to their parents about sex (Coles & Stokes, 1985). The parents may not find it any easier. Nearly half (47%) of the teens polled in a national survey in the United States said they would ask their friends, siblings, or sex partners if they desired information about sex. Only about a third (36%) would turn to their parents (Coles & Stokes, 1985). Three out of four say that it is hard to talk about sex with their fathers. More than half (57%) find it difficult to approach their mothers. Regrettably, information received from peers is likely to be strewn with inaccuracies. Misinformed teenagers run a higher risk of unwanted pregnancies and STIs.

Most young children are curious about where babies come from, about what makes little girls different from little boys, and so on. Parents who avoid answering such questions convey their own uneasiness about sex and may teach children that sex is something to be ashamed of, not something they should discuss openly.

Some parents resist talking about sex with their children because they are insecure in their own knowledge. Reinisch (1990) argues, however, that parents need not be sex experts to talk to their children about sex. Parents can turn to books in the local bookstore to fill in gaps in knowledge, or to books that are intended for parents to read to their children. They can also admit that they do not know the answer to a particular question.

In answering children's questions, parents need to be sensitive to what their children can understand. The four-year-old who wants to know where babies come from is probably not interested in detailed biological information. It may be sufficient to say "from Mommy's uterus" and then point to the mother's abdominal region. Why say "tummy"? "Tummy" is wrong and confusing.

In their *Family Book About Sexuality*, Calderone and Johnson (1989) offer parents some pointers:

1. *Be willing to answer your child's questions about sex.* Parents who respond by saying, "Why do you want to know that?" squelch questioning. The child is likely to interpret the parent's response as meaning "You shouldn't be interested in that."

2. *Use appropriate language.* As children develop awareness of their sexuality, they need to learn the names of their sex organs. They also need to learn that the "dirty words" that others use to refer to the sexual parts of the body are not acceptable in most situations.

3. *Give advice in the form of information that the child can use to make sound decisions, not as an imperial edict.* State your own convictions, but label your beliefs as your own rather than as something you are trying to impose on your child. Provide information and encourage discussion.

   Parents of teenagers often react to sexual experimentation with threats or punishments, which may cause adolescents to rebel or tune them out. Or the adolescent may learn to associate sex with fear and anger, which may persist even in adult relationships. Parents may find it more constructive to convey concern about the consequences of children's actions in a loving and nonthreatening way that invites an open response. Say, for example, "I'm worried about the way you are experimenting, and I'd like to give you some information that you may

   not have. Can we talk about it?" (Calderone & Johnson, 1989, p. 141).

4. *Share information in small doses.* Pick a time and place that feels natural for such discussions, such as when the child is preparing for bed or when you are riding in the car.

5. *Encourage the child to talk about sex.* Children may feel embarrassed about talking about sex, especially with family members. Make the child aware that you are always available to answer questions. Be "askable." But let the child postpone talking about a sensitive topic until the two of you are alone or the child feels comfortable. Books about sexuality may help a child open up. They can be left lying around or given to the child with a suggestion such as "This is a good book about sex, or at least I thought so. If you read it, then maybe we can talk about it" (Calderone & Johnson, 1989, p. 136).

6. *Respect privacy rights.* Most of us, parents and children alike, value our privacy at certain times. A parent who feels uncomfortable sharing a bathroom with a child can simply tell the child that Daddy (or Mommy) likes to be alone when using the bathroom. Or the parent might explain, "I like my privacy, so please knock and I'll tell you if it's okay to come in. I'll do the same for you" (Calderone & Johnson, 1989, p. 137). This can be said without a scolding or harsh tone. Privacy rights in the bedroom can be established by saying in a clear and unthreatening way, "Please knock when the door's closed and wait to be invited in" (Calderone & Johnson, 1989, p. 138). It is important for the parent to respect the same rights to privacy that the parent expects from the child.

Puberty

I remember when my friend got her first period better than when I got mine. I can't really remember mine. My period came and went without me ever talking to anyone, other than my friends who were shocked and amazed at how early I got it. Passed by my mother in the kitchen one day, two years after I had gotten it. She said, "Have you come across your period yet?" "Yes," I told her and that was that. The big period talk was over. She never talked to me about it before then, so I didn't want to talk about it now. Somehow I knew what to do and what it was all about.

My friend got her period at school in grade 5. She thought she was dying, in the bathroom, blood running down her leg, soaking her underpants. She started crying and screaming. Someone ran to get a teacher and the teacher came in and took her to the nurse's office. I thought, "It's true, maybe she is gonna die." You see, no one had ever told her about bleeding, especially from there. It was a shock and a bit of a wake up call for the teachers to start talking to us about "menstruation."

(Anonymous, 17, in St. Stephen's Community House, 2000, *The Little Black Book*, p. 36.)

These recollections of a young woman reflect common attitudes toward menstruation. Some pubescent girls see it as a sign of "becoming a woman." They anxiously await **menarche** (the onset of menstruation). They compete with friends to see who will be first to arrive on the doorstep of adulthood. Many people mistakenly believe that menstruation signals reproductive capacity. Yet such capacity may lag behind menarche by more than a year.

Menarche is one of the key events of puberty in girls. **Puberty** begins with the appearance of **secondary sex characteristics** and ends when the long bones make no further gains in length (see Table 11.1). The appearance of strands of pubic hair is often the first visible sign of puberty. Pubic hair tends to be light-coloured, sparse, and straight at first. Then it spreads and grows darker, thicker, and coarser. Puberty also involves changes in **primary sex characteristics**. Once puberty begins, most major changes occur within three years in girls and within four years in boys (Etaugh & Rathus, 1995).

Toward the end of puberty, reproduction becomes possible. The two principal markers of reproductive potential are menarche in the girl and the first ejaculation in the boy. But these events do not generally herald immediate fertility.

Girls typically experience menarche between the ages of 10 and 18. In the mid-1800s, European girls typically achieved menarche by about age 17. The age of menarche has declined sharply since then among girls in Western nations, most likely because of improved nutrition and health care. In North America, the average age of menarche by the 1960s and 1970s had dropped to between 12½ and 13 (Etaugh & Rathus, 1995). A U.S. study looked at the average age of menarche for two survey groups, 25 years apart, and found a further drop. In the years 1963–1970, the average age of menarche was 12.75; by 1988–1994, the average had fallen to 12.54 (Anderson et al., 2003). One view is that a critical body weight (perhaps 47 to 50 kg) triggers pubertal changes such as menarche, and children today do tend to achieve larger body sizes sooner. Menarche may also be triggered by the accumulation of a certain percentage of body fat. This theory is supported by the finding that menarche comes later to girls who have a lower percentage of body fat, such as athletes (Frisch, 1983). Whatever the exact triggering mechanism, the average age at which girls experience menarche has levelled off in recent years.

Pubertal Changes in the Female

First menstruation, or menarche, is the most obvious sign of puberty in girls. Yet other, less obvious changes have already taken place that have set the stage for menstruation. Between eight and 14 years of age, release of FSH (follicle-stimulating hormone) by the pituitary gland causes the ovaries to begin to secrete estrogen. Estrogen has several major effects on pubertal development. For one, it stimulates the growth of breast tissue ("breast buds"), perhaps as early as age eight or nine. The breasts usually begin to enlarge during the tenth year.

Menarche (pronounced men-AR-kee). The onset of menstruation; first menstruation. (From Greek roots meaning "month" [*men*] and "beginning" [*arche*].)

Puberty The stage of development during which reproduction first becomes possible. Puberty begins with the appearance of *secondary sex characteristics* and ends when the long bones make no further gains in length. (From the Latin *puber*, meaning "of ripe age.")

Secondary sex characteristics Physical traits that distinguish men from women but are not directly involved in reproduction.

Primary sex characteristics Physical characteristics that differentiate males and females and are directly involved in reproduction, such as the sex organs.

TABLE 11.1 Stages of pubertal development

IN FEMALES

Beginning sometime between ages 8 and 11	Pituitary hormones stimulate ovaries to increase production of estrogen. Internal reproductive organs begin to grow.
Beginning sometime between ages 9 and 15	Pituitary hormones stimulate ovaries to increase production of estrogen. Internal reproductive organs begin to grow. First the areola (the darker area around the nipple) and then the breasts increase in size and become more rounded. Pubic hair becomes darker and coarser. Growth in height continues. Body fat continues to round body contours. A normal vaginal discharge becomes noticeable. Sweat and oil glands increase in activity, and acne may appear. Internal and external reproductive organs and genitals grow, which makes the vagina longer and the labia more pronounced.
Beginning sometime between ages 10 and 16	Areola and nipples grow, often forming a second mound sticking out from the rounded breast mound. Pubic hair begins to grow in a triangular shape and to cover the centre of the mons. Underarm hair appears. Menarche occurs. Internal reproductive organs continue to develop. Ovaries may begin to release mature eggs capable of being fertilized. Growth in height slows.
Beginning sometime between ages 12 and 19	Breasts near adult size and shape. Pubic hair fully covers the mons and spreads to the top of the thighs. The voice may deepen slightly (but not as much as in males). Menstrual cycles gradually become more regular. Some further changes in body shape may occur into the young woman's early 20s.

IN MALES

Beginning sometime between ages 9 and 15	Testicles begin to grow. Skin of the scrotum becomes redder and coarser. A few straight pubic hairs appear at the base of the penis. Muscle mass develops, and the boy begins to grow taller. The areola grows larger and darker.
Beginning sometime between ages 11 and 16	The penis begins to grow longer. The testicles and scrotum continue to grow. Pubic hair becomes coarser, more curled, and spreads to cover the area between the legs. The body gains in height. The shoulders broaden. The hips narrow. The larynx enlarges, resulting in a deepening of the voice. Sparse facial and underarm hair appears.
Beginning sometime between ages 11 and 17	The penis begins to increase in circumference as well as in length (though more slowly). The testicles continue to increase in size. The texture of the pubic hair is more like an adult's. Growth of facial and underarm hair increases. Shaving may begin. First ejaculation occurs. In nearly half of all boys, gynecomastia (breast enlargement) occurs, which then decreases in a year or two. Increased skin oils may produce acne.
Beginning sometime between ages 14 and 18	The body nears final adult height, and the genitals achieve adult shape and size, with pubic hair spreading to the thighs and slightly upward toward the belly. Chest hair appears. Facial hair reaches full growth. Shaving becomes more frequent.

This table is a general guideline. Changes may normally appear sooner or later than shown, and not always in the indicated sequence.

For some young men, further increases in height, body hair, and muscle growth and strength continue into their early 20s.

Estrogen also promotes the growth of the uterus and the thickening of the vaginal lining. It also stimulates growth of fatty and supporting tissue in the hips and buttocks. This tissue and the widening of the pelvis cause the hips to become rounded and permit childbearing. But growth of fatty deposits and connective tissue varies considerably. Some women may have pronounced breasts; others may have relatively large hips.

Small amounts of androgens produced by the female's adrenal glands, along with estrogen, stimulate development of pubic and underarm hair, beginning at about age 11. Excessive androgen production can darken or thicken facial hair.

Estrogen causes the labia to grow during puberty, but androgens cause the clitoris to develop. Estrogen stimulates growth of the vagina and uterus. Estrogen typically brakes the female growth spurt some years before that of the male. Girls deficient in estrogen during their late teens may grow quite tall, but most tall girls reach their height because of normal genetically determined variations, not estrogen deficiency.

Estrogen production becomes cyclical in puberty and regulates the menstrual cycle. Following menarche, a girl's early menstrual cycles are typically **anovulatory**. Girls cannot become pregnant until ovulation occurs, which may lag behind menarche by as much as two years. At first ovulation may not be reliable, so a girl may be relatively infertile. Some teenagers, however, are highly fertile soon after menarche (Reinisch, 1990).

Anovulatory Without ovulation.

Pubertal Changes in the Male

At puberty the hypothalamus signals the pituitary to increase production of FSH and LH (luteinizing hormone). These releasing hormones stimulate the testes to increase their output of testosterone. Testosterone prompts growth of the male genitals: the testes, scrotum, and penis. It fosters differentiation of male secondary sex characteristics: the growth of facial, body, and pubic hair, and the deepening of the voice. Testicle growth, in turn, accelerates testosterone production and pubertal changes. The testes continue to grow, and the scrotal sac becomes larger and hangs loosely from the body. The penis widens and lengthens, and pubic hair appears.

By age 13 or 14, erections become frequent. Indeed, many junior high school boys dread that they may be caught between classes with erections, or asked to stand before the class. Under the influence of testosterone, the prostate and seminal vesicles—the organs that produce semen—increase in size, and semen production begins. Boys typically experience their first ejaculation by age 13 or 14, most often through masturbation. There is much variation, however. First ejaculations may occur as early as age eight or not until the early 20s (Reinisch, 1990). Mature sperm are not usually found in the ejaculate until about a year after the first ejaculation, at age 14 on the average (Kulin et al., 1989). But sperm may be present in the first ejaculate (Reinisch, 1990), so pubertal boys should not assume that they have an infertile "grace period" following first ejaculation. About a year after first ejaculation, boys may also begin **nocturnal emissions**, which are also called "wet dreams" because of the belief that nocturnal emissions accompany erotic dreams—which need not be so.

Underarm hair appears at about age 15. Facial hair is at first a fuzz on the upper lip. A beard does not appear for another two or three years. Only half of North American boys need to shave by age 17. The beard and chest hair continue to develop past the age of 20. At age 14 or 15 the voice deepens because of the growth of the **larynx** and the lengthening of the vocal cords. Development is gradual, and the voices of adolescent boys sometimes crack embarrassingly.

Boys and girls undergo general growth spurts during puberty. Girls usually shoot up before boys. Individuals differ, however, and some boys spurt sooner than some girls.

Increases in muscle mass produce increases in weight. The shoulders and the circumference of the chest widen. At the age of 18 or so, men stop growing taller because estrogen prevents the long bones from making further gains in length (Smith et al., 1994). Males normally produce some estrogen in the adrenal glands and testes. During puberty, nearly one in two boys experiences temporary enlargement of the breasts, or **gynecomastia**, which is also caused by estrogen.

Nocturnal emission Involuntary ejaculation of seminal fluid while asleep. Also referred to as a "wet dream," although the individual need not be dreaming about sex, or dreaming at all, at the time.

Larynx A structure of muscle and cartilage at the upper end of the trachea that contains the vocal cords; the voice box.

Gynecomastia Overdevelopment of a male's breasts. (From Greek roots meaning "woman" [*gyne*] and "breast" [*mastos*].)

Sexual Behaviour

Masturbation is a major sexual outlet during adolescence. There is considerable variation in the frequency of masturbation, but boys generally masturbate more frequently than girls do. Studies of university-aged students generally show that 80% to 100% of males and 40% to 80% of females have masturbated (Pinkerton et al., 2002). Researchers find no links between adolescent masturbation and early sexual activity (for example, frequency of intercourse, number of different partners, or age upon first intercourse) and sexual adjustment during young adulthood (Leitenberg et al., 1993).

Many teens still think of masturbation as shameful (Herold, 1984). Twenty-five percent of women who had ever masturbated reported feeling guilty about it, and younger teens were more likely to feel anxious about masturbating than older teens (Herold, 1984).

Young people today start dating and "going steady" earlier than in past generations. These changes have implications for teenage pregnancy. Research has shown that early dating is a precursor to early sexual activity (Miller et al., 1997; Longmore et al., 2001). Teens who initiate sexual intercourse earlier are also less likely to use contraception and more likely to incur an unwanted pregnancy. If the young woman decides to keep her baby, she is also more likely to experience difficulties reaching her educational and vocational goals. Early dating does not always lead to early coitus. Nor does early coitus always lead to unwanted pregnancies. Still, some young women find their options in adulthood restricted by a chain of events that began in early adolescence.

Petting Many adolescents use petting to express affection, satisfy their curiosities, heighten their sexual arousal, and reach orgasm while avoiding pregnancy and maintaining virginity. Petting is a form of preliminary sexual activity such as deep or open-mouth kissing, touching above the waist, and touching below the waist. Recent Canadian statistics show that 67% of Grade 9 girls and 65% of Grade 9 boys had engaged in deep kissing at least once. By Grade 11 the percentages of boys and girls who had kissed at least once rose to 81 and 82 respectively (Council of Ministers of Education, 2003).

Oral Sex The incidence of premarital oral sex has increased threefold since Kinsey's time. About six in ten (61%) of a sample of female university students reported that they had performed fellatio (Herold & Way, 1983). About a third of the boys reported performing cunnilingus. Many girls reported they had engaged in fellatio for the partner's pleasure, not their own. A recent Canadian study reports that 53% of Grade 11 boys and 52% of Grade 11 girls have experienced oral sex at least once (Council of Ministers of Education, 2003). Some couples maintain technical virginity by substituting oral sex for intercourse (Gagnon & Simon, 1987). Some adolescent couples use oral sex as a means of birth control. As one 17-year-old girl put it, "That's what we used to do before we could start having sex, because we didn't have protection and stuff" (Coles & Stokes, 1985, p. 60).

Premarital Intercourse Today, more than half of our teenagers engage in coitus (Haffner, 1993). Many young people feel as if they are caught betwixt and between. On the one hand, adults tell them to wait until they're older, to "just say no." On the other hand, the movies and television programs they see, and the stories they hear from their peers, reinforce the belief that everybody's "doing it."

The incidence of premarital intercourse, especially for females, has increased dramatically since Kinsey's day. In Kinsey's time, the sexual double standard held firm. Women were expected to remain virgins until marriage, but society looked the other way for men. Not surprisingly, Kinsey and his colleagues found a much greater incidence of premarital coitus among men. By the age of 20, 77% of the single men but only 20% of the single women reported that they had engaged in premarital coitus. Of those still single by age 25, the figures rose to 83% for men but only 33% for women. Kinsey found that 53% of the females who had engaged in premarital coitus had done so with one partner only (Kinsey et al., 1953).

Surveys in the late 1960s and early 1970s found that less than half (15% to 37% across studies) of Canadian women had engaged in premarital sex by the age of 19 (Herold, 1984). By 1979, 66%—two out of three—never-married women 19 years of age attending university had engaged in sexual intercourse (Herold, 1984). By 1988, the Canada Youth and Aids Study found that 49% of 17-year-old males and 46% of 17-year-old females had experienced sexual intercourse. In 2003, the percentage of Grade 11 boys who had experienced sexual intercourse decreased to 40% and the percentage of Grade 11 girls who had experienced sexual intercourse remained unchanged at 46% (Council of Ministers, 2003).

Young people today are also initiating intercourse at younger ages. Today, half of Canadian teens have their first sexual experience by the age of 17. Note, however, that sexual activity among teenagers tends to be episodic. Only half of the sexually experienced adolescents in one survey reported engaging in sexual intercourse during the month before the interview (Leigh et al., 1994). Another study, conducted among Alberta youth aged 18 to 22, showed that females were engaging in sexual intercourse more often and with fewer partners, while males had sex less often but with more partners. This difference may be explained by the fact that females have sex within relationships and they feel it is important to have an emotional connection with their partner (Schnirer, 2000).

In sum, the incidence of premarital sex has increased since Kinsey's day, dramatically so among females. Rates of premarital sex among young men have traditionally been higher, but the gender gap has narrowed considerably.

Motives for Intercourse Premarital intercourse is motivated by a number of factors. Sex hormones, especially testosterone, activate sexual arousal. Thus the pubertal surge of hormones directly activates sexual arousal, at least among boys (Brooks-Gunn & Furstenberg, 1989). The majority of both males and females report that the primary reasons for their first coital experience included curiosity and "readiness for sex" (McKenzie, 2000, unpublished data). For some adolescents, sexual intercourse is perceived as the natural outgrowth of love (Thompson, 1995). Adolescents may consider intercourse a sign of maturity, a way for girls to reward a boyfriend for remaining loyal, or a means of punishing parents (Thompson, 1995). Some adolescents engage in coitus in response to peer pressure, especially from close friends.

Factors in Premarital Intercourse Many young people abstain from premarital coitus for religious or moral reasons (Coles & Stokes, 1985; Miller & Bingham, 1989). Family influences and religious values are important determinants of adolescent sexual experience (White & DeBlassie, 1992). Other reasons include fear of being caught, fear of pregnancy, or fear of disease.

Teens who have higher educational goals and do better in school are less likely to engage in coitus than less academically oriented teens (Brooks-Gunn & Furstenberg, 1989; Hofferth & Hayes, 1987). The causal connection between school performance and premarital sex is difficult to discern, because adolescents who do well in school are also more likely to come from better-functioning families.

Other researchers focus on relationships between family factors and premarital intercourse. Children whose parents are separated or divorced are more likely than those from intact homes to engage in premarital intercourse (Coles & Stokes, 1985). Perhaps parents who have "failed" in their marital relationships lack credibility in advising their adolescent children (Coles & Stokes, 1985). Single parents, because of time constraints, may also be less capable of supervising their children. Teenagers from single-parent homes may have greater opportunities for privacy, especially when the parent works (Coles & Stokes, 1985). Moreover, a teenager may interpret a single parent's becoming sexually active with dates as tacit approval of premarital sex.

The quality of the relationship between teens and their parents may also be important (Brooks-Gunn & Furstenberg, 1989). Teens who feel that they can talk to their parents are less likely to engage in coitus than those who describe communication with their parents as poor.

Adolescents whose parents are very permissive and impose very few rules and restrictions are also more likely to engage in premarital intercourse (Hogan & Kitigawa, 1985; Miller et al., 1986). Parents who show an interest in their children's behaviour and communicate their concerns and expectations with understanding and respect may best influence their children to show sexual restraint.

Teenage Pregnancy

In 2000 in Canada, 17 350 babies were born to mothers between the ages of 15 and 19 (Statistics Canada, 2003b). Although Canada's teen pregnancy rate is higher than that of Japan, Switzerland, and Sweden, it is substantially lower than that of New Zealand and the U.S. The birth rate for teens aged 15–19 has dropped from 35.6 per 1000 in 1974 to 17.2 per 1000 in 2000 (Statistics Canada, 2003b). The decline in birth rates may be because of increased use of contraceptives among teens. Many studies have shown an increase in the use of condoms and other contraceptives over this period.

Consequences of Teenage Pregnancy In Canada, 60% of single mothers and their children live in poverty. Poverty, joblessness, and lack of hope for the future are recurrent themes in adolescent pregnancy (Desmond, 1994). Few receive consistent emotional or financial help from the fathers, who generally cannot support themselves, much less a family. In Quebec, approximately 80% of teenage mothers are raising their babies alone. Working teenage mothers earn just half as much as those who give birth in their 20s (National Research Council, 1993). Barely able to cope with one baby, many young mothers who give birth at age 15 or 16 have at least one more baby by the time they are 20.

Medical complications associated with teenage childbearing are highest among very young teens aged 11 to 15 years. Studies have shown that adverse obstetrical outcomes among older teens are often the result of inadequate prenatal care. Both Canadian and American research show that once income, maternal education levels, and racial/ethnic status are taken into account, maternal age alone is not predictive of low birthweight (National Council of Welfare, 1997; Stevenson et al., 1999). Poor health outcomes for teenage mothers and their children are due largely to non-biological factors associated with poverty. Easily accessible, comprehensive services for socially and economically disadvantaged teen mothers have far-reaching health and social benefits. Prenatal and

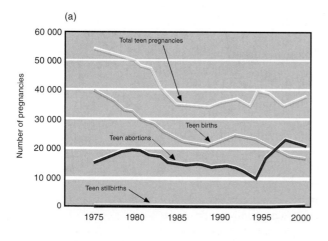

Figure 11.1a. Teenage pregnancies, Age 13–19, Canada, 1975–2000.

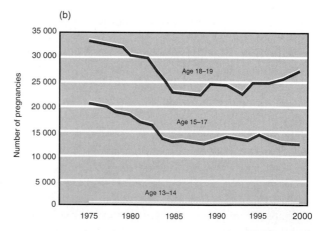

Figure 11.1b. Teenage pregnancies, by Age, Canada, 1975–2000.

Total teenage pregnancies have decreased over the years, as shown in part (a). Throughout this period, the largest number of pregnancies have been among older teenagers.
Source: Statistics Canada, 1999c, 2003a. "Teen pregnancy, by outcome of pregnancy and age group, count and rate per 1,000 women aged 15 to 19, Canada, provinces and territories, 1998–2000," is from the Statistics Canada website **www.statcan.ca/english/freepub/ 82-221-XIE/01103/rtables/htm;l/411.htm**, and "Teenage Pregnancies, by age 15-44, 1975–2000," is from the Statistics Canada website **www.statcabn.ca/english/freepub/82/223-XIE/tables.htm**

early parenting support services for teen mothers reduce the need for hospitalizations, emergency room visits, interventions by child protection workers, and foster home placements (National Council of Welfare, 1997). A number of factors contribute to teenage pregnancies, including a loosening of traditional taboos on adolescent sexuality (Hechtman, 1989). Impaired family relationships, problems in school, emotional problems, misunderstandings about reproduction or contraception, and lack of contraception also play roles (Hechtman, 1989). Some adolescent girls believe that a baby will elicit a commitment from their partner or fill an emotional void. Some become pregnant as a way of rebelling against parents. Many become pregnant because of misunderstandings about reproduction and contraception, or failure to use contraception consistently (Hechtman, 1989).

More attention has been focused on teenage mothers, but young fathers bear an equal responsibility for teenage pregnancies. A U.S. survey based on a nationally representative sample of 1880 young men ages 15 through 19 showed that socioeconomically disadvantaged young men in particular appeared to view paternity as a source of self-esteem and were consequently more likely than more affluent young men to say that fathering a child would make them feel like a real man and that they would be pleased, or at least not as upset, with an unplanned pregnancy (Marsiglio, 1993a). Consistent with these attitudes, poor young men were less likely to use a contraceptive.

Various factors determine use of contraceptives. Teenage girls who engage in more frequent intercourse are more likely to use contraception and to use more effective methods (DuRant & Sanders, 1989). Older teenagers are more likely than younger ones to use contraception (Mosher & Bachrach, 1987). Younger teens who are sexually active may be less likely to use contraception because they lack information about contraception and because they do not always perceive the repercussions of their actions (Handler, 1990). Younger teens may also have less access to contraceptives.

Recent Canadian statistics (2003) show that 42% of Grade 11 boys surveyed for the Canadian Youth, Sexual Health and HIV Study (Council of Ministers, 2003) reported using only a condom the last time they had sexual intercourse, compared to 28% of girls.

Applications

Combatting Teenage Pregnancy: A Role for the Schools?

Various means have been recommended to combat the problem of teenage pregnancy, including quality sex education, access to contraceptive services in schools, open discussion of sex between parents and children, and dissemination of information about responsible sex practices and contraception through the media. Many helping professionals believe that the rate of teenage pregnancy and the spread of sexually transmitted infections could be curtailed through sex education about contraception and provision of contraceptives.

Sex-education programs that focus on the development of skills needed to resist social and peer pressure are effective in encouraging teens to postpone sexual involvement (Fisher & Fisher, 1998). However, programs that rely on the "just say no" model to encourage abstinence are less effective (Wilson & Sanderson, 1988).

Alarmed by the threat of AIDS and teenage pregnancy, some schools now distribute contraceptives, such as condoms, to students, usually after consulting with parents. Whether public schools should make contraceptives available to sexually active teens is the focus of heated debate among parents, educators, health officials, and other public officials in Canada.

Misconceptions also decrease the likelihood of using birth control. Some adolescents believe that they are too young to become pregnant. Others believe that pregnancy results only from repeated coitus or will not occur if they are standing up. Still other adolescents simply do not admit to themselves that they are engaging in coitus.

Teenagers who focus on the long-term consequences of their actions are more likely to use contraceptives. The quality of the relationship is also a factor. Satisfaction with the relationship is associated with more frequent intercourse *and* more consistent use of contraception (Jorgensen et al., 1980). More consistent contraceptive use is found in relationships in which the young woman takes the initiative in making decisions and resolving conflicts.

Let us note that many adolescents today who use condoms do so more because of fear of AIDS than to protect themselves against unwanted pregnancies (Lewin, 1991). A reduction in teenage pregnancies may be a side effect of this trend.

The use of birth control pills and condoms was reported by 31% of Grade 11 boys and 30% of Grade 11 girls. The most common reason cited for not using a condom was that some other method of birth control was used. This was followed by the reason, "did not expect to have sex." Only 1.3% of boys and 0.3% of girls reported that they did not know how to use a condom, and virtually none of the students surveyed said that they were too embarrassed to use a condom. Poor family relationships and poor communication with parents are associated with inconsistent contraceptive use (Brooks-Gunn & Furstenberg, 1989). Poor performance in school and low educational ambitions predict irregular contraceptive use, as they also predict early sexual initiation. For many teenagers, coitus is an unplanned, "spur of the moment" experience.

Adulthood

People entering adulthood today face a wider range of sexual choices and lifestyles than those of earlier generations. The sexual revolution loosened traditional constraints on sexual choices, especially for women. Couples experiment with lifestyles that would have been unthinkable in earlier generations. An increasing number of young people choose to remain single as a way of life, not merely as a way station preceding the arrival of Mr. or Ms. Right.

In this section, we discuss diverse forms of adult sexuality, including singlehood, marriage, and cohabitation. Let us begin as people begin—with singlehood.

Singlehood

Recent years have seen a sharp increase in the numbers of single young people in our society. Singlehood, not marriage, is now the most common lifestyle among people in their early 20s. Though marriages may be made in heaven, many Canadians are saying heaven can wait. In 1996, 67% of men and 51% of women between the ages of 25 and 29 had never been married (compared to 35% of men and 21% of women in 1951) (Milan, 2000). The marriage rate has also dropped, from 9.2 per 1000 in 1972 to 5.1 per 1000 in 2000.

Several factors contribute to the increased proportion of singles. For one thing, more people are postponing marriage to pursue educational and career goals (Barringer, 1991). Many young people are deciding to "live together" (cohabit), at least for a while, rather than get married. Also, people are getting married at later ages (Milan, 2000). The increased prevalence of divorce also swells the ranks of single adults.

Less social stigma is attached to remaining single today. Though single people are less likely today to be perceived as socially inadequate or as failures, some unmarried people still encounter stereotypes. Men who have never married may be suspected of being gay. Single women may feel that men perceive them as "loose."

Many single people do not choose to be single. Some remain single because they have not yet found Mr. or Ms. Right. Yet many young people see singlehood as an alternative, open-ended way of life—not just a temporary stage that precedes marriage. As career options for women have expanded, they are not as financially dependent on men as were their mothers and grandmothers. A number of women, like young career-oriented men, choose to remain single (at least for a time) to focus their energies on their careers.

Singlehood is not without its problems. Many singles are lonely. Some singles express concerns about the lack of a steady, meaningful social relationship. Others, usually women, worry about their physical safety. Some people living alone may find it difficult to satisfy their needs for intimacy, companionship, sex, and emotional support. Despite these concerns, most singles are well adjusted and content. Singles who have a supportive social network tend to be more satisfied with their lifestyles.

There is no single "singles scene." Single people differ in their sexual interests and lifestyles. Many achieve emotional and psychological security through a network of intimate relationships with friends. Most are sexually active, and many practise **serial monogamy**. Other singles have a primary sexual relationship with one steady partner but occasional flings with others. A few, even in this age of AIDS, are "swinging singles." That is, they pursue casual sexual encounters, or "one-night stands."

Serial monogamy A pattern of involvement in one exclusive relationship after another, as opposed to engaging in multiple sexual relationships at the same time.

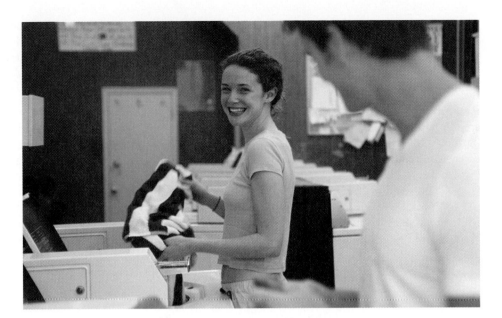

Some singles remain celibate, either by choice or for lack of opportunity. Nuns and priests choose **celibacy** for religious reasons. Others believe that celibacy allows them to focus their energies and attention on work or to commit themselves to an important cause. They see celibacy as a temporary accommodation to other pursuits. Others remain celibate because they view sex outside of marriage as immoral. Still others remain celibate because they find the prospects of sexual activity aversive or unalluring, or because of fears of STIs.

> **Celibacy** Complete sexual abstinence. (Sometimes used to describe the state of being unmarried, especially in the case of people who take vows to remain single.)

Cohabitation: Darling, Would You Be My POSSLQ?

> There is nothing I would not do
> If you would be my POSSLQ.
>
> (CHARLES OSGOOD)

POSSLQ? This unromantic abbreviation was introduced by the U.S. Bureau of the Census to refer to **cohabitation**. It stands for People of Opposite Sex Sharing Living Quarters and applies to unmarried couples who live together.

Some social scientists believe that cohabitation has become accepted within the social mainstream (Bumpass, 1995). Whether or not this is so, society in general has become more tolerant of it. We seldom hear cohabitation referred to as "living in sin" or "shacking up" as we once did. People today are more likely to refer to cohabitation with value-free expressions such as "living together."

The number of Canadian adults living in common-law relationships more than tripled between 1981 and 2000. It grew from 350 000 in 1981 to 1 158 400 in 2000 (Turcotte & Belanger, 1997; Statistics Canada, 2002). The 2001 Census showed that common-law couples accounted for 14% of all couples. This census was the first one to offer statistics on same-sex couples. Those who identified themselves as same-sex common-law couples accounted for 0.5% of all couples in the census.

> **Cohabitation** Living together as though married but without legal sanction (also known as common-law relationship).

Who Are the Cohabitors?
Even though most young adults plan to get married and stay married, 57% of Canadians live in a common-law relationship first (Turcotte & Belanger, 1997). In Quebec, people are even more likely to live together, as are francophones in the rest of Canada. Cohabitation is more common in younger women (teens and early twenties) than in those in their late 20s or early 30s. Women whose parents divorced before the age of 15 were much more likely to be in a common-law relationship. Men's behaviour is similar to women's, with the exception that age is not a determining factor (Turcotte & Belanger, 1997).

Willingness to cohabit is related to more liberal attitudes toward sexual behaviour, nontraditional views of marriage and gender roles (Huffman et al., 1994), and being employed. Cohabitors are also less likely than noncohabitors to attend church regularly. Although much of the attention on cohabitation has focused on university students, education was not a factor in forming common-law relationships (Turcotte & Belanger, 1997).

Reasons for Cohabitation Why do people cohabit? Cohabitation, like marriage, is an alternative to loneliness. Romantic partners may have deep feelings for each other but not be ready to get married. Some couples prefer cohabitation because it provides a consistent relationship without the legal and economic entanglements of marriage (Steinhauer, 1995).

Many cohabitors feel less commitment toward their relationships than married people do (Nock, 1995). Ruth, an 84-year-old woman, has been living with her partner, age 85, for four years. "I'm a free spirit," she says. "I need my space. Sometimes we think of marriage, but then I think that I don't want to be tied down" (cited in Steinhauer, 1995, p. C7).

Economic factors come into play as well. Emotionally committed couples may decide to cohabit because of the economic advantages of sharing household expenses. Some older people live together rather than marry because of resistance from adult children (Yorburg, 1995). Some children fear that a parent will be victimized by a needy senior citizen. Others may not want their inheritances to come into question or may not want to decide where to bury the remaining parent. Younger couples may cohabit secretly to maintain parental support that they might lose if they were to get married or to openly reveal their living arrangements.

Cohabitation and Later Marriage: Benefit or Risk? Cohabiting couples may believe that cohabitation will strengthen eventual marriage by helping them iron out the kinks in their relationship. Yet cohabitors who later marry may run a greater—not lesser—risk of divorce than noncohabitors. Statistics from a national survey of households reveal that the likelihood of divorce within ten years of marriage is nearly twice as great among married couples who cohabited before marriage (LeBourdais et al., 2000). A Swedish study found that the likelihood of marital dissolution was 80% greater among women who had cohabited before a first marriage than among women who had not (Bennett et al., 1988).

We must be cautious about drawing causal conclusions from correlational data, however. None of the couples in these studies were *randomly assigned* to cohabitation or noncohabitation. Therefore, *selection factors*—the factors that lead some couples and not others to cohabit—may explain the results (see Figure 11.2). Cohabitors tend to be more committed to personal independence (Bumpass, 1995). They also tend to be less traditional and less religious than noncohabitors. All in all, people who cohabit prior to marriage tend to be less committed to the values and interests traditionally associated with the institution of marriage. The attitudes of cohabitors, and not cohabitation itself, may thus account for their higher rates of marital dissolution.

About 40% of cohabiting couples eventually marry (Laumann et al., 1994). However, termination of the relationship is the more likely outcome (Willis & Michael, 1994).The majority of couples break up within three years. Recent research has found a relationship between a cohabiting couple's economic situation and the likelihood that they will marry or separate. It also shows that men and women react differently. Women in professional or semiprofessional occupations are less likely to marry their common-law partner, and more likely to end the relationship. Men in professional occupations, on the other hand, are more likely to marry their common-law partner (LeBourdais et al., 2000).

Marriage

Marriage is found in all human societies. In every known society, most people—in some societies nearly all people—get married at least once (Ember & Ember, 1990; Kammeyer, 1990).

In Canada in 2000, 157 395 couples married. This was up slightly from 1997 and down approximately 24% from 1972, when 200 470 ceremonies were conducted (Statistics Canada, 1999a; Statistics Canada, 2003c). With more people delaying marriage in favour of pursuing educational and career goals, the average age of first marriage has been rising steadily over the past few decades and is now 30 years for men and 28 years for women (Statistics Canada, 2003c).

Whom Do We Marry: Are Marriages Made in Heaven or in the Neighbourhood?

Most preliterate societies regulate the selection of spouses in some way. The universal incest taboo proscribes matings between close relatives. Societal rules and customs also determine which persons are desirable mates and which are not.

In Western cultures, mate selection is presumably free. Parents today seldom arrange marriages, although they may still encourage their child to date that wonderful son or daughter of the solid churchgoing couple who live down the street. Nevertheless, factors such as race, social class, and religion often determine the categories of persons within which we may seek mates (Laumann et al., 1994). People in our culture tend to marry others from the same geographical area and social class. Since neighbourhoods are often made up of people from a similar social class, storybook marriages like Cinderella's are the exception to the rule.

Because we make choices, we tend to marry people who attract us. These people are often similar to us in physical attractiveness and attitudes, even in minute details. We are more often than not similar to our mates in characteristics such as height, weight, personality traits, and intelligence (Buss, 1994; Lesnik-Oberstein & Cohen, 1984; Schafer & Keith, 1990). Those we marry are also those who seem likely to meet our material, sexual, and psychological needs.

The concept of like marrying like is termed **homogamy**. We usually marry people of the same racial/ethnic background, educational level, and religion. Marriages between individuals who are alike may stand a better chance of survival, since the partners are more likely to share values and attitudes (Michael et al., 1994).

We also tend to follow age homogamy (Michael et al., 1994). *Age homogamy*—the selection of a partner who falls in one's own age range—may reflect the tendency to marry early in adulthood. People who marry late or who remarry tend not to select partners so close in age.

Some marriages do show a **mating gradient**. The stereotype has been that an economically established older man would take an attractive, younger woman as his wife. But by and large, with boring predictability, we are attracted to and marry the boy or girl (almost) next door. Most marriages seem to be made not in heaven, but in the neighbourhood.

Homogamy The practice of marrying people who are similar in social background and standing. (From Greek roots meaning "same" [*homos*] and "marriage" [*gamos*].)

Mating gradient The tendency for women to "marry up" (in social or economic status) and for men to "marry down."

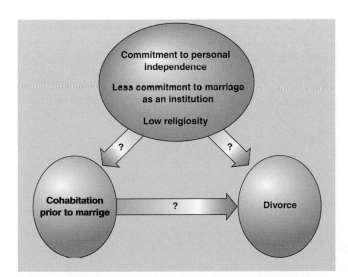

Figure 11.2. Does Cohabitation Prior to Marriage Increase the Risk of Eventual Divorce?

There is a correlation between cohabitation prior to marriage and the risk of divorce later on. Does cohabitation increase the risk of divorce, or do other factors—such as a commitment to personal independence—contribute to both the likelihood of cohabitation and eventual divorce?

Marital Sexuality Patterns of marital sexuality vary across cultures, yet anthropologists have noted some common threads (Ember & Ember, 1990). Privacy for sexual relations is valued in almost all cultures. Most cultures also place restrictions on coitus during menstruation, during at least some stages of pregnancy, and for a time after childbirth.

Until the sexual revolution of the 1960s and 1970s, Western culture could be characterized as sexually restrictive, even toward marital sex. Hunt noted that "Western civilization has long had the rare distinction of contaminating and restricting the sexual pleasure of married couples more severely than almost any other" (1974, p. 175).

The Sexual Revolution Hits Home We usually think of the sexual revolution in terms of the changes in sexual behaviours and attitudes that occurred among young, unmarried people. It also ushered in profound changes in marital sexuality, however. Compared to Kinsey's "prerevolution" samples from the late 1930s and 1940s, married couples today engage in coitus more frequently, with greater variety, and for longer durations of time. They report higher levels of sexual satisfaction.

The sexual revolution also helped dislodge traditional male dominance in sexual behaviour. In essence, male dominance is the view that sexual pleasure is meant for men but not women and that it is the duty of women to satisfy their husbands' sexual needs and serve as passive "receptacles."

Liberalizing trends were communicated through popular media. Hundreds if not thousands of books and magazines with sexual content crammed bookstore shelves and supermarket display cases. During Kinsey's day, books like Henry Miller's *Tropic of Cancer* and D. H. Lawrence's *Lady Chatterley's Lover* were censored in Canada and the United States. Now they are readily available but so tame when compared to today's explicit books and magazines that they barely raise an eyebrow. Similarly, since the late 1960s pornographic films have been shown in adult theatres across the nation. The VCR and the internet have brought sexually explicit films into middle-class suburban homes.

Scientific findings were also liberalizing influences. Kinsey's and Masters and Johnson's findings that women were capable not only of orgasm but also of multiple orgasms punctured traditional beliefs that sexual gratification was the birthright of men alone. TV shows, films, and radio talk shows began to portray women as sexual initiators who enjoy sex. All of these influences have encouraged North American women to forgo the traditional passive approach to sexuality.

The development of effective contraceptives also separated sex from reproduction. Motives for sexual pleasure became more open. The term *recreational sex* came into play. All these liberalizing forces have led to changes in the frequency of marital sex and in techniques of foreplay and coitus since Kinsey's day.

Duration and Techniques of Foreplay Married women in Kinsey's sample reported an average (median) length of foreplay of about 12 minutes. This figure rose to nearly 15 minutes among the wives in the *Playboy* survey (Hunt, 1974). Couples in more recent surveys report using a wider variety of foreplay techniques, including oral stimulation of the breasts and oral–genital contact (Blumstein & Schwartz, 1983; Hunt, 1974).

Frequency of Marital Coitus According to an Angus Reid poll (1998), the majority of married men and women in Canada now report engaging in sexual relations between five and ten times a month. The average is six times a month, although 17% said none, and 3% said more than 20 times a month.

Studies, from the Kinsey and *Playboy* studies shown in Table 11.2 to more recent studies, have consistently found that the frequency of sexual relations declines with age (Call et al., 1995; Laumann et al., 1994). Over the age of 55, for example, people reported an average of twice a month. Regardless of a couple's age, sexual frequency also appears to decline with years of marriage (Blumstein & Schwartz, 1990).

Techniques and Duration of Coitus In coitus, as in foreplay, the marital bed since Kinsey's day has become a stage on which the players act more varied roles. Today's couples use greater variety in coital positions. As many as 70% of Kinsey's males used the male-superior position exclusively (Kinsey et al., 1948). Perhaps three couples in ten used the female-superior position frequently. One in four or five used the lateral-entry position frequently, and about one in ten the rear-entry position. Younger and more highly educated men showed greater variety, however. Hunt (1974), by comparison, found that three-quarters of the married couples in the *Playboy* survey used the female-superior position at least occasionally. More than half had used the lateral-entry position, and about four in ten had used the rear-entry position.

An often overlooked but important difference between Kinsey's and current samples involves the length of intercourse. In Kinsey's time it was widely believed that the "virile" man ejaculated rapidly during intercourse. Kinsey estimated that most men reached orgasm within two minutes after penetration, many within 10 or 20 seconds. Kinsey recognized that women usually took longer to reach orgasm through coitus, and that some clinicians were already asserting that a man's ejaculation was "premature" unless he delayed it until "the female (was) ready to reach orgasm" (1948, p. 580).

Even today's less-educated couples appear to be more sophisticated than Kinsey's in their recognition of the need for sexual variety and their focus on exchanging sexual pleasure rather than rapidly reaching orgasm (Michael et al., 1994). According to surveys, the "duration of the last sexual event" of three out of four married couples was 15 minutes to an hour. Eight to nine percent of couples exceeded an hour (Michael et al., 1994). (About one unmarried, noncohabiting couple in three made love for an hour or more, suggesting that novelty and youth have their motivational aspects.)

Sexual Satisfaction One index by which researchers measure sexual satisfaction is orgasmic consistency. Men tend to reach orgasm more consistently than women do. After 15 years of marriage, 45% of the wives in Kinsey's study reported reaching orgasm 90% to 100% of the time. After 15 years of marriage, 12% of the wives in Kinsey's study had not experienced orgasm.

Orgasmic consistency now seems higher than in Kinsey's day. The surveys find that more than 90% of the men and about 70% of the women reported reaching orgasm "always" or "usually" with their primary partner during the 12 months prior to the survey (Laumann et al., 1994; Michael et al., 1994) (see Table 11.3). Three of four men (75%) and nearly three women in ten (28.6%) reported reaching orgasm on every occasion. Only 2% of the married women reported never reaching orgasm with their husbands during the past year.

Women in their 40s were somewhat more likely to reach orgasm consistently than younger and older women. Perhaps women in their 40s have had more time to get in touch with their sexuality and may be more secure in their relationships than younger women. Security in the relationship may promote orgasmic consistency. There do not seem to be notable racial or ethnic differences.

Orgasm is not the only criterion for measuring pleasure or satisfaction in marital sex. When asked whether they had been extremely physically satisfied with their primary partners during the past year, it is apparent, from Table 11.3, that men's and women's general physical satisfaction is comparable—about 47% and 41%, respectively.

TABLE 11.2 Median weekly frequency of marital coitus, male and female estimates combined (Kinsey and *Playboy* surveys)

KINSEY (1948, 1953)		PLAYBOY (1974)	
Age	Frequency	Age	Frequency
16–25	2.45	18–24	3.25
26–35	1.95	25–34	2.55
36–45	1.40	35–44	2.00
46–55	0.85	45–54	1.00
55–60	0.50	55 and over	1.00

Source: Hunt, M. (1974). *Sexual Behavior in the 1970's.* New York: Dell Books, p. 191.

TABLE 11.3 Sociocultural factors and sexual satisfaction in primary relationship during past year

Sociocultural Characteristics	Always or Usually Had an Orgasm with with Partner		Has Been Extremely Physically Satisfied with Partner		Has Been Extremely Emotionally Satisfied with Partner	
	Men (%)	Women (%)	Men (%)	Women (%)	Men (%)	Women (%)
Age						
8–24	92	61	44	44	41	39
25–29	94	71	50	39	46	40
30–39	97	70	45	41	39	38
40–49	97	78	44	42	38	42
50–59	91	73	53	32	52	32
Marital Status						
Noncohabiting	94	62	39	40	32	31
Cohabiting	95	68	44	46	35	44
Married	95	75	52	41	49	42

Source: Combined from Laumann, E. O., Gagnon, J. H., Michael, R. T., & Michaels, S. (1994). *The Social Organization of Sexuality: Sexual Practices in the United States*. Chicago: University of Chicago Press, Table 3.7, pp. 116–117, and Michael, R. T., Gagnon, J. H., Laumann, E. O., & Kolata, G. (1994). *Sex in America: A Definitive Survey*. Boston: Little, Brown, Table 9, pp. 128–129.

Orgasm, then, is not a guarantee of satisfaction. And lack of orgasm is not necessarily a sign of dissatisfaction.

The emotional satisfaction in a marital relationship is also linked to sexual satisfaction. Table 11.3 shows that about 40% of men and women report being extremely emotionally satisfied with their primary partners. Closer relationships are connected with more consistent orgasm.

Extramarital Sex

Extramarital sex (or an "affair") is usually conducted without the spouse's knowledge or approval. Such clandestine affairs are referred to as **conventional adultery**, infidelity, or simply "cheating." Some extramarital affairs are "one-night stands." Others persist for years.

In **consensual adultery**, extramarital relationships are conducted openly with the knowledge and consent of the partner and sometimes even with the partner's participation, as in **swinging.**

Extramarital sex Sexual relations between a married person and someone other than his or her spouse.

Conventional adultery Extramarital sex that is kept clandestine (hidden) from one's spouse.

Consensual adultery Extramarital sex that is engaged in openly with the knowledge and consent of one's spouse.

Swinging A form of consensual adultery in which both spouses share extramarital sexual experiences. Also referred to as *mate-swapping*.

Sexual Satisfaction. Marital closeness is linked to sexual satisfaction. Perhaps sexual pleasure contributes to marital closeness, or perhaps closeness helps couples achieve greater sexual satisfaction.

Some people engage in extramarital sex for variety (Lamanna & Riedmann, 1997). Some have affairs to break the routine of a confining marriage. Others enter affairs for reasons similar to the nonsexual reasons adolescents often have for coitus: as a way of expressing hostility toward a spouse or retaliating for injustice. Husbands and wives who engage in affairs often report that they are not satisfied with, or fulfilled by, their marital relationships.

Sometimes the sexual motive is less pressing than the desire for emotional closeness. Some women say they are seeking someone to talk to or communicate with (Lamanna & Riedmann, 1997). In a 2001 poll of Canadians, loneliness was cited as the main reason people would consider having an affair (Ipsos-Reid/CTV Poll, 2001). However, women (37%) were more likely than men (26%) to give loneliness as a prime motive for an affair. Curiosity and desire for personal growth were more prominent motives for affairs than marital dissatisfaction. Middle-aged people may have affairs to boost their self-esteem or prove that they are still attractive.

Men (whether single, married, or cohabiting) are generally more approving of extramarital affairs than are women (Glass & Wright, 1992). Men who have had affairs are more likely to cite a need for sexual excitement as a justification than women are— 75% versus 55% (Glass & Wright, 1992). Women are less accepting of sex without emotional involvement (Townsend, 1995). Women are more likely to cite "falling in love" as a justification for their affairs than are men: 77% versus 43%. These data support the widely held view that "men separate sex and love; women appear to believe that love and sex go together and that falling in love justifies sexual involvement" (Glass & Wright, 1992, p. 361).

Patterns of Extramarital Sex How many people engage in extramarital sex? Viewers of TV talk shows may get the impression that everyone cheats, but surveys paint a different picture. In a U.S. study conducted between 1988 and 1992 by the respected National Opinion Research Center, 21% of the husbands and 12% of the wives acknowledged marital infidelity ("Cheating," 1993). More than 90% of the married women and 75% of the married men say they remain loyal to their spouses (Laumann et al., 1994). The vast majority of those who were cohabiting also reported that they were loyal to their partners while they were living together (Laumann et al., 1994). Canadian statistics from the 2001 Ipsos-Reid/CTV poll reveal that one in ten Canadians (9%) say that they have had an extramarital affair (Ipsos-Reid/CTV poll, 2001).

Having presented the percentages of reported extramarital sex, let us note one compelling limitation to these data. These reports cannot be verified. People may be reluctant to reveal they have "cheated" on their spouses even when they are assured of anonymity. There is likely to be an overall tendency to underreport the incidence of extramarital sex.

Attitudes Toward Extramarital Sex The sexual revolution does not seem to have changed attitudes toward extramarital sex. Most people disapprove of it. A recent Canadian poll found that 80.8% of those surveyed considered extramarital relationships immoral (Léger Marketing, 2002). Most married couples espouse the value of monogamy as the cornerstone of their marital relationship (Blumstein & Schwartz, 1990).

Effects of Extramarital Sex The discovery of infidelity can evoke a range of emotional responses. The spouse may be filled with anger, jealousy, even shame. Feelings of inadequacy and doubts about one's attractiveness and desirability may surface. Infidelity may be seen by the betrayed spouse as a serious breach of trust and intimacy. Marriages that are not terminated in the wake of the disclosure may survive in a damaged condition (Charny & Parnass, 1995).

The harm an affair does to a marriage may reflect the meaning of the affair to the individual and his or her spouse. If a person has an affair because the marriage is deeply troubled, the affair may be one more factor that speeds its dissolution. The effects on the marriage may depend on the nature of the affair. It may be easier to understand that a spouse has fallen prey to an isolated, unplanned encounter than to accept an extended affair (Charny & Parnass, 1995). In some cases the discovery of infidelity stimulates the couple to work to improve their relationship. If the extramarital activity continues, however, it may undermine the couple's efforts to restore their relationship.

Divorce

Divorce: Facts, Causes and Consequences
www.vifamily.ca/library/cft/divorce.html
This paper by Dr. Ann-Marie Ambert of York University presents Canadian statistics on divorce and discusses causes and consequences of divorce for couples, families, and children of divorced parents.

Splitting Up: Canadians Get Divorced
http://archives.cbc.ca/IDD-1-69-760/life_society/divorce/
This CBC archive website looks at changes in how Canadians divorced from the 1960s to the 1980s.

More than one-third of marriages in Canada end in divorce within 30 years (Statistics Canada, 2000a). Divorce was unusual in Canada before the 1960s. The divorce rate more than tripled between 1960 and 1970, partly because in 1968 it became possible for the first time to obtain a divorce without proving adultery. The rate roughly doubled again between 1970 and the early 1980s, when it reached more than 300 divorces per 100 000 population. The divorce rate has fallen somewhat in the late 1980s and 1990s. In 2000, there were 231.2 divorces per 100 000 population (see Figure 11.3). About one-third of divorce cases involve minor children.

The relaxation of legal restrictions on divorce has made divorces easier to obtain. Under the Canadian *Divorce Act*, 1985, breakdown of the marriage is the only legal ground for divorce. Separation is considered proof of breakdown: a divorce can be granted if the couple has lived apart for more than one year. If there is adultery or physical or mental cruelty, the couple can be granted a divorce without having to live apart for a year.

The secularization of society and the increasing emphasis on individual choice are factors that have contributed to the rising divorce rate. Today, more people consider marriage an alterable condition than in prior generations. People today hold higher expectations of marriage than did their parents or grandparents. They expect it to be personally fulfilling as well as meeting the traditional expectation of marriage as an institution for rearing children. The most common reasons given for a divorce today are problems in communication and a lack of understanding. Years ago it was more likely to be lack of financial support.

The Cost of Divorce Divorce is often associated with financial and emotional problems. When a household splits, the resources often cannot maintain the earlier standard of living for each partner. A woman who has not pursued a career may struggle to compete with younger, more experienced workers. Divorced mothers often face the combined stress of the sole responsibility for rearing their children (women receive custody in the majority of divorce cases) and the need to increase their incomes to make ends meet. Divorced fathers may also find it difficult to pay alimony and child support while attempting to establish a new lifestyle. However, men are less likely than women to become poor as a result of divorce. In the first year following a divorce, women's income drops by 40%, while men's income actually rises slightly (Ambert, 2002).

Figure 11.3. Divorce Rates in Canada.

Divorce rates in Canada have increased, partly because of relaxation of legal restrictions.

Source: Adapted from the Statistics Canada website, **www.statcan.ca/english/Pgdb/People/Families/famil02.htm**, November 21, 2000, and Statistics Canada, *The Daily*, December 2, 2002, available at **www.statcan.ca/Daily/English/021202/d021202f.htm**.

Divorce may also prompt feelings of failure as a spouse and parent, loneliness and uncertainty about the future, and depression. Married people appear to be better able to cope with the stresses and strains of life, perhaps because they can rely on each other for emotional support. Divorced and separated people have the highest rates of physical and mental illness in the population (Bloom et al., 1978; Nevid et al., 2000). Divorced people also have higher rates of suicide than married people (Trovato, 1986). On the other hand, divorce may be a time of personal growth and renewal. It can provide an opportunity for people to take stock of themselves and establish a new, more rewarding life for themselves.

Although children suffer in a divorce, marital conflict also causes problems for children (Amato & Keith, 1991; Davies & Cummings, 1994). Marital relations spill over into parent–child relations and affect children's behaviour (Erel & Burman, 1995). Boys tend to show greater problems in adjusting to conflict or divorce, such as conduct problems at school and increased anxiety and dependence (Grych & Fincham, 1993; Holden & Ritchie, 1991). Children's adjustment is enhanced when parents maintain their parenting responsibilities and set aside their differences long enough to agree upon child-rearing practices (Wallerstein & Blakeslee, 1989).

Remarriage Despite the difficulties in adjusting to a divorce, most divorced people eventually bounce back. Many remarry. Among older people, divorced men are more likely than divorced women to remarry—in part because men usually die earlier than women (and so fewer prospective husbands are available), in part because older men tend to remarry younger women.

Remarriages are more likely than first marriages to end in divorce (Lown & Dolan, 1988). One reason is the selection factor. That is, divorced people may be less inclined than others to persist in a troubled marriage. Many divorced people who remarry are also encumbered with alimony and child-support payments that strain their new marriages. Many bring children from their earlier marriages to their new ones.

Today, the stepfamily is becoming one of the most common family units in Canada. In 1997, 34% of marriages involved at least one spouse who had previously been married; in almost half of these marriages, both spouses were remarrying (Milan, 2000).

Sex in the Later Years

Which is the fastest growing segment of the population? People aged 65 and older. Almost 4 million people in Canada are senior citizens, and their number is growing fast.

Researchers find that sexual daydreaming, sex drive, and sexual activity tend to decline with age, whereas negative sexual attitudes tend to increase (Purifoy et al., 1992). However, research does not support the belief that people lose their sexuality as they age. Nearly all (95%) of the older people in one sample reported that they liked sex, and 75% reported that orgasm was essential to their sexual fulfillment (Starr & Weiner, 1981). People who are exposed to cultural views that sex among older people is deviant may renounce sex as they age, however. Those who remain sexually active may be bothered by guilt (Reiss, 1988).

Sexual activity among older people, as among other groups, is influenced not only by physical structures and changes, but by psychological well-being, feelings of intimacy, and cultural expectations.

Physical Changes

Although many older people retain the capacity to respond sexually, physical changes do occur as the years pass (see Table 11.4). If we are aware of them, we will not view them as abnormal or find ourselves unprepared to cope with them. Many potential problems can be averted by changing our expectations or making some changes to accommodate the aging process.

Changes in the Female
Many of the physical changes in women stem from decline in the production of estrogen around the time of menopause. The vaginal walls lose

Sexual Issues for Aging Adults
**www.hs.ttu.edu/
sexuality&aging/**
This paper presents information on sexuality and aging as well as links to other resources.

TABLE 11.4 Changes in sexual arousal often associated with aging

Changes in the Female	Changes in the Male
Reduced myotonia (muscle tension)	Longer time to erection and orgasm
Reduced vaginal lubrication	Need for more direct stimulation for erection and orgasm
Reduced elasticity of the vaginal walls	Less semen emitted during ejaculation
Smaller increases in breast size during sexual arousal	Erections may be less firm
Reduced intensity of muscle spasms at orgasm	Testicles may not elevate as high into scrotum
	Less intense orgasmic contractions
	Lessened feeling of a need to ejaculate during sex
	Longer refractory period

Source: Copyright © 1990 by The Kinsey Institute for Research in Sex, Gender, and Reproduction. From THE KINSEY INSTITUTE NEW REPORT ON SEX. Reprinted with permission from St. Martin's Press, New York, NY.

much elasticity and the thick, corrugated texture of the childbearing years. They grow paler and thinner. Coitus may become irritating. The thinning of the walls may also place greater pressure against the bladder and urethra during coitus, leading in some cases to urinary urgency and burning urination.

The vagina also shrinks in size. The labia majora lose much of their fatty deposits and become thin. The introitus becomes relatively constricted, and penile entry may become somewhat difficult. This "problem" has a positive aspect: increased friction between the penis and vaginal walls may heighten sexual sensations. The body of the uterus decreases in size after menopause and no longer becomes so congested during sexual arousal. Following menopause, women also produce less vaginal lubrication, and the lubrication that is produced may take minutes, not seconds, to appear. Lack of adequate lubrication is also a major reason for painful coitus.

Many of these changes may be slowed or reversed through estrogen-replacement therapy, although prolonged use of estrogen-replacement therapy is controversial and not as widely accepted as it once was. Natural lubrication may also be increased through more elaborate foreplay. The need for more foreplay may encourage the man to become a more considerate lover. (He too will likely need more time to become aroused.) An artificial lubricant may also ease problems posed by difficult entry or painful thrusting.

Women's breasts show smaller increases in size with sexual arousal as they age, but the nipples still become erect. Because the muscle tone of the urethra and anal sphincters decreases, the spasms of orgasm become less powerful and fewer in number. They may feel less intense. The uterine contractions that occur during orgasm may become

Sexuality and Aging. *Despite stereotypes that stigmatize older people who are sexually active as abnormal or deviant, it is normal for older people to have sexual urges and maintain an active sex life.*

discouragingly painful for some postmenopausal women. Despite these changes, women can retain their ability to achieve orgasm well into their advanced years. The subjective experience of orgasm also remains highly satisfying, despite the lessened intensity of muscular contractions.

Changes in the Male Age-related changes tend to occur more gradually in men than in women and are not clearly connected with any one biological event, as they are with menopause in the woman. Male adolescents may achieve erection in a matter of seconds through sexual fantasy alone. After about age 50, men take progressively longer to achieve erection. Erections become less firm, perhaps because of lowered testosterone production. Older men may require minutes of direct stimulation of the penis to achieve an erection. Couples can adjust to these changes by extending the length and variety of foreplay.

Most men remain capable of erection throughout their lives. Erectile dysfunction is not inevitable with aging. Men generally require more time to reach orgasm as they age, however, which may also reflect lowered testosterone production. In the eyes of their sex partners, however, delayed ejaculation may make them better lovers.

The testes may decrease slightly in size and produce less testosterone. Testosterone production usually declines gradually from about age 40 to age 60 and then begins to level off. Sperm production tends to decline as the seminiferous tubules degenerate, but viable sperm may be produced quite late in life. Men in their 70s, 80s, and even 90s have fathered children.

Nocturnal erections tend to diminish in intensity, duration, and frequency as men age, but they do not normally disappear in healthy men (Reinisch, 1990; Schiavi et al., 1990). The refractory period tends to lengthen. An adolescent may require only a few minutes to regain erection and ejaculate again after a first orgasm, whereas a man in his 30s may require half an hour. Past age 50, the refractory period may increase to several hours.

Older men produce less ejaculate, and it may seep rather than shoot out. Though the contractions of orgasm still begin at 0.8-second intervals, they become weaker and fewer. Still, the number and strength of spasms do not translate precisely into subjective pleasure. An older male may enjoy orgasm as thoroughly as he did at a younger age. Attitudes and expectations can be as important as the contractions themselves.

Following orgasm, erection subsides more rapidly than it does in a younger man. A study of 65 healthy men aged 45 to 74 showed an age-related decline in sexual desire, arousal, and activity. Yet there were no differences between younger and older men in level of sexual satisfaction or enjoyment (Schiavi et al., 1990).

In sum, most physical changes do not bring a man's or a woman's sex life to a grinding halt. People's attitudes, sexual histories, and partners are usually more important factors in sexual behaviour and enjoyment.

Sexual Behaviour

Despite the decline in certain physical functions, older people can continue to lead a vibrant, fulfilling sex life. In fact, years of sexual experience may more than compensate for any diminution of physical responsiveness (Hodson & Skeen, 1994). In one survey of 800 people, aged 60 through 91, nearly three out of four who had remained sexually active reported that lovemaking had become more rewarding over the years (Starr & Weiner, 1981). Unfortunately, people who overreact to expected changes in sexual response may conclude that their sex lives are over and give up on sexual activity or even on expressing any physical affection (Reinisch, 1990).

Ninety-four percent of the men and 84% of the women in Kinsey's samples remained sexually active at the age of 60. Half of the 60- to 91-year-olds surveyed by Starr and Weiner (1981) reported sexual relations on a regular basis; and half of these, at least once a week. A study of 200 healthy 80- to 102-year-olds reported that 30% of the women and 62% of the men still engaged in intercourse (Bretschneider & McCoy, 1988). A study of 100 older men in England found that the key factor in whether they continued to engage in sexual activity was not physical condition but the availability of a partner (Jones et al., 1994).

Couples may accommodate to the physical changes of aging by broadening their sexual repertoire to include more diverse forms of stimulation. Many respondents to a *Consumer Reports* survey reported using oral–genital stimulation, sexual fantasy, sexually explicit materials, anal stimulation, vibrators, and other sexual techniques to offset problems in achieving lubrication or erection (Brecher, 1984).

The availability of a sexually interested and supportive partner may be the most important determinant of continued sexual activity. Many women discontinue sexual activity because of the death of their husbands.

Sex and Disability

Like older people, people with disabilities (especially those whose physical disabilities render them dependent on others) are often seen as sexless and childlike (Nosek et al., 1994). Such views are based on misconceptions about the sexual functioning of people with disabilities. Some of these myths and stereotypes may be eroding, however, in part due to the success of the civil and social rights movements of the disabled in the 1970s and the attention focused on the sexuality of people with disabilities in films such as *Coming Home, Born on the Fourth of July*, and *My Left Foot*.

A person may have been born with or acquire a bodily impairment, or suffer a loss of function or a disfiguring change in appearance. Although the disability may require the person to make adjustments in order to perform sexually, most people with disabilities have the same sexual needs, feelings, and desires as people without disabilities. Their ability to express their sexual feelings and needs depends on the physical limitations imposed by their disabilities, their adjustment to their disabilities, and the availability of partners. The establishment of mature sexual relationships generally demands some distance from one's parents. Therefore, persons with disabilities who are physically dependent on their parents may find it especially difficult to develop sexual relationships (Knight, 1989).

SIECUS Annotated Bibliography: Sexuality and Disability
http://www.siecus.org/ pubs/biblio/bibs0009.html
An annotated bibliography on sexuality and disability, provided by the Sexuality Information and Education Council of the United States.

Physical Disabilities

According to Margaret Nosek and her colleagues (1994), sexual wellness for people with disabilities involves five factors:

- Positive sexual self-concept; seeing oneself as valuable sexually and as a person
- Knowledge about sexuality
- Positive, productive relationships
- Coping with barriers to sexuality (social, environmental, physical, and emotional)
- Maintaining the best possible general and sexual health, given one's limitations

This model applies to all of us, of course. Let us now consider aspects of specific physical disabilities and human sexuality.

Cerebral Palsy **Cerebral palsy** does not generally impair sexual interest, capacity for orgasm, or fertility (Reinisch, 1990). Depending on the nature and degree of muscle spasticity or lack of voluntary muscle control, however, afflicted people may be limited to certain types of sexual activities and coital positions.

Cerebral palsy A muscular disorder that is caused by damage to the central nervous system (usually prior to or during birth) and characterized by spastic paralysis.

People with disabilities such as cerebral palsy often suffer social rejection during adolescence and perceive themselves as unfit or unworthy of intimate sexual relationships, especially with people who are not disabled. They are often socialized into an asexual role. Sensitive counselling can help them understand and accept their sexuality, promote a more positive body image, and provide the social skills to establish intimate relationships (Edmonson, 1988).

Spinal-Cord Injuries Spinal-cord injuries affect about 900 Canadians each year (Canadian Paraplegic Association, 2000). Eighty percent of people who suffer disabling

spinal-cord injuries are active males under 35. Automobile or pedestrian accidents account for about 40% of these cases. Other common causes include sports injuries and falls. Depending on the location of the injury to the spinal cord, a loss of voluntary control (paralysis) can occur in either the legs (*paraplegia*) or all four limbs (*quadriplegia*). A loss of sensation may also occur in parts of the body that lie beneath the site of injury.

The effect of spinal-cord injuries on sexual response depends on the site and severity of the injury. Overall, researchers find that about three of four men with spinal-cord injuries are able to achieve erections, but only about one in ten continues to ejaculate naturally (Geiger, 1981; Spark, 1991). Others can be helped to ejaculate with the aid of a vibrator (Szasz & Carpenter, 1989).

Women may lose the ability to experience genital sensations or to lubricate normally during sexual stimulation. However, breast sensations may remain intact, making this area even more erotogenic. Most women with spinal-cord injuries can engage in coitus, become impregnated, and deliver vaginally. A survey of 27 spinal-cord-injured women showed that about half were able to experience orgasm (Kettl et al., 1991). Some also report "phantom orgasms" that provide intense psychological pleasure and that are accompanied by nongenital physical sensations similar to those experienced by nondisabled women (Perduta-Fulginiti, 1992). Spinal-cord-injured women can heighten their sexual pleasure by learning to use fantasized orgasm, orgasmic imagery, and amplification of their physical sensations (Perduta-Fulginiti, 1992).

Couples facing the challenge of spinal-cord injury may expand their sexual repertoire to focus less on genital stimulation (except to attain the reflexes of erection and lubrication) and more on the parts of the body that retain sensation. Stimulation of some areas of the body, such as the ears, the neck, and the breasts (in both men and women) can yield pleasurable erotic sensations (Knight, 1989; Seftel et al., 1991).

Sensory Disabilities Sensory disabilities, such as blindness or deafness, do not directly affect genital responsiveness. Still, sexuality may be affected in many ways. A person who has been blind since birth or early childhood may have difficulty understanding a partner's anatomy. Sex-education curricula have been designed specifically to enable visually impaired people to learn about sexual anatomy via models. Anatomically correct dolls may be used to simulate positions of intercourse.

Deaf people, too, often lack knowledge about sex. Their ability to comprehend the social cues involved in forming and maintaining intimate relationships may also be impaired. Sex-education programs based on sign language are helping many hearing-

Sex and Disabled People.
Most people with disabilities have the same sexual needs, feelings, and desires as people without disabilities. They are capable of expressing their sexuality in ways that can be pleasurable for themselves and their partners.

impaired people become more socially perceptive as well as knowledgeable about the physical aspects of sex. People with visual and hearing impairments often lack self-esteem and self-confidence, which makes it difficult for them to establish intimate relationships. Sexual counselling may help them become more aware of their sexuality and develop social skills.

Arthritis A progressive disease that is characterized by inflammation or pain in the joints.

Other Physical Disabilities and Impairments Specific disabilities pose particular challenges to, and limitations on, sexual functioning. **Arthritis** may make it difficult or painful for sufferers to bend their arms, knees, and hips during sexual activity (Ehrlich, 1988). Coital positions that minimize discomfort and the application of moist heat to the joints before sexual relations may be helpful.

A male amputee may find that he is better balanced in the lateral or female-superior position than in the male-superior position (Knight, 1989). A woman with limited hand function may find it difficult or impossible to insert a diaphragm and may need to request assistance from her partner or switch to another contraceptive (Cole, 1988). Sensitivity to each other's needs is as vital to couples in which one member has a disability as it is to any couple.

Psychological Disabilities

People with psychological disabilities, such as mental retardation, are often stereotyped as incapable of understanding their sexual impulses. Developmentally delayed people are sometimes assumed to maintain childlike innocence throughout their lives, or to be devoid of sexuality. Some stereotype developmentally delayed people in the opposite direction: as having stronger-than-normal sex drives and being incapable of controlling them (Reinisch, 1990). Some developmentally delayed people do act inappropriately—by masturbating publicly, for example. The stereotypes are exaggerated, however, and even many of those who act inappropriately can be trained to follow social rules (Reinisch, 1990).

Parents and caretakers often discourage developmentally delayed people from learning about their sexuality or teach them to deny or suppress their sexual feelings. Although the physical changes of puberty may be delayed in developmentally delayed people, most develop normal sexual needs (Edmonson, 1988). Most are capable of learning about their sexuality and can be guided into rewarding and responsible intimate relationships.

One of the greatest impediments to sexual fulfillment among people with disabilities is finding a loving and supportive partner. Some people engage in sexual relations with people with disabilities out of sympathy. By and large, however, the partners are other people with disabilities or nondisabled people who have overcome stereotypes that portray disabled people as undesirable.

Summing Up

Fetuses have been found to have erections and to suck their fingers. Stimulation of the genitals in **infancy** may produce sensations of pleasure. Pelvic thrusting has been observed in humans as early as eight months of age. Masturbation may begin as early as six to twelve months. Some infants seem capable of sexual responses that closely resemble orgasm.

Statistics concerning the incidence of masturbation among **children aged three to eight** are inconclusive. In early childhood, children show curiosity about the genitals and may play "doctor." Same-gender sexual play may be more common than heterosexual play and does not presage adult sexual orientation.

Preadolescents (aged nine to 13 years) tend to socialize with best friends and with large groups and to become self-conscious about their bodies. Masturbation is apparently the primary means of achieving orgasm during preadolescence for both genders. Preadolescent sex play often involves mutual display of the genitals, with or without touching. Group dating and mixed-gender parties often provide preadolescents with their first exposure to heterosexual activities. Much preadolescent same-gender sexual behaviour involves sexual exploration and is short-lived. School-based **sex education** is a major source of information for Canadian teens.

Adolescence

Adolescence is bounded by the advent of puberty at the earlier end and by the capacity to take on adult responsibilities at the later. The conflicts and distress experienced by many adolescents apparently reflect the cultural expectations to which they are exposed.

Pubertal changes are ushered in by sex hormones. Puberty begins with the appearance of secondary sex characteristics and ends when the long bones make no further gains in length. Once puberty begins, most major changes in primary sex characteristics occur within three years in girls and within four years in boys.

Masturbation is a major sexual outlet during adolescence. Adolescents today date and "go steady" earlier than in past generations, a change that has apparently increased the incidence of teenage pregnancy. Many adolescents use petting as a way of achieving sexual gratification without becoming pregnant or ending one's virginity. The incidence of premarital intercourse, especially for females, has increased dramatically since Kinsey's day. Most adolescent same-gender sexual encounters are transitory. Coming to terms with adolescence is often more intense for gay males and lesbians, largely because gay male and lesbian sexual orientations are stigmatized in our society. Half of Canadian teens have their first sexual experience by 17.

Rates of **teenage pregnancy** are connected with socioeconomic status. Sexually active teenagers use contraception inconsistently, if at all.

Adulthood

Recent years have seen a sharp increase in the numbers of **single** young people in our society. Reasons include increased permissiveness toward premarital sex and, particularly for women, the desire to become established in a career. No one lifestyle characterizes single people.

The number of Canadian couples **cohabiting** has tripled since 1981. Some couples prefer cohabitation because it provides a consistent intimate relationship without the legal and economic entanglements of marriage. Some emotionally committed couples cohabit because of the economic advantages of sharing household expenses. Cohabitors who later marry may run a greater risk of divorce than noncohabitors, perhaps because cohabitors are a more liberal group.

Marriage is found in all human societies and is our most common lifestyle. In Western society today, romantic love is seen as an essential aspect of marriage. People in Canada tend to marry within their geographical area and social class. They tend to marry people similar to themselves in physical attractiveness, people whose attitudes are similar to their own, and people who seem likely to meet their material, sexual, and psychological needs.

Until the sexual revolution, Western culture could be characterized as sexually restrictive, even in its attitudes toward marital sex. Married couples today engage in coitus more frequently and for longer durations of time than in Kinsey's day. They report higher levels of sexual satisfaction and engage in a greater variety of sexual activities. Canadian women are more likely to reach orgasm through marital sex today than they were in Kinsey's day. Wives take more active sexual roles than in Kinsey's day.

In most cases, extramarital relationships are conducted without the spouse's knowledge or approval. People may have affairs for sexual variety, to punish their spouses, to achieve emotional closeness, or to prove that they are attractive. Precise figures on the prevalence of extramarital sex are lacking. Extramarital sex continues to be viewed negatively by the majority of people in our society. The discovery of infidelity can evoke anger, jealousy, even shame. Affairs often, but not always, damage marriages. Only a small minority of married couples engage in swinging.

About one-third of marriages in Canada end in **divorce**. Reasons include relaxed restrictions on divorce and wider acceptance of the idea that marriages should be happy. Divorce is often associated with financial and emotional problems, including feelings of failure and depression and difficulty rearing children.

Sex in the Later Years

There are a number of unfounded cultural myths about sexuality among older people, including the stereotypes that older people are sexless and that older people with sexual urges are abnormal.

Physical changes as the years pass can impair sexual activity. Many potential problems can be averted by altering expectations and making changes to accommodate the aging process.

Sexual activity tends to decline with age, but continued sexual activity can boost self-esteem and be an important source of gratification.

Sex and Disability

People with disabilities may suffer from prejudice that depicts them as sexless. Most people with **physical disabilities** have the same needs and desires as people without disabilities. Cerebral palsy does not usually impair sexual interest, capacity for orgasm, or fertility, but may limit types of sexual activities and coital positions. People with spinal cord injuries may be paralyzed and lose sensation below the waist. They often respond reflexively to direct genital stimulation. Sensory disabilities do not directly affect sexual response but may impair sexual knowledge and social skills.

Most people with **psychological disabilities,** including developmental disabilities, can learn the basics of their own sexuality and develop responsible intimate relationships.

Chapter Quiz

1. According to Kinsey and his colleagues, children first engage in behaviours that resemble orgasm
   (a) during the first year.
   (b) between the ages of two and five.
   (c) between the ages of five and eight.
   (d) between the ages of eight and adolescence.

2. All of the following are true about teenage pregnancy in Canada EXCEPT
   (a) more than 17 000 babies were born to girls aged 15 to 19.
   (b) Canada's teen pregnancy rate is higher than that of Japan, Switzerland, and Sweden.
   (c) the birth rate for girls aged 15–19 has dropped.
   (d) babies born to teenage mothers are healthier than babies born to mothers in their 20s.

3. Puberty ends
   (a) with the appearance of primary sex characteristics.
   (b) with the appearance of secondary sex characteristics.
   (c) when people take on adult responsibilities.
   (d) when the long bones make no further gains in length.

4. Estrogen is the main cause of all of the following EXCEPT
   (a) growth of the uterus.
   (b) growth of fatty and supporting tissue in the breasts and buttocks.
   (c) growth of underarm and pubic hair.
   (d) thickening of the vaginal lining.

5. Which of the following is connected with abstaining from premarital sexual intercourse among teenagers?
   (a) Curiosity about sex.
   (b) High educational goals.
   (c) Peer pressure.
   (d) Poor communication with one's parents.

6. All of the following are connected with getting married at later ages today EXCEPT
   (a) living together first to test compatibility.
   (b) the desire of many women to focus on careers during their 20s.
   (c) social pressure to remain single.
   (d) lengthy educations.

7. The text suggests that people who cohabit before getting married are more likely to get divorced later on because of
   (a) selection factors.
   (b) recognition that they were incompatible.
   (c) traditional religious values.
   (d) societal condemnation of cohabitation.

8. According to the text, all of the following have contributed to the high divorce rate in Canada EXCEPT
   (a) higher expectations from marriage.
   (b) relaxation of legal restrictions on divorce.
   (c) the secularization of society.
   (d) sexual dysfunctions.

9. In late adulthood
   (a) men's testes increase slightly in size.
   (b) most men do not remain capable of erection.
   (c) most men still like sex.
   (d) testosterone production increases.

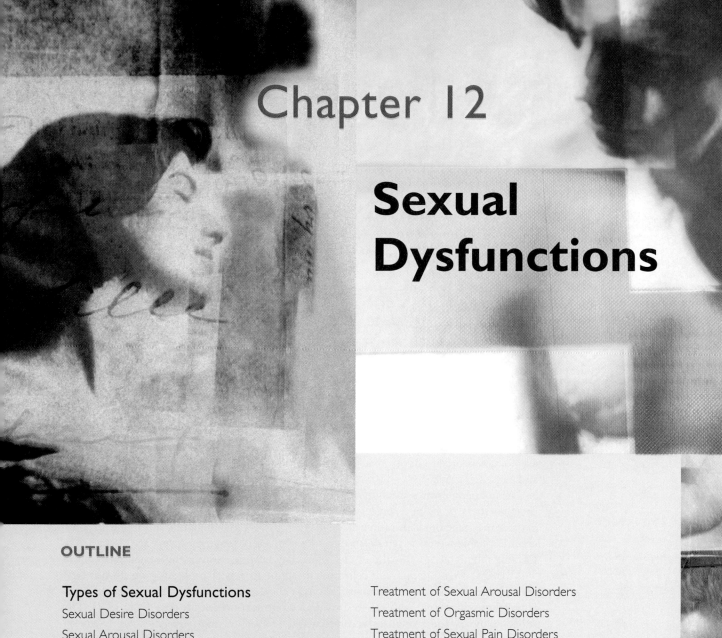

Chapter 12

Sexual Dysfunctions

Did You Know That...

- About one woman in three reports being uninterested in sex?
- About three men in ten report reaching climax too soon?
- The most common cause of painful intercourse in women is inadequate vaginal lubrication?
- Many people have difficulty performing sexually and then find that anxiety over performance makes it yet more difficult to perform the next time?
- In sex therapy, men with erectile disorder are taught that they should not try to obtain an erection?
- Many sex therapists recommend masturbation as the treatment for women who have never been able to reach orgasm?
- A man can be prevented from ejaculating by squeezing his penis when he feels that he is about to do so?
- Drugs are available to treat premature ejaculation and erectile disorder?

Sexual dysfunction A persistent or recurrent difficulty in becoming sexually aroused or reaching orgasm.

Sexual dysfunctions are problems in becoming sexually aroused or reaching orgasm. Many of us are troubled by sexual problems from time to time. Men occasionally cannot obtain an erection, or they ejaculate more rapidly than they would like. Most women occasionally have difficulty reaching orgasm or becoming sufficiently lubricated. People are not considered to have a sexual dysfunction, however, unless the problem is persistent and causes distress.

Many people with sexual dysfunctions find it difficult to talk about them, even with their partners or helping professionals. A woman who cannot reach orgasm with her partner may fake orgasms rather than "make a fuss." A man may find it difficult to admit erectile problems to his physician during a physical. Many physicians are also uncomfortable talking about sexual matters. They may never inquire about sexual problems.

Because many people are reluctant to admit to sexual problems, we do not have precise figures on their frequencies. The best current information we have on the sexual problems of women is the 1998 Canadian Contraception Study (see Table 12.1). This study analyzed the responses received from 1599 Canadian women aged 15 to 44. Respondents were asked if, during the past year, they had experienced any of the following: "My sexual desire is often much lower than I would like it to be; I often experience pain when I have intercourse; I usually do not have an orgasm during intercourse; my partner has had difficulties with premature ejaculation; my partner has had difficulties maintaining an erection" (Fisher, et al., 1999). The most commonly reported problem was low sexual desire (reported by 39% of respondents), followed by difficulties achieving orgasm through intercourse (21%). Problems with orgasm were more common in women aged 18–34 than in women over 35. Women over 35 were more likely to report that their partners had difficulty maintaining an erection (8%) than the younger women were (3%). Unfortunately, information on the sexual problems of Canadian males, based on a comparable national sample, is lacking. However, research suggests that premature ejaculation is the most common male sexual problem, followed by problems with erection (MacNeil & Byers, 1997).

Types of Sexual Dysfunctions

The most widely used system of classification of sexual dysfunctions is based upon the American Psychiatric Association's *Diagnostic and Statistical Manual of Mental Disorders* (DSM-IV, 1994). The DSM, which is now in its fourth edition, groups sexual dysfunctions into four categories:

TABLE 12.1 Current sexual dysfunctions according to the 1998 Canadian Contraception Study

	Percentage of women reporting the problem in the last year
Loss of sexual desire	39%
Unable to reach orgasm during intercourse	21%
Painful intercourse	14%
Partner—Premature ejaculation	5%
Partner—Difficulty in maintaining an erection	5%

Source: Fisher, W.A., et al. (1999). The 1998 Canadian contraception study. *The Canadian Journal of Human Sexuality, 8,* pp. 161-216. By permission.

1. **Sexual desire disorders**. These involve dysfunctions in sexual desire, interest, or drive, in which the person experiences a lack of sexual desire or an aversion to genital sexual contact.

2. **Sexual arousal disorders**. In men, sexual arousal disorders involve recurrent difficulty in achieving or sustaining erections sufficient to successfully engage in sexual intercourse. In women, they typically involve failure to become sufficiently lubricated.

3. **Orgasmic disorders**. Men or women may encounter difficulties achieving orgasm or may reach orgasm more rapidly than they would like. Women are more likely to have trouble reaching orgasm; men are more likely to experience overly rapid orgasm (premature ejaculation).

4. **Sexual pain disorders**. Both men and women may suffer from **dyspareunia** (painful intercourse). Women may experience **vaginismus**, which prevents penetration by the penis or renders penetration painful.

Sexual dysfunctions may also be classified as either lifelong or acquired. *Lifelong* dysfunctions have existed throughout the person's lifetime. *Acquired* dysfunctions develop following a period of normal functioning. They also may be classified as generalized or situational. *Generalized* dysfunctions affect a person's general sexual functioning. *Situational* dysfunctions affect sexual functioning only in some sexual situations (such as during coitus but not during masturbation) or occur with some partners but not with others. For example, a man may not be able to get an erection for sexual relations with a partner but can do so during masturbation. His dysfunction would be classified as situational.

Sexual Desire Disorders

Sexual desire disorders involve lack of sexual desire or interest, or aversion to genital sexual activity. Sex therapists report an increase in their frequency over the past generation (Schmidt, 1994).

Lack of Sexual Desire People with little or no sexual interest or desire are said to have *hypoactive sexual desire disorder*. They also often report an absence of sexual fantasies. According to the NHSLS Study (Laumann et al., 1994), the problem is more common among women than men. Recently, the definition of female hypoactive sexual desire disorder was revised to include the concept of "personal distress" (Basson et al., 2000). This means that periodic loss of sexual interest or desire, or even more lasting loss of desire, is not considered to be a disorder unless the individual is personally distressed by it. In cases where a partner is disturbed by a woman's lack of desire but the woman herself is not concerned, counselling would focus more on relationship conflict than on problems of sexual desire.

Sexual desire disorders Sexual dysfunctions in which people have persistent or recurrent lack of sexual desire or aversion to sexual contact.

Sexual arousal disorders Sexual dysfunctions in which people persistently or recurrently fail to become adequately sexually aroused to engage in or sustain sexual intercourse.

Orgasmic disorders Sexual dysfunctions in which people persistently or recurrently have difficulty reaching orgasm despite attaining a level of sexual stimulation of sufficient intensity to normally result in orgasm, or reach orgasm more rapidly than they would like.

Sexual pain disorders Sexual dysfunctions in which people persistently or recurrently experience pain during coitus.

Dyspareunia A sexual dysfunction characterized by persistent or recurrent pain during sexual intercourse. (From roots meaning "badly paired.")

Vaginismus A sexual dysfunction characterized by involuntary contraction of the muscles surrounding the vaginal barrel, preventing penile penetration or rendering penetration painful.

Lack of sexual desire does not imply that a person is unable to have an erection, lubricate adequately, or reach orgasm. Some people with low sexual desire do have such problems. Others can become sexually aroused and reach orgasm when stimulated adequately. Many enjoy sexual activity, even if they are unlikely to initiate it. Many appreciate the affection and closeness of physical intimacy, but have no interest in genital stimulation.

How much sexual interest or desire is "normal"? There is no standard level of sexual desire—no 37-degree reading on the "sexual thermometer." Lack of desire is usually considered a problem when couples recognize that their level of sexual interest has seriously declined. Sometimes the lack of desire is limited to one partner. When one member of a couple is more interested in sex than the other, sex therapists often recommend that couples try to reach a compromise. They also try to uncover and resolve problems in the relationship that may dampen sexual ardour.

Biological and psychosocial factors—hormonal deficiencies, depression, relationship dissatisfaction, and so on—contribute to lack of desire. A gradual decline in sexual desire, at least among men, may be explained in part by the reduction in testosterone levels that occurs in middle and later life (Brody, 1995b). Abrupt changes in sexual desire, however, are more often explained by psychological and interpersonal factors such as depression, emotional stress, and problems in the relationship (Leiblum & Rosen, 1988; Schreiner-Engle & Schiavi, 1986). Lingering anxiety and a history of sexual assault have also been linked to low sexual desire (Letourneau & O'Donohue, 1993).

Sexual Aversion Disorder People with low sexual desire may have little or no interest in sex, but they are not repelled by genital contact. Some people, however, find sex disgusting or aversive and avoid genital contact.

Sexual aversions are less common than lack of desire and remain poorly understood (Spark, 1991). Some researchers consider sexual aversion to be a *sexual phobia* or *sexual panic state*. It is characterized by intense, irrational fears of sexual contact and a pressing desire to avoid sexual situations (Kaplan, 1987). A history of sexual trauma, such as rape or childhood sexual abuse or incest, often figures prominently in cases of sexual aversion, especially in women.

Sexual Arousal Disorders

Vasocongestion The swelling of the genital tissues with blood, which causes erection of the penis and engorgement of the area surrounding the vaginal opening.

When we are sexually stimulated, our bodies normally respond with **vasocongestion**, which produces erection in the male and vaginal lubrication in the female. People with sexual arousal disorders, however, do not have, or maintain, the lubrication or erection necessary to facilitate sexual activity. Or they do not feel the sexual pleasure and excitement that normally accompany sexual arousal (American Psychiatric Association, 1994).

Male Erectile Disorder Sexual arousal disorder in the male is called **male erectile disorder** or *erectile dysfunction*. It is characterized by persistent difficulty in getting or maintaining an erection sufficient to allow the completion of sexual activity. In most cases the failure is limited to sexual activity with partners, or with some partners and not others. It can thus be classified as *situational*. In rare cases the dysfunction is found during any sexual activity, including masturbation. In such cases, it is considered *generalized*. Some men with erectile disorder are unable to attain an erection at all. Others can get an erection but not sustain it (or recover it) long enough for penetration and ejaculation.

Male erectile disorder Persistent difficulty achieving or maintaining an erection sufficient to allow the man to engage in or complete sexual intercourse. Also termed *erectile dysfunction*.

The incidence of erectile disorder increases with age and it is believed to affect one in three men over the age of 60. Men with *lifelong* erectile disorder never had adequate erectile functioning. Erectile disorder far more commonly develops after a period of normal functioning and is classified as *acquired erectile disorder*.

Performance anxiety Feelings of dread and foreboding experienced in connection with sexual activity (or any other activity that might be judged by another person).

Occasional problems in achieving or maintaining erection are quite common. Fatigue, alcohol, anxiety over impressing a new partner, and other factors may account for a transient episode. Even an isolated occurrence, however, can lead to a persistent problem if the man fears recurrence. The more anxious and concerned the man becomes about his sexual ability, the more likely he is to suffer **performance anxiety**. This anxiety can contribute to repeated failure, and a vicious circle of anxiety and failure may develop.

A man with erectile difficulties may try to "will" an erection, which can compound the problem. Each failure may further demoralize him. He may ruminate about his sexual inadequacy, setting the stage for yet more anxiety. His partner may try to comfort and support him by saying things like "It can happen to anyone," "Don't worry about it," or "It will get better in time." But attempts at reassurance may be to no avail. As one client put it,

> I always felt inferior, like I was on probation, having to prove myself. I felt like I was up against the wall. You can't imagine how embarrassing this (erectile failure) was. It's like you walk out in front of an audience that you think is a nudist convention and it turns out to be a tuxedo convention.

(THE AUTHORS' FILES)

The vicious circle of anxiety and erectile failure may be interrupted if the man does not overreact to occasional problems. However, the emphasis in our culture on men's sexual prowess may spur them to view occasional failures as catastrophes rather than transient disappointments.

Performance anxiety is a prominent cause of erectile disorder. So are other psychological factors such as depression, lack of self-esteem, and problems in the relationship (Leary, 1992). Biological factors can also play a causative role.

Female Sexual Arousal Disorder Women with sexual arousal disorder may have trouble becoming sexually excited or sufficiently lubricated in response to sexual stimulation. The problem can be lifelong or acquired, generalized or situational, and is the most commonly reported sexual problem in women (Fisher et al., 1999).

Female sexual arousal disorder, like its male counterpart, may have physical causes (Graber, 1993). A thorough evaluation by a medical specialist (a urologist in the case of a male; a gynecologist in the case of a female) is recommended. Any neurological, vascular, or hormonal problem that interferes with the lubrication or swelling response of the vagina to sexual stimulation may contribute to female sexual arousal disorder. For example, diabetes mellitus may lead to diminished sexual excitement in women because of blood vessel (vascular) damage or the degeneration of the nerves servicing the clitoris. Reduced estrogen production can also result in vaginal dryness.

However, female sexual arousal disorder more commonly has psychological causes. In some cases, women feel anger and resentment toward their partners. They may be exhausted from domestic responsibilities and resentful of partners who offer little support or affection. As one family physician has observed, "In short, if she's mad at him for not doing his share, why would she want to have sex with him?" (Candib, 2001). Many women find it difficult to turn off these feelings when they go to bed. In other cases, sexual trauma is involved. Survivors of sexual abuse—especially child sexual abuse—often find it difficult to respond sexually to their partners (Morokoff, 1993). Feelings of helplessness, anger, or guilt, or even flashbacks of the abuse, may surface when the woman begins sexual activity. Other psychosocial causes include anxiety or guilt about sex and ineffective stimulation by the partner (Morokoff, 1993).

Orgasmic Disorders

Three disorders concern the orgasm phase of the sexual response cycle: (1) female orgasmic disorder, (2) male orgasmic disorder, and (3) premature ejaculation.

In female or male orgasmic disorder, the woman or man is persistently delayed in reaching orgasm or does not reach orgasm at all, despite sexual stimulation of sufficient intensity to normally result in orgasm. The problem is more common among women than men. In some cases a person can reach orgasm without difficulty while engaging in sexual relations with one partner, but not with another.

Male Orgasmic Disorder Male orgasmic disorder may be lifelong or acquired, generalized or situational. In most cases the disorder is limited to coitus. The man may be capable of ejaculating during masturbation or oral sex, but find it difficult, if not impossible—despite high levels of sexual excitement—to ejaculate during intercourse.

Male Impotence
www.crha-health.ab.ca/ hlthconn/topics/mens.htm
Information on male impotence from the Calgary Health Region. Discusses causes, diagnosis, and treatment of impotence.

Female Sexual Dysfunction (FSD): A New Medical Myth
www.fsd-alert.org/
An educational campaign to challenge the medicalization of female sexual dysfunction and to examine female sexual problems from a feminist perspective.

Male orgasmic disorder is not common (Dekker, 1993). Research on the problem has been scarce (Dekker, 1993), and only a few case reports have appeared in the literature (e.g., Masters & Johnson, 1970; Rathus, 1978).

Male orgasmic disorder may be caused by physical problems such as multiple sclerosis (Kedia, 1983) or neurological damage that interferes with neural control of ejaculation. It may also be a side effect of certain drugs. Psychological factors, including performance anxiety, sexual guilt, and hostility toward the partner, may play a role. Helen Singer Kaplan (1974) suggests that some men with male orgasmic disorder may be unconsciously "holding back" their ejaculate from their partners because of underlying hostility or resentment. Masters and Johnson (1970) found that men with this problem frequently have strict religious backgrounds that may leave a residue of unresolved guilt about sex, which inhibits ejaculation. Fear of pregnancy or anger toward one's partner can also play a role.

Female Orgasmic Disorder
Women with female orgasmic disorder experience personal distress because they are unable to reach orgasm or have difficulty reaching orgasm following what would usually be an adequate amount of sexual stimulation. A woman who reaches orgasm through masturbation or oral sex may not necessarily reach orgasm dependably during coitus with her partner (Stock, 1993). Penile thrusting during coitus may not provide sufficient clitoral stimulation to facilitate orgasm. However, if this lack of orgasm during intercourse does not lead to personal distress then the diagnosis of female orgasmic disorder is not appropriate. Women who have never reached orgasm through any means are sometimes labelled **anorgasmic** or *preorgasmic*.

Women who try to force an orgasm may also find themselves unable to do so. They may assume a **spectator role** and observe, rather than fully participate in, their sexual encounters. "Spectatoring" may further decrease the likelihood of orgasm.

Premature Ejaculation
Premature ejaculation was the most common male sexual dysfunction reported in Canada (MacNeil & Byers, 1997). Men with this problem ejaculate too rapidly to permit their partners or themselves to fully enjoy sexual relations. The degree of prematurity varies. Some men ejaculate during foreplay, even at the sight of their partner disrobing. But most ejaculate either just prior to or immediately upon penetration, or following a few coital thrusts (Kaplan, 1974).

Just what makes an ejaculation "premature"? Some definitions focus on a particular time period during which a man should be able to control ejaculation. Is ejaculation within 30 seconds of intromission premature? Within one minute? Ten minutes? There is no clear cutoff. Some scholars argue that the focus should be on whether the couple is satisfied with the duration of coitus rather than on a specific time period.

Rapid Female Orgasm: Can Women Reach Orgasm Too Quickly?
The female counterpart to premature ejaculation, rapid orgasm, is so rarely recognized as a problem that it is generally ignored by clinicians and is not classified as a sexual dysfunction in the DSM. Still, some women experience orgasm rapidly and show little interest in continuing sexual activity so that their partners can receive gratification. Other women who reach orgasm rapidly are open to continued sexual stimulation and capable of experiencing successive orgasms.

Sexual Pain Disorders

For most of us, coitus is a source of pleasure. For some of us, however, coitus gives rise to pain and discomfort.

Dyspareunia
Dyspareunia, or painful coitus, can afflict men or women. Dyspareunia is one of the most common sexual dysfunctions and is also a common complaint of women seeking gynecological services (Quevillon, 1993). As many as 14% of women report this problem (Fisher, et al., 1999).

Pain is a sign that something is wrong—physically or psychologically. Dyspareunia may result from physical causes, emotional factors, or an interaction of the two (Meana

Anorgasmic Never having reached orgasm. (Literally, "without orgasm.")

Spectator role A role, usually taken on because of performance anxiety, in which people mentally observe rather than fully participate in their sexual encounters.

Premature ejaculation A sexual dysfunction in which the male persistently ejaculates too early to afford the couple adequate sexual gratification.

& Binik, 1994). Some question the accuracy of describing dyspareunia as a sexual problem and suggest that it is more helpful for the patient to view the condition as a chronic pain problem with sexual concerns resulting from the pain (Bourgeois-Law, 2001; Meana et al., 1997). The most common cause of coital pain in women is inadequate lubrication. In such a case, additional foreplay or artificial lubrication may help. Vaginal infections or sexually transmitted infections (STIs) may also produce coital pain. Allergic reactions to spermicides, even the latex material in condoms, can give rise to coital pain or irritation. Pain during deep thrusting may be caused by endometriosis or pelvic inflammatory disease (PID), by other diseases or structural disorders of the reproductive organs, or by penile contact with the cervix.

Psychological factors may also be involved, such as unresolved guilt or anxiety about sex or the lingering effects of sexual trauma. These factors may inhibit lubrication and cause involuntary contractions of the vaginal musculature, making penetration painful or uncomfortable.

Painful intercourse is less common in men and is generally associated with genital infections that cause burning or painful ejaculation. Smegma under the penile foreskin of uncircumcised men may also irritate the penile glans during sexual contact.

Vaginismus Vaginismus involves an involuntary contraction of the pelvic muscles that surround the outer third of the vaginal barrel. Vaginismus occurs reflexively during attempts at vaginal penetration, making entry by the penis painful or impossible. These reflexive contractions are accompanied by a deep-seated fear of penetration (Beck, 1993). Some women with vaginismus are unable to tolerate penetration by any object, including a finger, tampon, or a physician's speculum. Nevertheless, the woman with vaginismus usually is not aware that she is contracting her vaginal muscles.

Vaginismus is caused by a psychological fear of penetration, not by a physical injury or defect. Women with vaginismus often have histories of sexual trauma, rape, or botched abortions. They may desire sexual relations. They may be capable of becoming sexually aroused and achieving orgasm. However, fear of penetration triggers an involuntary spasm of the vaginal musculature at the point of penile insertion.

Vaginismus can be a *cause* or an *effect* of dyspareunia. Fear leads to involuntary vaginal contractions. Women with vaginismus may also experience pain if the couple tries to force penetration. Vaginismus and dyspareunia may also give rise to, or result from, erectile disorder in men (Speckens et al., 1995). Feelings of failure and anxiety come to overwhelm both partners.

Origins of Sexual Dysfunctions

Since sexual dysfunctions involve the sex organs, it was once assumed that they stemmed largely from organic or physical causes. Today it is accepted that both organic and psychological factors are important to varying degrees with different disorders. Many cases involve the interaction of both physical and psychological factors (Meisler & Carey, 1990; Mohr & Beutler, 1990).

Organic Causes

Physical factors, such as fatigue and lowered testosterone levels, can dampen sexual desire and reduce responsiveness. Testosterone deficiencies, thyroid problems, and epilepsy can all diminish sexual desire (Kresin, 1993). Sexual desire is stoked by testosterone, which is produced by men in the testes and by both genders in the adrenal glands. Women may experience less sexual desire when their adrenal glands are surgically removed. Low sexual interest, along with erectile difficulties, is also common among men with **hypogonadism**. (Hypogonadism is treated with testosterone [Brody, 1995b; Carani et al., 1990].) However, women with low sexual desire usually have normal levels of the hormones testosterone, estrogen, and progesterone (Schreiner-Engle et al., 1989; Stuart et al., 1987). The role of hormones in lack of desire among healthy people remains unclear.

Hypogonadism An endocrine disorder that reduces the output of testosterone.

Some medications, such as those used to control anxiety, allergies, or hypertension, may also reduce desire. Changing medications or dosage levels may return the person's previous level of desire.

Fatigue may cause erectile disorder and orgasmic disorder in men. It can cause orgasmic disorder and inadequate lubrication in women. These will be isolated incidents unless the person attaches too much meaning to them and becomes concerned about future performances. Various medical conditions can affect orgasmic functioning in both men and women, including diabetes mellitus, multiple sclerosis, spinal-cord injuries, complications from certain surgical procedures (such as removal of the prostate in men), endocrinological problems, and use of some pharmacological agents, such as drugs used to treat hypertension and psychiatric disorders (Segraves & Segraves, 1993). Painful coitus, however, often reflects organic problems such as infections.

It was once believed that 95% of cases of erectile disorder resulted from psychological causes (Masters & Johnson, 1970). It is now thought that organic factors are also widely involved (Rajfer et al., 1992). Psychological factors such as anxiety or depression may serve to perpetuate or exacerbate the problem even when there are underlying organic causes.

Organic causes of erectile disorder affect the flow of blood to and through the penis or damage to nerves involved in erection (Appell, 1986; Spark, 1991). Rajfer and his colleagues (1992) believe that most cases of erectile disorder involve failure of the body to produce sufficient quantities of the substance nitric oxide. When nitric oxide comes into contact with the muscles encircling blood vessels in the penis, the muscles relax, allowing vasocongestion to occur and causing the penis to swell. One treatment approach to erectile disorder is to inject the penis with a chemical that raises nitric oxide

A World of Diversity

Inis Beag and Mangaia— Worlds Apart

Let us invite you on a journey back in time and to two islands that are a world apart—sexually as well as geographically. We are going to accompany researchers on two classic anthropological expeditions to two quite different societies. The sexual attitudes and practices present at that time within these societies will shed some light on the role of cultural values in determining what is sexually normal and what is sexually dysfunctional.

Our first stop is the island of Inis Beag, which lies off the misty coast of Ireland. From the air Inis Beag was a green jewel, fertile and inviting. At ground level things did not appear quite so warm, however.

The residents of this Irish community did not believe that it was normal for women to experience orgasm. Anthropologist John Messenger (1971), who visited Inis Beag in the 1950s and 1960s, reported that any woman

who found pleasure in sex—especially the intense waves of pleasure that can accompany orgasm—was viewed as deviant. *Should women on Inis Beag, then, have been diagnosed as orgasmically impaired?*

Premarital sex was all but unknown on Inis Beag. Prior to marriage, men and women socialized apart. Marriage came relatively late—usually in the middle 30s for men and the middle 20s for women. Mothers taught their daughters that they would have to submit to their husbands' animal cravings in order to obey God's injunction to "be fruitful and multiply." After this indoctrination, women showed little interest in sex. *Should they be diagnosed as having hypoactive sexual desire?*

The women of Inis Beag did not need to be overly concerned about frequent sexual intercourse, however, since the men of the island believed that sexual activity would drain their strength. Consequently, men avoided sex on the eve of sporting activity or strenuous work. Because of taboos against nudity, married couples engaged in intercourse with their underclothes on. Intercourse

took place in the dark—literally as well as figuratively.

During intercourse the man took the male-superior position. The male was always the initiator. Foreplay was brief, rarely involving manual stimulation of the breasts and never including oral stimulation of the genitals. *Should people who have difficulty becoming sexually aroused under these circumstances be diagnosed as having sexual arousal disorders?* The man ejaculated as rapidly as he could, in the belief that he was the only partner with sexual needs and to spare his wife as best he could. Then he turned over and rapidly fell asleep. Once more the couple had done their duty. *Since the man ejaculated rapidly, should he be diagnosed as having premature ejaculation?*

Our next stop is Mangaia. Mangaia is a Polynesian pearl of an island. It lifts languidly out of the blue waters of the Pacific. It lies on the other side of the world from Inis Beag—in more ways than one. The sexual attitudes observed by researchers were quite different from those of the Irish island.

From an early age, Mangaian boys

levels and thus relaxes the penile muscles to permit blood to flow more freely. Erectile problems can also arise from clogged or narrow arteries to the penis (Lipschultz, 1996), diabetes, multiple sclerosis, syphilis, kidney disease, hypertension, cancer, emphysema, heart disease, and endocrine disorders.

Prescription drugs and illicit drugs are believed to account for one in four cases of erectile disorder (Leary, 1992). Antidepressant medication and antipsychotic drugs may impair erectile functioning and cause orgasmic disorders (Segraves, 1988b; Spark, 1991). Tranquillizers like Valium and Xanax may cause orgasmic disorder in either gender (Segraves, 1988b).

Women may also encounter vascular or nerve disorders that impair genital blood flow, reducing lubrication and sexual excitement, rendering intercourse painful, and reducing their ability to reach orgasm.

People with sexual dysfunctions are advised to undergo a physical examination to determine whether their problems are biologically based. Men with erectile disorder may be evaluated in a sleep centre to determine whether they attain erections while asleep. Healthy men usually have erections during rapid-eye-movement (REM) sleep, which occurs every 90 to 100 minutes. Men with organically based erectile disorder often do not have nocturnal erections. However, this technique, called nocturnal penile **tumescence** (NPT), may lead to misleading results in perhaps 20% of cases (Meisler & Carey, 1990). NPT may thus be helpful but not definitive in suggesting whether erectile disorder is organically based (Mohr & Beutler, 1990).

Central nervous system depressants such as alcohol, heroin, and morphine can reduce sexual desire and impair sexual arousal (Segraves, 1988a). Heavy drinking can damage the nerves that control erection and ejaculation (Spark, 1991). Narcotics also depress testosterone production, which can further reduce sexual desire and lead to erectile failure (Spark, 1991).

Tumescence Swelling; erection. (From the Latin *tumere*, meaning "to swell." *Tumour* has the same root.)

and girls were encouraged to get in touch with their own sexuality through sexual play and masturbation (Marshall, 1971). At about the age of 13, Mangaian boys were initiated into manhood by adults who instructed them in sexual techniques. Mangaian males were taught the merit of bringing their female partners to multiple orgasms before ejaculating. *Were Mangaian males who ejaculated before their partners had multiple orgasms suffering from premature ejaculation?*

Boys practised their new techniques with girlfriends on secluded beaches or beneath the listing fronds of palms. They sometimes visited girlfriends in the evening in the huts where they slept with their families. Parents often listened for their daughters to laugh and gasp so that they would know that their daughters had reached orgasm with a visiting young man, called a "sleepcrawler." Usually they pretended to be asleep so as not to interfere with courtship and impede their daughters' chances of finding a suitable mate. Daughters might receive a nightly succession of sleepcrawlers.

Girls, too, learned techniques of coitus from their elders. Typically they were initiated by an experienced male relative. Mangaians looked on virginity with disdain, because virgins did not know how to provide sexual pleasure. Thus, the older relative made his contribution to the family by initiating the girl.

Mangaians, by the way, expressed concern when they learned that many European and U.S. women did not regularly experience orgasm during coitus. Orgasm was apparently universal among Mangaian women. Therefore, Mangaians could only assume that Western women suffered from some abnormality of the sex organs. *Do they?*

All in all, the sharp contrasts between Inis Beag and Mangaia illustrate how concepts of normality are embedded within a cultural context. Behaviour that is judged to be normal in one culture may be regarded as abnormal in another. How might our own cultural expectations influence our judgments about sexual dysfunction?

Polynesia. *Cultural expectations affect our judgments as to what kinds of sexual behaviour are functional and dysfunctional. Some Polynesian cultures are sexually permissive. They encourage children to explore their sexuality. Men may be expected to bring their partners to orgasm several times before ejaculating. In such cultures, should men who ejaculate before their partners have multiple orgasms be diagnosed with premature ejaculation?*

Psychosocial Causes

Psychosocial factors connected with sexual dysfunctions include cultural influences, psychosexual trauma, relationship dissatisfaction, lack of sexual skills, and performance anxiety.

Cultural Influences Children reared in sexually repressive cultural or home environments may learn to respond to sex with feelings of anxiety and shame, rather than sexual arousal and pleasure. People whose parents instilled in them a sense of guilt over touching their genitals may find it difficult to accept their sex organs as sources of pleasure.

Despite the sexual revolution, women are more likely than men in our culture to be taught to repress their sexual desires and even to fear their sexuality (Nichols, 1990). Self-control and vigilance—not sexual awareness and acceptance—become identified as feminine virtues. Many women who are exposed to negative attitudes about sex during childhood and adolescence find it difficult to suddenly view sex as a source of pleasure and satisfaction once they are married. A lifetime of inhibiting sexual impulses may lead to problems in sexual response when an acceptable opportunity arises (Morokoff, 1993). Women may also feel inadequate if their body does not measure up to the cultural standards of feminine beauty and sexuality glorified in North American society. Feelings of inadequacy or shame can lead to sexual inhibition or avoidance (The Working Group for a New View of Women's Sexual Problems, 2001).

Psychosexual Trauma Sexual stimuli may bring about anxiety when they have been paired with painful experiences, such as rape, incest, or sexual molestation. Strong conditioned anxiety can stifle sexual arousal. Unresolved anger and misplaced guilt can also make it difficult for victims of rape and other sexual traumas to respond sexually, even years afterward. People who have been sexually victimized may harbour feelings of disgust and revulsion toward sex, or deep-seated fears of sex that make it difficult for them to respond sexually, even with loving partners.

Ineffective Sexual Techniques In some relationships, couples practise a narrow range of sexual techniques. Perhaps they have fallen into a routine. A man who remains unknowledgeable about the erotic importance of the clitoris may be unlikely to provide direct clitoral stimulation, and a woman who is uncomfortable with her own body may not be able to tell her partner what stimulation she needs. The couple who fail to communicate their sexual preferences or to experiment with altering their sexual techniques may find themselves losing interest. Brevity of foreplay and coitus may contribute to female orgasmic disorder.

Emotional Factors Orgasm involves a sudden loss of voluntary control. Fear of losing control or letting go may block sexual arousal. Other emotional factors, especially depression, are often implicated in sexual dysfunctions (Beck, 1988). People who are depressed frequently report lessened sexual interest and may find it difficult to respond sexually. Stress may also lessen sexual interest and response.

Problems in the Relationship Problems in the relationship are important and often pivotal factors in sexual dysfunctions (Catalan et al., 1990; Fish et al., 1994; Leiblum & Rosen, 1991). Couples usually find that their sexual relationships are no better than the other facets of their relationships. Research has shown that couples who experience greater relationship satisfaction are less likely to report sexual problems (Byers, 2001). Couples who harbour resentments toward one another may make sex their arena of combat. They may fail to become aroused by their partners or "withhold" orgasm to make their partners feel guilty or inadequate.

Troubled relationships are usually characterized by poor communication. Partners who have difficulty communicating about other matters may be unlikely to communicate their sexual desires to each other.

Psychological Conflicts Within Freud's psychoanalytic theory, sexual dysfunctions are rooted in the failure to successfully resolve the Oedipus or Electra complexes of early childhood. Sexual encounters in adulthood arouse unconscious anxieties and hostilities that are believed to reflect unresolved conflicts, thereby inhibiting sexual response.

A modern psychoanalytic theorist, Helen Singer Kaplan (1974), believed that sexual dysfunctions represent an interaction of immediate causes (such as poor techniques, marital conflict, performance anxiety, and lack of effective communication) and deep-seated or remote causes (such as unresolved childhood conflicts that predispose people to encounter sexual anxiety and hostility in adulthood). Kaplan recommended combining direct behavioural techniques, which deal with the immediate causes of sexual dysfunctions, with psychoanalytic techniques that deal with the remote causes.

Lack of Sexual Skills Sexual competency involves the acquisition of sexual knowledge and skills. We generally learn what makes us and others feel good through trial and error and by talking and reading about sex. Some people may not develop sexual competency because of a lack of opportunity to acquire knowledge and experience—even within a relationship. People with sexual dysfunctions may have been reared in families in which discussions of sexuality were off limits and early sexual experimentation was harshly punished. Such early influences may have squelched the young person's sexual learning and experimentation or led her or him to associate anxiety or guilt with sex.

Irrational Beliefs Psychologist Albert Ellis (1962, 1977) points out that irrational beliefs and attitudes may contribute to sexual dysfunctions. Negative feelings like anxiety and fear, Ellis submits, do not stem directly from the events we experience, but rather from our interpretations of these events. If a person encounters a certain event, such as an isolated instance of not becoming erect or not reaching orgasm, and then believes that the event is awful or catastrophic, he or she will exaggerate feelings of disappointment and set the stage for future problems.

Performance Anxiety Anxiety—especially performance anxiety—plays an important role in the development of sexual dysfunctions. Performance anxiety occurs when a person becomes overly concerned with how well he or she performs a certain act or task. Performance anxiety may place a dysfunctional individual in a spectator rather than a performer role. Rather than focusing on erotic sensations and allowing involuntary responses like erection, lubrication, and orgasm to occur naturally, he or she focuses on self-doubts and fears, and thinks, "Will I be able to do it this time? Will this be another failure?"

Performance anxiety can set the stage for a vicious circle in which a sexual failure increases anxiety. Anxiety then leads to repeated failure, and so on. Sex therapists emphasize the need to break this vicious circle by removing the need to perform.

In men, performance anxiety can inhibit erection while also triggering a premature ejaculation. (Erection, mediated by the parasympathetic nervous system, can be blocked by activation of the sympathetic nervous system in the form of anxiety. Since ejaculation, like anxiety, is mediated by the sympathetic nervous system, arousal of this system in the form of anxiety can increase the level of stimulation and thereby heighten the potential for premature ejaculation.)

In women, performance anxiety can reduce vaginal lubrication and contribute to orgasmic disorder. Women with performance anxieties may try to force an orgasm, only to find that the harder they try, the more elusive it becomes.

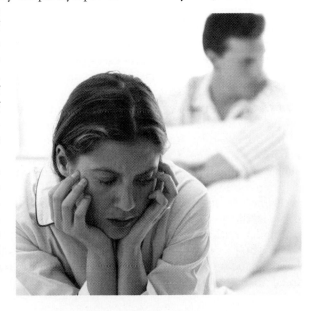

A Failure to Communicate.
Problems in communication cause or exacerbate sexual problems. It is irrational to believe that one's partner would know what to do if she or he "really loved me." Sex therapy enhances communication skills.

Treatment of Sexual Dysfunctions

When Kinsey conducted his surveys in the 1930s and 1940s, there was no effective treatment for sexual dysfunctions. At the time the predominant model of therapy for sexual dysfunctions was long-term psychoanalysis. Psychoanalysts believed that the sexual problem would abate only if the presumed unconscious conflicts that lay at the root of the problem were resolved through long-term therapy. Evidence of the effectiveness of psychoanalysis in treating sexual dysfunctions is still lacking, however.

Since that time behavioural models of short-term treatment, collectively called **sex therapy**, have emerged. These models aim to modify the dysfunctional behaviour as directly as possible. Sex therapists also recognize the roles of childhood conflicts, self-defeating attitudes, and the quality of the partners' relationship. Therefore, they draw upon various forms of therapy, as needed (LoPiccolo, 1994; Rosen et al., 1994).

Although the particular approaches vary, sex therapies aim to:

1. Change self-defeating beliefs and attitudes
2. Teach sexual skills
3. Enhance sexual knowledge
4. Improve sexual communication
5. Reduce performance anxiety

Sex therapy usually involves both partners, although individual therapy is preferred in some cases. Therapists find that granting people "permission" to sexually experiment or discuss negative attitudes about sex helps many people overcome sexual problems without the need for more intensive therapy.

While reading the following sections, it is important to keep in mind that the treatments outlined were originally formulated for use with heterosexual couples. Therapists who work with lesbian, gay, bisexual, and transgendered individuals point out that such treatments are not necessarily appropriate for use with their clients because of this heterosexual bias (Nichols, 2000; Sandfort and de Keizer, 2001; Hall, 2002). More research is needed to understand the issues that contribute to sexual dysfunction in the non-heterosexual population, so that therapeutic interventions can be used effectively.

Let us begin with the groundbreaking work of Masters and Johnson.

The Masters and Johnson Approach

Masters and Johnson pioneered the use of direct behavioural approaches to treating sexual dysfunctions (Masters & Johnson, 1970). A female–male therapy team focuses on the couple as the unit of treatment during a two-week residential program. Masters and Johnson consider the couple, not the individual, dysfunctional. A couple may describe the husband's erectile disorder as the problem, but this problem is likely to have led to problems in the couple by the time they seek therapy. Similarly, a man whose wife has an orgasmic disorder is likely to be anxious about his ability to provide effective sexual stimulation.

The dual-therapist team permits each partner to discuss problems with a member of his or her own gender. It reduces the chance of therapist bias in favour of the female or male partner. It allows each partner to hear concerns expressed by another member of the other gender. Anxieties and resentments are aired, but the focus of treatment is behavioural change. Couples perform daily sexual homework assignments, such as **sensate focus exercises**, in the privacy of their own rooms.

Sensate focus sessions are carried out in the nude. Partners take turns giving and receiving stimulation in nongenital areas of the body. Without touching the breasts or genitals, the giver massages or fondles the receiving partner in order to provide pleasure under relaxing and nondemanding conditions. Since genital activity is restricted, there is no pressure to perform. The giving partner is freed to engage in trial-and-error learning about the receiving partner's sensate preferences. The receiving partner is also freed to enjoy the experience without feeling rushed to reciprocate or obliged to

Sex therapy A collective term for short-term behavioural models for treatment of sexual dysfunctions.

Sensate focus exercises Exercises in which sex partners take turns giving and receiving pleasurable stimulation in nongenital areas of the body.

perform by becoming sexually aroused. The receiving partner's only responsibility is to direct the giving partner as needed. In addition to these general sensate focus exercises, Masters and Johnson used specific assignments designed to help couples overcome particular sexual dysfunctions.

Masters and Johnson were pioneers in the development of sex therapy. Yet many sex therapists have departed from the Masters and Johnson format. Many do not treat clients in an intensive residential program. Many question the necessity of female–male therapist teams. Researchers find that one therapist, regardless of gender, is about as effective as two (Libman et al., 1985). Nor does the therapeutic benefit seem to depend to any great extent on whether the sessions are conducted within a short period of time, as in the Masters and Johnson approach, or spaced over time (Libman et al., 1985). Therapists have also departed from the Masters and Johnson approach by working individually with preorgasmic women rather than with the couple.

The Helen Singer Kaplan Approach

Kaplan (1974) called her approach *psychosexual therapy*. Psychosexual therapy combines behavioural and psychoanalytic methods. Kaplan, as noted, believed that sexual dysfunctions have both *immediate* causes and *remote* causes (childhood conflicts). Kaplan began therapy with the behavioural approach. She focused on improving the couple's communication, eliminating performance anxiety, and fostering sexual skills and knowledge. She used a brief form of insight-oriented therapy when it appeared that remote causes impede response to the behavioural program. In so doing, she hoped to bring to awareness unconscious conflicts that she believed stifle a person's sexual desires or responsiveness. Although Kaplan reported a number of successful case studies, there are no controlled studies demonstrating that the combination of behavioural and insight-oriented, or psychoanalytic, techniques is more effective than the behavioural techniques alone.

Let us now consider some of the specific techniques that sex therapists have introduced in treating several of the major types of sexual dysfunction.

Treatment of Sexual Desire Disorders

Some sex therapists help kindle the sexual appetites of people with hypoactive sexual desire by prescribing self-stimulation exercises combined with erotic fantasies (LoPiccolo & Friedman, 1988). Sex therapists may also assist dysfunctional couples by prescribing sensate focus exercises, enhancing communication, and expanding the couple's repertoire of sexual skills. Sex therapists recognize that hypoactive sexual desire is often a complex problem that requires more intensive treatment than do problems of the arousal or orgasm phases (Leiblum & Rosen, 1988). Helen Singer Kaplan (1987) argued that insight-oriented approaches are especially helpful in the treatment of hypoactive sexual desire and sexual aversion to help people with deep-seated conflicts.

When lack of desire is connected with depression, sexual interests may rebound when the depression lifts. Treatment in such cases may involve psychotherapy or drug therapy, not sex therapy per se. When problems in the relationship are involved, marital or couples therapy may be indicated to improve the relationship. Once interpersonal problems are ironed out, sexual interest may return.

Treatment of sexual aversion disorder may involve medications to reduce anxiety and psychological treatments designed to help the individual overcome the underlying sexual phobia. Couples therapy may be used in cases in which sexual aversions arise from problems in relationships (Gold & Gold, 1993). Sensate focus exercises may be used to lessen generalized anxiety about sexual contact. But fears of specific aspects of the sexual act may need to be overcome through behavioural exercises in which the client learns to manage the stimuli that evoke fears of sexual contact:

> Bridget, 26, and Bryan, 30, were married for four years but had never consummated their relationship because Bridget would panic whenever Bryan

attempted coitus with her. While she enjoyed foreplay and was capable of achieving orgasm with clitoral stimulation, her fears of sexual contact were triggered by Bryan's attempts at vaginal penetration. The therapist employed a program of gradual exposure to the feared stimuli to allow Bridget the opportunity to overcome her fears in small, graduated steps. First she was instructed to view her genitals in a mirror when she was alone—this in order to violate her long-standing prohibition against looking at and enjoying her body. While this exercise initially made her feel anxious, with repeated exposure she became comfortable performing it and then progressed to touching her genitals directly. When she became comfortable with this step, and reported experiencing pleasurable erotic sensations, she was instructed to insert a finger into the vagina. She encountered intense anxiety at this step and required daily practice for two weeks before she could tolerate inserting her finger into her vagina without discomfort. Her husband was then brought into the treatment process. The couple was instructed to have Bridget insert her own finger in her vagina while Bryan watched. When she was comfortable with this exercise, she then guided his finger into her vagina. Later he placed one and then two fingers into her vagina, while she controlled the depth, speed and duration of penetration. When she felt ready, they proceeded to attempt penile penetration in the female superior position, which allowed her to maintain control over penetration. Over time, Bridget became more comfortable with penetration to the point that the couple developed a normal sexual relationship.

(ADAPTED FROM KAPLAN, 1987, PP. 102–103)

Treatment of Sexual Arousal Disorders

Men with chronic erectile disorder may believe that they have "forgotten" how to have an erection. They may ask their therapists to "teach" them or "show them" how. Erection is an involuntary reflex, however, not a skill. A man need not learn how to have an erection any more than he need learn how to breathe. The descriptions that follow refer to hetersosexual couples, but any of the treatments for male arousal disorders can be used by gay male couples as well.

In sex therapy, women who have trouble becoming lubricated and men with erectile problems learn that they need not do anything to become sexually aroused. As long as their problems are psychologically and not organically based, they need only receive sexual stimulation under relaxed circumstances so that anxiety does not inhibit their natural reflexes.

In order to reduce performance anxiety, the partners engage in nondemanding sexual contacts: contacts that do not demand lubrication or erection. They may start with nongenital sensate focus exercises in the style of Masters and Johnson. After a couple of sessions, sensate focus extends to the genitals. The position shown in Figure 12.1 allows the woman easy access to her partner's genitals. She repeatedly "teases" him to erection and allows the erection to subside. Thus she avoids creating performance anxiety that could lead to loss of erection. By repeatedly regaining his erection, the man loses the fear that loss of erection means it will not return. He learns also to focus on erotic sensations for their own sake. He experiences no demand to perform, as the couple is instructed to refrain from coitus.

When the dysfunctional partner can consistently become sexually excited (denoted by erection in the male and lubrication in the female), the couple does not immediately attempt coitus, since this might rekindle performance anxiety. Rather, the couple engages in a series of nondemanding, pleasurable sexual activities, eventually culminating in coitus.

In Masters and Johnson's approach, the couple begin coitus after about 10 days of treatment. The woman teases the man to erection while she is sitting above him,

Figure 12.1. The Training Position Recommended by Masters and Johnson for Treatment of Erectile Disorder and Premature Ejaculation.

Lying in front of her partner, who has his legs spread, the woman has ready access to his genitals. In one part of a program designed to overcome erectile disorder, she repeatedly "teases" him to erection and allows the erection to subside. Thus she avoids creating performance anxiety that could lead to loss of erection. Through repeated regaining of erection, the man loses the fear that loss of erection means it will not return.

straddling his thighs. When he is erect, she inserts the penis—to avoid fumbling attempts at entry—and moves slowly back and forth in a *nondemanding* way. Neither attempts to reach orgasm. If erection is lost, teasing and coitus are repeated. Once the couple become confident that erection can be retained—or regained if lost—they may increase coital thrusting gradually to reach orgasm.

Treatment of Orgasmic Disorders

Women who have never experienced orgasm often harbour negative sexual attitudes that cause anxiety and inhibit sexual response. Treatment in such cases may first address these attitudes.

Masters and Johnson use a couples-oriented approach in treating anorgasmic women. They begin with sensate focus exercises. Then, during genital massage and later during coitus, the woman guides her partner in the caresses and movements that she finds sexually exciting. Taking charge helps free the woman, psychologically speaking, from the traditional stereotype of the passive, subordinate female role.

Masters and Johnson recommend a training position (see Figure 12.2) that gives the man access to his partner's breasts and genitals. She can guide his hands to show him the types of stimulation she enjoys. The genital play is nondemanding. The goals are to learn to provide and enjoy effective sexual stimulation, not to reach orgasm. The clitoris is not stimulated early, since doing so may produce a high level of stimulation before the woman is prepared.

After a number of occasions of genital play, the couple undertake coitus in the female-superior position (see Figure 12.3). This position allows the woman freedom of

Figure 12.2. The Training Position for Nondemanding Stimulation of the Female Genitals.

This position gives the man access to his partner's breasts and genitals. She can guide his hands to show him the types of stimulation she enjoys.

movement and control over her genital sensations. She is told to regard the penis as her "toy." The couple engages in several sessions of deliberately slow thrusting to sensitize the woman to sensations produced by the penis and break the common counter-productive pattern of desperate, rapid thrusting.

Orgasm cannot be willed or forced. When a woman receives effective stimulation, feels free to focus on erotic sensations, and feels that nothing is being demanded of her, she will generally reach orgasm. Once the woman is able to attain orgasm in the female-superior position, the couple may extend their sexual repertoire to other positions.

Masters and Johnson prefer working with the couple in cases of anorgasmia, but other sex therapists prefer to begin working with the woman individually through masturbation (Barbach, 1975; Heiman & LoPiccolo, 1987). This approach assumes that the woman accepts masturbation as a therapy tool. Masturbation provides women with opportunities to learn about their own bodies at their own pace. It frees them of the need to rely on partners or to please partners. The sexual pleasure they experience helps counter lingering sexual anxieties. Although there is some variation among therapists, the following elements are commonly found in directed masturbation programs:

1. *Education.* The woman and her sex partner (if she has one) are educated about female sexuality.

Figure 12.3. Coitus in the Female-Superior Position.

In treatment of female orgasmic disorder, the couple undertake coitus in the female-superior position after a number of occasions of genital play. This position allows the woman freedom of movement and control over her genital sensations. She is told to regard the penis as her "toy." The couple engages in several sessions of deliberately slow thrusting to sensitize the woman to sensations produced by the penis and to break the common counterproductive pattern of desperate, rapid thrusting.

2. *Self-exploration.* Self-exploration is encouraged as a way of increasing the woman's sense of body awareness. She may hold a mirror between her legs to locate her sexual anatomic features. Exercises may be prescribed to help tone and strengthen the pubococcygeus (PC) muscle that surrounds the vagina and increase her awareness of genital sensations and sense of control.

3. *Self-massage.* Once the woman feels comfortable about exploring her body, she creates a relaxing setting for self-massage. She chooses a time and place where she is free from external distractions. She begins to explore the sensitivity of her body to touch, discovering and then repeating the caresses that she finds pleasurable. At first self-massage is not concentrated on the genitals. It encompasses other sensitive parts of the body. She may incorporate stimulation of the nipples and breasts and then direct genital stimulation, focusing on the clitoral area and experimenting with hand movements. Nonalcohol-based oils and lotions may be used to enhance the sensuous quality of the massage and to provide lubrication for the external genitalia. Some women use their dominant hand to stimulate their breasts while the other hand massages the genitals. No two women approach masturbation in quite the same way. During the first few occasions the woman does not attempt to reach orgasm, so as to prevent performance anxiety.

4. *Giving oneself permission.* The woman may be advised to practise assertive thoughts to dispel lingering guilt and anxiety about masturbation. For example, she might repeat to herself, "This is my body. I have a right to learn about my body and receive pleasure from it."

5. *Use of fantasy.* Arousal is heightened through the use of sexual images, fantasies, and fantasy aids, such as erotic written or visual materials.

6. *Allowing, not forcing, orgasm.* It may take weeks of masturbation to reach orgasm, especially for women who have never had an orgasm. By focusing on her erotic sensations and fantasies, but not demanding orgasm, the woman lowers performance anxiety and creates the stimulating conditions needed to reach orgasm.

7. *Use of a vibrator.* A vibrator may be recommended to provide more intense stimulation, especially for women who find that manual stimulation is insufficient.

8. *Involvement of the partner.* Once the woman is capable of regularly reaching orgasm through masturbation, the focus may shift to the woman's sexual relationship with her partner. Nondemanding sensate focus exercises may be followed by

nondemanding coitus. The female-superior position is often used. It enables the woman to control the depth, angle, and rate of thrusting. She thus ensures that she receives the kinds of stimulation needed to reach orgasm.

Kaplan (1974) suggests a bridge manoeuvre to assist couples who are interested in making the transition from a combination of manual and coital stimulation to coital stimulation alone as a means for reaching orgasm. Manual stimulation during coitus is used until the woman senses that she is about to reach orgasm. Manual stimulation is then stopped and the woman thrusts with her pelvis to provide the stimulation necessary to reach orgasm. Over time the manual clitoral stimulation is discontinued earlier and earlier. Although some couples may prefer this "hands-off" approach to inducing orgasm, Kaplan points out that there is nothing wrong with combining manual stimulation and penile thrusting. There is no evidence that reliance on clitoral stimulation means that women are sexually immature. (Evidence has not borne out the theoretical psychoanalytic distinction between clitoral and vaginal orgasms.)

Our focus has been on sexual techniques, but it is worth noting that a combination of approaches that focuses on both sexual techniques and underlying interpersonal problems may be more effective than focusing on sexual techniques alone, at least for couples whose relationships are troubled (Killmann et al., 1987; LoPiccolo & Stock, 1986).

Male Orgasmic Disorder Treatment of male orgasmic disorder generally focuses on increasing sexual stimulation and reducing performance anxiety (LoPiccolo & Stock, 1986). Masters and Johnson instruct the couple to practise sensate focus exercises for several days, during which the man makes no attempt to ejaculate. The couple is then instructed to bring the man to orgasm in any way they can, usually by the woman's stroking his penis. Once the man can ejaculate in the woman's presence, she brings him to the point at which he is about to ejaculate. Then, in the female-superior position, she inserts the penis and thrusts vigorously to bring him to orgasm. If he loses the feeling he is about to ejaculate, the process is repeated. Even if ejaculation occurs at the point of penetration, it often helps break the pattern of inability to ejaculate within the vagina.

Premature Ejaculation In the Masters and Johnson approach, sensate focus exercises are followed by practice in the training position shown in Figure 12.1. The woman teases her partner to erection and uses the **squeeze technique** when he indicates that he is about to ejaculate. She squeezes the tip of the penis, which temporarily prevents ejaculation. This process is repeated three or four times in a 15- to 20-minute session before the man purposely ejaculates.

In using the squeeze technique (which should be used only following personal instruction from a sex therapist), the woman holds the penis between the thumb and first two fingers of the same hand. The thumb presses against the frenulum. The fingers straddle the coronal ridge on the other side of the penis. Squeezing the thumb and forefingers together fairly hard for about 20 seconds (or until the man's urge to ejaculate passes) prevents ejaculation. The erect penis can withstand fairly strong pressure without discomfort, but erection may be partially lost.

After two or three days of these sessions, Masters and Johnson have the couple begin coitus in the female-superior position because it creates less pressure to ejaculate. The woman inserts the penis. At first she contains it without thrusting, allowing the man to get used to intravaginal sensations. If he signals that he is about to ejaculate, she lifts off and squeezes the penis. After some repetitions, she begins slowly to move backward and forward, lifting off and squeezing as needed. The man learns gradually to tolerate higher levels of sexual stimulation without ejaculating.

The alternate "stop-start" method for treating premature ejaculation was introduced by urologist James Semans (1956). The method can be applied to manual stimulation or coitus. For example, the woman can manually stimulate her partner until he is about to ejaculate. He then signals her to suspend sexual stimulation and allows his arousal to subside before stimulation is resumed. This process enables the man to recognize the cues that precede his point of ejaculatory inevitability or "point of no

Squeeze technique
A method for treating premature ejaculation whereby the tip of the penis is squeezed temporarily to prevent ejaculation.

return," and to tolerate longer periods of sexual stimulation. When the stop-start technique is applied to coitus, the couple begin with simple vaginal containment with no pelvic thrusting, preferably in the female-superior position. The man withdraws if he feels he is about to ejaculate. As the man's sense of control increases, thrusting can begin, along with variations in coital positions. The couple again stop when the man signals that he is approaching ejaculatory inevitability.

Treatment of Sexual Pain Disorders

Dyspareunia Dyspareunia, or painful intercourse, generally calls for medical intervention to ascertain and treat any underlying physical problems, such as genital infections, that might give rise to pain. When dyspareunia is caused by vaginismus, treatment of vaginismus through a behavioural approach, described below, may eliminate pain.

Vaginismus Vaginismus is generally treated with behavioural exercises in which plastic vaginal dilators of increasing size are inserted to help relax the vaginal musculature. A gynecologist may first demonstrate insertion of the narrowest dilator. Later the woman herself practises insertion of wider dilators at home. The woman increases the size of the dilator as she becomes capable of tolerating insertion and containment (for 10 or 15 minutes) without discomfort or pain. The woman herself—not her partner or therapist—controls the pace of treatment (LoPiccolo & Stock, 1986). The woman's or her partner's fingers (first the littlest finger, then two fingers and so on) may be used in place of the plastic dilators, with the woman controlling the speed and depth of penetration. When the woman is able to tolerate dilators (or fingers) equivalent in thickness to the penis, the couple may attempt coitus. Still, the woman should control insertion. Circumstances should be relaxed and nondemanding. The idea is to avoid resensitizing her to fears of penetration. Since vaginismus often occurs among women with a history of sexual trauma, such as rape or incest, treatment for the psychological effects of these experiences may also be in order (LoPiccolo & Stock, 1986).

Evaluation of Sex Therapy

Masters and Johnson (1970) reported an overall success rate of about 80% in treating sexual dysfunctions in their two-week intensive program. Some dysfunctions proved more difficult to treat than others. An analysis of treatment results from 1950 to 1977 showed success rates ranging from 67% for primary erectile disorder to 99% for vaginismus (Kolodny, 1981). A follow-up of 226 initial successes after a five-year period showed that 16 people, or 7%, experienced a "treatment reversal."

Yet, Masters and Johnson's sample may have been biased in at least two ways. It consisted only of people who were willing and financially able to spend two weeks at their institute for full-time therapy. These people were better educated, more affluent, and more highly motivated than the general population. So some of the success of treatment may have been due to the clients' high level of motivation rather than to the treatment they received.

Other researchers have reported more modest levels of success in treating erectile disorder than those reported at the Masters and Johnson Institute (Barlow, 1986). Nevertheless, long-term follow-up evaluations support the general effectiveness of sex therapy for erectile disorder (Everaerd, 1993). The addition of biological treatments to the arsenal of treatments for erectile disorder has improved success rates to the point that virtually all erection problems can be successfully treated in one way or another (Reinisch, 1990).

Sex therapy approaches to treating vaginismus and premature ejaculation have produced more consistent levels of success (Beck, 1993; O'Donohue et al., 1993). Reported success in treating vaginismus has ranged as high as 80% (Hawton & Catalan, 1990) to 100% in Masters and Johnson's (1970) original research. Treatment of premature ejaculation has resulted in success rates above 90% using the squeeze or stop-start techniques (Killmann & Auerbach, 1979). Because the squeeze technique carries with it some risk of discomfort, many therapists prefer using the stop-start method.

LoPiccolo and Stock (1986) found that 95% of a sample of 150 previously anorgasmic women were able to reach orgasm through a directed masturbation program. About 85% of these women were able to reach orgasm through manual stimulation by their partners. Only about 40% had an orgasm during coitus, however. Generally speaking, couples-oriented treatment helps facilitate orgasm during coitus but is no guarantee (Heiman & LoPiccolo, 1987; LoPiccolo & Stock, 1986). Nevertheless, the goal of reaching orgasm through some form of genital stimulation with a cooperative partner, whether through coitus, oral sex, or direct manual clitoral stimulation, is realistic for most women (LoPiccolo & Stock, 1986).

Biological Treatments of Premature Ejaculation and Erectile Disorder

Sex therapy is by definition psychological or behavioural. However, biological treatments are also being used, especially in the cases of premature ejaculation and male erectile disorder.

Premature Ejaculation Drugs that are usually used for psychological problems have been helpful in treating premature ejaculation. One, clomipramine, is normally used to treat people with obsessive–compulsive disorder or schizophrenia. However, in a pilot study with 15 couples, low doses of clomipramine helped men engage in coitus five times longer than usual without ejaculating (Althof, 1994). So-called antidepressant drugs have also been helpful in treatment of premature ejaculation (Forster & King, 1994; Waldinger et al., 1994; Wise, 1994).

Erectile Disorder Biological or biomedical approaches may also be helpful in treating erectile disorder, especially in cases in which organic factors are involved. Treatments include oral drugs, penile implants, vascular surgery, hormone treatments, self-injections of drugs that induce erections, and a vacuum constriction device.

Oral Drugs In 1999, the drug Viagra became available in Canada. This drug has had a significant impact on couples seeking treatment for erectile disorders. Viagra, taken in pill form, enhances the natural processes of erection, making it possible for many men with erectile disorders to engage in sexual intercourse (Casey, 1998).

Penile Implants A penile implant is surgically implanted. Two types of implants are currently used: semirigid and inflatable. The semirigid implant is made of two rods of silicone rubber that remain in a permanent semirigid position. The inflatable type requires more extensive surgery. Cylinders are implanted in the penis, a fluid reservoir is placed near the bladder, and a tiny pump is inserted in the scrotum. To attain erection, the man squeezes the pump, releasing fluid into the cylinders. When the erection is no longer needed, a release valve returns the fluid to the reservoir, deflating the penis (DATTA, 1988). The inflatable type more closely duplicates the normal processes of tumescence and detumescence.

Some adverse side effects of penile implants have been reported, including infection, pain, and damage to the spongy tissues of the penis. Yet most men who receive penile implants, and their partners, are generally pleased with them (Anderson & Wold, 1986; LoPiccolo & Stock, 1986; Spark, 1991).

Vascular Surgery Vascular surgery may be helpful when the blood vessels that supply the penis are blocked, or when structural defects in the penis restrict blood flow (Carmignani et al., 1987; Goldstein, 1987; Mohr & Beutler, 1990).

Hormone Treatments Hormone (testosterone) treatments may help restore sex drive and erectile ability in men with abnormally low levels of testosterone (Bagatell & Bremner, 1996; Carani et al., 1990; Spark, 1991). There is no evidence for its effectiveness in men with normal hormone levels. Testosterone has been shown to help women who complain of lack of desire after their adrenal glands and ovaries have been removed (Bagatell & Bremner, 1996).

Penile Injection The muscle relaxants papaverine and alprostadil work after injection into the corpus cavernosum of the penis. A physician teaches the man how to inject himself. The drugs work by relaxing the muscles that surround the small blood vessels in the penis. The majority of men with erectile failure get an erection sufficient for coitus through injection (Linet & Ogrinc, 1996). A six-month study of self-injections with alprostadil in 296 men found that 94% of the men reported erections adequate for sexual activity (Linet & Ogrinc, 1996).

Penile injections may have side effects, including local pain and prolonged, painful erections (priapism) (Linet & Ogrinc, 1996; Lipschultz, 1996). Many men find the idea of penile injections distasteful and reject them out of hand or drop out after a trial (Lipschultz, 1996). Researchers are investigating alternatives to injections, such as creams that can be rubbed on the penis.

Vacuum Constriction Device A noninvasive vacuum constriction device (VCD) helps men get erections through vacuum pressure. The device (brand name: ErecAid) consists of a cylinder that is connected to a hand-operated vacuum pump. The vacuum increases the flow of blood into the penis, inducing an erection. Rubber bands placed around the base of the penis can maintain the erection for as long as 30 minutes. However, side effects such as pain and black-and-blue marks are common (Spark, 1991). The rubber bands can also injure penile tissue and prevent normal ejaculation, so semen remains trapped in the urethra until the bands are released (Spark, 1991).

Applications

Finding a Qualified Sex Therapist

How would you find a sex therapist if you had a sexual dysfunction? You might find advertisements for "sex therapists" in the Yellow Pages. But beware. The term "sex therapist" is not regulated in Canada.

Thus, it is essential to determine that a sex therapist is a member of a recognized profession (such as psychology, social work, or medicine) with training and supervision in sex therapy. Professionals are usually licensed or certified by their province.

If you are uncertain as to how to locate a qualified sex therapist in your area, you may obtain names of local practitioners from various sources, such as your university or college psychology department, local clinic or hospital, a family physician, or your instructor.

Ethical professionals are not annoyed or embarrassed if you ask them (1) what their profession is, (2) where they earned their advanced degree, (3) whether they are licensed or certified by the province, (4) their fees, (5) their plans for treatment, and (6) the nature of their training in human sexuality and sex therapy. If the therapist hems and haws, asks why you are asking such questions, or fails to provide a direct answer, beware.

Professionals are also restricted by the ethical principles of their professions from engaging in unethical practices, such as sexual relations with their clients. Any therapist who makes a sexual overture toward a client, or tries to persuade a client to engage in sexual relations, is acting unethically.

Summing Up

Types of Sexual Dysfunctions

Sexual dysfunctions are difficulties in becoming sexually aroused or reaching orgasm. **Sexual desire disorders** involve dysfunctions in sexual desire, interest, or drive, in which the person experiences a lack of sexual desire or an aversion to genital sexual contact. In men, **sexual arousal disorders** involve recurrent difficulty in achieving or sustaining an erection sufficient to engaging successfully in sexual intercourse. In women, they typically involve failure to become sufficiently lubricated. With **orgasmic disorders**, women are more likely to encounter difficulties reaching orgasm, while men are more likely to have premature ejaculation. **Sexual pain disorders** include dyspareunia and vaginismus.

Origins of Sexual Dysfunctions

Many sexual dysfunctions involve the interaction of organic and psychological factors.

Organic causes include fatigue, which may lead to erectile disorder in men and to arousal and orgasmic disorders in women. Dyspareunia often reflects vaginal infections and STIs. Organic factors are involved in many cases of erectile disorder. Medications and other drugs may also impair sexual functioning. **Psychosocial causes** include cultural influences, psychosexual trauma, relationship dissatisfaction, psychological conflict, lack of sexual skills, irrational beliefs, and performance anxiety. Children reared in sexually repressive cultural or home environments may learn to respond to sex with feelings of anxiety and shame rather than sexual arousal and pleasure. Many people do not acquire sexual competencies because they have had no opportunity to acquire knowledge and experience, even within a relationship. Irrational beliefs and attitudes, such as a belief that an isolated instance of dysfunction is catastrophic, may also contribute to sexual problems. Performance anxiety may place a dysfunctional individual in a spectator rather than performer role.

Treatment of Sexual Dysfunctions

Sex therapy aims to modify dysfunctional behaviour directly by changing self-defeating beliefs and attitudes, fostering sexual skills and knowledge, enhancing sexual communication, and suggesting behavioural exercises to enhance sexual stimulation while reducing performance anxiety. **Masters and Johnson** pioneered the direct, behavioural approach to treating sexual dysfunctions. A male-and-female therapy team is employed during an in-residence program that focuses on the couple as the unit of treatment. Sensate focus exercises are used to enable the partners to give each other pleasure in a nondemanding situation. **Helen Singer Kaplan's** psychosexual therapy combines behavioural and psychoanalytic methods. In the treatment of **sexual desire disorders**, some sex therapists help kindle the sexual appetites of people with inhibited sexual desire by prescribing self-stimulation exercises combined with erotic fantasies. In the treatment of **sexual arousal disorders**, clients receive sexual stimulation from their partners under relaxed circumstances so that anxiety does not inhibit their natural reflexes. Biological treatments such as the drug Viagra are also used with male erectile disorder. For the treatment of **orgasmic disorders,** Masters and Johnson use a couples-oriented approach. Other sex therapists prefer a program of directed masturbation to enable anorgasmic women to learn about their own bodies at their own pace and free them of the need to rely on a partner or please a partner. Premature ejaculation is usually treated with the squeeze technique or the stop-start method. In the treatment of **sexual pain disorders,** dyspareunia, or painful intercourse, is generally treated with medical intervention. Vaginismus is generally treated with plastic vaginal dilators of increasing size. The success of **sex therapy** has varied with the type of sexual dysfunction treated. **Biological treatment methods** for premature ejaculation are under development. Erectile disorders can be treated with drugs, penile implants, vascular surgery, hormone treatments, or injections.

Chapter Quiz

1. According to a study by MacNeil and Byers, the most common male sexual dysfunction is
   (a) male orgasmic disorder.
   (b) erectile disorder.
   (c) premature ejaculation.
   (d) performance anxiety.

2. Which of the following is most likely to have organic causes?
   (a) Dyspareunia.
   (b) Vaginismus.
   (c) Female orgasmic disorder.
   (d) Performance anxiety.

3. According to the 1998 Canadian Contraception study, the most common female sexual dysfunction is
   (a) dyspareunia.
   (b) lack of interest in sex.
   (c) reaching climax too early.
   (d) having trouble lubricating.

4. Masters and Johnson used all of the following treatment methods except
   (a) sensate focus exercises.
   (b) a male-and-female therapy team.
   (c) a two-week residential program.
   (d) guided masturbation.

5. According to the text, which of the following is most likely to be connected with a history of sexual trauma?
    (a) Dyspareunia.
    (b) Rapid ejaculation.
    (c) Performance anxiety.
    (d) Vaginismus.

6. Papaverine is used in the treatment of
    (a) premature ejaculation.
    (b) male erectile disorder.
    (c) female orgasmic disorder.
    (d) hypoactive sexual desire.

7. According to the text, a low level of _____ has been connected with lack of sexual desire.
    (a) testosterone
    (b) estrogen
    (c) Depo-Provera
    (d) alprostadil

8. Helen Singer Kaplan's approach to sex therapy is termed
    (a) couples therapy.
    (b) family therapy.
    (c) medical therapy.
    (d) psychosexual therapy.

9. All of the following are sex therapy methods, with the exception of
    (a) penile implants.
    (b) improving sexual communication.
    (c) reducing performance anxiety.
    (d) sensate focus exercises.

10. Under what circumstances may a sex therapist ethically engage in sexual relations with a client?
    (a) When the client requests it.
    (b) When the client is an adult.
    (c) When the client does not have a partner of his or her own.
    (d) Under no circumstances, ever.

Chapter 13

Sexually Transmitted Infections

Did You Know That...

- The most common bacterial STI in Canada is genital chlamydia?

- The majority of women who contract gonorrhea have no symptoms in the early stages of the infection?

- A few sexually transmitted infections actually can be contracted from toilet seats in public rest rooms?

- Three-quarters of Canadian women will have at least one yeast infection during their reproductive years?

- As you are reading this page, your body is engaged in search-and-destroy missions against foreign agents?

- Most people who are infected by HIV remain symptom-free and appear healthy for years?

- Genital herpes can be transmitted at any time, not only during flare-ups of the infection?

- Pubic lice may be referred to as "crabs," but they are not of the same family?

Today another generation of young people is becoming sexually active with the threat of a lethal disease hanging over every sexual encounter. AIDS has changed the expression of human sexuality. The vision of an earlier generation of youth, that sexual expression could be completely spontaneous and innocent, seems dangerously outmoded today.

AIDS is indeed a scary thing, yet other **sexually transmitted infections** (STIs) pose much wider threats. According to Health Canada, only 1.5% of all positive HIV tests reported to the Laboratory Centre for Disease Control as of June 30, 2002, were among youth aged 15 to 19 (Health Canada, 2003a). *Chlamydia trachomatis* (the bacterium that causes genital chlamydia) is primarily a disease of young people. In 1999, approximately 69% of chlamydia infections occurred among Canadians between the ages of 15 and 24 (Health Canada, 2000a). Younger women are especially vulnerable—in 1999, 38% of all reported infections occurred in women between the ages of 15 and 19 (Health Canada, 2000a). *Human papilloma virus* (HPV), the virus that causes genital warts, may infect as many as 33% of Canadian women (Health Canada, 2000b). One study of 955 women in Ontario found that women aged 20 to 24 had the highest prevalence rate at 24% (Sellors et al., 2000). Figure 13.1 shows the cumulative totals of the most common sexually transmitted infections (STIs) in Canada from January to June 2002 and 2003. College and university students may be reasonably well versed about AIDS, but many are unaware that chlamydia can go undetected for years. Moreover, if it is left untreated, it can cause pelvic inflammation and infertility. Many, perhaps most, students are ignorant of HPV, which is linked to cervical cancer.

Sexually transmitted infections (STIs) are transmitted primarily through sexual means, such as vaginal or anal intercourse or oral sex. They were formerly called *venereal diseases* (VD)—after Venus, the Roman goddess of love. In this chapter we discuss STIs that are caused by bacteria, viruses, protozoa, and parasites.

Bacterial Infections

Bacteria are one-celled micro-organisms that cause many diseases such as pneumonia, tuberculosis, and meningitis—along with the common STIs chlamydia, gonorrhea, and syphilis.

Chlamydia

Although you may be more familiar with gonorrhea and syphilis, **chlamydia**, another bacterial STI, is actually more common in Canada (Health Canada, 2003b). Chlamydial

Sexually transmitted infections Infections that are communicated primarily through sexual contact. Abbreviated *STIs.*

Bacteria Plural of *bacterium,* a class of one-celled micro-organisms that have no chlorophyll and can give rise to many illnesses. (From the Greek *baktron,* meaning "stick," referring to the fact that many bacteria are rod-shaped.)

Chlamydia A common STI caused by the *Chlamydia trachomatis* bacterium.

Figure 13.1. Sexually Transmitted Infections, Cumulative Totals— Preliminary (January to June 2003 and 2002).

Genital chlamydia is by far the most common bacterial STI in Canada.
Source: *Notifiable Disease Monthly Report,* Health Canada, January–June 2003 and 2002. © Minister of Public Works and Government Services Canada, 2003. Accessed from PDF at **www.hc-sc.gc.ca/ pphb-dgspsp/bid-bmi/ dsd-dsm/ndmr-rmmdo/ pdf/2003/06-2003e.pdf.** *Reproduced with the permission of the Minister of Public Works and Government Services Canada, 2004.*

Sexually Transmitted Diseases
Cumulative Totals - Preliminary (January – June 2003 and 2002)

	Chlamydia, Genital	Gonococcal Infections	Syphilis, Infectious	Syphilis, Other - Unspecified
☐ J-J 2003	22 294	2741	277	171
■ J-J 2002	22 916	2772	140	180

These numbers are preliminary and are subject to change.

infections are caused by the *Chlamydia trachomatis* bacterium. This bacterium can cause several different types of infection, including *nongonococcal urethritis* (NGU) in men and women, *epididymitis* (infection of the epididymis) in men, and *cervicitis* (infection of the cervix), *endometritis* (infection of the endometrium), and *pelvic inflammatory disease* (PID) in women (See page 293 for a discussion of PID.)

More than 40 000 cases may occur annually. The incidence of chlamydia is especially high among young Canadians aged 15 to 24 (see Figure 13.2). About 1 in 100 female university students will acquire a chlamydia infection during the year.

Transmission *Chlamydia trachomatis* is usually transmitted through sexual intercourse—vaginal or anal. It may also cause an eye infection if a person touches his or her eyes after handling the genitals of an infected partner. Oral sex with an infected partner can infect the throat. Newborns can acquire potentially serious chlamydial eye infections as they pass through the cervix of an infected mother during birth. Even newborns delivered by caesarean section may be infected if the amniotic sac breaks before delivery (Reinisch, 1990). Infants infected with the bacterium during birth may develop eye infections or pneumonia.

Symptoms Chlamydial infections usually produce symptoms that are similar to, but milder than, those of gonorrhea. In men, *Chlamydia trachomatis* can lead to nongonococcal urethritis (NGU). *Urethritis* is an inflammation of the urethra. NGU refers to forms of urethritis that are not caused by the gonococcal bacterium. (NGU is generally diagnosed only in men. In women, an inflammation of the urethra caused by *Chlamydia trachomatis* is called a chlamydial infection or simply chlamydia.) NGU was formerly called nonspecific urethritis or NSU. Many organisms can cause NGU. *Chlamydia trachomatis* accounts for about half of the cases among men (Centers for Disease Control, 1985).

NGU in men may give rise to a thin, whitish discharge from the penis and some burning or other pain during urination. These symptoms contrast with the yellow-green discharge and more intense pain produced by gonorrhea. There may be soreness in the scrotum and a feeling of heaviness in the testes. In men, chlamydia is much more prevalent than gonorrhea (Health Canada, 2001).

In women, chlamydial infections usually give rise to infections of the urethra or cervix. Women, like men, may experience burning when they urinate, genital irritation, and a mild (vaginal) discharge. Women are also likely to encounter pelvic pain and irregular menstrual cycles. The cervix may look swollen and inflamed.

Yet, as many as 25% of men and 70% of women infected with chlamydia are asymptomatic (Cates & Wasserheit, 1991). For this reason, chlamydia has been dubbed the "silent disease." People without symptoms may go untreated and unknowingly pass

What You Need to Know About STIs: Chlamydia
www.hc-sc.gc.ca/ pphb-dgspsp/publicat/ std-mts/sti_g.html
This Health Canada website gives basic information, including symptoms and treatment, about chlamydia.

along their infections to their partners. In women, an untreated chlamydial infection can spread throughout the reproductive system, leading to PID and to scarring of the fallopian tubes, resulting in infertility (Garland et al., 1990; Hodgson et al., 1990). About half of all cases of PID are attributed to chlamydia (Schachter, 1989). Women with a history of exposure to *Chlamydia trachomatis* also stand twice the normal chance of incurring an ectopic (tubal) pregnancy (Sherman et al., 1990).

Untreated chlamydial infections can also damage the internal reproductive organs of men. About 50% of cases of epididymitis are caused by chlamydial infections (Crum & Ellner, 1985). Yet only about 1% or 2% of men with untreated NGU caused by *Chlamydia trachomatis* go on to develop epididymitis (Bowie, 1990). The long-term effects of untreated chlamydial infections in men remain undetermined. The fact that chlamydia is found far more often in women than in men (Figure 13.2) suggests that while health authorities may be missing a large number of infections in women, they are missing even more in men. The development of urine tests for chlamydia, rather than inserting a swab into the urethra, may encourage more men to be tested (Health Canada, 1999a).

Chlamydial infections also frequently occur together with other STIs, most often gonorrhea. As many as 40% of men and 60% of women with chlamydia also have gonorrhea (Health Canada, 1997).

Diagnosis and Treatment The Abbott Testpack permits physicians to verify a diagnosis of chlamydia in women in about half an hour (Reichart et al., 1990; Reinisch, 1990). The test analyzes a cervical smear (like a Pap smear) and identifies 75% to 80% of infected cases. There are relatively few **false positives** (incorrect positive findings). In men, a swab is inserted through the penile opening, and the extracted fluid is analyzed to detect the presence of *Chlamydia trachomatis*.

Antibiotics other than penicillin are highly effective in eradicating chlamydial infections (CDC, 1989; Toomey & Barnes, 1990). (Penicillin, effective in treating gonorrhea, is ineffective against *Chlamydia trachomatis*.) Treatment of sex partners is considered critical regardless of whether the partner shows symptoms, so as to prevent the infection from bouncing back and forth (Martin, 1990).

Gonorrhea

Gonorrhea is the second most commonly reported bacterial STI in Canada. Although the rate of gonorrhea infection has decreased steadily since 1980, in 2002, over 3300 new cases were reported, and almost 5000 new cases were reported between January and

False positive An erroneous positive test result or clinical finding.

Gonorrhea An STI caused by the *Neisseria gonorrhoeae* bacterium and characterized by a discharge and burning urination. Left untreated, gonorrhea can give rise to pelvic inflammatory disease (PID) and infertility. (From the Greek *gonos*, meaning "seed," and *rheein*, meaning "to flow," referring to the fact that in ancient times the penile discharge characteristic of the illness was erroneously interpreted as a loss of seminal fluid.)

Figure 13.2. Reported Genital Chlamydia Rates in Canada by Age Group and Sex, 1999.

Genital chlamydia is predominantly a disease of the young. In 1999, youth and young adults between the ages of 15 and 24 accounted for 69% of infections. Chlamydia rates were highest in young females aged 15 to 24.

Source: Health Canada, *Sexual Health and Sexually Transmitted Infections,* STD Data Tables, Appendix 1.1: Reported Genital Chlamydia Cases and Rates in Canada by Age Group and Sex, 1991–2000. (Updated January 3, 2002.) Accessed at **www .hc-sc.gc.ca/ pphb-dgspsp/ std-mts/stddata1201/ tab1-1_e.html,** January 29, 2004.

Reproduced with the permission of the Minister of Public Works and Government Services Canada, 2004.

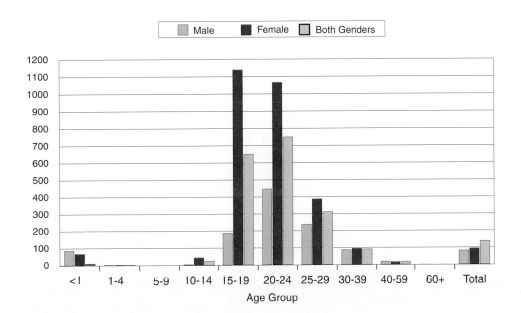

September 2003 (Health Canada, 2003b). The rate of gonorrhea varies widely between the provinces. The highest rates are found in the Northwest Territories, Manitoba, and Saskatchewan, while New Brunswick, Prince Edward Island, Newfoundland, Nova Scotia, and Quebec were all significantly below the national average (Health Canada, 2003c). It should be noted that incidence rates measure the number of cases in relation to the population (usually per 100 000). This allows us to make meaningful comparisons between groups of different sizes (Ontario and Prince Edward Island, for example). Explaining these provincial differences in rates of infection is difficult; they could be due to differences in screening methods, educational programs, or many other factors. Although in 2000 Nunavut had the highest rate of infection for gonorrhea, at nearly 350 per 100 000 population, Ontario had the largest number of reported cases (2795), followed by British Columbia (724), Quebec (671), and Manitoba (658) (Health Canada, 2003d).

Gonorrhea is primarily a disease of young Canadians. In 2000, just under half of all reported cases were found in people between the ages of 15 and 24 (Health Canada, 2003e). Gonorrhea is caused by the *Gonococcus* bacterium (see Table 13.1).

Transmission Gonococcal bacteria require a warm, moist environment, like that found along the mucous membranes of the urinary tract in both genders or the cervix in women. Outside the body, they die in about a minute. Gonorrhea is almost always transmitted by unprotected vaginal, oral, or anal sexual activity, or from mother to newborn during delivery (Reinisch, 1990).

A person who performs fellatio on an infected man may develop **pharyngeal gonorrhea**, which produces a throat infection. Mouth-to-mouth kissing and cunnilingus are less likely to spread gonorrhea. The eyes provide a good environment for the bacterium. Thus, a person whose hands come into contact with infected genitals and who inadvertently touches his or her eyes afterward may infect them. Babies have contracted gonorrhea of the eyes (**ophthalmia neonatorum**) when passing through the birth canals of infected mothers. This disorder may cause blindness but has become rare because the eyes of newborns are treated routinely with silver nitrate or penicillin ointment, which are toxic to gonococcal bacteria.

A gonorrheal infection may be spread from the penis to the partner's rectum during anal intercourse. A cervical gonorrheal infection can be spread to the rectum if an infected woman and her partner follow vaginal intercourse with anal intercourse. Gonorrhea is less likely to be spread by vaginal than penile discharges.

Symptoms Most men experience symptoms within two to five days after infection. Symptoms include a penile discharge that is clear at first. Within a day it turns yellow to yellow-green, thickens, and becomes puslike. The urethra becomes inflamed, and urination is accompanied by a burning sensation. Thirty to forty percent of males have swelling and tenderness in the lymph glands of the groin. Inflammation and other symptoms may become chronic if left untreated.

The initial symptoms of gonorrhea usually abate within a few weeks without treatment, leading people to think of gonorrhea as being no worse than a bad cold. However, the gonococcus bacterium will usually continue to damage the body even though the early symptoms fade.

In women the primary site of the infection is the cervix, where it causes **cervicitis**. Cervicitis may cause a yellowish to yellow-green puslike discharge that irritates the vulva. If the infection spreads to the urethra, women may also note burning urination. About 80% of the women who contract gonorrhea are **asymptomatic** during the early stages of the disease, however. Unfortunately, therefore, many infected women do not seek treatment until more serious symptoms develop. They may also inadvertently infect another sex partner.

When gonorrhea is not treated early, it may spread through the urogenital systems in both genders and strike the internal reproductive organs. In men, it can lead to **epididymitis**, which can cause fertility problems. Swelling and feelings of tenderness or pain in the scrotum are the principal symptoms of epididymitis. Fever may also be present. Occasionally the kidneys are affected.

Pharyngeal gonorrhea A gonorrheal infection of the pharynx (the cavity leading from the mouth and nasal passages to the larynx and esophagus) that is characterized by a sore throat.

Ophthalmia neonatorum A gonorrheal infection of the eyes of newborn children who contract the disease by passing through an infected birth canal. (From the Greek *ophthalmos*, meaning "eye.")

Cervicitis Inflammation of the cervix.

Asymptomatic Without symptoms.

Epididymitis Inflammation of the epididymis.

TABLE 13.1 Causes, modes of transmission, symptoms, diagnosis, and treatment of major sexually transmitted infections (STIs)

STI and Pathogen	Modes of Transmission	Symptoms	Diagnosis	Treatment
Bacterial Infections				
Gonorrhea ("clap," "drip"): gonococcus bacterium (*Neisseria gonorrhoeae*).	Vaginal, oral, or anal sexual activity, or from mother to newborn during delivery.	In men, yellowish, thick penile discharge; burning urination. In women, increased vaginal discharge, burning urination, irregular menstrual bleeding (most women show no early symptoms).	Clinical inspection, culture of sample discharge.	Antibiotics: ceftixime, azithromycin, doxycycline.
Syphilis: *Treponema pallidum*.	Vaginal, oral, or anal sexual activity, or touching an infectious chancre.	In primary stage, a hard, round, painless chancre or sore appears at site of infection within 2 to 4 weeks. May progress through secondary, latent, and tertiary stages, if left untreated.	Primary-stage syphilis is diagnosed by clinical examination and by examination of fluid from a chancre. Secondary-stage syphilis is diagnosed by blood test (the VDRL).	Penicillin; or doxycycline, tetracycline, or erythromycin for nonpregnant, penicillin-allergic patients.
Chlamydia and nongonococcal urethritis (NGU): *Chlamydia trachomatis* bacterium; NGU in men may also be caused by *Urea-plasma urealycticum* bacterium and other pathogens.	Vaginal, oral, or anal sexual activity; to the eye by touching one's eyes after touching the genitals of an infected partner, or to newborns passing through the birth canal of an infected mother.	In women, frequent and painful urination, lower abdominal pain and inflammation, and vaginal discharge (but most women are symptom-free. In men, symptoms are similar to but milder than those of gonorrhea—burning or painful urination, slight penile discharge (most men are also asymptomatic), Sore throat may indicate infection from oral–genital contact.	The Abbott Testpack analyzes a cervical smear in women; in men, an extract of fluid from the penis is analyzed.	Antibiotics:: doxycycline, cefixime, or azithromycin.
Vaginitis				
Bacterial vaginosis: *Gardnerella vaginalis* bacterium and others.	Can arise by over-growth of organisms in vagina, allergic reactions, etc.; also transmitted by sexual contact.	In women, thin, foul-smelling vaginal discharge. Irritation of genitals and mild pain during urination. In men, inflammation of penile foreskin and glans, urethritis, and cystitis. May be asymptomatic in both genders.	Culture and examination of bacterium.	Oral treatment with metronidazole (brand name: Flagyl).

continued

TABLE 13.1 Causes, modes of transmission, symptoms, diagnosis, and treatment of major sexually transmitted infections (STIs)   *(continued)*

STI and Pathogen	Modes of Transmission	Symptoms	Diagnosis	Treatment
Candidiasis (moniliasis, thrush, "yeast infection"): *Candida albicans*—a yeastlike fungus.	Can arise by overgrowth of fungus in vagina; may also be transmitted by sexual contact or by sharing a washcloth with an infected person.	In women, vulval itching; white, cheesy, foul-smelling discharge; soreness or swelling of vaginal and vulval tissues.\n\nIn men, itching and burning on urination, or a reddening of the penis.	Usually on basis of symptoms.	Vaginal suppositories, creams, or tablets containing miconazole, clotrimazole, or tioconazole; modification of use of other medicines and chemical agents; keeping infected area dry.
Trichomoniasis ("trich"): *Trichomonas vaginalis*—a protozoan (one-celled animal).	Almost always transmitted sexually.	In women, foamy, yellowish, odorous vaginal discharge; itching or burning sensation in vulva. Many women are asymptomatic.\n\nIn men, usually asymptomatic, but mild urethritis is possible.	Microscopic examination of a smear of vaginal secretions, or of culture of the sample (latter method preferred).	Metronidazole (Flagyl).

Viral Infections

STI and Pathogen	Modes of Transmission	Symptoms	Diagnosis	Treatment
Acquired immuno-deficiency syndrome (AIDS): *Human immunodeficiency virus (HIV).*	HIV is transmitted by sexual contact, by infusion with contaminated blood, from mother to fetus during pregnancy, or through childbirth or breast-feeding.	Infected people may initially be asymptomatic or develop mild flulike symptoms, which may then disappear for many years prior to the development of AIDS. AIDS symptoms include fever, weight loss, fatigue, diarrhea, and opportunistic infections such as rare forms of cancer (Kaposi's sarcoma) and pneumonia (PCP).	Blood, saliva, or urine tests detect HIV antibodies. The Western blot blood test may be used to confirm the results when HIV antibodies are present. The diagnosis of AIDS is usually made on the basis of antibodies, a low count of CD4 cells and/or presence of indicator diseases.	There is no cure for AIDS or HIV infections. HIV is treated with a combination of protease inhibitors and nucleoside analogues.
Oral herpes: *Herpes simplex virus-type 1 (HSV-1).*	Touching, kissing, sexual contact with sores or blisters; sharing cups, towels, toilet seats.	Cold sores or fever blisters on the lips, mouth, or throat; herpetic sores on the genitals.	Usually clinical inspection.	Over-the counter lip balms, cold-sore medications; check with your physician, however.
Genital herpes: *Herpes simplex virus-type 2 (HSV-2).*	Almost always by means of vaginal, oral, or anal sexual activity; most contagious during active outbreaks of the infection.	Painful, reddish bumps around the genitals, thighs, or buttocks; in women, may also be in the vagina or on the cervix. Bumps become blisters or sores that fill with pus and break, shedding viral particles. Other possible symptoms: burning urination, fever, aches and pains, swollen glands; in women, vaginal discharge.	Clinical inspection of sores; culture and examination of fluid drawn from the base of a genital sore.	The antiviral drug acyclovir (brand name: Zovirax) may provide relief and prompt healing, but is not a cure; people with herpes often profit from counselling and group support as well.

continued

TABLE 13.1 Causes, modes of transmission, symptoms, diagnosis, and treatment of major sexually transmitted infections (STIs) *(continued)*

STI and Pathogen	Modes of Transmission	Symptoms	Diagnosis	Treatment
Viral hepatitis: hepatitis A, B, C, and D type viruses.	Sexual contact, especially involving the anus (especially for hepatitis A); contact with infected fecal matter; transfusion of contaminated blood (especially for hepatitis B and C).	Ranges from being asymptomatic to mild flulike symptoms and more severe symptoms including fever, abdominal pain, vomiting, and "jaundiced" (yellowish) skin and eyes.	Examination of blood for hepatitis antibodies; liver biopsy.	Bed rest, intake of fluids, and, sometimes, antibiotics to ward off bacterial infections that might take hold because of lowered resistance. Alpha interferon is sometimes used in treating hepatitis C.
Genital warts (venereal warts): *human papilloma virus* (HPV).	Sexual and other forms of contact, *such* as with infected towels or clothing.	Appearance of painless warts often resembling cauliflowers, on the penis, foreskin, scrotum, or internal urethra in men; on the vulva, labia, wall of the vagina, or cervix in women. May occur around the anus and in the rectum of both genders.	Clinical inspection.	Cryotherapy (freezing), podophyllin, burning, surgical removal.
Ectoparasitic Infestations				
Pediculosis ("crabs"): *Pthirus pubis* (pubic lice).	Sexual contact, or by contact with an infested towel, sheet, or toilet seat.	Intense itching in pubic area and other hairy regions to which lice can attach.	Clinical examination.	Nonprescription medications containing pyrethrins or piperonal butoxide (brand names: R&C, Nix) or lindane (Kwellada).
Scabies: *Sarcoptes scabiei.*	Sexual contact, or by contact with infested clothing, bed linen, towels, and other fabrics.	Intense itching; reddish lines on skin where mites have burrowed in; welts and pus-filled blisters in affected areas.	Clinical examination.	Lindane (Kwellada).

Source: Adapted from Rathus, S. A. (1996). *Psychology,* 6th ed. Fort Worth: Harcourt Brace College Publishers.

In women, the bacterium can spread through the cervix to the uterus, fallopian tubes, ovaries, and other parts of the abdominal cavity, causing **pelvic inflammatory disease (PID)**. Symptoms of PID include cramps, abdominal pain and tenderness, cervical tenderness and discharge, irregular menstrual cycles, coital pain, fever, nausea, and vomiting. PID may also be asymptomatic. PID can cause scarring that blocks the fallopian tubes, leading to infertility. PID is a serious illness that requires aggressive treatment with antibiotics or surgery to remove infected tissue.

Diagnosis and Treatment
When diagnosed and treated early, gonorrhea clears up rapidly in more than 90% of cases. Diagnosis of gonorrhea involves clinical inspection of the genitals by a physician and the culturing and examination of a sample of genital discharge.

Pelvic inflammatory disease (PID) Inflammation of the pelvic region—possibly including the cervix, uterus, fallopian tubes, abdominal cavity, and ovaries—that can be caused by organisms such as *Neisseria gonorrhoeae.* Its symptoms are abdominal pain, tenderness, nausea, fever, and irregular menstrual cycles. The condition may lead to infertility.

Antibiotics are the standard treatment for gonorrhea. Penicillin was once the favoured antibiotic, but the rise of penicillin-resistant strains of *Neisseria gonorrhoeae* has required that alternative antibiotics be used (Goldstein & Clark, 1990). Since gonorrhea and chlamydia often occur together, persons infected with gonorrhea are usually also treated for chlamydia through the use of another antibiotic. Sex partners of people with gonorrhea should also be examined.

Syphilis

Syphilis A sexually transmitted infection that is caused by an infection with the *Treponema pallidum* bacteria.

The bacterium that causes **syphilis** is *Treponema pallidum* (*T. pallidum*, for short). Because of its spiral shape, *T. pallidum* is also called *a spirochete*, from Greek roots meaning "spiral" and "hair."

The incidence of syphilis has decreased since the introduction of penicillin in the 1940s. The number of reported cases decreased from 400 in 1987 to a low of 116 in 1997. However, the incidence of syphilis appears to be on the rise again—from 166 in 1998 to 171 in 2002 and 362 cases in the first six months of 2003 (Health Canada, 2003f; Health Canada, 2003g). This increase, which began in the middle of 1997 in Vancouver, and which has, so far, not responded to public health interventions, has been associated with the sex trade (Patrick et al., 2000). British Columbia has both the highest incidence and greatest number of cases of syphilis in Canada. Early detection and treatment of syphilis is extremely important, as the presence of syphilis may increase the sexual transmission of HIV (Health Canada, 1999b). HIV often co-exists with other sexually transmitted infections, and it is possible that the presence of these infections may increase susceptibility to infection by HIV. Many cases go unreported. Cocaine users risk contracting syphilis through sex with multiple partners or with prostitutes, not through cocaine use per se (Rolfs et al., 1990).

Transmission Syphilis, like gonorrhea, is most often transmitted by vaginal or anal intercourse, or oral–genital or oral–anal contact with an infected person. The spirochete is usually transmitted when open lesions on an infected person come into contact with the mucous membranes or skin abrasions of the partner's body during sexual activity. The chance of contracting syphilis from one sexual contact with an infected partner is estimated at one in three (Reinisch, 1990). Syphilis may also be contracted by touching an infectious **chancre**, but not from using the same toilet seat as an infected person.

Chancre A sore or ulcer.

Congenital syphilis A syphilis infection that is present at birth.

Pregnant women may transmit syphilis to their fetuses, because the spirochete can cross the placental membrane. Miscarriage, stillbirth, or **congenital syphilis** may result. Congenital syphilis may impair vision and hearing or deform bones and teeth. Blood tests are administered routinely during pregnancy to diagnose syphilis in the mother so that congenital problems in the baby may be averted. The fetus will probably not be harmed if an infected mother is treated before the fourth month of pregnancy.

Symptoms and Course of Illness Syphilis develops through several stages. In the first or *primary* stage of syphilis, a chancre (a painless, hard, round, ulcerlike lesion with raised edges) appears at the site of infection two to four weeks after contact. When women are infected, the chancre usually forms on the vaginal walls or the cervix. It may also form on the external genitalia, most often on the labia. When men are infected, the chancre usually forms on the penile glans. It may also form on the scrotum or penile shaft. If the mode of transmission is oral sex, the chancre may appear on the lips or tongue. If the infection is spread by anal sex, the rectum may serve as the site of the chancre. The chancre disappears within a few weeks, but if the infection remains untreated, syphilis will continue to work within the body.

The *secondary* stage begins a few weeks to a few months later. A skin rash develops, consisting of painless, reddish, raised bumps that darken after a while and burst, oozing a discharge. Other symptoms include sores in the mouth, painful swelling of joints, a sore throat, headaches, and fever. A person with syphilis may thus wrongly assume that he or she has the flu.

1998/1999 Canadian Sexually Transmitted Diseases Surveillance Report www.hc-sc.gc.ca/ pphb-dgspsp/publicat/ ccdr-rmtc/00vol26/ 26s6/index.html
This report includes statistics and data on chlamydia, gonorrhea, and syphilis.

These symptoms also disappear. Syphilis then enters the latent stage and may lie dormant for 1 to 40 years. But spirochetes continue to multiply and burrow into the circulatory system, central nervous system (brain and spinal cord), and bones. The person may no longer be contagious to sex partners after several years in the latent stage, but a pregnant woman may pass along the infection to her fetus at any time.

In many cases the disease eventually progresses to the late or *tertiary* stage. A large ulcer may form on the skin, muscle tissue, digestive organs, lungs, liver, or other organs. This destructive ulcer can often be successfully treated, but still more serious damage can occur as the infection attacks the central nervous system or the cardiovascular system (the heart and the major blood vessels). Either outcome can be fatal. **Neurosyphilis** can cause brain damage, resulting in paralysis or the mental illness called **general paresis.**

The primary and secondary symptoms of syphilis inevitably disappear. Infected people may thus be tempted to believe that they are no longer at risk and fail to see a doctor. This is indeed unfortunate, because failure to eradicate the infection through proper treatment may lead to dire consequences.

Diagnosis and Treatment Primary-stage syphilis is diagnosed by clinical examination. If a chancre is found, fluid drawn from it can be examined under a microscope. The spirochetes are usually quite visible. Blood tests are not definitive until the secondary stage begins. The most frequently used blood test is the **VDRL.** The VDRL tests for the presence of **antibodies** to *Treponema pallidum* in the blood.

Penicillin is the treatment of choice for syphilis, although other antibiotics are sometimes used. Sex partners of persons infected with syphilis should also be evaluated by a physician.

Other Bacterial Infections

Several other types of bacterial STIs occur less commonly in Canada and the United States. These include chancroid, shigellosis, granuloma inguinale, and lymphogranuloma venereum.

Chancroid **Chancroid**, or "soft chancre," is caused by the bacterium *Hemophilus ducreyi*. It is more commonly found in the tropics and Eastern nations than in Western countries. The chancroid sore consists of a cluster of small bumps or pimples on the genitals, perineum (the area of skin that lies between the genitals and the anus), or the anus itself. These lesions usually appear within seven days of infection. Within a few days the lesion ruptures, producing an open sore or ulcer. Several ulcers may merge with other ulcers, forming giant ulcers. There is usually an accompanying swelling of a nearby lymph node. In contrast to the syphilis chancre, the chancroid ulcer has a soft rim (hence the name) and is painful in men. Women frequently do not experience any pain and may be unaware of being infected. The bacterium is typically transmitted through sexual or bodily contact with the lesion or its discharge. Diagnosis is usually confirmed by culturing the bacterium, which is found in pus from the sore, and examining it under a microscope. Antibiotics (erythromycin or ceftriaxone) are usually effective in treating the disease.

Shigellosis **Shigellosis** is caused by the *Shigella* bacterium and is characterized by fever and severe abdominal symptoms, including diarrhea and inflammation of the large intestine. Nearly 1200 cases of shigellosis were reported in the first nine months of 2003 (Health Canada, 2003b). It is often contracted by oral contact with infected fecal material, which may occur as the result of oral–anal sex. It can be treated with antibiotics, such as tetracycline or ampicillin.

Granuloma Inguinale **Granuloma inguinale**, like chancroid, is more common in tropical regions. It is caused by the bacterium *Calymmatobacterium granulomatis* and is not as contagious as many other STIs. Primary symptoms are painless red bumps or sores in the groin area that ulcerate and spread. Like chancroid, it is usually spread by intimate bodily or sexual contact with a lesion or its discharge. Diagnosis is confirmed

Neurosyphilis Syphilitic infection of the central nervous system, which can cause brain damage and death.

General paresis A progressive form of mental illness caused by neurosyphilis and characterized by gross confusion.

VDRL The test, named after the Venereal Disease Research Laboratory of the U.S. Public Health Service, that tests for the presence of antibodies to *Treponema pallidum* in the blood.

Antibodies Specialized proteins produced by the white blood cells of the immune system in response to disease organisms and other toxic substances. Antibodies recognize and attack the invading organisms or substances.

Chancroid An STI caused by the *Hemophilus ducreyi* bacterium. Also called *soft chancre*.

Shigellosis An infection caused by the *Shigella* bacterium.

Granuloma inguinale A tropical STI caused by the *Calymmatobacterium granulomatis* bacterium.

by microscopic examination of tissue from the rim of the sore. The antibiotics tetracycline and streptomycin are effective in treating this disorder. If left untreated, however, the disease may lead to the development of fistulas (holes) in the rectum or bladder, destruction of the tissues or organs that underlie the infection, or scarring of skin tissue that results in a condition called **elephantiasis**, a condition that afflicted the so-called Elephant Man in the nineteenth century.

Lymphogranuloma venereum (LGV) Lymphogranuloma venereum (LGV) is another tropical STI that occurs only rarely in Canada and the United States. It is caused by several strains of the *Chlamydia trachomatis* bacterium. LGV usually enters the body through the penis, vulva, or cervix, where a small, painless sore may form. The sore may go unnoticed, but a nearby lymph gland in the groin swells and grows tender. Early symptoms mimic those of flu: chills, fever, and headache. Other symptoms that may occur include backache (especially in women) and arthritic complaints (painful joints). If LGV is untreated, complications such as growths and fistulas in the genitals and elephantiasis of the legs and genitals may occur. Diagnosis is made by skin tests and blood tests. The antibiotic doxycycline is the usual treatment.

Vaginal Infections

Vaginitis refers to any kind of vaginal infection or inflammation. Women with vaginitis may experience genital irritation or itching and burning during urination, but the most common symptom is an odorous discharge.

Most cases of vaginitis are caused by organisms that reside in the vagina or by sexually transmitted organisms. Organisms that reside in the vagina may overgrow and cause symptoms when the environmental balance of the vagina is upset by factors such as birth-control pills, antibiotics, dietary changes, excessive douching, or nylon underwear or pantyhose. Still other cases are caused by sensitivities or allergic reactions to various chemicals.

As many as 90% of vaginal infections involve bacterial vaginosis (BV), candidiasis (commonly called a "yeast" infection), or trichomoniasis ("trich"). Bacterial vaginosis is the most common form of vaginitis, followed by candidiasis, then by trichomoniasis (Reinisch, 1990), but some cases involve combinations of the three.

The microbes causing vaginal infections in women can also infect the man's urethral tract. In some cases, a "vaginal infection" can be passed back and forth between sex partners.

Bacterial Vaginosis

Bacterial vaginosis (BV—formerly called *nonspecific vaginitis*) is most often caused by the bacterium *Gardnerella vaginalis*. The bacterium is primarily transmitted through sexual contact. The most characteristic symptom in women is a thin, foul-smelling vaginal discharge, but infected women are often asymptomatic. Accurate diagnosis requires culturing the bacterium in the laboratory (Reinisch, 1990). Besides causing troublesome symptoms in some cases, BV may increase the risk of various gynecological problems, including pelvic inflammatory disease (Hillier & Holmes, 1990). Oral treatment with metronidazole (brand name: Flagyl) for seven days is recommended (CDC, 1989; Health Canada, 1998) and is effective in about 90% of cases (Reinisch, 1990). Recurrences are common, however.

Questions remain about whether the male partner should also be treated. The bacterium can usually be found in the male urethra but does not generally cause symptoms (Reinisch, 1990). Lacking symptoms, the male partner may unknowingly transmit the bacterium to others. There is no evidence, however, that treating the male with metronidazole benefits either partner (CDC, 1989; Moi et al., 1989), and Canadian treatment guidelines do not recommend it.

Elephantiasis A disease characterized by enlargement of parts of the body, especially the legs and genitals, and by hardening and ulceration of the surrounding skin. (From the Greek *elephas,* meaning "elephant," referring to the resemblance of the affected skin areas to elephant hide.)

Lymphogranuloma venereum A tropical STI caused by the *Chlamydia trachomatis* bacterium.

Vaginitis Vaginal inflammation.

Vaginitis (Yeast Infections and Trichomonas)
www.bchealthguide.org/ healthfiles/hfile08j.stm
This website from British Columbia's Ministry of Health Planning provides information and resources on vaginal infections.

Bacterial vaginosis A form of vaginitis usually caused by the *Gardnerella vaginalis* bacterium.

Candidiasis

Also known as *moniliasis, thrush,* or, most commonly, a yeast infection, **candidiasis** is caused by a yeastlike fungus, *Candida albicans.* Candidiasis commonly produces soreness, inflammation, and intense (sometimes maddening!) itching around the vulva that is accompanied by a white, thick, curdlike vaginal discharge. Yeast generally produces no symptoms when the vaginal environment is normal (Reinisch, 1990). Yeast infections can also occur in the mouth and anus in both men and women and in the penis in men.

Infections most often arise from changes in the vaginal environment that allow the fungus to overgrow. Factors such as the use of antibiotics or birth-control pills, pregnancy, and diabetes may alter the vaginal balance, allowing the fungus that causes yeast infections to grow to infectious levels. Wearing nylon underwear and tight, restrictive, poorly ventilated clothing may also set the stage for a yeast infection.

Diet may play a role in recurrent yeast infections. Reducing one's intake of substances that produce excessive excretion of urinary sugars (such as dairy products, sugar, and artificial sweeteners) apparently reduces the frequency of recurrent yeast infections (Friedrich, 1985). In one study, daily ingestion of one pint of yogourt containing active bacterial (*Lactobacillus acidophilus*) cultures helped reduce the rate of recurrent infections (Hilton et al., 1992).

Candidiasis can be passed back and forth between sex partners through vaginal intercourse. It may also be passed back and forth between the mouth and the genitals through oral–genital contact and infect the anus through anal intercourse. However, most infections in women are believed to be caused by an overgrowth of "yeasts" normally found in the vagina, not by direct sexual transmission. Still, it is advisable to evaluate both partners simultaneously. Whereas most men with *Candida* are asymptomatic (Hillier & Holmes, 1990), some may develop NGU or a genital thrush that is accompanied by sensations of itching and burning during urination, or a reddening of the penis (Hillier & Holmes, 1990). Candidiasis may also be transmitted by nonsexual means, as between women who share a washcloth.

About 75% of women will experience an episode of candidiasis at some point during their reproductive years (Reinisch, 1990). About half of these women will have recurrent infections. Three to seven days of treatment with vaginal suppositories, creams, or tablets containing miconazole, or clotrimazole, among others, is usually recommended (Health Canada, 1994). These medications are available without a prescription. Even so, women with vaginal complaints should consult their physicians before using any medication, to ensure that they receive the proper diagnosis and treatment.

Trichomoniasis

Trichomoniasis ("trich") is caused by *Trichomonas vaginalis,* a one-celled parasitic animal (technically, a protozoan). Trichomoniasis is the most common parasitic STI (Levine, 1991). Symptoms in women include burning or itching in the vulva, mild pain during urination or coitus, and an odorous, foamy whitish to yellowish green discharge. Lower abdominal pain is reported by 5% to 12% of infected women (Rein & Muller, 1990). Many women notice symptoms appearing or worsening during, or just following, their menstrual periods. Trichomoniasis is also linked to the development of tubal adhesions that can result in infertility (Grodstein et al., 1993). As with many other STIs, about half of infected women are asymptomatic (Reinisch, 1990).

Unlike candidiasis, trichomoniasis is almost always sexually transmitted. Because the parasite may survive for several hours on moist surfaces outside the body, trich can be communicated from contact with infected semen or vaginal discharges on towels, washcloths, and bedclothes. This parasite is one of the few disease agents that could possibly be picked up from a toilet seat, but it would have to directly touch the penis or vulva (Reinisch, 1990).

Trichomonas vaginalis can cause NGU in the male, which can be asymptomatic or cause a slight penile discharge that is usually noticeable only upon awakening before one first urinates in the morning. There may be tingling, itching, and other irritating sensations in the urethral tract. Yet most infected men are symptom-free (Rein & Muller, 1990). Therefore, they may unwittingly transfer the organism to their sex partners. Perhaps three or four in ten male partners of infected women are found to harbour *Trichomonas vaginalis* themselves (Reinisch, 1990). Diagnosis is frequently made by microscopic examination of a smear of a woman's vaginal fluids in a physician's office (Levine, 1991). However, diagnosis based on examination of cultures grown from the vaginal smear is considered more reliable (Thomason & Gelbart, 1989).

Except during the first three months of pregnancy, trichomoniasis is treated in both genders with metronidazole (brand name: Flagyl). Both partners are treated, whether or not they report symptoms. When both partners are treated simultaneously, the success rate approaches 100% (Thomason & Gelbart, 1989).

Viral Infections

Viruses are tiny particles of DNA coated by protein. They cannot reproduce on their own. When they invade a body cell, however, they can direct the cell's own reproductive machinery to spin off new viral particles that spread to other cells, causing infection. In this section we discuss several viral STIs: AIDS, herpes, viral hepatitis, and genital warts.

AIDS

Acquired immunodeficiency syndrome (AIDS) A sexually transmitted infection that destroys white blood cells in the immune system, leaving the body vulnerable to various opportunistic diseases.

Human immunodeficiency virus (HIV) A sexually transmitted virus that destroys white blood cells in the immune system, leaving the body vulnerable to life-threatening diseases.

AIDS is the acronym for **acquired immunodeficiency syndrome**. AIDS is a fatal disease that is caused by the **human immunodeficiency virus (HIV)**. HIV attacks and disables the immune system, the body's natural line of defence, stripping it of its ability to fend off disease-causing organisms. No one knows where HIV originated, but some investigators suspect that it may be a variant of viruses found in monkeys and chimpanzees.

Prevalence The first reported case of AIDS in Canada occurred in 1982. By June 30, 2002, 18 336 Canadians were diagnosed as having AIDS (Health Canada, 2003h).

More than 50 000 people in Canada are infected with HIV. The World Health Organization (WHO) estimated that more than 42 million people around the world were living with HIV by the end of 2002. Almost half of the people infected with HIV are women, and over 3 million are children under the age of 15. Of the five million people who were newly infected with HIV in 2002, nearly three million were women and children. The WHO also estimates that 3.1 million people died of AIDS-related causes in 2002 (WHO, 2002).

In 1981, when AIDS-related problems were first described in medical journals, they were labelled as problems that affected only gay males. For many years, a large majority of cases of AIDS in North America were found among men who have sex with men. In 1989, nearly 80% of all Canadian cases of AIDS in adults were attributed to men who have sex with men. By the end of 1999, however, only 41% fell in this category (Health Canada, 2000c).

However, recent Health Canada HIV updates suggest that HIV infections in men who have sex with men increased again (CMA, 2000). One study found a significant increase in the rate of new HIV infections in Ontario between 1996 and 1999. Another study found that the belief that a cure for HIV is just around the corner encourages men to have unsafe sex (Canadian Press Newswire, 2000). Over the last few years, about half of new positive HIV tests among adult men were attributable to men having sex with men (Health Canada, 2003i).

The percentage of new adult AIDS cases caused by injection drug use has increased, from 2.5% in the early 1980s to 14% in 2001 and nearly 24% for the first half of 2002 (Health Canada, 2003j).

HIV is also increasing in women. By June 30, 2002, 26% of positive HIV tests were in women of all ages, and among those 15 to 29 years old, 42% of positive tests were

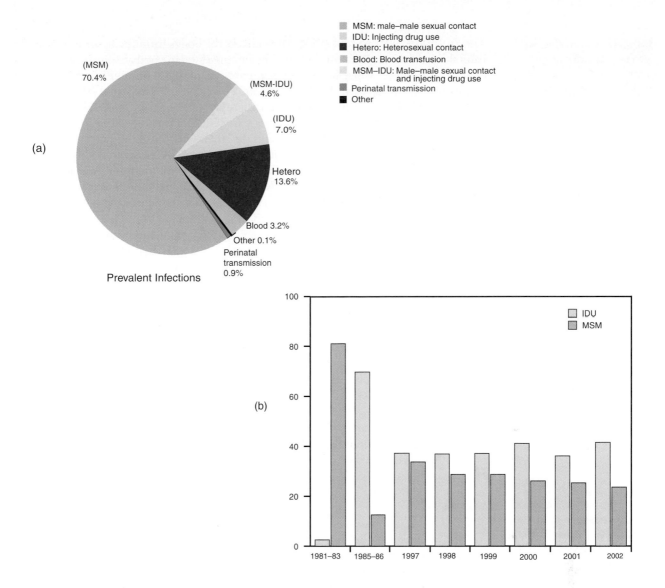

Figure 13.3. (a) AIDS Cases by Exposure Category, Canada (All Ages), to December 31, 2002, and (b) Category of Exposure among New HIV Infections in Canada (Age 15 and Over), by Time Period (Results before 1985 by Back-calculation)

Part (a) and Part (b) show the differences in categories of exposure to HIV over time. Part (a) shows the types of exposure among people with prevalent AIDS cases (those living with an infection diagnosed in an earlier year). Male–male sexual contact (MSM) was the predominant source of those earlier infections. Part (b) shows t a decline in the proportion of MSM among incident (new) infections, from more than 80% during 1981–83 to41.5 in 2002, and a sharp increase in the proportion of exposure through injecting drug use (IDU).

Source: Health Canada. *HIV and AIDS in Canada. Surveillance Report to December 31, 2002.* Division of HIV/AIDS Epidemiology and Surveillance, Centre for Infectious Disease Prevention and Control, Health Canada, 2003, pp. 56, 16. Accessed from PDF at **www.hc-sc.gc.ca/pphb-dgspsp/publicat/ aids-sida/haic-vsac1202/index.html**

found in women. Heterosexual sexual contact accounts for 62% of HIV infections in women, while injection drug use is responsible for 35% (Health Canada, 2003k). The increasing incidence of HIV in women is of concern because HIV infection may be passed from mother to offspring during pregnancy, delivery, or through breastfeeding (known as perinatal transmission). Of the 208 cases of AIDS in infants and children under 14 years of age, 79% were due to perinatal transmission (Health Canada 2003l). Screening pregnant women for HIV is important, as the transmission of HIV from a woman to her fetus during pregnancy can be reduced by treating the mother with antiretroviral drugs. All provinces offer HIV testing to pregnant women, by either an opt-in or an opt-out approach (Health Canada, 2003l). In an opt-in approach, the woman must consent specifically to an HIV test. In an opt-out approach, the woman is informed that an HIV test will be carried out as part of routine prenatal screening unless she refuses the test.

Immune system A term for the body's complex of mechanisms for protecting itself from disease-causing agents.

Pathogen An agent, especially a micro-organism, that can cause a disease. (From the Greek *pathos,* meaning "suffering" or "disease," and *genic,* meaning "forming" or "coming into being.")

Leukocytes White blood cells that are essential to the body's defences against infection. (From the Greek *leukos,* meaning "white," and *kytos,* meaning "a hollow," and used in combination with other word forms to mean "cell.")

Antigen A protein, toxin, or other substance to which the body reacts by producing antibodies. (Combined word formed from *anti*body *gen*erator.)

Inflammation Redness and warmth that develop at the site of an injury, reflecting dilation of blood vessels that permits the expanded flow of leukocytes to the region.

Opportunistic diseases Diseases that take hold only when the immune system is weakened and unable to fend them off.

Health Canada: AIDS
www.hc-sc.gc.ca/english/
diseases/aids.html
This site contains information on AIDS transmission and prevention, statistics, references, and links to AIDS resources.

The Immune System and AIDS AIDS attacks the body's **immune system**—the body's natural line of defence against disease. The immune system combats disease in a number of ways. It produces white blood cells that envelop and kill **pathogens** such as bacteria, viruses, and funguses; worn-out body cells; and cancer cells. White blood cells are referred to as **leukocytes**. Leukocytes engage in microscopic warfare. They undertake search-and-destroy missions. They identify and eradicate foreign agents and debilitated cells.

Leukocytes recognize foreign agents by their shapes. The shapes are termed **antigens** because the body develops antibodies in response to them. Antibodies attach themselves to the foreign bodies, inactivate them, and mark them for destruction.

Other leukocytes, called "memory lymphocytes," are held in reserve. Memory lymphocytes can remain in the bloodstream for years, and they form the basis for a quick immune response to an invader the second time around.[1]

Another function of the immune system is to promote **inflammation**. When you suffer an injury, blood vessels in the region initially contract to check bleeding. Then they dilate. Dilation expands blood flow to the injured region, causing the redness and warmth that identify inflammation. The elevated blood supply also brings in an army of leukocytes to combat invading microscopic life forms, like bacteria, that might otherwise use the local injury to establish a beachhead into the body.

Like other viruses, HIV uses the cells it invades to spin off copies of itself. HIV uses the enzyme *reverse transcriptase* to cause the genes in the cells it attacks to make proteins that the virus needs in order to reproduce.

HIV directly attacks the immune system by invading and destroying a type of lymphocyte called the CD4 cell (or helper T-cell). The CD4 cell is the "quarterback" of the immune system. CD4 cells "recognize" invading pathogens and signal B-lymphocytes, or B-cells—another kind of white blood cell—to produce antibodies that inactivate pathogens and mark them for annihilation. CD4 cells also signal another class of T-cells, called killer T-cells, to destroy infected cells. By attacking and destroying helper T-cells, HIV disables the very cells that the body relies on to fight off this and other infections.

The blood normally contains about 1000 CD4 cells per cubic millimetre. The numbers of CD4 cells may remain at about this level for years following HIV infection. Many people show no symptoms and appear healthy while CD4 cells remain at this level. Then, for reasons that are not clearly understood, the levels of CD4 cells begin to drop off, although symptoms may not appear for a decade or more. As the numbers of CD4 cells decline, symptoms generally increase, and people fall prey to diseases that their weakened immune systems are unable to fight off. People become most vulnerable to opportunistic infections when the level of CD4 cells falls below 200 per cubic millimetre.

Progression of HIV Infection and AIDS Most people who are infected with HIV remain symptom-free for years. Some have symptoms such as chronically swollen lymph nodes and intermittent weight loss, fever, fatigue, and diarrhea. The severity of symptomatic HIV infection depends on various factors, such as the person's general health. This symptomatic state does not constitute full-blown AIDS, but shows that HIV is undermining the integrity of the person's immune system.

The beginnings of full-blown cases of AIDS are often marked by symptoms such as swollen lymph nodes, fatigue, fever, "night sweats," diarrhea, and weight loss that cannot be attributed to dieting or exercise. People with AIDS develop **opportunistic diseases** such as *Pneumocystis carinii* pneumonia (PCP), other forms of pneumonia, Kaposi's sarcoma (an otherwise rare form of cancer), toxoplasmosis of the brain (a parasitic infection), *Herpes simplex* with chronic ulcers, invasive cancer of the cervix, and tuberculosis. AIDS has almost always resulted in death within a few years. Whether current treatments will make a dent in the mortality rate remains to be seen.

---

[1] Vaccination is the placement of a weakened form of an antigen in the body, which activates the creation of antibodies and memory lymphocytes. Smallpox has been annihilated by vaccination, and researchers are trying to develop a vaccine against the virus that causes AIDS.

Transmission HIV can be transmitted by certain contaminated bodily fluids—blood, semen, vaginal secretions, or breast milk. The first three of these may enter the body through vaginal, anal, or oral–genital intercourse with an infected partner. Other avenues of infection include sharing a hypodermic needle with an infected person (as do many people who inject drugs), transfusion with contaminated blood, transplants of organs and tissues that have been infected with HIV, artificial insemination with infected semen, or being stuck by a needle used previously on an infected person. HIV may enter the body through tiny cuts or sores in the mucosal lining of the vagina, rectum, and even the mouth. These cuts or sores may be so tiny that you may not be aware of them.

What of kissing? There need be no concern about closed-mouth kissing. Moreover, saliva does not transmit HIV. However, deep (open-mouth) kissing may pose a threat because blood mixed with saliva may be transmitted from person to person, if there is blood in an infected person's mouth (e.g., from active gum disease or vigorous tooth brushing) and cuts or sores in the partner's mouth. Though the risk of passing HIV through deep kissing is extremely small, it may be prudent to avoid the practice with partners not known to be HIV-negative.

When a person injects drugs, a small amount of blood remains inside the needle and syringe. If the person is HIV-infected, the virus may be found in the blood remaining in the needle or syringe. When others use the same needle, they inject the infected blood into their bloodstream. HIV may also be spread by sharing needles used for other purposes, such as injecting steroids, ear piercing, or tattooing.

HIV may also be transmitted from mother to fetus during pregnancy or from mother to child through childbirth or breast-feeding (Peckham & Gibb, 1995). Transmission is most likely to occur during the birth process.

Male-to-female transmission through vaginal intercourse is about twice as likely as female-to-male transmission (Allen & Setlow, 1991), partly because more of the virus is found in the ejaculate than in vaginal secretions. A man's ejaculate may also remain for many days in the vagina, providing greater opportunity for infection to occur. Male–female or male–male anal intercourse is especially risky, particularly to the recipient, since it often tears or abrades rectal tissue, facilitating entry of the virus into the bloodstream (Caceres & van-Griensven, 1994). Worldwide, male–female sexual intercourse accounts for 75% of cases of HIV infection. In Canada, heterosexual transmission continues to be an important risk factor for HIV infection in women.

In the early years of the AIDS epidemic, HIV spread rapidly among hemophiliacs who had unknowingly been transfused with contaminated blood. In 1985, the test to detect HIV antibodies (revealing the presence of HIV infection) became available. Although precautions were not taken immediately in Canada, within a few years blood banks began universal screening of donor blood. Medical authorities today consider the risk of HIV transmission through transfusion of screened blood to be negligible (Lackritz et al., 1995; Schreiber et al., 1996; Vyas et al., 1996).

Some people seem more likely to communicate HIV, and others seem to be especially vulnerable to HIV infection. Why, for instance, are some people infected by one sexual contact with an infected partner, whereas others are not infected during months or years of unprotected sex? Several factors appear to affect the risk of HIV infection and development of AIDS:

- The number of sexual contacts with an infected partner
- The type of sexual activity (Anal intercourse, for example, provides a convenient port of entry for HIV because it often tears or abrades the rectal lining.)
- The amount of virus in semen
- Unprotected vaginal sexual contact during menses (It increases the probability of female-to-male transmission.)
- Presence of other STIs (Many STIs either inflame the genital region or produce genital ulcers, both of which heighten vulnerability to HIV infection.)
- Circumcision (It *decreases* the risk of infection.)

- Genetic factors (HIV apparently enters cells in the immune system through certain receptors. About 1% of people of western European descent have a gene from both parents that prevents development of these receptors and are apparently immune to HIV infection. Perhaps 20% of individuals of western European descent have inherited the gene from one parent. HIV disease appears to progress more slowly in these people. Some prostitutes in Thailand and Africa, where HIV infection has been running rampant, also appear to be immune to HIV infection ["Genes that protect," 1996].)

Diagnosis The most widely used test for HIV infection is the *enzyme-linked immunosorbent assay* (ELISA, for short). ELISA detects HIV antibodies in the blood, saliva, or urine. (HIV itself is not found in measurable quantities in saliva or urine. However, HIV *antibodies* may be.) Saliva and urine tests are not as accurate as blood tests but they may encourage people who avoid blood tests to be tested. Positive ELISA results may be confirmed by the Western blot test, which detects a pattern of protein bands that are linked to the virus.

Treatment For many years, researchers were frustrated by failure in the effort to develop effective vaccines and treatments for HIV infection and AIDS. There is still no safe, effective vaccine, although research is ongoing in this area, but recent developments in drug therapy have raised hopes about treatment. Today, there are many drugs being used to treat HIV infections.

Zidovudine (formerly known as AZT) has been the most widely used HIV/AIDS drug. This drug is one of a number of so-called nucleoside analogues that inhibit replication (reproduction) of HIV by targeting the enzyme called *reverse transcriptase*. Other nucleoside analogues include ddI, ddC, d4T, and 3TC. Most studies suggest that zidovudine can delay the progression of infection from the symptom-free to the symptomatic state (Cooper et al., 1993) and increase the blood count of CD4 cells (Kinloch-de Loes et al., 1995).

Researchers also found that zidovudine administered to HIV-infected pregnant women reduced the rate of HIV infection in their newborns by two-thirds (Connor et al., 1994). The drug also helps prevent transmission during childbirth by reducing the amount of the virus in the mother's bloodstream. Only 8% of the babies born to the zidovudine-treated women became infected with HIV, compared to 25% of the babies born to women in the placebo group. According to Health Canada, as the number of

Applications

How HIV Is Not Transmitted

Much misinformation has been spread about the transmission of HIV. Although knowledge about transmission of HIV is valuable, even lifesaving, many people have needless concerns. Let us set aside some of these concerns by considering some of the ways in which HIV is not transmitted:

1. *Closed-mouth kissing.*
2. *Donating blood.* AIDS cannot be contracted by donating blood because needles are discarded after a single use.
3. *Casual, everyday contact.* There is no evidence of transmission of HIV through hugging someone, shaking hands, bumping into strangers on buses and trains; handling money, doorknobs, or other objects that have been touched by infected people; sharing drinking fountains, public telephones, public toilets, or swimming pools; or trying on clothing that has been worn by an infected person.
4. *Massage.*
5. *Insect bites.*
6. *Airborne germs or contact with contaminated food.* People do not contract HIV from contact with airborne germs, as by sneezing or coughing, or by contact with contaminated food or eating food prepared by a person infected with HIV (CDC, 1992).
7. *Sharing work or home environments.* HIV has not been shown to be transmitted from infected people to family members or others they live with through any form of casual contact, such as hugging or touching, or through sharing bathrooms, food, or eating utensils, so long as there is no exchange of blood or genital secretions (CDC, 1992; Hatcher et al., 1990). But do not share razor blades or toothbrushes with an infected person.

A World of Diversity

Ethnicity and AIDS in Canada

Although the majority of people with AIDS in Canada are white, Aboriginals and blacks are overrepresented. Although the reported number of cases of AIDS has declined over the last 10 years, the rate of decline has not been the same for all ethnic groups. Less than 15% of the population of Canada identify themselves as belonging to a visible minority, but they accounted for 34% of all cases of AIDS reported in 1999. Since 1980, the proportion of visible minorities among AIDS cases has risen from 11% to 36% (Health Canada, 2003m). Aboriginal people, who represent 3.3% of the population of Canada, accounted for 5.3% of reported cases with known ethnicity in 2001, and 25.5% of positive HIV tests with known ethnicity. Similarly, blacks, who represent only 2.2% of the population, accounted for 13.9% of reported cases of AIDS. Figure 13.4 shows the percentage distribution of AIDS cases diagnosed through 2001 according to ethnic background.

Compared with people from other ethnic groups who test positive for HIV, Aboriginals who tested positive between 1998 and 2002 were more likely to be young (28% were under 30, compared to 17% of whites), female (45% vs. 17%), and injection drug users 60% vs. 35%). The higher proportion of females is of particular concern because of the risk of maternal–fetal transmission of HIV. In British Columbia, 36% of babies born to an HIV-positive mother were Aboriginals (Health Canada, 2000d).

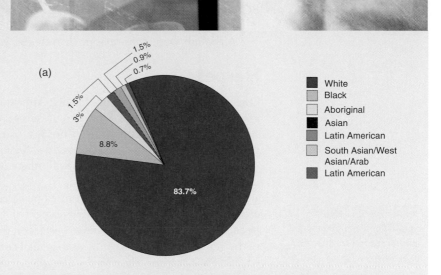

Figure 13.4a. Distribution of AIDS Cases by Ethnic Group in Canada. The figure reflects cumulative totals for men and women combined from 1997 to 2002.

Figure 13.4b. Percentage Distribution of Reported AIDS Cases for Selected Ethnic Groups in Canada, 1990–2002

Source: Health Canada. *HIV and AIDS in Canada. Surveillance Report to December 31, 2002.* Division of HIV/AIDS Epidemiology and Surveillance, Centre for Infectious Disease Prevention and Control, Health Canada, 2003, p. 58. Accessed from PDF at **www.hc-sc.gc.ca/ pphb-dgspsp/publicat/aids-sida/haic-vsac1202/index.html**

Canadian women receiving antiretroviral therapy increased from 37% in 1994 to 84% in 1998, perinatal transmission of HIV also decreased (Health Canada, 2003l). Research in Europe suggests that combining zidovudine treatment during pregnancy with caesarean delivery can reduce the transmission of HIV from mother to infant dramatically (Ricci, et al., 2000). Although zidovudine is helpful, it may eventually lose effectiveness.

A new generation of drugs that block the replication of HIV, called *protease inhibitors*, are more effective in treating HIV infection and AIDS (Corey & Holmes, 1996). Protease inhibitors block reproduction of HIV particles by targeting the protease enzyme. A cocktail of antiviral drugs such as zidovudine, other nucleoside analogues, and protease inhibitors is now the treatment of choice for HIV. However, drug therapy is expensive, and many people who could benefit from it cannot afford it (Kolata, 1996b).

Promising results are also reported in treating the opportunistic infections, such as PCP (Bozzette et al., 1995) and fungal infections (Powderly et al., 1995), that take hold in people with weakened immune systems (Clumeck, 1995).

Although there is more hope than there has been, make no mistake: AIDS is a killer.

Herpes

Once you get herpes, it's yours for life. After the initial attack, it remains an unwelcome guest in your body. It causes recurrent outbreaks that often happen at the worst times, such as around final exams. This is not just bad luck. Stress can depress the functioning of the immune system and heighten the likelihood of outbreaks. On the other hand, some people have no recurrences. Still others have mild, brief recurrences that become less frequent over time.

Different types of herpes are caused by variants of the *Herpes simplex* virus. The most common type, ***Herpes simplex* virus type 1** (HSV-1 virus), causes oral herpes. Oral herpes is denoted by cold sores or fever blisters on the lips or mouth. It can also be transferred to the genitals by the hands or by oral–genital contact. **Genital herpes** is caused by a related but distinct virus, the ***Herpes simplex* virus type 2** (HSV-2). This virus produces painful shallow sores and blisters on the genitals. HSV-2 can also be transferred to the mouth through oral–genital contact. Both types of herpes can be transmitted sexually.

Since genital herpes is not reportable in Canada, there is no way of knowing how many people are infected with HSV-2. However, one study of women giving birth in a Vancouver hospital found that the more sexual partners a woman had, the higher her risk for HSV (Steben & Sacks, 1997).

Transmission Herpes can be transmitted through oral, anal, or vaginal sexual activity with an infected person (Mertz et al., 1992; Wald et al., 1995). The herpes virus can also survive for several hours on toilet seats or other objects, where it can be picked up by direct contact. Therefore, reasonable precautions should be taken, such as washing hands. Oral herpes is easily contracted by drinking from the same cup as an infected person, by kissing, even by sharing towels. But genital herpes is generally spread by coitus or by oral or anal sex.

Many people do not realize that they are infected. They can thus unknowingly transmit the virus through sexual contact. Though genital herpes is most contagious during active flare-ups, it may also be transmitted when an infected partner has no symptoms (genital sores or feelings of burning or itching in the genitals) (Mertz et al., 1992; Wald et al., 1995). Any intimate contact with an infected person carries some risk of transmission of the virus, even if the infected person never has another outbreak.

Herpes may also be spread from one part of the body to another by touching the infected area and then touching another body part. One potentially serious result is a herpes infection of the eye: **ocular herpes**. Thorough washing with soap and water after touching an infected area may reduce the risk of spreading the infection to other parts of the body.

Women with genital herpes are more likely than the general population to have miscarriages. Passage through the birth canal of an infected mother can infect babies with genital herpes, damaging or killing them (Whitley et al., 1991). Obstetricians thus often perform caesarean sections if the mother has herpes (Osborne & Adelson, 1990). Herpes also appears to place women at greater risk of genital cancers, such as cervical cancer (Graham et al., 1982).

Symptoms Genital lesions or sores appear about six to eight days after infection with genital herpes. At first they appear as reddish, painful bumps, or papules, along the penis or the vulva. They may also appear on the thighs or buttocks, in the vagina, or on the cervix. These papules turn into groups of small blisters that are filled with fluid containing infectious viral particles. The blisters are attacked by the body's immune system (white blood cells). They fill with pus, burst, and become extremely painful, shallow sores or ulcers that are surrounded by a red ring. People are especially infectious during

Herpes simplex virus type 1 The virus that causes oral herpes, which is characterized by cold sores or fever blisters on the lips or mouth. Abbreviated *HSV-1*.

Genital herpes An STI caused by the *Herpes simplex* virus type 2 and characterized by painful shallow sores and blisters on the genitals.

Herpes simplex virus type 2 The virus that causes genital herpes. Abbreviated *HSV-2*.

Ocular herpes A herpes infection of the eye, usually caused by touching an infected area of the body and then touching the eye.

such outbreaks, as the ulcers shed millions of viral particles. Other symptoms may include headaches and muscle aches, swollen lymph glands, fever, burning urination, and a vaginal discharge. The blisters crust over and heal within one to three weeks. Internal sores in the vagina or on the cervix may take ten days longer than external (labial) sores to heal completely.

Although the symptoms disappear, the virus burrows into nerve cells in the base of the spine, where it may lie dormant for years or a lifetime. The infected person is least contagious during this dormant stage.

Recurrences may be related to factors such as infections, stress, fatigue, depression, exposure to the sun, and hormonal changes, such as those that occur during pregnancy or menstruation. Recurrences tend to occur within three to twelve months of the initial episode and to affect the same part of the body.

Diagnosis and Treatment Genital herpes is first diagnosed by clinical inspection of herpetic sores or ulcers in the mouth or on the genitals. A sample of fluid may be taken from the base of a genital sore and cultured in the laboratory to detect the growth of the virus.

There is no cure for herpes. Viruses, unlike the bacteria that cause gonorrhea or syphilis, do not respond to antibiotics. The antiviral drug acyclovir (brand name: Zovirax) may be taken orally to reduce the severity and length of an initial outbreak, or to reduce the frequency of recurrences. It may also be applied directly to sores in ointment form. It can relieve pain, speed healing, and reduce the duration of viral shedding. Acyclovir must be administered orally to combat internal lesions in the vagina or on the cervix. Oral acyclovir may reduce the severity of the initial episode and, if taken regularly, the frequency and duration of outbreaks (Brody, 1993a; Goldberg et al., 1993).

Warm baths, loose fitting clothing, aspirin, and cold, wet compresses may relieve pain during flare-ups. People with herpes are advised to maintain regular sleeping habits and to learn to manage stress.

Herpes Lesion on the Male Genitals. *Herpes lesions or sores can appear on the genitals in women or men and be associated with flu-like symptoms.*

Viral Hepatitis

Hepatitis is an inflammation of the liver that may be caused by factors such as chronic alcoholism and exposure to toxic materials. Viral hepatitis refers to several different types of hepatitis caused by related, but distinct, viruses. The major types are *hepatitis A* (formerly called *infectious hepatitis*), *hepatitis B* (formerly called *serum hepatitis*), *hepatitis C* (formerly called *hepatitis non-A, non-B*), and *hepatitis D*. In Canada, hepatitis C is the most common, with almost 19 000 cases reported in 2000; that same year, approximately 500 cases of Hepatitis A and 1000 cases of Hepatitis B were reported (Health Canada, 2003n).

Most people with acute hepatitis have no symptoms. When symptoms do appear, they often include **jaundice**, feelings of weakness and nausea, loss of appetite, abdominal discomfort, whitish bowel movements, and brownish or tea-coloured urine. The symptoms of hepatitis B tend to be more severe and long-lasting than those of hepatitis A or C. In about 10% of cases, hepatitis B can lead to chronic liver disease. Hepatitis C tends to have milder symptoms but often leads to chronic liver disease such as cirrhosis or cancer of the liver. Hepatitis D—also called *delta hepatitis* or *type D hepatitis*—occurs in the presence of hepatitis B. Hepatitis D, which has symptoms similar to those of hepatitis B, can produce severe liver damage and often leads to death.

The hepatitis A virus is transmitted through contact with infected fecal matter found in contaminated food or water, and by oral contact with fecal matter, as through oral–anal sexual activity (licking or mouthing the partner's anus). (It is largely because of the risk of hepatitis A that restaurant employees are required to wash their hands after using the toilet.) Ingesting uncooked, infected shellfish is also a frequent means of transmission of hepatitis A (Lemon & Newbold, 1990).

Hepatitis B can be transmitted through anal, vaginal, or oral intercourse with an infected partner; through transfusion with contaminated blood supplies; by the sharing of contaminated needles or syringes; and by contact with contaminated saliva, menstrual blood, nasal mucus, or semen (Lemon & Newbold, 1990). Sharing razors, toothbrushes,

Hepatitis An inflammation of the liver. (From the Greek *hepar*, meaning "liver.")

Jaundice A yellowish discoloration of the skin and the whites of the eyes. (From the French *jaune*, meaning "yellow.")

Lovers and Livers: Hepatitis B as an STD www.hc-sc.gc.ca/ pphb-dgspsp/publicat/ cjhs/cjhs6.html This article provides information on Hepatitis B Virus (HBV) infection in Canada, including risk factors, transmission, and prevention.

or other personal articles with an infected person may also transmit hepatitis B. Hepatitis C and hepatitis D may also be transmitted sexually or through contact with contaminated blood. A person can transmit the viruses that cause hepatitis even if he or she is unaware of having any symptoms of the disease.

Hepatitis is usually diagnosed by testing blood samples for the presence of hepatitis antigens and antibodies. There is no cure for viral hepatitis. Bed rest and fluids are usually recommended until the acute stage of the infection subsides, generally in a few weeks.

Full recovery may take months. Vaccines provide protection against hepatitis A and B, either separately or in a combined form (brand name Twinrix). The introduction of school-based vaccination programs is expected to reduce the incidence of hepatitis B substantially. No vaccine is yet available for hepatitis C.

Genital Warts

Genital warts An STI that is caused by the human papilloma virus and takes the form of warts that appear around the genitals and anus.

The *human papilloma virus* (HPV) causes **genital warts** (formerly termed venereal warts). HPV is extremely widespread, possibly infecting as many as 20% to 33% of sexually active women in Canada (Health Canada, 2000e). Though the warts may appear in visible areas of the skin, in perhaps seven of ten cases they appear in areas that cannot be seen, such as on the cervix in women or in the urethra in men (Reinisch, 1990). Within a few months following infection, the warts are usually found in the genital and anal regions. Women are more susceptible to HPV infection because cells in the cervix divide swiftly, facilitating the multiplication of HPV (Blakeslee, 1992). Women who initiate coitus prior to the age of 18 and who have many sex partners are particularly susceptible to infection (Blakeslee, 1992). A study of university women in Montreal found that 22% were infected with HPV (Richardson et al., 2000).

Genital warts are similar to common plantar warts—itchy bumps that vary in size and shape. Genital warts are hard and yellow-grey when they form on dry skin. They take on pink, soft, cauliflower shapes in moist areas such as the lower vagina. In men they appear on the penis, foreskin, and scrotum, and within the urethra. They appear on the vulva, along the vaginal wall, and on the cervix in women. They can occur outside the genital area in either gender—for example, in the mouth; on the lips, eyelids, or nipples; around the anus; or in the rectum.

Genital warts may not cause any symptoms, but those that form on the urethra can cause bleeding or painful discharges. HPV itself is believed to be harmless in most cases (Penn, 1993), but it has been implicated in cancers of the genital organs, particularly cervical cancer (Health Canada, 2000e) and penile cancer. Moreover, women whose husbands visit prostitutes or have many sexual partners are 5 to 11 times as likely as other married women to develop cervical cancer ("Roving mates," 1996).

HPV can be transmitted sexually through skin-to-skin contact during vaginal, anal, or oral sex (Penn, 1993). It can also be transmitted by other forms of contact, such as touching infected towels or clothing. The incubation period may vary from a few weeks to a couple of years.

Freezing the wart (*cryotherapy*) with liquid nitrogen is the preferred treatment (Health Canada, 2000e). One alternative treatment involves painting the warts over a period of several days with an alcohol-based podophyllin solution, which causes them to dry up and fall off. The warts may also be treated (by a doctor!) with electrodes (burning) or surgery (by laser or surgical removal). Although such treatments may remove the warts, they do not rid the body of the virus (CDC, 1989). There may thus be recurrences. Podophyllin is not recommended for use with pregnant women or for treatment of warts that form on the cervix (CDC, 1989).

Unfortunately, no vaccine against HPV exists or appears to be in the offing. Latex condoms help reduce the risk of contracting HPV. They do not eliminate the risk entirely because the virus may be transmitted from areas of the skin not protected by

Genital Warts. Genital warts are caused by the human papilloma virus (HPV) and often have a cauliflower-like appearance.

condoms, such as the scrotum (Ochs, 1994). People with active warts should probably avoid sexual contact until the warts are removed and the area heals completely.

Ectoparasitic Infestations

Ectoparasites, as opposed to *endoparasites*, live on the outer surfaces of animals (*ecto* means "outer"). *Trichomonas vaginalis*, which causes trichomoniasis, is an endoparasite (*endo* means "inner"). Ectoparasites are larger than the agents that cause other STIs. In this section we consider two types of STIs caused by ectoparasites: pediculosis and scabies.

Pediculosis

Pediculosis is caused by *Pthirus pubis* (pubic lice). Pubic lice are commonly called "crabs" because under the microscope they are somewhat similar in appearance to crabs (see Figure 13.5). In the adult stage, pubic lice are large enough to be seen with the naked eye. They are spread sexually but may also be transmitted by contact with an infested towel, sheet, or—yes—toilet seat. They can survive for only about 24 hours without a human host, but they may deposit eggs that can take up to seven days to hatch in bedding or towels (Reinisch, 1990). Therefore, all bedding, towels, and clothes that have been used by an infested person must be washed in hot water and dried on the hot cycle, or dry-cleaned. Fingers may also transmit the lice from the genitals to other hair-covered parts of the body, including the scalp and armpits. Sexual contact should be avoided until the infestation is eradicated.

Itching, ranging from the mildly irritating to the intolerable, is the most prominent symptom of a pubic lice infestation. The itching is caused when "crabs" attach themselves to the pubic hair and pierce the skin to feed on the blood of their hosts. The life span of these insects is only about one month, but they are prolific egg-layers and may spawn several generations before they die.

An infestation can be treated effectively with nonprescription medications containing pyrethrins or piperonyl butoxide (brand names: R&C, Nix, and others, as well as those containing lindane (Kwellada). Kwellada is not recommended for use by pregnant or lactating women (CDC, 1989).

Scabies

Scabies (short for *Sarcoptes scabiei*) is a parasitic infestation caused by a tiny mite that may be transmitted through sexual contact or contact with infested clothing, bed linen, towels, and other fabrics. The mites attach themselves to the base of pubic hair and burrow into the skin, where they lay eggs and subsist for the duration of their 30-day life span. Like pubic lice, scabies cause itching and discomfort. They are also responsible for reddish lines (created by burrowing) and sores, welts, or blisters on the skin. Unlike lice, they are too tiny to be seen by the naked eye. Diagnosis is made by detecting the mite or its by-products on microscopic examination of scrapings from suspicious-looking areas of skin. Scabies are most often found on the hands and wrists, but they may also appear on the genitals, buttocks, armpits, and feet (Reinisch, 1990).

Scabies, like pubic lice, may be treated effectively with 1% lindane (Kwellada). The entire body from the neck down must be coated with a thin layer of the medication, which should not be washed off for eight hours (CDC, 1989). But lindane should not be used by women who are pregnant or lactating. To avoid reinfection, sex partners and others in close bodily contact with infected persons should also be treated. Clothing and bed linen used by the infected person must be washed and dried on the hot cycle or dry-cleaned. As with "crabs," sexual contact should be avoided until the infestation is eliminated.

Ectoparasites Parasites that live on the outside of the host's body—as opposed to *endoparasites*, which live within the body. (From the Greek *ektos*, meaning "outside.")

Pediculosis A parasitic infestation by pubic lice (*Pthirus pubis*) that causes itching.

Figure 13.5. Pubic Lice.

Pediculosis is an infestation by pubic lice (Pthirus pubis), commonly called "crabs" because of their appearance under a microscope.

Scabies A parasitic infestation caused by a tiny mite (*Sarcoptes scabiei*) that causes itching.

Preventing AIDS and Other Sexually Transmitted Infections

Make no mistake about it. Although protease inhibitors have brought new hope to people infected with HIV, AIDS remains a deadly disease. Other STIs are also connected with serious health problems.

What, then, can we do to curb the spread of AIDS and other STIs? Given that many STIs have no vaccine or cure, prevention is our best hope. Most prevention efforts focus on education. Sexually active people have been advised to alter their sexual behaviour either by practising abstinence, by limiting their sexual experiences to a lifelong monogamous relationship, or by practising "safe sex"—which, as we shall see, could be more accurately dubbed "safer sex."

1. *Consider abstinence or monogamy.* The only fully effective strategies to prevent the sexual transmission of STIs are abstinence or maintaining a monogamous sexual relationship with an uninfected partner.

2. *Be aware of the risks involved in sexual behaviour.* Don't use denial. Many of us try to put the risks of STIs out of our minds—especially in moments of passion. Refuse to play the dangerous game of pretending that you are immune to STIs.

3. *Stay sober.* Alcohol and other mood-altering drugs increase the likelihood of engaging in risky sexual behaviour.

4. *Avoid high-risk sexual behaviours, unless you are absolutely certain that your partner is not infected.* Use latex condoms ("protection"). Latex condoms block nearly all sexually transmissible organisms, and are clearly the best method other than abstinence to protect oneself. Although it had been thought that combining condoms with spermicides containing nonoxynol-9 would increase the effectiveness of condoms, recent research suggests that nonoxynol-9 may actually increase the risk of HIV infection by causing lesions and ulcerations to the mucous membranes of the genitals (Cherniak, 1999). A recent Health Canada HIV/AIDS update concluded that this spermicide should not be considered effective in prevention of HIV infection, with or without a condom (Health Canada, 2003o). Several brands of condoms coated with nonoxynol-9 have been withdrawn from the market. Unprotected anal intercourse is one of the riskiest sexual practices. Other high-risk behaviours include unprotected oral–genital activity, oral–anal activity, insertion of a hand or fist into someone's rectum or vagina, or any activity in which you or your partner would come into contact with the other's blood, semen, or vaginal secretions.

5. *Be selective.* Choose partners carefully. Avoid sexual contact with someone who has engaged in high-risk sexual or drug-use practices and is not known to be uninfected with STIs. It is not enough to ask your partner about past sexual behaviour and drug use. You need to know the person well enough to judge the truthfulness of his or her answers. Until you are sure you are safe, use a condom.

6. *Limit your number of sex partners.* The more sexual contacts you have, the greater your risk of exposing yourself to STIs. Also avoid sex with a partner who has had multiple partners.

7. *Inspect your sex organs and those of your partner.* Inspect yourself for a discharge, bumps, rashes, warts, blisters, chancres, sores, lice, or foul odours. Check out any unusual feature with a physician before you engage in sexual activity.

8. *Engage in "outercourse," not "intercourse."* Hugging, massage, caressing, mutual masturbation, and rubbing bodies together without vaginal, anal, or oral contact are low-risk ways of finding sexual pleasure, so long as semen or vaginal fluids do not come into contact with mucous membranes or breaks in the skin. These activities may be termed *outercourse* to distinguish them from sexual intercourse.

9. *Use barrier devices when practising oral sex (fellatio or cunnilingus).* Use a condom before practising fellatio and a dental dam (a square piece of latex rubber used by dentists during oral surgery) to cover the vagina before engaging in cunnilingus.

10. *Wash the sex organs before and after sex.* Washing removes many potentially harmful agents, but is not an effective substitute for safer sex.

11. *Have regular medical checkups and test specifically for STIs.* Many people are asymptomatic carriers of STIs, especially of chlamydial infections. Medical tests can reveal "silent" diseases, which can then be treated, but you have to ask for them. Routine gynecological exams and Pap tests will not pick up STIs.

12. *Consult your physician or a local health clinic if you suspect that you have been exposed to an STI.* Early intervention may prevent serious health problems.

13. *When in doubt, avoid sex.*

Summing Up

Although public attention has been riveted on AIDS, other STIs, such as chlamydia and genital warts, pose wider threats.

Bacterial Infections

Bacteria are one-celled micro-organisms that cause many illnesses. **Chlamydia**, the most common bacterial STI in Canada, is caused by the *Chlamydia trachomatis* bacterium. The symptoms of chlamydial infections resemble those of gonorrhea but tend to be milder. Chlamydial infections also respond to antibiotics. **Gonorrhea** is caused by the *Gonococcus* bacterium. For men, symptoms include a penile discharge and burning urination. Most women are asymptomatic. If left untreated, gonorrhea can attack the internal reproductive organs and lead to PID in women. Gonorrhea is treated with antibiotics. **Syphilis** is caused by the *Treponema pallidum* bacterium. Syphilis undergoes several stages of development. Although it can lie dormant for many years, it may also be lethal. Syphilis is treated with antibiotics. **Other bacterial STIs** that occur less commonly in Canada include chancroid, shigellosis, granuloma inguinale, and lymphogranuloma venereum.

Vaginal Infections

Vaginitis is usually characterized by a foul-smelling discharge, genital irritation, and burning during urination. Most cases involve bacterial vaginosis, candidiasis, or trichomoniasis. **Bacterial vaginosis** is usually caused by the *Gardnerella vaginalis* bacterium. **Candidiasis** is caused by a yeast-like fungus, *Candida albicans*. Infections usually arise from changes in the vaginal environment that allow the fungus to overgrow. **Trichomoniasis** ("trich") is caused by a protozoan called *Trichomonas vaginalis*.

Viral Infections

Viruses are particles of DNA that reproduce by invading a body cell and directing the cell's own reproductive machinery to spin off new viral particles.

Acquired immunodeficiency syndrome, or **AIDS**, is caused by human immunodeficiency virus (HIV), which attacks the body's immune system. Worldwide, more than 42 million people are infected with HIV. AIDS is caused by HIV, which attacks the body's immune system. As HIV disables the body's natural defences, the person becomes vulnerable to opportunistic diseases, such as serious infections and cancers that are normally held in check. HIV is a blood-borne virus that is also found in semen, vaginal secretions, and breast milk. Common avenues of transmission include sexual intercourse, transfusion with contaminated blood, sharing a hypodermic needle with an infected person, childbirth, and breastfeeding. HIV infection is usually diagnosed through blood, saliva, and urine tests that detect HIV antibodies. There is no cure for AIDS, and an effective, safe vaccine has not yet been developed. The most effective form of treatment so far is a combination of antiviral drugs including zidovudine and protease inhibitors.

Herpes is a lifelong infection. Oral herpes is caused by the *Herpes simplex* virus type 1 (HSV-1). Genital herpes is caused by the *Herpes simplex* virus type 2 (HSV-2), which produces painful, shallow sores and blisters on the genitals. Antiviral drugs can relieve pain and speed healing during flare-ups. There are several types of **viral hepatitis** caused by different hepatitis viruses. Most cases of hepatitis are transmitted sexually or by contact with contaminated blood or fecal matter. **Genital warts** are caused by the human papilloma virus (HPV). HPV has been linked to cancers of the genital tract. Freezing the wart is a preferred treatment for removal of the wart, but the virus remains in the body afterward.

Ectoparasitic Infestations

Pediculosis ("crabs") is caused by pubic lice (*Pthirus pubis*). Pubic lice attach themselves to pubic hair and feed on the blood of their hosts, which often causes itching. Infestations can be treated with the prescription medication lindane or with nonprescription medications that contain pyrethrins or piperonal butoxide. Scabies (*Sarcoptes scabiei*) is a parasitic infestation with a tiny mite that causes itching. Scabies, like pubic lice, is treated with lindane.

Strategies for **preventing STIs** include abstinence, monogamy, inspecting oneself and one's partner, using latex condoms, avoiding high-risk sex, washing the genitals before and after sex, having regular medical checkups, and getting to know one's partner before engaging in sexual activity.

Chapter Quiz

1. Which of the following is the most widespread STI?
   (a) AIDS.
   (b) Syphilis.
   (c) Genital herpes.
   (d) Genital warts.

2. Silver nitrate is used to prevent
   (a) PCP.

(b) ophthalmia neonatorum.

(c) general paresis.

(d) hepatitis C.

3. In women the primary site of a gonorrhea infection is the

(a) cervix.

(b) endometrium.

(c) perineum.

(d) introitus.

4. *Treponema pallidum* is the organism that causes

(a) gonorrhea.

(b) syphilis.

(c) chlamydia.

(d) genital herpes.

5. The Abbott Testpack is used to diagnose _____ in women.

(a) trichomoniasis

(b) HIV infection

(c) chlamydia

(d) candidiasis

6. Miconazole is used to treat

(a) candidiasis.

(b) hepatitis.

(c) pediculosis.

(d) syphilis.

7. Protease inhibitors in combination with nucleoside analogues have been shown to decrease the amount of _____ in the bloodstream.

(a) Herpes simplex virus, type 1

(b) HPV

(c) HIV

(d) Pthirus pubis

8. Which of the following is an antiviral drug?

(a) Acyclovir.

(b) Podophyllin.

(c) Lindane.

(d) Penicillin.

9. General paresis may develop during the _____ stage of syphilis.

(a) primary

(b) secondary

(c) tertiary

(d) all of the above

10. People with AIDS may suffer from

(a) PCP, a form of pneumonia

(b) Kaposi's sarcoma

(c) otherwise unexplained weight loss

(d) all of the above

Chapter 14

Atypical Sexual Variations

Did You Know That...

- Nude sunbathers and stripteasers are not considered exhibitionists?
- It is normal—not voyeuristic—to enjoy watching one's sex partner undress?
- Exhibitionists and voyeurs are sometimes violent?
- Some people cannot become sexually aroused unless they are bound, flogged, or humiliated by their sex partners?
- It is considered normal to enjoy some mild forms of pain during sexual activity?
- There is a subculture in which sexual sadists and sexual masochists form liaisons to inflict and receive pain and humiliation during sexual activity?

What is normal, and what is abnormal or deviant sexual behaviour? In this chapter we explore a number of sexual behaviours that deviate from the norm in one sense or another.

Normal Versus Deviant Sexual Behaviour

One common approach to defining normality is based on a statistical norm. From this perspective, rare or unusual sexual behaviours are considered abnormal or deviant. In our own culture, sexual practices such as oral sex and masturbation were once considered to be deviant or abnormal. Today, however, they are practised so widely in our society that few people would label them as deviant practices. The American Psychiatric Association (APA) classified homosexuality as a sexual disorder until 1973. Gay rights activists were largely responsible for getting rid of this psychiatric diagnosis (Kleinplatz & Moser, 2003). Another basis for determining sexual deviance is to classify sexual practices as deviant when they involve a persistent preference for nongenital sexual outlets. If a man prefers fondling a woman's panties to engaging in sexual relations with her, or prefers to masturbate against her foot rather than engage in coitus, his behaviour is likely to be labelled deviant.

Because of the confusing array of meanings of the terms *deviant* and *abnormal*, we prefer to speak about unusual patterns of sexual arousal or behaviour as "atypical variations" in sexual behaviour rather than as "sexual deviations." Atypical patterns of sexual arousal or behaviour that are problematic in the eyes of the individual or society are labelled *paraphilias* by both the American Psychiatric Association (2000) and the Canadian Psychiatric Association.

The Paraphilias

Paraphilia A diagnostic category used by the American Psychiatric Association to describe atypical patterns of sexual arousal or behaviour that become problematic in the eyes of the individual or society, such as fetishism or exhibitionism. (From Greek roots meaning "to the side of" [*para*-] and "loving" [*philos*].)

Paraphilias involve sexual arousal in response to unusual stimuli such as children or other nonconsenting persons (such as unsuspecting people whom one watches or to whom one exposes one's genitals), nonhuman objects (such as shoes, leather, rubber, or undergarments), or pain or humiliation. Psychiatrists diagnose paraphilias when sexual fantasies, urges, or behaviours cause significant distress or interfere with a person's ability to function socially or to carry out everyday tasks, such as work. For specific paraphilias defined as criminal (exhibitionism, frotteurism, pedophilia, sexual sadism, and voyeurism), a diagnosis is made when an individual acts on the atypical urges, regardless of whether the person experiences personal distress or dysfunction.

People with paraphilias often feel that their urges have an insistent, demanding, or compulsory quality (Brody, 1990a; Money, 1988). People with paraphilias tend to experience their urges as beyond their control, much as drug addicts or compulsive gamblers might regard themselves as helpless to resist urges to gamble or use drugs.

Paraphilias vary in severity. In some cases the person can function sexually in the absence of paraphilic stimuli and seldom if ever acts upon paraphilic urges. In other cases the person resorts to paraphilic behaviour only in times of stress. In more extreme forms the person may not be able to become sexually aroused without either fantasizing about the paraphilic stimulus or having it present. For some people paraphilic behaviour is the only means of attaining sexual gratification.

The person with a paraphilia typically replays the paraphilic act in sexual fantasies to stimulate arousal during masturbation or sexual relations. It is as if he or she is mentally replaying a videotape of the paraphilic scene. The scene grows stale after a while, however. According to sex researcher John Money, "the tape wears out and he has to perform another paraphilic act, in effect, to create a new movie" (quoted in Brody, 1990, p. C12). Except in the case of sexual masochism, paraphilias are believed to occur almost exclusively among men (Money & Wiedeking, 1980).

Fetishism

In **fetishism**, an inanimate object elicits sexual arousal. Articles of clothing (for example, women's panties, bras, lingerie, stockings, gloves, shoes, or boots) and materials made of rubber, leather, silk, or fur are common fetishistic objects. Leather boots and high-heeled shoes are popular ones.

The fetishist may act on the urges to engage in fetishistic behaviour, such as by masturbating by stroking an object or while fantasizing about it, or he may be distressed about such urges or fantasies but not act upon them. In a related paraphilia, **partialism**, people are excessively aroused by a particular body part, such as the feet, breasts, or buttocks.

Most fetishes and partialisms are harmless. Fetishistic practices are almost always private and involve masturbation or are incorporated into coitus with a willing partner. Only rarely have fetishists coerced others into paraphilic activities. Yet some partialists have touched parts of women's bodies in public. And some fetishists have committed burglaries to acquire the fetishistic objects (Sargent, 1988).

Transvestism

Transvestism may be viewed as a type of fetish. Transvestites become excited by wearing articles of clothing—the fetishistic objects—of the other gender. Transvestites are almost always males. Most are married and otherwise masculine in behaviour and style of dress.

The origins of transvestism are unknown. Family relationships appear to play a role, however. Transvestites are more likely than other people to be oldest children or only children (Schott, 1995). They also report closer relationships with their mothers than their fathers (Schott, 1995). Some transvestites report a history of "petticoat punishment" during childhood. That is, they were humiliated by being dressed in girl's attire. Perhaps the adult transvestite is trying psychologically to convert humiliation into mastery by achieving an erection and engaging in sexual activity despite being attired in female clothing (Geer et al., 1984). Transvestism can also be looked at as an attempt by males to escape the narrow confines of the masculine role (Bullough, 1991).

What Sexual Scientists Know About... Compulsive Sexual Behaviour
www.sexscience.org/
publications/index.php?
category_id=440&
subcategory_id=334
An article summarizing and explaining paraphilic and non-paraphilic compulsive sexual behaviours.

Fetishism A paraphilia in which an inanimate object, such as an article of clothing, or an item made of rubber, leather, or silk, elicits sexual arousal.

Partialism A paraphilia related to fetishism, in which sexual arousal is exaggeratedly associated with a particular body part, such as feet, breasts, or buttocks.

Transvestism A paraphilia in which a person repeatedly cross-dresses to achieve sexual arousal or gratification, or is troubled by persistent, recurring urges to cross-dress. (From the Latin roots *trans-*, meaning "cross," and *vestis*, meaning "garment.")

Fetishism. In fetishism, inanimate objects such as leather shoes or boots elicit sexual arousal. Fetishists may derive sexual gratification by fondling, manipulating, or fantasizing about the object during masturbation. They may want the object to be present during sexual activity with, or to be worn by, their partners.

Transvestism. Transvestites cross-dress for the purpose of sexual gratification. Some transvestites sport feminine attire in public. Others cross-dress only in the privacy of their own homes.

Transvestism ranges from wearing a single female garment when alone to sporting dresses, wigs, makeup, and feminine mannerisms at a transvestite club. Most transvestites do not engage in antisocial or illegal behaviour. Most practise their sexual inclination in private and would be horrified or embarrassed to be discovered by associates while dressed as women.

Some transvestites persuade their female partners to permit them to wear feminine attire during their sexual activities. Most keep their transvestism a secret.

Exhibitionism

Exhibitionism A paraphilia characterized by persistent, powerful urges and sexual fantasies involving exposing one's genitals to unsuspecting strangers to achieve sexual arousal or gratification.

Exhibitionism ("flashing") involves persistent, powerful urges and sexual fantasies involving exposing one's genitals to unsuspecting strangers for the purpose of achieving sexual arousal or gratification. The urges are either acted upon or are disturbing to the individual. Exhibitionists are almost always males. What we know of exhibitionists is almost entirely derived from studies of men who have been apprehended or treated by mental health professionals. Such knowledge may yield a biased picture of exhibitionists. Relatively few reported incidents result in apprehension and conviction (Cox, 1988).

The prevalence of exhibitionism in the general population is unknown, but a survey of 846 college women at nine randomly selected U.S. universities found exposure to exhibitionism to be widespread. A third of the women reported that they had run into a "flasher" (Cox, 1988). Only 15 of the women had reported these incidents to the police.

The urge to exhibit oneself, if not the actual act, usually begins in early adolescence, generally between the ages of 13 and 16 (Freund et al., 1988). The frequency of exhibitionism declines markedly after the age of 40 (American Psychiatric Association, 2000).

It is understandable that an unsuspecting woman who is exposed to an exhibitionist may react with shock, surprise, or fear. Unfortunately, her display of shock or fear may reinforce the flasher's tendencies to expose himself. She may fear that the flasher is likely to assault her physically as well. Fortunately, most exhibitionists do not seek actual sexual contact with their victims and run away before they can be caught.

Some women may respond with anger, insults, even arguments that the offender should feel ashamed. A display of anger may reinforce exhibitionism. We do not recommend that the victim insult the flasher, lest it provoke a violent response. Although most exhibitionists are nonviolent, about one in ten has considered or attempted sexual assault (Gebhard et al., 1965).

When possible, showing no reaction or simply continuing on one's way may be the best response. If women do desire to respond to the flasher, they might calmly say something like "You really need professional help. You should see a professional to help you with this problem." They should report the incident to police, so that they can catch the offender.

Obscene Telephone Calling

Telephone scatologia A paraphilia characterized by the making of obscene telephone calls. (From the Greek *skatos*, meaning "excrement" and *logos*, meaning "speech.")

Like exhibitionists, obscene phone callers (almost all of whom are male) seek to become sexually aroused by shocking their victims. The American Psychiatric Association (2000) labels this type of paraphilia **telephone scatologia** (lewdness).

How to Respond to an Exhibitionist

The typical exhibitionist does not attempt further sexual contact with the victim. Thus, he does not usually pose a physical threat (American Psychiatric Association, 2000).

Victims of exhibitionism may feel violated and be bothered by recurrent images or nightmares. They may harbour misplaced guilt that they had somehow tempted the exhibitionist. They may also develop fears of venturing out on their own.

Geer and his colleagues (1984) see exhibitionism as an indirect means of expressing hostility toward women. Exposure may be an attempt by the exhibitionist to strike back at women because of a belief that women have wronged him or damaged his self-esteem by failing to notice him or take him seriously.

Other studies show exhibitionists to be shy, dependent, passive, lacking in sexual and social skills, even inhibited (Dwyer, 1988). They tend to be self-critical, to have doubts about their masculinity, and to suffer from feelings of inadequacy and inferiority (Blair &

Lanyon, 1981; Dwyer, 1988). Many have had poor relationships with their fathers and have overprotective mothers (Dwyer, 1988). Exhibitionists who are socially shy or inadequate may be using exhibitionism as a substitute for the intimate relationships they cannot develop.

The preferred victims are typically girls or young women (Freund & Blanchard, 1986). Exhibitionists may also need to risk being caught to experience a heightened erotic response (Stoller, 1977). The exhibitionist may even situate himself to increase the risk. For example, he may repeatedly expose himself in the same location or while sitting in his own easily identifiable car.

Since exhibitionism usually does not involve physical contact it has generally been regarded as a "nuisance" offence rather than a dangerous one. However, Canadian research with men either convicted of exhibitionism or diagnosed as exhibitionists according to psychiatric criteria suggests that a small but significant number will go on to commit other sexual (11.7%), violent (16.8%), or criminal offences (32.7%) (Greenberg et al., 2002). In another study, about 10% of rapists and child molesters began their

"sexual careers" by exposing themselves to strangers (Abel et al., 1984).

In the Criminal Code, exhibitionism is a crime under section 173, which deals with indecent acts.

Definitions of exhibitionism also bring into focus the boundaries between normal and abnormal behaviour. Are exotic dancers (stripteasers) or nude sunbathers exhibitionists? After all, aren't they also exposing themselves to strangers? But exotic dancers—male or female—usually remove their clothes to sexually excite or entertain an expectant audience, not themselves. Their motive is to earn a living or (arguably) to express themselves in dance. Sunbathers in their "birthday suits" may also seek to sexually arouse others, not themselves. Of course, they may also be seeking an all-over tan or trying to avoid feeling encumbered by clothing. In any case, stripteasers and sunbathers do not expose themselves to unsuspecting others. Thus these behaviours are not regarded as exhibitionistic.

It is also normal to become sexually excited while stripping before one's sex partner. Such stripping is done to elicit a positive response from one's partner, not to surprise or shock a stranger.

Obscene phone callers are generally motivated by a desire for sexual excitement and usually choose their victims randomly from the phone book or by chance dialling. They typically masturbate during the phone call or shortly afterwards. Most obscene phone callers are not dangerous. Most do not make repeat calls to the same person (Reinisch, 1990). However, research indicates that some men who engage in telephone scatalogia also exhibit other paraphilic behaviours, especially exhibitionism and voyeurism (Price et al., 2002; Bradford 1992). There are many patterns of obscene phone calling (Matek, 1988). Some callers limit themselves to obscenities. Others make sexual overtures. Some just breathe heavily. Others describe their masturbatory activity. Some profess to have previously met the victim at a social gathering or through a mutual acquaintance. Some even present themselves as "taking a sex survey" and ask provocative questions.

The typical obscene phone caller is a socially inadequate heterosexual male. The relative safety and anonymity of the telephone may shield him from the risk of rejection. A reaction of shock or fright from his victims may fill him with feelings of power and control that are lacking in his life, especially in his relationships with women. The obscenities may vent the rage that he holds against women who have rejected him.

What should a woman do if she receives an obscene phone call? Advice generally parallels that given to women who are victimized by exhibitionists. Above all, women are advised to remain calm and not reveal shock or fright, since such reactions tend to reinforce the caller and increase the probability of repeat calls. The best response is to hang up. If she should receive repeated calls, the woman might request an unlisted number, obtain caller ID from the telephone company, or contact the police about tracing the calls. Under the Criminal Code, this behaviour could constitute criminal harassment.

Voyeurism

Voyeurism A paraphilia characterized by strong, repetitive urges and related sexual fantasies of observing unsuspecting strangers who are naked, disrobing, or engaged in sexual relations. (From the French verb *voir*, meaning "to see.")

Voyeurism involves strong, repetitive urges to observe unsuspecting strangers who are naked, disrobing, or engaged in sexual relations (American Psychiatric Association, 2000). The voyeur becomes sexually aroused by the act of watching and typically does not seek sexual relations with the observed person. Like fetishism and exhibitionism, voyeurism is found almost exclusively among males. It usually begins before the age of 15 (American Psychiatric Association, 2000).

The voyeur may masturbate while "peeping" or afterward while "replaying" the incident. The voyeur may fantasize about making love to the observed person but have no intention of actually doing so.

Are people voyeurs who become sexually aroused by the sight of their lovers undressing? What about people who enjoy watching pornographic films or stripteasers? No, no, and no. The people being observed are not unsuspecting strangers. The lover knows that his or her partner is watching. Porn actors and strippers know that others will be viewing them. They would not be "performing" if they did not expect or have an audience.

It is perfectly normal for men and women to be sexually stimulated by the sight of other people who are nude, undressing, or engaged in sexual relations. Voyeurism is characterized by urges to "peep" on *unsuspecting* strangers.

Voyeurs often put themselves in risky situations in which they face the prospect of being discovered or apprehended. They may risk physical injury by perching themselves in trees or otherwise assuming precarious positions to catch a preferred view of their target. They will occupy rooftops and fire escapes in brutal winter weather. Peepers can be patient. They may wait hour after hour, night after night, for a glimpse of an unsuspecting person. Part of the sexual excitement seems to stem from the risks voyeurs run.

Although most voyeurs are nonviolent, some commit violent crimes like assault and rape (Langevin et al., 1985). Voyeurs who break into and enter homes or buildings, or who tap at windows to gain the attention of victims, are among the more dangerous. Voyeurism can be a prosecutable crime in Canada, under section 177 of the Criminal Code (trespassing at night).

Compared to other types of sex offenders, voyeurs tend to be less sexually experienced and are less likely to be married (Gebhard et al., 1965). Like exhibitionists, voyeurs tend to harbour feelings of inadequacy and to lack social and sexual skills (Dwyer, 1988). They may thus have difficulty forming romantic relationships with women. Yet not all voyeurs are socially awkward and inept with women.

Sexual Masochism

Although pleasure and pain may seem like polar opposites, some people experience sexual pleasure through having pain or humiliation inflicted on them by their sex partners. People who associate the receipt of pain or humiliation with sexual arousal are called sexual masochists. A sexual masochist either acts upon or is distressed by persistent urges and sexual fantasies involving the desire to be bound, flogged, humiliated, or made to suffer in some way by a sexual partner so as to achieve sexual excitement. In extreme cases the person is incapable of becoming sexually aroused unless pain or humiliation is incorporated into the sexual act.

Sexual masochism A paraphilia characterized by the desire or need for pain or humiliation to enhance sexual arousal so that gratification may be attained. (From the name of the author Leopold von Sacher-Masoch.)

Sexual masochism is the only paraphilia that is found among women with some frequency (American Psychiatric Association, 2000; Baumeister, 1988). Even sexual masochism is much more prevalent among men than women, however. Male masochists may outnumber females by a margin of 20 to 1 (American Psychiatric Association, 2000).

The word *masochism* is derived from the name of the Austrian storyteller Leopold von Sacher-Masoch (1835–1895). He wrote tales of men who derived sexual satisfaction from having a female partner inflict pain on them, typically by flagellation (beating or whipping).

Sexual masochists may derive pleasure from various types of punishing experiences, including being restrained (a practice known as **bondage**), blindfolded (sensory bondage), spanked, whipped, or made to perform humiliating acts, such as walking around on all fours and licking the boots or shoes of the sex partner, or being subjected to vulgar insults. Some masochists have their partners humiliate them by urinating or defecating on them. Some masochists seek pain. Sexual masochists and **sexual sadists** often form sexual relationships to meet each other's needs. Some sexual masochists enlist the services of prostitutes or obtain the cooperation of their regular sexual partners to enact their masochistic fantasies.

It may seem contradictory for pain to become connected with sexual pleasure. The association of sexual arousal with mildly painful stimuli is actually quite common, however. Kinsey and his colleagues (1953) reported that perhaps as many as one person in four has experienced erotic sensations from being bitten during lovemaking. The eroticization of mild forms of pain (love bites, hair pulls, minor scratches) may fall within the normal range of sexual variation.

Baumeister (1988) proposes that independent and responsible selfhood becomes burdensome or stressful at times. Sexual masochism provides a temporary reprieve from the responsibilities of independent selfhood. It is a blunting of one's ordinary level of self-awareness that is achieved by "focusing on immediate sensations (both painful and pleasant) and on being a sexual object" (Baumeister, 1988, p. 54).

Sexual masochism can range from relatively benign to potentially lethal practices, like **hypoxyphilia**. People who practise hypoxyphilia may place plastic bags over their heads or nooses around their necks during sexual acts to enhance their sexual arousal by being temporarily deprived of oxygen. Or they may apply pressure to their chests. Oxygen deprivation is usually accompanied by sexual fantasies of being strangled by a lover. People usually discontinue oxygen deprivation before they lose consciousness, but some miscalculations result in death by suffocation (Blanchard & Hucker, 1991; Cosgray et al., 1991).

Sexual Sadism

Sadism is named after the infamous Marquis de Sade (1774–1814), a Frenchman who wrote tales of becoming sexually aroused by inflicting pain or humiliation on others. The virtuous Justine, the heroine of his best-known novel of the same name, endures terrible suffering at the hands of fiendish men. She is at one time bound and spread-eagled so that bloodhounds can savage her. She then seeks refuge with a surgeon who tries to dismember her. Later she falls into the clutches of a sabre-wielding mass murderer, but Nature saves her with a timely thunderbolt.

Sexual sadism is characterized by persistent, powerful urges and sexual fantasies involving the inflicting of pain and suffering on others to achieve sexual excitement or gratification. The urges are acted on or are disturbing enough to cause personal distress. Some sexual sadists cannot become sexually aroused unless they make their sex partners suffer. Others can become sexually excited without such acts.

Some sadists hurt or humiliate willing partners, such as prostitutes or sexual masochists. Others—clearly a small minority—stalk and attack nonconsenting victims.

Sadomasochism Sadomasochism (or S&M) involves *mutually gratifying* sexual interactions between *consenting partners*. Occasional S&M is quite common among the general population. Couples may incorporate mild or light forms of S&M in their lovemaking now and then, such as mild dominance and submission games or gentle physical restraint. It is also not uncommon for lovers to scratch or bite their partners to heighten their mutual arousal during coitus. They generally do not inflict severe pain or damage, however.

Twenty-two percent of the men and 12% of the women surveyed by Kinsey and his colleagues (1953) reported at least some sexual response to sadomasochistic stories. Although some milder forms of sadomasochism may fall within the boundaries of normal sexual variation, sadomasochism becomes pathological when such fantasies are acted

Bondage Ritual restraint, as by shackles, as practised by many sexual masochists.

Sexual sadists People who become sexually aroused by inflicting pain or humiliation on others.

Hypoxyphilia A practice in which a person seeks to enhance sexual arousal, usually during masturbation, by becoming deprived of oxygen. (From the Greek root meaning "under" [hypo-].)

Sadism A paraphilia characterized by the desire or need to inflict pain or humiliation on others to enhance sexual arousal so that gratification is attained. (From the name of the author Marquis de Sade.)

Sadomasochism A mutually gratifying sexual interaction between consenting sex partners in which sexual arousal is associated with the infliction and receipt of pain or humiliation. Commonly known as S&M.

upon in ways that become destructive, dangerous, or distressing to oneself or others, as we find in the following case example:

> A 25-year-old female graduate student described a range of masochistic experiences. She reported feelings of sexual excitement during arguments with her husband when he would scream at her or hit her in a rage. She would sometimes taunt him to make love to her in a brutal fashion, as though she were being raped. She found the brutality and sense of being punished to be sexually stimulating. She had also begun having sex with strange men and enjoyed being physically punished by them during sex more than any other type of sexual stimulus. Being beaten or whipped produced the most intense sexual experiences she had ever had. Although she recognized the dangers posed by her sexual behaviour, and felt somewhat ashamed about it, she was not sure that she wanted treatment for "it" because of the pleasure that it provided her.

(Adapted from Spitzer et al., 1989, pp. 87–88)

In one subculture, sadomasochism is the preferred or even the exclusive form of sexual gratification. People in this subculture seek one another out through mutual contacts, S&M social organizations, or personal ads in S&M magazines. The S&M subculture has spawned magazines and clubs catering to people who describe themselves as "into S&M," as well as sex shops that sell sadomasochistic paraphernalia. These include leather restraints and leather face masks that resemble the ancient masks of executioners.

Sadomasochists often engage in highly elaborate rituals involving dominance and submission. Rituals are staged like scenes in a play (Weinberg et al., 1984). In the "master and slave" game, the sadist leads the masochist around by a leash. The masochist performs degrading or menial acts. In "bondage and discipline" (B&D), the dominant partner restrains the submissive partner and flagellates (spanks or whips) or sexually stimulates the submissive partner. The erotic appeal of bondage seems connected with controlling or being controlled.

Various types of stimulation may be used to administer pain during S&M encounters, but pain is not always employed. When it is, it is usually mild or moderate. Psychological pain, or humiliation, may be as common as physical pain. Pain may also be used symbolically, as in the case of a sadist who uses a harmless, soft rubber paddle to spank the masochist. So the erotic appeal of pain for some S&M participants may derive from the ritual of control rather than from the pain itself (Weinberg, 1987).

S&M participants may be heterosexual, gay, or bisexual (Breslow et al., 1986). They may assume either the masochistic or the sadistic role, or may alternate roles. Persons who seek to enact both sadistic and masochistic roles are known as *sadomasochists*. In heterosexual relationships the partners may reverse traditional gender roles. The man may assume the submissive or masochistic role, and the woman may take the dominant or sadistic role (Reinisch, 1990).

S&M Paraphernalia. *People who participate in S&M often incorporate handcuffs and other paraphernalia into their sadomasochistic encounters.*

The causes of sexual masochism and sadism, as of other paraphilias, are unclear. Ford and Beach (1951) speculated that humans may possess a physiological capacity to experience heightened sexual arousal from the receipt or infliction of pain (which may explain the prevalence of love bites). Mild pain may heighten physiological arousal both in the aggressor and victim, adding to the effects of sexual stimulation. Yet intense pain is likely to decrease rather than increase sexual arousal.

Pain may also have more direct biological links to pleasure. Natural chemicals called endorphins, similar to opiates, are released in the brain in response to pain and produce feelings of euphoria and general well-being. Perhaps, then, pleasure is derived from pain due to the release or augmentation of endorphins (Weinberg, 1987). This theory fails to explain the erotic appeal of sadomasochistic encounters that involve minimal pain, however. Nor does it explain the erotic appeal to the sadist of inflicting pain.

Whatever their causes, the roots of sexual masochism and sadism apparently date to childhood. Sadomasochistic behaviour commonly begins in early adulthood, but sadomasochistic fantasies are likely to have been present during childhood (American Psychiatric Association, 1994; Breslow et al., 1986).

Frotteurism

Frotteurism (also known as "mashing") is rubbing against or touching a nonconsenting person. Mashing has been reported exclusively among males (Spitzer et al., 1989).

Most mashing takes place in crowded places, such as buses, subway cars, or elevators. The man finds the rubbing or the touching, not the coercive nature of the act, to be sexually stimulating. While rubbing against a woman, he may fantasize a consensual, affectionate sexual relationship with her. Typically the man incorporates images of his mashing within his masturbation fantasies. Mashing also incorporates a related practice, **toucherism**: fondling nonconsenting strangers.

Mashing may be so fleeting and furtive that the woman may not realize what has happened (Spitzer et al., 1989). Mashers thus stand little chance of being caught.

Many mashers have difficulties forming relationships with women and are handicapped by fears of rejection. Mashing provides sexual contact in a relatively nonthreatening context.

Other Paraphilias

Let us consider some other less common paraphilias.

Zoophilia A person with **zoophilia** experiences repeated, intense urges and related fantasies involving sexual contact with animals. As with other paraphilias, the urges may be acted upon or cause personal distress. A child or adolescent who shows some sexual response to an occasional episode of rough-and-tumble play with the family pet is thus not displaying zoophilia.

The term *bestiality* applies to actual sexual contact with an animal. Kinsey and his colleagues (1948, 1953) found that men more often had sexual contact with farm animals, such as calves and sheep. Women more often reported sexual contacts with household pets. Urban–rural differences also emerged. Sexual contact with an animal is an offence under section 160 of the Criminal Code.

Necrophilia In **necrophilia**, a rare paraphilia, a person desires sex with corpses. Three types of necrophilia have been identified (Rosman & Resnick, 1989). In *regular necrophilia*, the person has sex with a deceased person. In *necrophilic homicide*, the person commits murder to obtain a corpse for sexual purposes. In *necrophilic fantasy*, the person fantasizes about sex with a corpse but does not actually carry out necrophilic acts. Necrophiles often obtain jobs that provide them with access to corpses, such as working in cemeteries, morgues, or funeral homes. The primary motivation for necrophilia appears to be the desire to sexually possess a completely nonresistant and nonrejecting partner (Rosman & Resnick, 1989). Many necrophiles are clearly mentally disturbed. In Canada, sexual contact with a corpse is a crime punishable by five years in prison.

Less Common Paraphilias In **klismaphilia**, sexual arousal is derived from use of enemas. Klismaphiles generally prefer the receiving role to the giving role. Klismaphiles may have derived sexual pleasure in infancy or childhood from the anal stimulation provided by parents giving them enemas.

In **coprophilia**, sexual arousal is connected with feces. The person may desire to be defecated on or to defecate on a sex partner. The association of feces with sexual arousal may also be a throwback to childhood. Many children appear to obtain anal sexual pleasure by holding in and then purposefully expelling feces. It may also be that the incidental connection between erections or sexual arousal and soiled diapers during infancy eroticizes feces.

Frotteurism A paraphilia characterized by recurrent, powerful sexual urges and related fantasies involving rubbing against or touching a nonconsenting person. (From the French *frotter*, meaning "to rub.")

Toucherism A practice related to frotteurism and characterized by the persistent urge to fondle nonconsenting strangers.

Zoophilia A paraphilia involving persistent or repeated sexual urges and related fantasies involving sexual contact with animals.

Necrophilia A paraphilia characterized by desire for sexual activity with corpses. (From the Greek *nekros*, meaning "dead body.")

Klismaphilia A paraphilia in which sexual arousal is derived from use of enemas.

Coprophilia A paraphilia in which sexual arousal is attained in connection with feces. (From the Greek *copros*, meaning "dung.")

Urophilia A paraphilia in which sexual arousal is associated with urine.

In **urophilia**, sexual arousal is associated with urine. As with coprophilia, the person may desire to be urinated upon or to urinate upon a sexual partner. Also like coprophilia, urophilia may have childhood origins. Stimulation of the urethral canal during urination may become associated with sexual pleasure. Or urine may have become eroticized by experiences in which erections occurred while the infant was clothed in a wet diaper.

Theoretical Perspectives

The paraphilias are among the most fascinating and perplexing variations in sexual behaviour. Let us consider explanations that have been advanced from the major theoretical perspectives.

Biological Perspectives

Little is known about whether there are biological factors in paraphilic behaviour. Efforts to date to find concrete evidence of brain damage or abnormalities among people with paraphilias have failed (e.g., Langevin et al., 1989). Because testosterone is linked to sex drive, researchers have also focused on differences in testosterone levels between people with paraphilias and people without them. A study of hormonal differences between a group of 16 male exhibitionists and controls found no differences in overall levels of testosterone, but the exhibitionists had elevated levels of the measure of testosterone believed to be most closely linked to sex drive (Lang et al., 1989). Yet many of the people with paraphilias studied fell within the normal range.

Psychoanalytic Perspectives

Nymphomania An excessive, insatiable sexual appetite or drive in women. (From the Greek roots *nymphe*, meaning "a bride," and *mania*, which means "madness.")

Satyriasis An excessive, insatiable sexual appetite or drive in men. (After *satyr*, a sexually insatiable, goat-legged creature with pointed ears and short horns in Greek mythology. Satyrs were part man, part beast.)

Don Juanism An excessive, insatiable sexual appetite or drive in men. (After the fictional Spanish nobleman who was unable to obtain true sexual gratification despite numerous affairs.)

Hypersexuality An excessive or apparently insatiable sex drive that disrupts the person's ability to concentrate on other needs or leads to self-defeating behaviour, such as indiscriminate sexual contacts.

Classical psychoanalytic theory suggests that paraphilias are psychological defences, usually against unresolved castration anxiety dating back to the Oedipus complex (Fenichel, 1945). To the transvestic man, the sight of a woman's vagina threatens to arouse castration anxiety. It reminds him that women do not have penises and that he might suffer the same fate. Sequestering his penis beneath women's clothing symbolically asserts that women do have penises, which provides unconscious reassurance against his own fears of castration.

By exposing his genitals, the exhibitionist unconsciously seeks reassurance that his penis is secure. It is as if he were asserting, "Look! I have a penis!" Shock or surprise on the victim's face acknowledges that his penis still exists, temporarily relieving unconscious castration anxiety.

Masturbation with a fetishistic object (a shoe, for example) allows the fetishist to gratify his sexual desires while keeping a safe distance from the fantasized dangers that he unconsciously associates with sexual contact with women. Or the fetishistic object itself—the shoe—may unconsciously symbolize the penis. Stroking a woman's shoe during sexual relations, or fantasizing about one, may unconsciously provide reassurance that the man's own penis, symbolically represented by the fetishistic object, is secure.

In one psychoanalytic view of voyeurism, the man is unconsciously denying castration by searching for a penis among women victims. Other psychoanalytic views suggest that the voyeur is identifying with the man in the observed couple as he had identified with his own father during childhood observations of the parental coitus—the so-called primal scene. Perhaps he is trying to "master" the primal scene by compulsively reliving it.

Psychoanalytic explanations of sadism suggest that sadists are attempting to defend themselves against unconscious feelings of impotence and powerlessness by inflicting pain on others. The recipients' shouts of pain or confessions of unworthiness make sadists feel masculine and powerful.

Psychoanalytic theory suggests that masochism in the male may be the turning inward of aggressive impulses originally aimed toward the powerful, threatening father. The flagellation or bondage may also be unconsciously preferred to castration as a form of punishment for having unacceptable sexual feelings. Like the child who experiences

Theoretical Perspectives 321

A World of Diversity

Nymphomania, Satyriasis, and the Sexual Double Standard

Sarah R., a never-married, 39-year-old artist became sexually active in her junior year in high school and has rarely been without at least one or two lovers ever since. Whenever she has not had an opportunity for sexual intercourse for several weeks or longer, for one reason or another, she has felt quite uncomfortable, or as she put it, "horny and hard-up." She has had two unwanted pregnancies, both of which resulted in abortions, and has contracted gonorrhea on three separate occasions and has suffered several times from infestations of pubic lice. She continues to be troubled with recurrent episodes of genital herpes. She generally limits her sexual relationships to one or two partners, but has on occasion maintained sexual relationships at the same time with three or four men. She engages in sexual intercourse two or three times a week, on the average, and engages in masturbation to relieve her sexual urges when intercourse is not possible.

Both her family practitioner and gynecologist, who have treated her for years, consider her to be a nymphomaniac. Her gynecologist says of her, "Of course she has herpes. What can you expect with the kind of sexual excesses she indulges in? She's a real nympho."

(Goldberg, 1987, p. 204)

Would you have reached the same conclusion as Sarah's physicians did? Why, or why not? What criteria would you use to define **nymphomania**? Perhaps most readers have heard of nymphomania, but only a few are likely to be acquainted with the terms describing the same condition in men, **satyriasis or Don Juanism**.

The fact that nymphomania is more commonly used in our society than the male counterpart underscores the traditional double standard in Western society (Groneman, 1994). Greater sexual liberties are accorded to men than women. A man who has a number of flings is likely to be labelled a "playboy," a "Casanova," or even a "stud." A woman who does so is likely to be branded with labels that carry negative connotations, such as "nympho," "slut," or "whore."

Clinicians prefer to use the term **hypersexuality** to refer to nymphomania in women and satyriasis in men, thereby avoiding disparaging connotations. No absolute criteria exist, however, for determining hypersexuality or establishing the boundary between normal sexuality and hypersexuality. Some people might consider a person who requires a sexual release through masturbation or coitus more than once daily to be hypersexual. Others draw the line at two, three, or perhaps six or ten or more times daily. Among some couples, the partner desiring less frequent sexual activity may label the other as "oversexed." But what defines "oversexed" in one relationship may be considered normal, or subnormal, in another.

Clinicians may determine the boundaries of hypersexuality not by the sheer frequency of sexual activity but by the compulsive or self-defeating nature of the behaviour.

Hypersexual people may use sex as a means of buttressing a flagging sense of self-esteem. They may feel driven to a series of sexual conquests or brief encounters to reassure themselves that they are desirable, or masculine or feminine enough. Because they lack true intimacy, however, the encounters leave them feeling empty and sexually unfulfilled. Such relationships provide only a temporary salve for feelings of self-doubt or unworthiness. The person quickly loses sexual interest in the new partner once the conquest or brief encounter has occurred and begins searching for another. Partners are treated like objects to be used and discarded.

Return to Sarah. Do the facts of her case suggest hypersexuality? Did Sarah feel a lack of control over her sexual urges? Did she feel compelled to engage in sexual behaviours that put herself at risk of incurring unwanted pregnancies or sexually transmitted diseases?

Goldberg (1987) argues that Sarah's physicians labelled her as a nymphomaniac because her behaviour did not meet social expectations of female sexuality. Goldberg (1987) comments, "In all likelihood, a 39-year-old man living the sort of life that Sarah is living would not be regarded as suffering from satyriasis or, indeed, as being sexually abnormal in any way" (p. 204). Does the label of nymphomania represent a sexist tendency to judge women and men by different sets of social standards?

relief when punishment is over, the sexual masochist willingly accepts immediate punishment in the form of flagellation or bondage in place of the future punishment of castration. Or a woman who witnessed her parents having coitus at an early age may have misperceived the father to be assaulting the mother. Her masochism then represents her unconscious reliving of her mother's (imagined) role with her father. Sexual masochists of either gender may also have such high levels of sex guilt that they can permit themselves to experience sexual pleasure only if they are adequately punished for it during sex.

The paraphilias have provided a fertile ground for psychoanalytic theories. However, there is a lack of evidence to support the role of such unconscious processes as unresolved castration anxiety. The basic shortcoming of psychoanalytic theory is that many of its key concepts involve unconscious mechanisms that cannot be directly observed or measured. So psychoanalytic theories remain interesting but speculative hypotheses about the origins of atypical sexual behaviour patterns.

Nymphomania: The Historical Construction of Female Sexuality
www.academicarmageddon .co.uk/library/GRONE.htm
An article by Carol Groneman that examines the medical history of nymphomania in the late nineteenth and early twentieth centuries.

Learning Perspectives

Learning theorists believe that fetishes and other paraphilias are learned behaviours that are acquired through experience. An object may acquire sexually arousing properties through association with sexual arousal or orgasm. Like Pavlov's dogs, who learned to salivate to the ringing of a bell that had been repeatedly paired with food, "an animal may become conditioned to respond not only to particular stimuli, but to objects and other phenomena which were associated with the original experience… In the laboratory, male animals may respond to particular dishes, to particular boards, or to particular pieces of furniture with which some female has had contact" (Kinsey et al., 1953, p. 647).

According to the conditioning model, a boy who catches a glimpse of his mother's stockings hanging on the towel rack while he is masturbating may go on to develop a fetish for stockings (Breslow, 1989). Orgasm in the presence of the object would reinforce the erotic connection, especially if the experience occurs repeatedly.

Breslow (1989) proposes a learning theory explanation that describes the development of paraphilias in terms of the gradual acquisition of sexual arousal to an unusual object or activity through its incorporation in masturbatory fantasies. A transvestite, for example, may have had an erection while trying on his mother's panties in childhood. The paraphilic object or activity is then incorporated within masturbatory fantasies and is reinforced by orgasm. The paraphilic object or activity is then repeatedly used as a masturbatory aid, further strengthening the erotic bond.

Fetishistic interests can often be traced to early childhood. Some rubber fetishists, for example, recall erotic interests in rubber objects since early childhood. Reinisch (1990) speculates that for some rubber fetishists, the earliest awareness of sexual arousal or response (such as erection) may have been associated with the presence of rubber pants, diapers, and so forth, such that a connection was formed between the two. The fetishistic act may represent an attempt to recapture sexual or loving feelings from early childhood.

McGuire and his colleagues (1965) report a case that provides some support for the role of learning in the development of exhibitionism. Two young males were surprised by an attractive woman while urinating. Although embarrassed at the time, their memories of the incident were sexually stimulating, and they masturbated repeatedly while fantasizing about it. The fantasies persisted, possibly reinforced by frequent orgasms. After a while, the young men purposely began to expose themselves to rekindle the high level of sexual excitement.

Friedrich and Gerber (1994) studied five adolescent boys who practised hypoxyphilia and found extensive early histories of choking in combination with physical or sexual abuse. The combination seems to have encouraged each of the boys to associate choking with sexual arousal.

Learning explanations of sexual masochism focus on the pairing of sexual excitement with punishment. For example, a child may be punished when discovered masturbating. Or a boy may reflexively experience an erection if his penis accidentally rubs against the parent's body as he is being spanked. With repeated encounters like these, pain and pleasure may become linked in the person's sexual arousal system. Another learning explanation focuses on the association of pain with parental affection (Breslow, 1989; Sue et al., 1981). A child with cold and indifferent parents may be hugged only following a spanking. The pain or humiliation associated with the spanking becomes associated with the affection of the hug, which leads in later life to pain becoming a prerequisite for sexual pleasure.

Why do some people who are exposed to early conditioning experiences develop paraphilic interests, whereas others do not? Predisposing factors may include poor self-esteem and difficulties forming intimate relationships. Many exhibitionists, voyeurs, frotteurs, and other people with paraphilias have few interpersonal skills in relating to women. They may avoid customary social interactions with women for fear of rejection. Their furtive, paraphilic behaviours may provide a sexual release with minimal risks of rejection or apprehension and be maintained because they represent the only available source of sexual gratification or reinforcement. Some paraphilias, such as voyeurism, exhibitionism, and frotteurism, may also be conceptualized as *courtship disorders*, involving an exaggeration or distortion of the steps normally taken during courtship in identifying, approaching, and becoming more intimate with new sexual partners (Freund & Blanchard, 1986).

Sociological Perspectives

Martin Weinberg (1987) proposes a sociological model that focuses on the social context of sadomasochism. Weinberg notes that S&M rituals generally involve some form of dominance and submission and attributes their erotic appeal to the opportunity to reverse the customary power relationships that exist between the genders and social classes in society at large. Within the confines of the carefully scripted S&M encounter, the meek can be powerful and the powerful meek (Geer et al., 1984). Dominance and submission games also allow opportunities to accentuate or reverse the gender stereotypes that identify masculinity with dominance and femininity with submissiveness.

Individual sadomasochistic interests may become institutionalized as an S&M subculture in societies (like ours) that have certain social characteristics: (1) dominance–submission relationships are embedded within the culture, and aggression is socially valued; (2) there is an unequal distribution of power between people from different gender or social class categories; (3) there are enough affluent people to enable them to participate in such leisure-time activities; and (4) imagination and creativity, important elements in the development of S&M scripts and fantasies, are socially valued and encouraged (Weinberg, 1987).

An Integrated Perspective: The "Lovemap"

The paraphilias may have multiple biological, psychological, and sociocultural origins (Money, 1994). Money and Lamacz (1989) trace the origins of paraphilias to childhood. They believe that childhood experiences etch a pattern in the brain, called a **lovemap**, that determines the types of stimuli and activities that become sexually arousing to the individual. In the case of paraphilias, these lovemaps become distorted or "vandalized" by early traumatic experiences, such as incest, overbearing antisexual upbringing, and physical abuse or neglect.

Research suggests that voyeurs and exhibitionists often were the victims of childhood sexual abuse (Dwyer, 1988). Not all children exposed to such influences develop paraphilic compulsions, however. A genetic predisposition, hormonal factors, brain abnormalities, or a combination of these and other factors may play a role in determining one's vulnerability to vandalized lovemaps (Brody, 1990).

Lovemap A representation in the mind and in the brain of the idealized lover and the idealized erotic activity with the lover.

Review of Lovemaps
www.sexuality.org/l/pl/pl06.html
A review of *Lovemaps*, a book in which John Money outlines his ideas on the origins and treatment of paraphilias.

Treatment of the Paraphilias

The treatment of these atypical patterns of sexual behaviour raises a number of issues. First, people with paraphilias usually do not want or seek treatment, at least not voluntarily. They are generally seen by mental health workers only when they come into conflict with the law or at the urging of their family members or sexual partners. Second, helping professionals traditionally help clients clarify or meet their own goals; it is not their role to impose societal goals on the individual. Many helping professionals believe that the criminal justice system, and not they, ought to enforce social standards. Third, unless the motivation to change is present, therapeutic efforts may be wasted. Fourth, most therapies require that people accept personal responsibility for their actions as a prelude to change. Yet sex offenders tend to claim that they are unable to control their urges.

Despite these issues, many offenders are referred for treatment by the courts. A few seek therapy themselves because they have come to see that their behaviour is harmful. Let us consider some of the ways in which therapists treat people with these atypical sexual behaviours.

Behaviour therapy The systematic application of the principles of learning to help people modify problem behaviour.

Systematic desensitization A method for terminating the connection between a stimulus (such as a fetishistic object) and an inappropriate response (such as sexual arousal to the paraphilic stimulus). Muscle relaxation is practised in connection with each stimulus in a series of increasingly arousing stimuli, so that the person learns to remain relaxed (and not sexually aroused) in their presence.

Aversion therapy A method for terminating undesirable sexual behaviour in which the behaviour is repeatedly paired with an aversive stimulus, such as electric shock, so that a conditioned aversion develops.

Covert sensitization A form of aversion therapy in which thoughts of engaging in undesirable behaviour are paired repeatedly with imagined aversive stimuli.

Pedophiles Persons with pedophilia, a paraphilia involving sexual interest in children.

Social skills training Behaviour therapy methods for building social skills that rely on a therapist's coaching and practice.

Orgasmic reconditioning A method for strengthening the connection between sexual arousal and appropriate sexual stimuli (such as fantasies about an adult of the other gender) by repeatedly pairing the desired stimuli with orgasm.

Psychotherapy

Psychoanalysis focuses on resolving the unconscious conflicts that are believed to originate in childhood and to give rise in adulthood to pathological problems such as paraphilias. The aim of therapy is to help bring unconscious conflicts, principally Oedipal conflicts, into conscious awareness so that they may be worked on. Although some favourable case results have been reported (e.g., Rosen, 1967), psychoanalytic therapy of the paraphilias has not been subjected to experimental analysis. We thus do not know whether successes are due to the psychoanalytic treatment itself or to other factors, such as spontaneous improvement or a client's willingness to change.

Behaviour Therapy

Behaviour therapy focuses directly on changing behaviour. A number of techniques have been used to help eliminate paraphilic behaviours. **Systematic desensitization** attempts to break the link between the sexual stimulus (such as a fetishistic stimulus) and the inappropriate response (sexual arousal). The client is taught to relax muscle groups. Muscle relaxation is then paired repeatedly with paraphilic images or fantasies. Relaxation comes to replace sexual arousal in response to these stimuli. In one case study, a fetishistic transvestite who had become attracted to his mother's lingerie at age 13 was taught to relax when presented with audiotaped scenes representing transvestite or fetishistic themes (Fensterheim & Kantor, 1980). He played such tapes daily while remaining relaxed. He later reported a complete absence of transvestite thoughts or activities.

In **aversion therapy**, the undesirable sexual behaviour (for example, masturbation to fetishistic fantasies) is paired repeatedly with an aversive stimulus (such as a harmless but painful electric shock or a nausea-inducing chemical) in the hope that the client will develop a conditioned aversion toward the paraphilic behaviour.

Covert sensitization is a variation of aversion therapy in which paraphilic fantasies are paired with an aversive stimulus in imagination. In a broad-scale application, 38 **pedophiles** and 62 exhibitionists, more than half of whom were court-referred, were treated by pairing imagined aversive odours or images with fantasies of the problem behaviour (Maletzky, 1980). Clients were instructed to fantasize pedophiliac or exhibitionistic scenes. Then,

> at a point... when sexual pleasure is aroused, aversive images are presented....
> Examples might include a pedophiliac fellating a child, but discovering a festering
> sore on the boy's penis; an exhibitionist exposing to a woman but suddenly being
> discovered by his wife or the police; or a pedophiliac laying a young boy down in a
> field, only to lie next to him in a pile of dog feces.
>
> (MALETZKY, 1980, P. 308)

Maletzky used this treatment weekly for six months, then followed it with "booster sessions" every three months over a three-year period. The procedure resulted in at least a 75% reduction of the deviant activities and fantasies for over 80% of the study participants at follow-up periods of up to 36 months.

Social skills training focuses on helping the individual improve his ability to relate to other people and to develop appropriate sexual relationships.

Orgasmic reconditioning aims to increase sexual arousal to socially appropriate sexual stimuli by pairing culturally appropriate imagery with orgasmic pleasure. The person is instructed to become sexually aroused by masturbating to paraphilic images or fantasies. But as he approaches the point of orgasm, he switches to "appropriate imagery," such as photos of *Playboy* models. Orgasm is thus paired with socially acceptable images, which gain the capacity to elicit sexual arousal.

Biochemical Approaches

No drug or surgical technique eliminates paraphilic urges and behaviour. Yet some progress has been reported in using antidepressants (fluoxetine, sertraline, fluvoxamine) in treating exhibitionism, voyeurism, and fetishism (Emmanuel et al., 1992; Lorefice, 1991; Miller, 1995; Bradford, 2001). In addition to treating depression, antidepressants have been helpful in treating obsessive–compulsive disorder, a type of emotional disorder involving recurrent obsessions (intrusive ideas) and/or compulsions (urges to repeat a certain behaviour or thought). Paraphilias involve obsessions and compulsions.

People who experience such intense urges that they are at risk of committing sexual offences may be helped by **anti-androgen drugs**, which reduce the level of testosterone in the bloodstream (Marshall et al., 1991). Medroxyprogesterone acetate (MPA) (trade name: Depo-Provera), which can be administered in weekly injections, has been used extensively in the treatment of sex offenders. Anti-androgens reduce sexual desire and the frequencies of erections and ejaculations (Cooper, 1986; Money, 1987b). Yet Depo-Provera does not change the types of stimuli that the individual finds arousing.

Although we have amassed a great deal of research on atypical variations in sexual behaviour, our understanding of and treatment approaches to them remain largely in their infancy.

Anti-androgen drug
A chemical substance that reduces the sex drive by lowering the level of testosterone in the bloodstream.

Summing Up

Normal Versus Deviant Sexual Behaviour

What is considered normal in one culture or at a particular time may be considered abnormal in other cultures or at other times. Atypical patterns of sexual arousal or behaviour that become problematic in the eyes of the individual or society are labelled *paraphilias*.

The Paraphilias

Paraphilias involve sexual arousal in response to unusual stimuli such as children or other nonconsenting persons, certain objects, or pain or humiliation. The psychiatric diagnosis of paraphilia requires that the person has acted on these persistent urges or is distinctly distressed by them. Except in the case of sexual masochism, paraphilias are believed to occur almost exclusively among men.

In **fetishism**, an inanimate object comes to elicit sexual arousal. In partialism, people are inordinately aroused by a particular body part, such as the feet. Whereas other fetishists become sexually aroused by handling the fetishistic object while they masturbate, **transvestites** become excited by wearing articles of clothing—the fetishistic objects—of the other gender. An **exhibitionist** experiences the compulsion to expose himself to strangers. The typical exhibitionist does not attempt further sexual contact with the victim and does not pose a physical threat. The **obscene telephone caller** is motivated to become sexually aroused by shocking his victim. Such callers typically masturbate during the phone call or shortly afterward. **Voyeurs** become sexually aroused by watching and do not seek sexual relations with the target. The voyeur may masturbate while peeping or afterward while engaging in voyeuristic fantasies. Like exhibitionists, voyeurs tend to harbour feelings of inadequacy and poor self-esteem and to lack social and sexual skills. **Sexual masochists** associate the receipt of pain or humiliation with sexual arousal. Sexual masochists and sexual sadists sometimes form liaisons to meet each other's needs. **Sexual sadism** is characterized by persistent, powerful urges and sexual fantasies involving the inflicting of pain and suffering on others to achieve sexual excitement or gratification. Sadomasochists enjoy playing both sadistic and masochistic roles. Most acts of **frotteurism**—rubbing against nonconsenting persons, also known as mashing—take place in crowded places, such as buses, subway cars, or elevators. **Other paraphilias** include zoophilia (the desire to have sexual contact with animals) and necrophilia (the desire to have sexual contact with dead bodies).

Theoretical Perspectives

The links between paraphilias and **biological** factors have yet to be fully explored. Classical **psychoanalytic** theory suggests that paraphilias in males are psychological defences against castration anxiety.

Some **learning** theorists have argued that unusual stimuli may acquire sexually arousing properties through association with sexual arousal or orgasm. Another possibility is that unusual stimuli gradually acquire sexually arousing properties by being incorporated into masturbatory fantasies.

According to Weinberg's **sociological** model, the erotic appeal of S&M rituals may result from the opportunity to reverse the customary power relationships that exist between the gender and social classes in society at large.

Money and Lamacz suggest that childhood experiences etch a pattern in the brain—a **lovemap**—that determines the types of stimuli and activities that become sexually arousing. In the case of paraphilias, these lovemaps become distorted by early traumatic experiences.

Treatment of the Paraphilias

People with paraphilias may be motivated to seek help because of fears of exposure, criminal prosecution, or humiliation, but they seldom desire to surrender their sexual preferences. In **psychotherapy**, psychoanalysis aims to bring unconscious Oedipal conflicts into awareness so that they can be worked through in adulthood. **Behaviour therapy** attempts to eliminate paraphilic behaviours through techniques such as systematic desensitization, aversion therapy, social skills training, covert sensitization, and orgasmic reconditioning. With **biochemical approaches**, antidepressants have shown some promise in treating paraphilias. By reducing sex drives, anti-androgen drugs can help people who have difficulty combatting paraphilic urges.

Chapter Quiz

1. What is the most accurate statement about gender and paraphilias?
   (a) All people with paraphilias are male.
   (b) All people with paraphilias are female.
   (c) People with paraphilias are about equally divided among males and females.
   (d) The great majority of people with paraphilias are male.

2. People who are excessively aroused by a particular body part, such as the feet, breasts, or buttocks, are said to have
   (a) voyeurism.
   (b) frotteurism.
   (c) partialism.
   (d) transvestism.

3. Hypoxyphilia is an activity related to
   (a) sexual sadism.
   (b) sexual masochism.
   (c) fetishism.
   (d) zoophilia.

4. Which of the following is NOT a problem in treating people with paraphilias?
   (a) They usually do not see their behaviour as undesirable.
   (b) They see their behaviour as being beyond their control.
   (c) "Treatment" often requires encouragement to conform to social norms rather than therapy.
   (d) No treatments are available.

5. According to psychoanalytic theory, the _____ is declaring, "Look, I have a penis!"
   (a) exhibitionist
   (b) voyeur
   (c) masher
   (d) sexual sadist

6. A "lovemap" is most likely to become distorted or "vandalized" by
   (a) alcohol.
   (b) physical abuse or neglect.
   (c) unconscious conflicts from the Oedipal period.
   (d) the sadomasochistic subculture.

7. Transvestism is considered to be most closely related to
   (a) fetishism.
   (b) exhibitionism.
   (c) mashing.
   (d) sadomasochism.

8. Telephone scatalogia is considered to be most closely related to
   (a) coprophilia.
   (b) sexual sadism.
   (c) voyeurism.
   (d) exhibitionism.

9. Which of the following are most likely to need to risk capture to heighten their sexual arousal?
   (a) Sadomasochists
   (b) Coprophiliacs
   (c) Exhibitionists
   (d) Mashers

10. Which of the following are most likely to report a history of "petticoat punishment" during childhood?
    (a) Transvestites
    (b) Sexual sadists
    (c) Sexual masochists
    (d) Sadomasochists

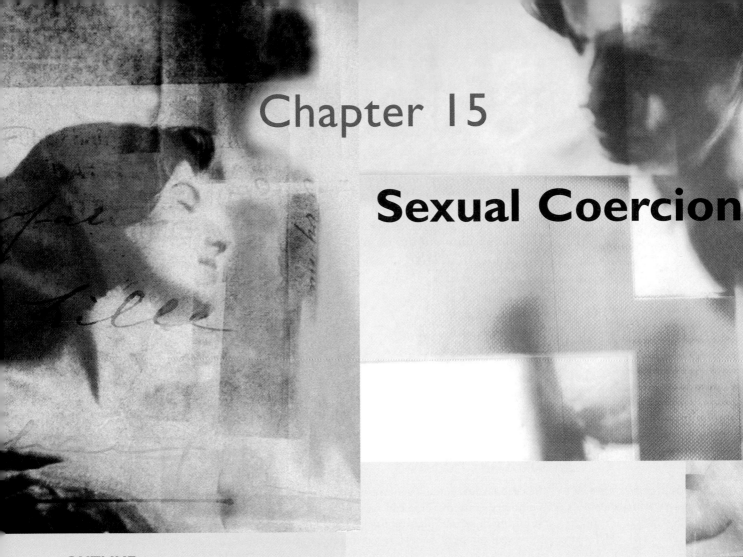

Chapter 15

Sexual Coercion

Did You Know That...

- A child cannot legally consent to sexual activity?
- A woman is sexually assaulted nearly every fifteen minutes in Canada?
- The majority of sexual assaults are committed not by strangers in deserted neighbourhoods or darkened alleyways but by people known to the victim?
- The great majority of men who sexually assault other men are heterosexual?
- The belief that women say no when they mean yes is the type of cultural myth that encourages sexual assault?
- Most men who commit sexual assault are "normal" in the sense that they are neither mentally ill nor intellectually disabled?
- Women who plead are more likely to be assaulted than women who scream or try to run away?

Sexual coercion, as the term is used in this chapter, includes sexual assault and other forms of sexual pressure, including sexual harassment, as well as sexual activity between an adult and a child. Sexual relations with children are considered coercive, even when children cooperate, because children are not considered by the law to be capable of giving consent.

Sexual Assault

Sexual assault Any form of sexual contact without voluntary consent.

Rape Sexual assault involving penetration. (The term was removed from the Criminal Code of Canada in 1983 and replaced with *sexual assault*.)

Sexual assault with a weapon Sexual contact with a non-consenting person involving a weapon, threats, or bodily harm.

Aggravated sexual assault Sexual contact with a non-consenting person that results in wounding, maiming, disfigurement, or endangering the life of the victim.

Sexual assault is the legal term used in Canada for any form of sexual contact without voluntary consent. This can range from unwanted sexual touching to sexual violence resulting in serious physical injury. Kissing, oral sex, and vaginal or anal intercourse are all sexual offences if they are performed without consent. People often refer to sexual assault as rape. **Rape**, which implies penetration, was removed from the Criminal Code in 1983, along with the related crimes of attempted rape and indecent assault. They were replaced with the new crime of sexual assault. Sexual assaults are assigned levels depending on the seriousness of the assault:

- **Level 1 Sexual assault:** involves no physical injury or minor physical injury; carries a maximum sentence of 10 years
- **Level 2 Sexual assault with a weapon, threats to a third party, or causing bodily harm:** carries a maximum sentence of 14 years
- **Level 3 Aggravated sexual assault:** involves wounding, maiming, disfigurement, or endangering the victim's life; carries a maximum of life sentence (Canadian Centre for Justice Statistics, 1999)

Although the actual behaviours involved in sexual assault were not specifically defined in the 1983 legislation, a 1987 ruling by the Supreme Court of Canada differentiated sexual assault from other forms of assault by the part of the body touched, the situation, or other circumstances (Canadian Centre for Justice Statistics, 1999). Changes to the law also meant that men, as well as women, could be considered victims of sexual assault. Lawmakers hoped that emphasizing the violent, rather than the sexual, nature of the assault, and eliminating the need to prove penetration, would encourage victims to report incidents to the police, make the complaint process less traumatic for the victims, and increase the number of convictions.

Incidence of Sexual Assault

According to Statistics Canada, 27 094 sexual assaults were reported to police in 2002 (Kong, et al., 2003). Sexual assaults account for 8% of all violent crimes reported to the police. Almost all (88%) were classified as Level 1.

Applications

A Guide to Understanding "Consent"

In the Canadian Criminal Code, "consent" is defined as a "voluntary agreement" to engage in sexual activity. Anyone over the age of 18 can consent to any legal sexual behaviour. Agreement obtained by pressure, coercion, force, or threat of force is not voluntary, and therefore, is not consent. Consent is not considered to be given if:

- someone else gives it (e.g., a partner)
- the person is not able to consent (i.e., he or she is high on drugs or alcohol, unconscious, or sleeping)
- someone in a position of trust, power, or authority (e.g., a teacher or employer) abuses that position in order to obtain consent
- the person shows, by words or behaviour, that he or she does not agree (e.g., crying, saying no)
- the person changes his or her mind about engaging in sexual activity

This means that, under Canadian law, a person can be convicted of sexual assault for:

- using threats to force someone into unwanted sexual activity
- using his or her authority (e.g., as an employer or teacher) to coerce someone into unwanted sexual activity by threatening his or her job or grade in a course, for example
- engaging in any form of sexual activity, including touching and kissing, with someone who is unconscious
- engaging in any form of sexual activity, including touching and kissing, with someone who is legally unable to consent because of a physical or mental disability or because he or she is under the age of consent

A person between the ages of 14 and 17 can consent to sexual activity with another person if:

- there is no relationship of trust, authority, or dependency
- there is no payment or offer of payment
- there is no anal intercourse, unless both people are legally married to each other. This means that, since same-sex marriage is not (as yet) available across Canada, a common form of sex is generally illegal for gay males if one of them is under the age of 18.

Under Canadian law, no one under the age of 14 is considered able to give consent. This means that even if the person said yes to the sexual activity, the consent is not valid. The fact that the other person did not know that his or her partner was underage is no defence either, unless he or she "took all reasonable steps to ascertain the age of the complainant" (Criminal Code, 2000).

There are exceptions in the case of statutory rape. If one of the persons is aged 12–14, and the other is

- aged 12 to 16
- less than two years older than the complainant, and
- not in a position of trust or authority over the complainant

he or she will not be tried for statutory rape. In addition, a person aged 12 or 13 will not be tried for statutory rape unless he or she is in a position of trust or authority over the complainant.

Studies that rely mainly on crime statistics underreport the incidence of sexual assault. The Uniform Crime Reporting Survey (UCR2), used by Statistics Canada to track the incidence of crime in Canada, collects data from 154 police departments in nine provinces, but is not a nationally representative sample (Kong et al., 2003). Results from victimization studies, such as the General Social Survey on Victimization, a telephone survey of 26 000 Canadians 15 years and older, indicate that fewer than 10% of women who are sexually assaulted report the incident to the police (Federal/Provincial Territorial Ministers Responsible for the Status of Women [Canada], 2002). Many women choose not to report assaults because of concern that they will be humiliated by the criminal justice system. Others fear negative reactions from their families or reprisal from the perpetrator. Some simply assume that the offender will not be apprehended or prosecuted.

According to Statistics Canada, in 2002:

- Eighty-five percent of the victims of sexual assault were female.
- Sixty percent of the victims of sexual assault were under age 18.
- Male victims were even younger, with the highest rates of sexual assault among boys aged 3 to 14.

Types of Sexual Assault

Are most sexual assaults perpetrated by strangers lurking in dark alleyways or by intruders who climb through open windows in the middle of the night? No. Most women are assaulted by men they know—often by men they have come to trust. Figure 15.1 shows that in 2002, only 20% of assaults were committed by strangers (Kong et al., 2003).

The perpetrator of a sexual assault can be a stranger, an acquaintance, a spouse, or a date. Men can be victims as well as perpetrators.

Stranger Sexual Assault

Stranger sexual assault refers to a sexual assault that is committed by someone previously unknown. These men often select targets who seem vulnerable—poor women, women who live alone, who are older or disabled, who are walking down deserted streets, or who are asleep or intoxicated. After choosing a target, the man may search for a safe time and place to commit the assault—a deserted, run-down part of town, a darkened street, a second-floor apartment without window bars or locks. According to the 1993 Violence Against Women survey, 3% of Canadian women over the age of 18 have been sexually assaulted by a stranger. Women between 18 and 44 were most likely to be attacked. Most of the assaults took place in public places—on the street (20%), at bars or clubs (15%), or in public buildings (13%), but 7% of the women reported being assaulted in their own homes (Strike, 1995).

Acquaintance Sexual Assault

Victims of sexual assault are more likely to be assaulted by people they know, such as classmates, co-workers, and even family friends, than by strangers (Kong et al., 2003). However, the victim may not perceive what happened as a sexual assault, especially if there has previously been consensual intercourse. Only 27% of women in a college/university survey who had been sexually assaulted saw themselves as victims of rape (Koss et al., 1987). Some women fail to acknowledge coercive sexual experiences as sexual assault if there has not been significant violence involved (Bondurant, 2001). Sociocultural beliefs in North America tend to support the definition of sexual assault as a violent crime committed by a stranger. If a woman is assaulted by someone known to her and she does not perceive the assault to be violent, then she may not identify her experience as a sexual assault. Studies on the prevalence of unwanted sexual encounters among university women stress the importance of challenging societal myths regarding sexual assault.

Women can also be assaulted in a dating situation. Such an assault most often involves intercourse. In a national study of Canadian college and university students, 20% of women said they had given in to pressure to have unwanted sexual intercourse, 7% said that they had been threatened or physically forced to have intercourse, and 14% said that a man attempted unwanted intercourse when they were drunk or high (DeKeseredy & Kelly, 1993). UCR2 data shows that the highest rates of reported sexual assault in a dating situation were among young women 16 years of age and younger (Kong et al., 2003).

Sexual assaults are more likely to occur when the couple have had too much to drink and then park in the man's car or go back to his residence. If a man perceives his partner's willingness to return home with him as a signal of sexual interest, even if she resists his advances, he may ignore her protests and overcome her resistance by force. In Canadian studies, 48% of victims of sexual assault reported that the attacker had used drugs or alcohol, as had 10% of victims (Kong et al., 2003).

Stranger sexual assault Sexual assault that is committed by someone previously unknown to the person who is assaulted.

Acquaintance sexual assault Sexual assault by an acquaintance of the person who is assaulted.

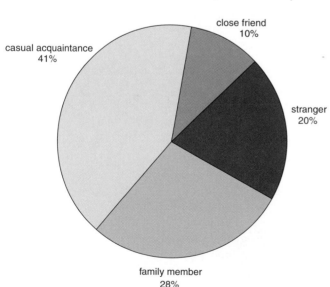

Figure 15.1. Perpetrators of Sexual Assaults on Women, 2002

Most sexual assaults on women are perpetrated by men whom they know—either a family member or a casual acquaintance.

Source: Statistics Canada, *Juristat,* Cat. 85-002, Vol. 23, No. 6.

Note: Percentages in pie charts in this chapter may not add to 100 because of rounding.

Men who sexually assault a date may believe that acceptance of a date indicates willingness to engage in coitus. They may think that women should reciprocate with coitus if they are taken to dinner. Other men assume that women who frequent settings such as singles bars are expressing tacit agreement to engage in coitus with men who show interest in them.

The issue of consent lies at the heart of determining whether a sexual act is an assault. Unlike situations where the victim and assailant are strangers, acquaintance sexual assault occurs within a context in which sexual relations could occur voluntarily. Thus, the question can arise of whether consent was freely given.

Multiple Perpetrators Many men who participate in group sexual assaults (gang rapes) are trying to conform to the stereotype of the tough, competent, "masculine" he-man. Exercise of power appears to be the major motive behind gang assaults, although some attackers may also be expressing anger against women. Gang members often believe that once women engage in coitus they are "whores." Thus, each offending gang member may become more aggressive as he takes his turn.

Combatting Sexual Assault on Campus. *Many colleges and universities have instituted sexual assault awareness programs to combat the problem of date rape and other sexual assaults on campus. What is the prevalence of sexual assaults on your campus? What are you going to do about it?*

Sexual Assault of Men The prevalence of sexual assaults on men is unknown because most men do not report. Some estimates suggest that perhaps 1 in 10 victims of sexual assaults is a man (Gibbs, 1991). Recent Canadian statistics indicate that men make up about 8% of reported adult sexual assault victims (Kong et al., 2003). A study of male sexual assault victims seen at a Toronto crisis centre found that the majority were young gay men. Many were vulnerable because of physical or cognitive disabilities, a history of child sexual abuse (34%), or previous sexual assault. Half of the victims knew their assailants and half were assaulted by strangers (Stermac et al., 1996).

Most men who sexually assault other men are heterosexual. Their motives may include domination and control, revenge and retaliation, and gang status and affiliation (Groth & Birnbaum, 1979, Hodge & Canter, 1998). These assaults are more likely to be committed by strangers, and anti-gay sentiments may or may not be a motivating factor (Stermac et al., 1996). However, one British study found that assaults by an acquaintance were most often sexually motivated (Hodge & Canter, 1998).

There are many reasons why men do not report sexual assaults. Men are not socialized to express fear or to admit to feelings of powerlessness and victimization. Male sexual assault survivors may, however, suffer traumatic effects similar to those suffered by female survivors (Calhoun & Atkeson, 1991). And support services for male survivors are not always available.

Spousal Sexual Assault A husband may believe that he is entitled to sexual access to his wife any time he desires it. He may believe it is his wife's duty to satisfy his sexual needs even when she is uninterested. The 1993 Violence Against Women survey found that 8% of women reported being sexually assaulted by their partner (Rodgers, 1994).

Coercion by spouses goes largely unreported and unrecognized by survivors as sexual assault (Russell, 1982). Women may fail to report the incident because of fear that no one will believe them.

Motives for spousal assault vary. Some men use sex to dominate their wives. Others degrade their wives through sex, especially after arguments. Sexual coercion often occurs within a context of marital violence, battering, and physical intimidation (Finkelhor & Yllo, 1982; Russell, 1982). In some cases, though, violence is limited to the sexual relationship (Finkelhor & Yllo, 1982). Some men see sex as the solution to all marital disputes. They think that if they can force their wives into coitus, "everything will be OK."

A World of Diversity

Sexual-Assault-Prone and Sexual-Assault-Free Societies

Cross-cultural studies suggest that sexual violence is not unique to our culture. It may in fact be culturally sanctioned in some societies. Sexual assault is more common in violent cultures, especially in the minority of cultures in which violence toward women is legitimized (Ember & Ember, 1990; Powell, 1991). Among the Yanomamö people of the Amazon jungle, a tribe known to be among the fiercest and most aggressive people in the world, men often raid neighbouring villages and literally carry away the women to keep as their wives (Ember & Ember, 1990). Wives are often savagely beaten, stabbed with sticks,

or burned with glowing firewood by husbands as punishment for misbehaviour. Wives come to accept punishment as part of their marital role. They may also come to regard the scars as signs that their husbands must care deeply for them to have beaten them so badly.

Sanday (1981) characterized 18% of the 156 cultures she studied as being prone to sexual assault. These "cultures of violence" tended to treat women as property. By contrast, Sanday found 45 "rape-free" cultures in which sexual assault was absent or rare. Such societies were characterized by sexual equality in which both genders shared power and were deemed to make important contributions, albeit in different ways, to the welfare of the society. In such societies, women did not economically depend on

men and were able to control their own resources. Such societies also reared their children to be nurturant and to shun interpersonal violence. It thus appears that sexual violence occurs within the cultural context of interpersonal violence and male dominance (Stock, 1991).

Such cultural factors may help to explain the high rate of sexual assault in the United States (Renzetti & Curran, 1989). The United States has both a high level of violent behaviour, including the highest homicide rate among industrialized nations, and unequal gender relations. However, while Canada has a much lower overall rate of violent crime, the rate of violence in intimate relationships is similar to that of the United States (DeKeseredy, 2000).

Survivors of spousal sexual assault may be as fearful of serious injury or death as survivors of stranger sexual assault (Kilpatrick et al., 1987). The long-term effects are also similar (Calhoun & Atkeson, 1991), including fear, depression, and sexual dysfunctions (Kilpatrick et al., 1987). Moreover, the woman who is sexually assaulted by her husband usually continues to live with her assailant and may fear repeated attacks.

Sexual Assault by Women Sexual assault by women is rare. In 2002, only 3% of those accused of sexual assault in Canada were women (Kong et al.). When it does occur, it often involves aiding or abetting men who are attacking another woman. Sexual assault by women may occur in gang attacks in which women follow male leaders to gain their approval. In such cases, a woman may be used to lure another woman to a secluded place for the sexual assault. Or the woman may hold the other woman down while she is assaulted. Men have also been sexually assaulted by women (Sarrel & Masters, 1982; Struckman-Johnson, 1988). Women may also aid in the sexual assault of a male (Stermac et al., 1996).

Social Attitudes and Myths That Encourage Sexual Assault

Many people believe a number of myths about sexual assault, such as that "women say no when they mean yes," "all women like a man who is pushy and forceful," "the way women dress, they are just asking to be raped," and "rapists are crazed by sexual desire" (Powell, 1996, p. 139). Yet another myth is that deep down inside, women want to be forced to have sex. Many women report sexual assault fantasies, but they are in control of their fantasies. Sexual assault is a complete lack of control, which no one wants (Powell, 1996). The belief that women desire to be overpowered and forced by men into sexual relations is a rationalization for violence (Powell, 1996).

These myths create a social climate that legitimizes sexual assault. Though both men and women are susceptible to sexual assault myths, researchers find that male students

Applications

If You Are Sexually Assaulted...

The following suggestions, adapted from Powell (1991), outline steps to follow if you should be involved in a sexual assault (and especially if penetration occurred):

1. Don't change anything about your body—don't wash or even comb your hair. Leave your clothes as they are. Otherwise you could destroy evidence.

2. Consider reporting the incident to police. You may prevent another woman from being assaulted, and you will be taking charge, starting on the path from victim to survivor. However, the decision to report an assault is ultimately up to you.

3. Ask a relative or friend to take you to a hospital, if you can't get an ambulance or a police car. If you call the hospital, tell them why you're requesting an ambulance, in case they are able to send someone trained to deal with sexual assault cases.

4. Seek help in an assertive way. Seek medical help. Injuries you are unaware of may be detected. Insist that a written or photographic record be made to document your condition. If you decide to file charges, the prosecutor may need this evidence to obtain a conviction.

5. Question health professionals. Ask about your biological risks. Ask what treatments are available. Ask for whatever will help make you comfortable. Call the shots. Demand confidentiality if that's

what you want. Refuse what you don't want. You may also wish to call a sexual assault hotline or sexual assault crisis centre for advice, if one is available in your area. A sexual assault crisis volunteer may be available to accompany you to the hospital and help see you through the medical evaluation and police investigation if you report the attack. It is not unusual for survivors of sexual assault to try to erase the details of the incident from their minds. However, trying to remember details clearly will permit you to provide an accurate description of the offender to the police, including his clothing, type of car, and so on. This information may help police apprehend the offender and assist in the prosecution.

---

show greater acceptance of such myths than do female students (Brady et al., 1991; Margolin et al., 1989). Men also cling more stubbornly to these myths, even after classes designed to challenge these views (Lenihan et al., 1992). College and university men who endorse these myths are more likely to see themselves as likely to force someone to have sex (Malamuth, 1981). Such myths do not occur in a social vacuum. They are related to other social attitudes, including gender-role stereotyping, the perception of sex as adversarial, and the acceptance of violence in interpersonal relationships (Burt, 1980).

Sociocultural Factors in Sexual Assault

Many observers contend that our society supports sexual assaults by socializing males into socially and sexually dominant roles (Lisak, 1991; Powell, 1996). Men are often reinforced from early childhood for stereotypically aggressive and competitive behaviour (Lisak, 1991). Gender typing may also lead men to reject or repress traits such as tenderness and empathy that might restrain sexual aggression but that are associated with the feminine gender role (Lisak, 1991).

Research with college students supports the connection between stereotypical masculine identification and tendencies to sexually assault or condone sexual assault. One U.S. study compared male students who adhered strictly to stereotypical gender-role beliefs with men holding less rigid attitudes. The stereotypical men expressed a greater likelihood of committing sexual assault, were more accepting of violence against women, were more likely to blame sexual assault survivors, and were more aroused by depictions of sexual assault (Check & Malamuth, 1983). American researchers also found that male students who more closely identified with the traditional masculine gender role more often reported having engaged in verbal sexual coercion and forcible sex (Muehlenhard & Falcon, 1990). One study of Canadian male university students found that sexually aggressive men also tended to be physically aggressive and masculine and to hold traditional sex role beliefs and were more accepting of interpersonal violence (Lackie & deMan, 1997).

Women may be socialized into assuming the helpless role. The stereotypical feminine gender role includes characteristics such as submissiveness, passivity, cooperativeness, even obedience to male authority. Such qualities may make it difficult for a woman to resist when faced with the possibility of sexual assault. A woman may lack skills in aggressiveness and believe that physical resistance is inappropriate or that she is incapable of resisting. Women are also taught that it is important to be sexually attractive to men. Women may thus unfairly blame themselves for the assault, believing that they somehow enticed the assailant.

Social influences may reinforce cultural themes that underlie sexual assault, such as the belief that a truly masculine man is expected to be sexually aggressive and overcome a woman's resistance until she "melts" in his arms (Stock, 1991). The popular belief that women fantasize about being overpowered sanctions coercive tactics to "awaken" a woman's sexual desires. Images from popular books and movies reinforce these themes, such as that of Rhett Butler in *Gone with the Wind* carrying a protesting Scarlett O'Hara up the stairs to her bedroom. Violent pornography, which fuses violence and erotic arousal, may also serve to legitimize sexual assault (Stock, 1991).

Young men may come to view dates not as chances to get to know their partners but as opportunities for sexual conquest, in which the object is to overcome their partners' resistance. In one U.S. study, male students expressed support for a man's right to kiss his female partner even if she resists (Margolin et al., 1989). Malamuth (1981) found that 35% of the university men in his sample said they would force a woman into sexual relations if they knew they could get away with it.

The lessons learned in competitive sports may also predispose young men to sexual violence (Levy, 1991). Coaches often encourage them to win at all costs. They are taught to be dominant and to vanquish their opponents, even if winning means injuring or "taking out" the opposition. This philosophy may be carried from the playing field into relationships with women. Some athletes distinguish between sports and dating relationships. Others do not. Past research has indicated that student athletes commit a disproportionate number of sexual assaults (Eskenazi, 1990). However, recent research has questioned this assumption and has shown that male athletes are not a homogeneous group but rather reflect a range of attitudes and behaviours. One study has suggested that male athletes who participate in physically aggressive team sports are more accepting of sexual assault myths and display more sexual aggression than male athletes involved in individually focused sports such as swimming, tennis, or track. Researchers raise the question of whether team sports encourage sexual aggression or tend to attract males with aggressive tendencies (Sawyer et al., 2002). Further research is needed to fully understand the interplay between socially sanctioned aggression in sports and aggression against women.

Psychological Characteristics of Sex Offenders

Although sexual aggressiveness may be embedded within our social fabric, not all men are equally vulnerable to such cultural influences (Burkhart & Fromuth, 1991). Not all men become sex offenders. Personal factors are thus also involved. What are they? Are sex offenders mentally disturbed or intellectually disabled? Driven by insatiable sexual urges?

Much of our knowledge of the psychological characteristics of sexual offenders derives from studies of samples of incarcerated sex offenders (Harney & Muehlenhard, 1991). One conclusion that emerges is that there is no single type of sex offender. Sex offenders vary in their psychological characteristics, family backgrounds, mental health, and criminal histories (Prentky & Knight, 1991). As a group, sex offenders are no less intelligent and no more likely to be mentally ill than comparison groups (Renzetti & Curran, 1989). This does not mean that their behaviour is "normal." It means that the great majority of sex offenders are in control of their behaviour, and they know that it is illegal.

Data from a sample of 169 Canadian police departments in six provinces found that in 1997, 98% of accused sex offenders were male. Men who commit sexual offences tend

Looking at Men's Violence Against Women
**www.whiteribbon.ca/
educational_materials**
"The Seven P's of Men's Violence," by Michael Kaufman of the Canadian White Ribbon Campaign, examines the sociocultural roots of men's violence against women.

to be older than other violent offenders. For men accused of sex offences, 37% were between the ages of 18 and 34, 21% between 35 and 44, and 23% were 45 or older. Only 12% of men accused of other violent crimes were older than 45. The median age of sex offenders was 32 (Canadian Centre for Justice Statistics, 1999). Other research suggests that sex offenders generally have less than a grade 12 education and few marketable job skills.

Some sex offenders feel socially inadequate and report that they cannot find willing partners. Some lack social skills and avoid social interactions with women (Overholser & Beck, 1986). Others, however, are no less skilful socially than non-offenders in the same socioeconomic group (Segal & Marshall, 1985). Some sex offenders are basically antisocial and have long histories of violent behaviour (Knight et al., 1991). They tend to act upon their impulses regardless of the cost to the person they attack. An examination of the case files of 785 convicted sex offenders found that 60% had been removed from the care of their parents before age 16, more than one-third had been physically abused or neglected by their caretakers, and one-third had been sexually abused before the age of 16. More than 75% of the abused offenders had been abused by males, and in many cases, the sexual abuse was accompanied by physical abuse (Motiuk & Porporino, 1993). As adults, they may be identifying with the aggressor role in interpersonal relationships. The use of alcohol may also dampen self-restraint and spur sexual aggressiveness.

For some sex offenders, violence and sexual arousal become enmeshed. Thus, they seek to combine sex and violence to enhance their sexual arousal (Quinsey et al., 1984). Some sex offenders are more sexually aroused than other people (as measured by the size of erections) by verbal descriptions, films, or audiotapes that portray themes of sexual assault (Barbaree & Marshall, 1991). Other researchers, however, have failed to find deviant patterns of arousal in sex offenders (e.g., Baxter et al., 1986; Hall, 1989). These researchers find that, as a group, sex offenders, like most other people, are more aroused by stimuli depicting mutually consenting sexual activity than forced sex.

Harney and Muehlenhard (1991) summarized research findings on self-identified sexually aggressive men. They are more likely than other men to:

- Condone sexual assault and violence against women
- Hold traditional gender-role attitudes
- Be sexually experienced
- Be hostile toward women
- Engage in sexual activity in order to express social dominance
- Be sexually aroused by depictions of sexual assault
- Be irresponsible and lack a social conscience
- Have peer groups, such as fraternities, that pressure them into sexual activity

The Motives for Sexual Assault

Although sexual arousal is an obvious and important element in sexual assault (Barbaree & Marshall, 1991), some researchers argue that sexual desire is not the basic motivation for sexual assault (Gebhard et al., 1965; Groth & Birnbaum, 1979). Other researchers believe that sexual motivation plays a key role in at least some sexual assaults (Hall & Hirschman, 1991). Based on their clinical work with more than 1000 sex offenders, Groth and Birnbaum believe that there are three basic motives for sexual assault—anger, desire for power, and sadistic motives:

1. *Anger motive.* The sexual assault motivated by anger is a vicious, unplanned attack that is triggered by anger and resentment toward women. These offenders usually employ more force than is needed to obtain compliance. The person they assault is often coerced into performing degrading and humiliating acts, fellatio, or anal intercourse. Typically, such a sex offender reports that he had suffered humiliations at the hands of women and used the assault as a means of revenge.

2. *Power motive.* The desire to control and dominate women is the motivation behind this form of sexual assault. Sexual gratification is secondary. It is an attempt "to resolve disturbing doubts about [his] masculine identity and worth, [or] to combat deep-seated feelings of insecurity and vulnerability" (Groth & Hobson, 1983, p. 165). Only enough force to subdue the woman is used.

3. *Sadistic motive.* This form of sexual assault is a ritualized, savage attack. These sex offenders often carefully plan their assaults and use a "con" or pretext to approach their targets, such as asking for directions or offering or requesting assistance (Dietz et al., 1990). Some sadists bind their victims and subject them to humiliating and degrading experiences and threats. Some torture or murder their victims (Dietz et al., 1990). Mutilation of the victim is unfortunately common. Groth and Birnbaum (1979) suggest that sadistic sex offenders are often preoccupied with violent pornography but have little or no interest in nonviolent (consensual) pornography. Groth (Groth & Birnbaum, 1979) estimated that about 40% of sexual assaults are motivated by anger; 55% by power; and 5% by sadistic urges.

Applications

Reducing the Risk of Sexual Assault

The elimination of sexual assault would require massive changes in cultural attitudes and socialization processes. Educational intervention on a smaller scale may, however, reduce its incidence. Most Canadian universities have support services for victims of sexual assault. Most of these services also offer educational programs. The point of such programs is for men to learn that no means no, despite the widespread belief that some women like to be "talked into" sex.

Until the basic cultural attitudes that support sexual assault change, however, "sexual assault prevention" will require that women take a number of precautions. Why, a reader may wonder, should women be advised to take measures to avoid sexual assault? Is not the very listing of such measures a subtle way of blaming the woman if she should fall prey to an attacker? No, providing the information does not blame the person who is attacked. The perpetrator is always responsible for the assault. However, *The New Our Bodies, Ourselves* (Boston Women's Health Book Collective, 1992) lists several suggestions that may help reduce the risk of sexual assault:

- Establish a set of signals with other women in the building or neighbourhood.
- List yourself in the phone directory and on the mailbox by your first initials only.
- Use dead-bolt locks.
- Lock windows, and install iron grids on first-floor windows.
- Keep doorways and entries well lit.
- Keep your keys handy when approaching the car or the front door.
- Do not walk by yourself after dark.
- Avoid deserted areas.
- Do not allow strange men into your house or apartment without first checking their credentials.
- Keep your car doors locked and the windows up.
- Check out the back seat of your car before entering.
- Don't give rides to hitchhikers (including women hitchhikers).
- Don't converse with strange men on the street.
- Shout "Fire!" not "Rape!" People are likely to flock to fires but to avoid scenes of violence.

Powell (1996) adds the following suggestions for avoiding date sexual assault:

- Communicate your sexual limits to your date. Tell your partner how far you would like to go so that he will know what the limits are. For example, if your partner starts fondling you in ways that make you uncomfortable, you might say, "I'd prefer if you didn't touch me there. I really like you, but I prefer not getting so intimate at this point in our relationship."
- Meet new dates in public places, and avoid driving with a stranger or a group of people you've never met. When meeting a new date, drive in your own car and meet your date at a public place. In some cases of date sexual assault, the group disappears just prior to the assault.
- State your refusal definitively. Be firm in refusing a sexual overture. Look your partner straight in the eye. The more definite you are, the less likely your partner will be to misinterpret your wishes. If your date continues to pursue unwanted sexual activity, talking will probably not be effective. You are justified in leaving such a situation in any way possible, without an explanation or apology.
- Become aware of your fears. Take notice of any fears of displeasing your partner that might stifle your

Adjustment for Survivors of Sexual Assault

Many women who are sexually assaulted fear for their lives during the attack (Calhoun & Atkeson, 1991). Whether or not weapons or threats are used, the experience of being dominated by an unpredictable and threatening assailant is terrifying. The woman does not know whether she will survive and may feel helpless to do anything about it. Afterwards, many survivors enter a state of **crisis.**

Many survivors are extremely distraught in the days and weeks following the sexual assault (Calhoun & Atkeson, 1991; Valentiner et al., 1996). They have trouble sleeping and cry frequently. They report eating problems, cystitis, headaches, irritability, mood changes, anxiety and depression, and menstrual irregularity. They may become withdrawn, sullen, and mistrustful (McArthur, 1990). One myth regarding sexual assault is that women who are sexually assaulted are at least partly to blame for the assault (Bell et al., 1994). Therefore, some survivors experience feelings of guilt and shame (McArthur, 1990).

Sexual assault survivors may also suffer physical injuries and sexually transmitted diseases, even AIDS, as a result of a sexual assault. In one study, concerns about contracting AIDS were reported by about one in four survivors (Baker et al., 1990).

Survivors may also encounter problems at work, such as problems relating to co-workers or bosses or difficulties in concentrating. Work adjustment, however, usually returns to normal levels within a year (Calhoun & Atkeson, 1991). Relationships with

Crisis A highly stressful situation that can involve shock, loss of self-esteem, and lessened capacity for making decisions.

Canadian Association of Sexual Assault Centres **www.casac.ca/** Discussion of the legal, social, and attitudinal changes needed to prevent, and ultimately eradicate, sexual assault, as well as news articles and links to other resources.

assertiveness. If your partner is truly respectful of you, you need not fear an angry or demeaning response. But if your partner is not respectful, it is best to become aware of it and end the relationship right there.

- Pay attention to your instincts. Trust your gut-level feelings. Many victims of acquaintance sexual assault said afterward that they had had a strange feeling about the man but failed to pay attention to it.
- Be especially cautious if you are in a new environment, such as a new college or university or a foreign country. You may be especially vulnerable to exploitation when you are becoming acquainted with a new environment, different people, and different customs.
- If you have broken off a relationship with someone you don't really like or feel good about, don't let him into your place. Many sexual assaults are committed by ex-lovers and ex-boyfriends.

Confronting an Attacker: Should You Fight, Flee, or Plead?

But what if you are accosted by an attacker? Should you try to fight him off, flee, or try to plead with him to stop?

Some women have thwarted attacks by pleading or crying. Yet research has shown that less forceful forms of resistance, such as pleading, begging, or reasoning, can be dangerous strategies. They may not fend off the attack and may heighten the probability of injury (Bart & O'Brien, 1985). Screaming may be particularly effective in warding off some attacks (Byers & Lewis, 1988). Running away is sometimes an effective strategy (Bart & O'Brien, 1985), but may not be effective if you are outnumbered by a group of assailants (Gidycz & Koss, 1990). No suggestion is likely to be helpful in all sexual assault cases.

Self-defence training may help women become better prepared to fend off an assailant. Courses given by women for women can be effective in developing assertive responses to threatening or dangerous situations. Research shows that women who use two strategies of resistance such as fleeing, yelling, or using physical force increase their chances of preventing the completion of a rape by 80% (Bart & O'Brien, 1984). Some research suggests that resistance increases the odds of being physically injured by as much as threefold (Brody, 1992). However, other research points out that women who resisted an assault did so

because they were injured. Resistance was not a cause of injury but rather a consequence (Siegel, et al., 1989). A study of 116 sexual assaults showed that women were more likely to physically resist if the attacker was a friend or relative, if the attacker made verbal threats, and if the attacker physically restrained her or injured her (Atkeson et al., 1989).

It is difficult, if not impossible, for people to think through their options clearly and calmly when they are suddenly attacked. Sexual assault experts recommend that women rehearse alternative responses to an attack. A U.S. Police Department recommends that whatever form of self-defence a woman intends to use, she should carefully think through how it is used and practise using it (Brody, 1992a). Thompson (1991) suggests that effective self-defence is built upon the use of multiple strategies, ranging from attempts to avoid potential sexual assault situations (such as installing home security systems or walking only in well-lit areas), to acquiescence when active resistance would seem too risky, to the use of more active verbal or physical forms of resistance in some low-risk situations.

Applications

For Men: How You Can Avoid Sexual Violence

Most self-help tips on the prevention of sexual assault are aimed at women. Here are some things men can do to help reduce sexual violence. Sexual assault is motivated mainly by a desire to control or dominate rather than by sex. It is never all right to force yourself on a woman, even when she:

- teases you
- leads you on
- says no even if you think she means yes
- is under the influence of drugs or alcohol.

People do not always communicate clearly. If you think you are getting a double message, ask her what she really wants. If she seems unsure, back off. When in doubt, don't.

Remember that when you put pressure on a woman, you may be forcing her into doing something she doesn't want to do. In one study of Canadian university and college women, 20% said that they had given in to unwanted sexual intercourse because the man continued to pressure them. Below are things to consider:

- Stay in touch with your own sexual feelings. Are you really hearing what she wants, or are your hormones talking?
- Communicate your sexual needs and desires as clearly and honestly as possible. It is all right to ask, but back off if she says no.

- Just because she wants to be kissed and caressed doesn't mean that she wants to have intercourse.
- Taking advantage of someone who is incapable of giving consent is sexual assault. If she has had too much to drink, or is high on drugs, she is not able to consent.
- The fact that you are drunk or high is no defence either.
- Be aware that you may be intimidating to some women just because you are male, even if you don't see yourself as threatening.

If you are trying to decide what to do in any situation, ask yourself whether you would want a man to sexually force himself on your sister. If not, why would you want to do it to your girlfriend, or to any other woman?

---

spouses or partners may also be impaired. Disturbances in sexual functioning are common and may last for years or a lifetime. Survivors often report a lack of sexual desire, fears of sex, and difficulty becoming sexually aroused (Becker et al., 1986). Some women simply do not experience the level of sexual enjoyment they found before the assault (Calhoun & Atkeson, 1991).

Sexual Assault and Psychological Disorders Survivors of sexual assault are at higher-than-average risk of developing psychological disorders such as depression, alcohol and substance abuse, and anxiety (Koss, 1993). **Posttraumatic stress disorder (PTSD)** is an anxiety disorder brought on by exposure to a traumatic event and is also often seen in soldiers who were in combat. Features of PTSD include flashbacks to the traumatic experience, disturbing dreams, emotional numbing, and nervousness. PTSD may persist for years. A person with the disorder may also develop fears of situations connected with the traumatic event. For example, a woman who was sexually assaulted on an elevator may develop a fear of riding elevators by herself. Researchers also report that women who blame themselves for the sexual assault tend to suffer more severe depression and adjustment problems, including sexual problems (Frazier, 1990; Wyatt et al., 1990).

Rape Trauma Syndrome Burgess and Holmstrom (1974) identified some common patterns in people's responses to sexual assault. For several weeks following the attack, people behave in a disorganized manner. They may cry uncontrollably and often experience feelings of anger, shame, fear, and nervousness. Although some survivors present a calm, composed face to the world, inwardly they have not yet come to terms with the experience. Most people will benefit from counselling at this time. Long-term adjustment, which may last for years, involves dealing with feelings and being able to remember the event without re-experiencing it. Survivors may make major changes to their lives, including changing jobs and phone numbers, and moving to what they feel are safer surroundings, out of fear of retaliation by the perpetrator of the assault.

Treatment of Sexual Assault Survivors Treatment of sexual assault survivors typically involves a two-stage process of helping the woman (the vast majority are

Posttraumatic stress disorder (PTSD) A type of stress reaction brought on by a traumatic event and characterized by flashbacks of the experience in the form of disturbing dreams or intrusive recollections, a sense of emotional numbing or restricted range of feelings, and heightened body arousal. Abbreviated *PTSD*.

Rape trauma syndrome A two-phase reaction to sexual assault that is characterized by disruption of the survivor's lifestyle (the acute phase) and reorganization of the survivor's life (the long-term phase).

female) through the crisis following the attack and then helping to foster long-term adjustment. Crisis intervention typically provides the survivor with support and information to help her express her feelings and develop strategies for coping with the trauma (Resick & Schnicke, 1990). Psychotherapy, involving group or individual approaches, can help the survivor cope with the emotional consequences of sexual assault, avoid self-blame, improve self-esteem, validate the welter of feelings surrounding the experience, and help her establish or maintain loving relationships. Therapists also recognize the importance of helping the sexual assault survivor identify supportive social networks (Ledray, 1990; Valentiner et al., 1996). Family, friends, religious leaders, and health care specialists are all potential sources of help. In major cities and many towns, concerned men and women have formed sexual assault crisis centres and hotlines, peer counselling groups, and referral agencies geared to assessing and treating survivors' needs after the assault. Some counsellors are specially trained to mediate between survivors of sexual assault and their loved ones—husbands, lovers, and so forth. These counsellors help people to discuss and work through the often complex emotional legacy of sexual assault. Phone numbers for these services can be obtained from a local sexual assault centre or women's centre. Many Canadian universities offer sexual assault counselling.

Sexual Abuse of Children

Many view child sexual abuse as among the most heinous of crimes. Children who are sexually assaulted often suffer social and emotional problems that impair their development and persist into adulthood, affecting their self-esteem and their ability to form intimate relationships.

The National Clearinghouse on Family Violence: Child Sexual Abuse **www.hc-sc.gc.ca/hppb/ familyviolence/ nfntsabus_e.html** This site presents a number of papers on child sexual abuse.

No one knows how many children are sexually abused. There are few national statistics on child sexual abuse in Canada. Abuse data are collected through the Uniform Crime Reporting Survey (UCR2), a survey of a number of police departments (primarily in Quebec and Ontario), and by the General Social Survey (GSS), an annual national telephone survey that asks respondents about a variety of topics including victimization. Because not all sexual offences are reported to police, the UCR2 does not provide complete information on the prevalence of child sexual abuse in Canada. And while the GSS is a national probability sample, it only surveys Canadians 15 years of age or older, so it cannot provide direct information about children who are being abused. Combining information from the two sources gives a more detailed but still incomplete picture of sexual abuse of children in Canada. There are many reasons why sexual abuse continues to be underreported, including the fact that since children are generally dependent on their abusers, they may be afraid to speak out. Adults may fail to report abuse they suffered as children due to faulty memories or because of shame or embarrassment.

U.S. researchers estimate that the prevalence of sexual abuse among boys ranges from 4% to 16% (Genuis et al., 1991; Janus & Janus, 1993; Kohn, 1987) and among girls exceeds 20% (Janus & Janus, 1993; Kohn, 1987).

Most victims of reported sexual abuse are girls. In 2002, boys were victims of sexual assault in 29% of cases reported to the police involving victims 12 years of age and younger, and in 12% of reported cases involving youth aged 12 to 18 (Kong et al., 2003). In 2002, 61% of sexual assaults reported through the Uniform Crime Reporting Survey 2 involved child victims. Of these, 71% of victims were female and 29% were male (Kong et al., 2003).

What Is Child Sexual Abuse?

Sexual abuse of children may range from exhibitionism, kissing, fondling, and sexual touching to oral sex and anal intercourse and, in the case of girls, vaginal intercourse (Knudsen, 1991). Any form of sexual contact between an adult and a child is considered abusive, even if the child is willing, since children are below the age of consent.

In addition to sexual assault, the Canadian Criminal Code includes other sexual offences primarily relating to sexual abuse of children. They include:

- sexual interference—sexual touching of a child under the age of 14 by an adult or older teen. The maximum sentence is 10 years.

- invitation to sexual touching—encouraging, asking, or forcing a child under the age of 14 to touch an adult or older teen's body for sexual purposes (e.g., having a child masturbate an adult). The maximum sentence is 10 years.

- sexual exploitation—when a person in a position of trust or authority (e.g., a teacher or babysitter), or in a relationship of dependency with a young person (e.g., a parent or guardian), commits sexual interference or invitation to sexual touching. In this case, a young person is defined as a person 14 to 18 years of age. The maximum sentence is five years.

- incest—sexual intercourse with a person where there is a known blood relationship. The maximum sentence is 14 years. (Incest will be discussed further later in the chapter.)

- anal intercourse and bestiality—also included in the category of "other" sexual offences. The offences may be, but are not always, directed against children. The maximum sentence is 10 years.

Voluntary sexual activity between children of similar ages is not sexual abuse. Children often engage in sex play with peers or siblings, as in "playing doctor" or mutual masturbation. When the experience involves coercion, however, or when one child is significantly older or in a position of power over the other, the sexual contact may be considered sexual abuse, and is a crime.

Patterns of Abuse

Children from stable, middle-class families appear to be generally at lower risk of encountering sexual abuse than children from poorer, less cohesive families (Finkelhor, 1984). In most cases, children who are sexually abused are not accosted by the proverbial stranger lurking in the schoolyard. In nine out of ten cases, children are abused by relatives or family friends or acquaintances, as shown in Figure 15.2 (Kong et al., 2003).

The average age at which most children are first sexually abused ranges from six to twelve years for girls and seven to ten years for boys (Knudsen, 1991). Canadian police statistics show that boys between the ages of four and six are at the highest risk of experiencing family-related sexual assault, while girls are at the highest risk in the 11 to 14 age range (Statistics Canada, 2002). Parents who discover that their child has been abused by a family member are often reluctant to notify authorities. Some may feel that such problems are "family matters" that are best kept private. Others may be reluctant to notify authorities for fear that it may shame the family or that they may be held accountable for failing to protect the child.

Typically, the child initially trusts the abuser. Physical force is seldom needed to gain compliance, largely because of the child's helplessness, gullibility, and submission to adult authority. Whereas most sexually abused children are abused only once, those who are abused by family members are more likely to suffer repeated acts of abuse (Briere & Runtz, 1987; Dube & Hebert, 1988).

Genital fondling is the most common type of abuse (Knudsen, 1991). In one sample of women who had been molested in childhood, most of the contacts involved genital fondling (38% of cases) or exhibitionism (20% of cases). Intercourse occurred in only 4% of cases (Knudsen, 1991). Repeated abuse by a family member, however, commonly follows a pattern that begins with affectionate fondling during the preschool years, progresses to oral sex or mutual masturbation during the early school years, and then to sexual penetration (vaginal or anal intercourse) during preadolescence or adolescence (Waterman & Lusk, 1986).

Abused children rarely report the abuse, often because of fear of retaliation from the abuser or because they believe they will be blamed for it. Adults may suspect abuse if a

(a)   Relationship to Victim—Girls under 12

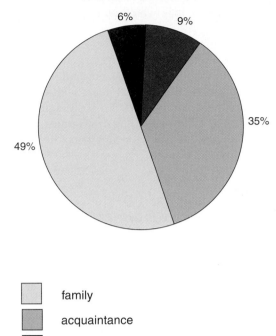

6%   9%

49%

35%

family

acquaintance

stranger

close friend

Figure 15.2a Relationship of child sexual assaulters to victims—girls under 12.

Figure 15.2b Relationship of child sexual assaulters to victims—boys under 12.

Statistics indicate that most boys and girls who were sexually assaulted fell victim to acquaintances.

Source: Statistics Canada, *Juristat*, Cat. 85-002, vol. 23, no. 6.

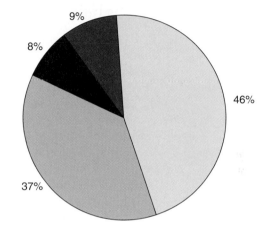

(b)   Relationship to Victim—Boys under 12

9%

8%

46%

37%

child shows sudden personality changes or develops fears, problems in school, or eating or sleeping problems. A pediatrician may discover physical signs of abuse during a medical exam. Despite laws requiring adults to report any suspected child abuse or neglect to authorities, it has been estimated that as many as 90% of all cases of sexual abuse of children are not reported (MacMillan et al., 1996b).

Types of Abusers

Researchers find that the overwhelming majority of perpetrators of child sexual abuse of both boys and girls are males (Thomlison et al., 1991). Although most sexual abusers are adults, some are adolescents. Male adolescent sexual offenders are more likely than nonoffenders to have been molested themselves as young boys (Becker et al., 1989; Muster, 1992). Some adolescent sexual offenders may be imitating their own victimization. One Canadian study found that 43% of adolescent male sex offenders had experienced some form of sexual abuse in childhood (Worling, 1995). Adolescent child molesters also tend to feel socially inadequate and to be fearful of social interactions with age-mates of the other gender (Katz, 1990).

Why do men molest children? Banning (1989) suggests that males in our culture are socialized into seeking partners who are younger and weaker, whom they can easily dominate. This pattern of socialization may take the extreme form of development of sexual interest in children and adolescent girls, who because of their age are more easily dominated than adult women. Yet sexual interest in children may also be motivated by unusual patterns of sexual arousal in which children become the objects of sexual desire, sometimes to the exclusion of more appropriate (adult) stimuli.

Although the great majority of sexual abusers are male, the number of female sexual abusers may be greater than has been generally believed (Banning, 1989). Many female sexual abusers may go undetected because society accords women a much freer range of physical contact with children than it does men. A woman who fondles a child might be seen as affectionate, or at worst seductive, whereas a man would be more likely to be perceived as a child molester (Banning, 1989).

What motivates a woman to sexually abuse children, even her own children? Little research has been done to explore this question, but some factors have begun to emerge (Matthews et al., 1990). Some appear to have been manipulated into engaging in sexual abuse by their husbands. Others appear to have unmet emotional needs and low self-esteem and may have been seeking acceptance, closeness, and attention through sexual acts with children. Some, motivated by unresolved feelings of anger, revenge, powerlessness, or jealousy, may view their own and others' children as safe targets for venting these feelings. Some view their crimes as expressions of love.

Pedophilia

Pedophilia is a paraphilia that involves persistent or recurrent sexual attraction to children. Although pedophiles are sometimes called child molesters, not all child molesters are pedophiles. Some molesters may seek sexual contacts with children only when they are under unusual stress or lack other sexual outlets. Thus, they do not meet the clinical definition of pedophilia.

Research suggests that sexual attraction to children may be more common than is generally believed. Researchers in one U.S. study administered an anonymous survey to a sample of 193 university men (Briere & Runtz, 1989). A surprisingly high percentage of the students—21%—admitted to having been sexually attracted to small children. Nine percent reported sexual fantasies involving young children. Five percent reported masturbating to such fantasies. Seven percent reported that there was some likelihood that they would have sex with a young child if they knew they could avoid detection and punishment. Fortunately, most people with such erotic interests never act upon them.

Pedophilia A type of paraphilia that is defined by sexual attraction to children. (From the Greek *paidos*, meaning "child," not the Latin *pedis*, meaning "foot.")

Applications

Preventing Child Sexual Abuse

Many of us were taught by our parents never to accept a ride or an offer of candy from a stranger. However, many instances of child sexual abuse are perpetrated by familiar adults, often a family member or friend. Prevention programs help children understand what sexual abuse is and how they can avoid it. In addition to learning to avoid strangers, children need to recognize the differences between acceptable touching, as in an affectionate embrace or pat on the head, and unacceptable or "bad" touching. Even elementary-school-age children can learn the distinction between "good touching and bad touching" (Tutty, 1992). Good school-based programs are generally helpful in preparing children to handle an actual encounter with a potential

molester (Goleman, 1993). Children who receive comprehensive training are more likely to use strategies such as running away, yelling, or saying no when they are threatened by an abuser. They are also more likely to report incidents to adults.

Researchers recognize that children can easily be intimidated or overpowered by adults or older children. Children may be unable to say no in a sexually abusive situation, even though they want to and know it is the right thing to do (Waterman et al., 1986). Although children may not always be able to prevent abuse, they can be encouraged to tell someone about it. Most prevention programs emphasize teaching children messages such as "It's not your fault," "Never keep a bad or scary secret," and "Always tell your parents about this, especially if someone says you shouldn't tell them" (Waterman et al., 1986).

Children also need to be alerted to the types of threats they might receive for disclosing the abuse. They are more likely to resist threats if they are reassured that they will be believed if they disclose the abuse, that their parents will continue to love them, and that they and their families will be protected from the molester.

School-based prevention programs focus on protecting the child. Teachers and helping professionals are required to report suspected abuse to authorities. Tighter controls and better screening are needed to monitor the hiring of daycare employees. Administrators and teachers in preschool and daycare facilities also need to be educated to recognize the signs of sexual abuse and to report suspected cases (Waterman et al., 1986). Treatment programs to help people who are sexually attracted to children before they commit abusive acts would also be of use.

Pedophiles are almost exclusively male, although some isolated cases of female pedophiles have been reported (Cooper et al., 1990). Some pedophiles are sexually attracted only to children. Others are sexually attracted to adults as well. Some pedophiles limit their sexual interest in children to incestuous relationships with family members. Others abuse children to whom they are unrelated. Some pedophiles limit their sexual interest in children to looking at them or undressing them. Others fondle them or masturbate in their presence. Some manipulate or coerce children into oral, anal, or vaginal intercourse.

Children tend not to be worldly-wise. They can often be taken in by pedophiles who tell them that they would like to "show them something," "teach them something," or do something with them that they would "like." Some pedophiles seek to gain the child's affection and discourage the child from disclosing the sexual activity by showering the child with attention and gifts. Others threaten the child or the child's family to prevent disclosure.

There is no consistent personality profile of the pedophile (Okami & Goldberg, 1992). Most pedophiles do not fit the common stereotype of the "dirty old man" in the trench coat who hangs around schoolyards. Most are otherwise law-abiding, well-respected citizens, generally in their 30s and 40s. Many are married or divorced, with children of their own.

Pedophilia may have complex and varied origins. Some pedophiles who are lacking in social skills may turn to children after failing to establish gratifying relationships with adult women (Overholser & Beck, 1986; Tollison & Adams, 1979). Research generally supports the stereotype of the pedophile as weak, passive, and shy—a socially inept, isolated man who feels threatened by mature relationships (Ames & Houston, 1990; Wilson & Cox, 1983).

Pedophiles who engage in incestuous relationships with their own children tend to present a somewhat different picture. They tend to fall at one end or the other of the dominance spectrum. Some are very dominant; others, very passive. Few are found between these extremes (Ames & Houston, 1990).

Some pedophiles were sexually abused as children and may be attempting to establish feelings of mastery by reversing the situation (de Young, 1982). Cycles of abuse may be perpetuated from generation to generation if children who are sexually abused become victimizers or partners of victimizers as adults.

Incest

Incest refers to sexual relationships among people who are closely related by blood, or *consanguineous*. Although a few societies have permitted incestuous pairings among royalty, all known cultures have some form of an incest taboo. In Canada, sexual relations are illegal between parent and child, between siblings, between uncle or aunt and niece or nephew, and between grandparent and grandchild. In this section we will be talking about incest within the household unit that affects children or adolescents.

Most of our knowledge of incestuous relationships concerns father–daughter incest. Why? Most identified cases involve fathers who were eventually incarcerated.

There is little national data on incest in Canada. Figure 15.3 shows that, of reported cases, parent–child sexual assault is the most common, followed by sibling sexual assault. However, some U.S. surveys of adults suggest that brother–sister incest is greatly under-reported, and may be the most common (Finkelhor et al., 1990; Waterman & Lusk, 1986).

Father–daughter incest often begins with affectionate cuddling or embraces and then progresses to teasing sexual play, lengthy caresses, hugs, kisses, and genital contact, even penetration. In some cases genital contact occurs more abruptly, usually when the father has been drinking or arguing with his wife. Force is not typically used to gain compliance, but daughters are sometimes physically overcome and injured by their fathers.

In sibling incest, the brother usually initiates sexual activity and assumes the dominant role (Meiselman, 1978). Some brothers and sisters may view their sexual activity as natural and not know that it is taboo (Knox, 1988). Evidence on the effects of incest between brothers and sisters is mixed. In a study of college undergraduates, those who

Incest Marriage or sexual relations between people who are so closely related (by "blood") that sexual relations are prohibited and punishable by law. (From the Latin *in-*, meaning "not," and *castus*, meaning "chaste."

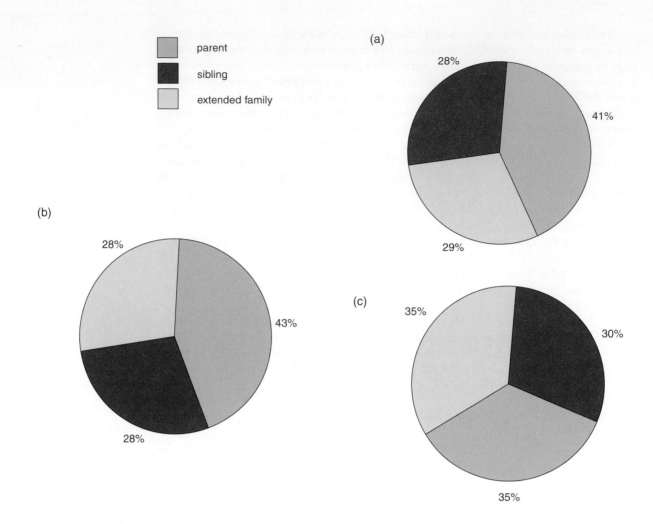

Figure 15.3a. Sexual Assault by Family Members, 2001.

Figure 15.3b. Sexual Assault on Girls, by Family Members, 2001.

Figure 15.3c. Sexual Assault on Boys, by Family Members, 2001.

Parent–child sexual assault is the most commonly reported.

Source: Statistics Canada, *Family Violence in Canada: A Statistical Profile,* Cat. 85-224.

reported childhood incest with siblings did not reveal greater evidence of sexual adjustment problems than other undergraduates (Greenwald & Leitenberg, 1989). Sibling incest is most likely to be harmful when it is recurrent or forced or when parental response is harsh (Knox, 1988; Laviola, 1989).

Family Factors in Incest Incest frequently occurs within the context of general family disruption, as in families in which there is spouse abuse, a dysfunctional marriage, or alcoholic or physically abusive parents (Alter-Reid et al., 1986; Sirles & Franke, 1989; Waterman, 1986). Stressful events in the father's life, such as the loss of a job or problems at work, often precede the initiation of incest (Waterman, 1986).

Fathers who abuse older daughters tend to be domineering and authoritarian with their families (Waterman, 1986). Fathers who abuse younger, preschool daughters are more likely to be passive, dependent, and low in self-esteem. As Waterman (1986) notes:

> [The fathers] may need soothing and comforting, and may feel especially safe with preschool children: "I felt safe with her.... I didn't have to perform. She was so little that I knew she wouldn't and couldn't hurt me." (p. 215)

Marriages in incestuous families tend to be characterized by an uneven power relationship between the spouses. The abusive father is usually dominant. Another thread that frequently runs through incestuous families is a troubled sexual relationship between the spouses. The wife often rejects the husband sexually (Waterman, 1986).

Gebhard and his colleagues (1965) found that many fathers who committed incest with their daughters were religiously devout, fundamentalist, and moralistic. Perhaps such men, when sexually frustrated, are less likely to seek extramarital and extrafamilial sexual outlets or to turn to masturbation as a sexual release. In many cases the father is under stress but does not find adequate emotional and sexual support from his wife (Gagnon, 1977). He turns to a daughter as a wife surrogate, often when he has been drinking alcohol (Gebhard et al., 1965). The daughter may become, in her father's fantasies, the "woman of the house." This fantasy may become his justification for continuing the incestuous relationship. In some incestuous families, a role reversal occurs. The abused daughter assumes many of the mother's responsibilities for managing the household and caring for the younger children (Waterman, 1986).

Incestuous abuse is often repeated from generation to generation. One study found that in 154 cases of children who were sexually abused within the family, more than a third of the male offenders and about half of the mothers had either been abused themselves or exposed to abuse as children (Faller, 1989).

Sociocultural factors, such as poverty, overcrowded living conditions, and social or geographical isolation, may contribute to incest in some families (Waterman, 1986). Sibling incest may be encouraged by the crowded living conditions and open sexuality that occur among some economically disadvantaged families (Waterman, 1986).

Effects of Child Sexual Abuse

Aboriginal Healing Foundation
www.ahf.ca/
This group supports Aboriginals in the healing processes that address the legacy of abuse, including sexual abuse in residential schools.

Child sexual abuse often inflicts great psychological harm on the child, whether the abuse is perpetrated by a family member, acquaintance, or stranger. Children who are sexually abused may suffer from a litany of short- and long-term psychological complaints, including anger, depression, anxiety, eating disorders, inappropriate sexual behaviour, aggressive behaviour, self-destructive behaviour, sexual promiscuity, drug abuse, suicide attempts, posttraumatic stress disorder, low self-esteem, sexual dysfunction, mistrust of others, and feelings of detachment (Beitchman et al., 1992; Finkelhor, 1984; Goodwin et al., 1990; McLaren & Brown, 1989). Child sexual abuse may also have physical effects such as genital injuries and may cause psychosomatic problems such as stomachaches and headaches.

Abused children commonly "act out." Younger children have tantrums or display aggressive or antisocial behaviour. Older children turn to substance abuse (Finkelhor, 1984). Some abused children become withdrawn and retreat into fantasy or refuse to leave the house. Regressive behaviours, such as thumb sucking, fear of the dark, and fear of strangers, are also common among sexually abused children. On the heels of the assault and in the ensuing years, many survivors of childhood sexual abuse—like many survivors of sexual assault—show signs of posttraumatic stress disorder. They have flashbacks, nightmares, numbing of emotions, and feelings of estrangement from others (Finkelhor, 1984).

A study of more than 1000 women attending an inner-city community health clinic in Winnipeg found that women who had been sexually abused as children were more likely to have their first consensual sexual intercourse early (less than 12 years of age) than women who were not abused, and on average had more lifetime sexual partners and more partners in the past year. Sexual abuse was also associated with smoking and a history of sexually transmitted infections such as chlamydia, gonorrhea, and genital warts, and divorce, especially for the non-Aboriginal women in the sample (Young & Katz, 1998).

Researchers generally find more similarities than differences between the genders with respect to the effects of sexual abuse in childhood (Finkelhor, 1984). For example, both boys and girls tend to suffer fears and sleep disturbance. There are some gender differences, however. The most consistent gender difference appears to be that boys more often externalize their problems, perhaps by becoming more physically aggressive.

Girls more often internalize their difficulties, as by becoming depressed (Finkelhor, 1984; Gomez-Schwartz et al., 1990).

Late adolescence and early adulthood seem to pose especially difficult periods for survivors of childhood sexual abuse. Studies of women in these age groups reveal more psychological and social problems in abused women than are found among nonabused reference groups (Jackson et al., 1990; Roland et al., 1989).

Effects of childhood sexual abuse are often long-lasting. In one study, researchers found evidence of greater psychological distress in a group of 54 women, ranging from 23 to 61 years of age, who had been sexually abused as children than in a matched group of nonabused women (Greenwald et al., 1990). Women who blame themselves for the abuse apparently have relatively lower self-esteem and more depression than those who do not (Hoagwood, 1990).

Treatment of Survivors of Child Sexual Abuse

At least 75% of cases of child sexual abuse go unreported. Psychotherapy in adulthood often becomes the first opportunity for survivors to confront leftover feelings of pain, anger, and misplaced guilt (Alter-Reid et al., 1986; Ratican, 1992). Group or individual therapy can help improve survivors' self-esteem and ability to develop intimate relationships. Confronting the trauma within a supportive therapeutic relationship may also help prevent the cycle of abuse from perpetuating itself from one generation to another (Alter-Reid et al., 1986).

Special programs have begun to appear that provide therapeutic services to abused children and adolescents. Most therapists recommend a multicomponent treatment approach, which may involve individual therapy for the child, mother, and father; group therapy for the adolescent or even preadolescent survivor; art therapy or play therapy for the younger child (e.g., using drawings or puppets to express feelings); marital counselling for the parents; and family therapy for the entire family (de Luca et al., 1992; Waterman, 1986). Services for survivors of child sexual abuse may be found through university and college health services, local community centres, and women's groups. Unfortunately, fewer resources are available for male survivors than for female survivors of sexual abuse.

Treatment of Sex Offenders

What does treatment mean? When a helping professional treats someone, the goal is usually to help that individual. When we speak of treating a sex offender, the goal is more often to help society by eliminating the problem behaviour.

Sex offenders are criminals, not patients. Most convicted offenders are incarcerated as a form of punishment, not treatment. They may, however, receive psychological treatment or rehabilitation in prison to help prepare them for release and reentry into society. The most common form of treatment is group therapy, which is based on the belief that though offenders may fool counsellors, they do not easily fool one another (Kaplan, 1993).

The results of prison-based treatment programs are mixed at best. Consider a Canadian study of 54 rapists who participated in a treatment program. Following release from prison, 28% were later convicted of a sexual offence, and 43% were convicted of a violent offence (Rice et al., 1990). Treatment also failed to curb recidivism among a sample of 136 child molesters (Rice et al., 1991).

More promising findings resulted from innovative programs in prison facilities in California and Vermont (Goleman, 1992). In the Vermont program, the average rate of conviction for additional sex crimes following release was reduced by at least half in a group of sex offenders who received the treatment program, as compared to a control group who did not. These innovative programs used a variety of techniques. Empathy training was used to increase the offender's sensitivity to his victims. One empathy exercise had offenders write about their crimes from the perspective of the victim. The technique of covert sensitization was used to help offenders resist deviant sex fantasies, which often lead to deviant behaviour. The offender would pair, in his imagination, scenes involving rape and molestation with aversive consequences. An exhibitionist, for example, might be asked to practise imagining that he is about to expose himself and is discovered in the act by his parents. A child molester might fantasize about sexually approaching a child, only to find himself confronted by police officers.

Social skills training teaches offenders how to communicate appropriately with others, and, in the case of child abusers, how to develop relationships with suitable individuals. Cognitive interventions help offenders become aware of the thoughts and feelings that lead to abusive behaviour and to replace them with more appropriate ones (Statistics Canada, 1999b).

A number of programs have also been developed to treat Aboriginal sex offenders. These programs make use of traditional healing and Aboriginal spirituality to help offenders maintain their self-identity and cultural awareness (Williams et al., 1997).

Another approach uses medical interventions to reduce testosterone levels and, consequently, offenders' sex drives. In a few European countries, some offenders who claimed they were unable to control their sex drives have been castrated to reduce testosterone levels (Wille & Beier, 1989). The effects of castration are mixed. Many castrated sexual offenders report markedly lowered sex drives, but they may retain sexual interest and remain capable of erection. And some do repeat their crimes. Other researchers report lower recidivism rates among castrated offenders than among non-castrated offenders. In any event, the use of castration with sex offenders appears to be declining (Wille & Beier, 1989).

Anti-androgen drugs such as Depo-Provera induce "chemical castration" (Ayres, 1996). Unlike surgical castration, chemical castration is reversible (Ayres, 1996). In 1996, California passed a bill that requires repeat child molesters to undergo chemical castration upon release unless they have undergone voluntary surgical castration ("Injections approved," 1996).

Sexual Harassment

What is **sexual harassment**? There is no simple or universally accepted definition of sexual harassment, but its definition in the workplace is generally any sexually oriented conduct—physical, verbal, or by innuendo—that is a condition of employment, interferes with job performance, or creates a hostile or offensive work environment. In Canada, harassment may be considered a crime under the Criminal Code, and is also addressed by provincial human rights legislation.

Among the complaints reported to the Canadian Human Rights Commission between 1978 and 1993 were (Welsh, 2000):

- harassment and insults
- subtle pressure to engage in sexual activity
- personal remarks and comments
- leering at or ogling a person's body
- touching or brushing against a person's body
- demands for sexual favours accompanied by the promise of a job or promotion
- coerced sex

Men or women can both commit, and be subjected to, sexual harassment. However, the great majority of harassers are men.

Charges of sexual harassment are often ignored or trivialized by co-workers and employers. The victim may hear, "Why make a big deal out of it? It's not like you were attacked in the street." Yet some find harassment on the job so unbearable that they resign. University women have dropped courses, switched majors, or changed graduate programs or even universities because they were unable to stop professors from sexually harassing them (Dziech & Weiner, 1984; Fitzgerald, 1993a, 1993b).

Sexual harassment Any sexually oriented conduct that is a condition of employment, interferes with job performance, or creates a hostile or offensive work environment is sexual harassment.

Sexual Harassment. *Any sexually oriented conduct that is a condition of employment, interferes with job performance, or creates a hostile or offensive environment is sexual harassment.*

One reason that sexual harassment is so stressful is that, as with so many other forms of sexual exploitation or coercion, the blame tends to fall on the victim (Powell, 1996). Some harassers seem to believe that charges of harassment were exaggerated or that the victim "overreacted" or "took me too seriously." In our society, women are expected to be "nice"—to be passive and not "make a scene." The woman who assertively protects her rights may be seen as "strange" and disturbing, or a "troublemaker." "Women are damned if they assert themselves and victimized if they don't" (Powell, 1991, p. 114).

Sexual harassment may have more to do with the abuse of power than with sexual desire (Goleman, 1991; Tedeschi & Felson, 1994). Relatively few cases of sexual harassment involve outright requests for sexual favours. Most involve the expression of power as a tactic to control or frighten someone, usually a woman. The harasser is usually in a dominant position and abuses that position by exploiting the victim's vulnerability. Sexual harassment may be used as a tactic of social control, a means of keeping women "in their place." This is especially so in work settings that are traditional male preserves, such as the firehouse, the construction site, or the military academy. Sexual harassment expresses resentment and hostility toward women who venture beyond the boundaries of the traditional feminine role (Fitzgerald, 1993b).

Sexual harassment is not confined to the workplace or the university. It may also occur between doctors and patients and between therapists and clients. Therapists may use their power and influence to pressure clients into sexual relations. The harassment may be disguised, expressed in terms of the "therapeutic benefits" of sexual activity.

Criminal Harassment

Suppose someone you know repeatedly follows you to school, work, or home, lurks outside your house, apartment, or classroom, phones you at all hours of the day or night, sends you unwanted emails, sends you gifts or letters threatening you or a family member. Is this a crime? Under the Canadian Criminal Code, it is. According to police statistics, most victims of criminal harassment are women; most stalkers are men (Kong, 1997). The majority of stalkers are former boyfriends or husbands, but women may also be stalked by casual acquaintances or co-workers, including employers, customers, or teachers. Male victims are more likely to be harassed by casual acquaintances or co-workers than by ex-wives or girlfriends (Kong, 1997).

Resisting Sexual Harassment

What would you do if you were sexually harassed by an employer or a professor? How would you handle it? Would you try to ignore it and hope that it would stop? What actions might you take? We offer some suggestions, adapted from Powell (1996), that may be helpful. Recognize, however, that responsibility for sexual harassment always lies with the perpetrator and the organization that permits sexual harassment to take place, not with the person subjected to the harassment.

1. *Familiarize yourself with your university's or employer's policy on sexual harassment.* Colleges, universities, and corporations have policies on sexual harassment, which you can usually find in your student handbook or employee package. The policy should state what the institution considers to be sexual harassment and outline reporting procedures and penalties.
2. *Convey a professional attitude.* Harassment may be stopped cold by responding to the harasser with a businesslike, professional attitude.
3. *Discourage harassing behaviour, and encourage appropriate behaviour.* Harassment may also be stopped cold by shaping the harasser's behaviour. Your reactions to the harasser may encourage businesslike behaviour and discourage flirtatious or suggestive behaviour. If a harassing professor suggests that you come back after school to review your term paper so that the two of you will be undisturbed, set limits assertively. Tell the professor that you'd feel more comfortable discussing the paper during regular office hours. Remain task-oriented. Stick to business. The harasser should get the message that you wish to maintain a professional relationship. If the harasser persists, do not blame yourself. You are

responsible only for your own actions. If the harasser persists, you may try a more direct response: "Professor Jones, I'd like to keep our relationship on a purely professional basis, okay?"
4. *Avoid being alone with the harasser.* If you are being harassed by your professor but need some advice about preparing your term paper, approach him or her after class when other students are milling about, not privately during office hours. Or bring a friend to wait outside the office while you consult the professor.
5. *Maintain a record.* Keep a record of incidents of harassment as documentation in the event you decide to lodge a complaint. The record should include the following: (1) where the incident took place; (2) the date and time; (3) what happened, including the exact words that were used, if you can recall them; (4) how you felt; and (5) the names of witnesses.
6. *Talk with the harasser.* It may be uncomfortable to address the issue with a harasser, but doing so puts the offender on notice that you want the harassment to stop. It may be helpful to frame your approach in terms of a description of the offending actions (e.g., "When we were alone in the office, you repeatedly attempted to touch me or brush up against me"), your feelings about the offence ("It made me feel like my privacy was being violated. I'm very upset about this and haven't been sleeping well"), and what you would like the offender to do ("So I'd like you to agree never to attempt to touch me again, okay?"). Having a talk with the harasser may stop the harassment. If the harasser denies the accusations, it may be necessary to take further action.
7. *Write a letter to the harasser.* Set

down on paper a record of the offending behaviour, and put the harasser on notice that the harassment must stop. Your letter might (1) describe what happened ("Several times you have made sexist comments about my body"), (2) describe how you feel ("It made me feel like a sexual object when you talked to me that way"), and (3) describe what you would like the harasser to do ("I want you to stop making sexist comments to me").
8. *Seek support.* Support from people you trust can help you through the often trying process of resisting sexual harassment. Talking with others allows you to express your feelings and receive emotional support, encouragement, and advice. In addition, it may strengthen your case if you have the opportunity to identify and talk with other people who have been harassed by the offender.
9. *File a complaint.* Companies and organizations are required by law to respond reasonably to complaints of sexual harassment. In large organizations, a designated official (sometimes an ombudsman or sexual harassment advisor) is usually charged to handle such complaints. Set up an appointment with this official to discuss your experiences. Ask about the grievance procedures in the organization and your right to confidentiality. Have available a record of the dates of the incidents, what happened, how you felt about it, and so on.
10. *Seek legal remedies.* Sexual harassment is illegal and actionable. If you are considering legal action, consult a lawyer familiar with this area of law. You may be entitled to back pay (if you were fired for reasons arising from the sexual harassment), job reinstatement, and punitive damages.

Summing Up

Sexual Assault

Sexual assault includes any form of sexual contact without voluntary touching. The term *rape* has been replaced in Canadian criminal law with sexual assault at three levels of severity. The definition of sexual assault involves more than just sexual intercourse. The **incidence of sexual assault** is difficult to determine because many assaults go unreported.

Types of sexual assault include stranger sexual assault, acquaintance sexual assault, marital sexual assault, gang sexual assault, male sexual assault, and sexual assault by females. Women are more likely to be sexually assaulted by men they know than by strangers. Most male sexual assaults occur in prison settings. Husbands who sexually assault their wives can now be prosecuted under the Canadian sexual assault laws.

Social attitudes and myths that encourage sexual assault include gender-role stereotyping, seeing sex as adversarial, and the belief that women want to be coerced. Many observers contend that our society breeds sexual assault by socializing males to be socially and sexually dominant.

Psychological characteristics of sexual assailants vary: some feel socially inadequate, lack social skills, and avoid social interactions with women. Some are basically antisocial and have long histories of violent behaviour. **Motives for sexual assault** include anger, a desire for power, and sadistic motives.

Sexual assault survivors often experience post-traumatic stress disorder (PTSD). Burgess and Holmstrom identified some common response patterns in sexual assault survivors that they labelled the sexual assault trauma syndrome. Treatment of sexual assault survivors typically involves helping them through the crisis period following the attack and then helping to foster long-term adjustment.

Sexual assault prevention involves educating society at large and familiarizing women with a number of precautions that they can take. Whether or not women take precautions to prevent sexual assault, however, the assailant is always the one responsible for the assault.

Sexual Abuse of Children

Like sexual assault, sexual abuse of children is greatly underreported. Sexual **abuse of children** includes any form of sexual contact between an adult and a child is abusive, even if force or physical threat is not used, because children are legally incapable of consenting to sexual activity with adults.

Patterns of abuse show that children from poorer, less cohesive families are at increased risk. In most cases, the molesters are close to the children they abuse—relatives, step-relatives, family friends, and neighbours. Genital fondling is the most common type of abuse. Most abusers are male.

Pedophilia is a type of paraphilia in which adults are sexually attracted to children. Pedophiles are almost exclusively male.

Incest is marriage or sexual relations between people who are so closely related that sex is prohibited and punished by virtue of the kinship tie. Father–daughter incest is more likely to be reported and prosecuted, but brother–sister incest is the most common type of incest. Incest frequently occurs within the context of general family disruption.

Children who are sexually abused often suffer social and emotional problems that impair their development and persist into adulthood, affecting their self-esteem and their formation of intimate relationships.

Treatment includes psychotherapy, which may help adult survivors of sexual abuse improve their self-esteem and ability to develop intimate relationships. Sexual assault prevention involves children learning not only to avoid strangers, but the difference between acceptable touching, such as an affectionate embrace or pat on the head, and unacceptable or "bad" touching. Children who may not be able to prevent abuse may nevertheless be encouraged to tell someone about the experience.

Treatment of Sexual Offenders

The effectiveness of prison-based rehabilitation programs and anti-androgen drugs in curbing repeat offences requires further empirical support.

Sexual Harassment

The definition of sexual harassment in the workplace has been expanded to include any behaviour of a sexual nature that interferes with an individual's work performance or creates a hostile, intimidating, or offensive work environment. There is no guaranteed way to put an end to sexual harassment, but suggestions include conveying a professional attitude, avoiding being alone with the harasser, keeping a record of incidents, and seeking legal remedies. Whether or not these efforts are effective, responsibility for harassment lies with the harasser and with the institution that failed to prevent harassment of the student or employee.

Chapter Quiz

1. All forms of sexual activity between adults and children are considered coercive because
    (a) the children resist.

(b) the adults have a need to dominate the children.

(c) the children are invariably hurt by the sexual activity.

(d) the children are below the age of consent.

2. Which of the following is NOT a reason why the incidence of sexual assault is underreported?

(a) Some women fear that they will be humiliated by the criminal justice system.

(b) Some women fear reprisal from their families or the assailant.

(c) Some women assume that the offender will not be apprehended or prosecuted.

(d) Some women are assaulted by total strangers.

3. The most common type of sexual assault is

(a) assault by an acquaintance.

(b) assault by a stranger.

(c) spousal assault.

(d) assault by females.

4. Most men who sexually assault other men are

(a) heterosexual.

(b) gay.

(c) pedophiles.

(d) insane.

5. Which one of the following is NOT a cultural myth that encourages sexual assault?

(a) Women say no when they mean yes.

(b) The way women dress, they are asking to be sexually assaulted.

(c) Women do not wish to be forced into sexual activity.

(d) Women want a truly masculine man—one who is sexually aggressive.

6. Which of the following is TRUE of sex offenders?

(a) Sex offenders are opposed to violence as a way of encouraging other people to do their will.

(b) Sex offenders cannot control their behaviour.

(c) Sex offenders vary in their psychological characteristics and family backgrounds.

(d) Sex offenders are less intelligent than most other people.

7. Which of the following statements is NOT TRUE of survivors of sexual assault?

(a) They often behave in a disorganized manner for several weeks after the assault.

(b) If they get through the first few weeks without breaking down, they will be fine.

(c) They can benefit from counselling.

(d) Long-term adjustment may take years.

8. Most of our knowledge of incestuous relationships concerns

(a) father–daughter incest.

(b) father–son incest.

(c) mother–son incest.

(d) brother–sister incest.

9. Which of the following is the most common form of child sexual abuse?

(a) Genital fondling

(b) Exhibitionism

(c) Oral–genital sex

(d) Sexual intercourse

10. Which of the following has been used to induce "chemical castration" in sex offenders?

(a) Testosterone

(b) Estrogen

(c) Depo-Provera

(d) Progesterone

Chapter 16

Commercial Sex

Did You Know That...

- Prostitution itself has never been illegal in Canada?
- Many massage parlours and escort services are fronts for prostitution?
- Many prostitutes were sexually abused as children?
- One of the lures of prostitution is that it provides sex without the need to make a commitment?
- Sex with prostitutes is a key factor in the male–female transmission of HIV in Africa?
- Some studies have linked exposure to violent pornography to increased acceptance of sexual assault?
- Both men and women are sexually aroused by pornography?
- Sexy ads can backfire in that viewers focus so much on the sexy imagery that they forget what the product is?

Sex as commerce runs the gamut from adult movie theatres and bookshops to strip shows, sex toy shops, erotic hotels and motels, escort/outcall services, "massage parlours," "900" telephone services, and the use of sex appeal in advertisements for legitimate products. The "world of commercial sex is a kind of X-rated amusement park—Disneyland for Adults" (Edgley, 1989, p. 372).

In this chapter, we discuss three commercial aspects of sexuality: prostitution, pornography, and the use of sex in advertising. Though the streetwalker, the purveyor of "adult" movies, and the advertising copywriter may otherwise have little else in common, they all have learned to use sex to make a profit.

Prostitution

Were you surprised to read that **prostitution** per se has never been illegal in Canada? Although it is legal for any two consenting adults to have sex with each other, the Criminal Code has many provisions concerning the taking of money for sex. Most are aimed at either the prostitute or **pimp**. For instance, procuring or soliciting someone to have illicit sexual intercourse, enticing someone who is not a prostitute to a "house of assignation" for the purpose of illicit sexual intercourse, concealing someone in or transporting someone to a common bawdy house, and living on the proceeds of prostitution are all punishable by not more than 10 years imprisonment. In addition, a prostitute can be charged for stopping people on the street or in a car in order to solicit money for sex.

Soliciting the services of a prostitute is also illegal. The customer, or "john," may also be charged. In 1998 46% of adults charged with prostitution-related offences were male and 54% were female. Although prostitutes and their clients can be male or female, most prostitutes are female and virtually all customers are male.

No one knows how many prostitutes there are in Canada. The little we know of prostitution derives from American sex surveys and police statistics. Almost two-thirds of the white males in Kinsey's sample (Kinsey et al., 1948) reported visiting a prostitute at least once. About 15% to 20% visited them regularly. The use of prostitutes varied with educational level, however. By the age of 20, about 50% of Kinsey's non-college-educated single males, but only 20% of his college-educated males, had visited a prostitute. By the age of 25, the figures swelled to about two-thirds for non-college-educated males but only slightly above 25% for college men.

Kinsey's data foreshadowed a falling off of experience with prostitutes that seems linked to the decay of the sexual double standard. Kinsey found that 20% of his college-educated men had been sexually initiated by prostitutes. A more recent survey of sexual behaviour in the United States reported that 7% of men who came of age in the 1950s

Prostitution The sale of sexual activity for money or goods of value, such as drugs. (From the Latin *prostituere*, meaning "to offer for sale.")

Pimps Men who serve as agents for prostitutes and live off their earnings. (Possibly from the Middle French *pimper*, meaning "to dress smartly.")

had their first sexual experience with a prostitute, compared to 1.5% of men who came of age in the 1980s (Laumann et al., 1994). Why are young men less likely to visit prostitutes than they were in Kinsey's day? For one thing, young men in recent generations were more likely to become sexually initiated with their girlfriends. As Edgley (1989) put it, "An old and hallowed economic principle was at work; those who charge for a service cannot compete with those who give it away" (p. 392). Concern about sexually transmitted infections, especially AIDS, has also limited the use of prostitution. Nevertheless, prostitution continues to flourish.

Types of Female Prostitutes

Female prostitutes—commonly called *hookers, whores, working girls,* or *escorts*—are usually classified according to the settings in which they work. The major types of prostitutes today are streetwalkers; brothel or "house" prostitutes, many of whom work in "massage parlours" and for "escort services" (often listed in the Yellow Pages); and call girls. Traditional brothel prostitution is much less common today than before World War II.

Streetwalkers Prostitutes who solicit customers on the streets.

Streetwalkers Most prostitutes are **streetwalkers**. They occupy the bottom rung in the hierarchy of prostitutes. They earn the lowest incomes and are usually the least desirable. They also incur the greatest risk of abuse by customers and pimps. Streetwalkers tend to come from poverty and to have had unhappy childhoods (Edgley, 1989). Perhaps as many as 80% are survivors of sexual assault, sexual abuse, or incest (Gordon & Snyder, 1989). Many were teenage runaways who turned to prostitution to survive (Wolff & Geissel, 1994).

Streetwalkers operate in the open. They are thus more likely than other prostitutes to draw attention to themselves and risk arrest. To avoid arrest, streetwalkers may be indirect about their services. They may ask passersby if they are interested in a "good time" or some "fun" rather than sex per se. In many cities, streetwalkers dress in revealing or provocative fashions.

A U.S. study of male, female, and transgendered street prostitutes found that female prostitutes were least likely to report any sexual enjoyment with clients. A small percentage of women in the sample reported enjoying sex with clients, and then only "sometimes" or "rarely." However, the male and transgendered sex workers reported enjoying sex with clients far more often. The authors of the study speculate that female sex workers are more likely to create an "emotional distance" from their work as a form of "survival strategy" (Weinberg et al., 1999). Most criminal charges relating to prostitution are for *communicating* (soliciting), as these charges are easier to prove than procuring, which may require extensive police investigation. The prostitute, however, is likely to receive a more severe sentence than the customer, especially if she has previous convictions. Sentencing may also vary from province to province. In Ontario in 1991–1992, 44% of charges against prostitutes (mostly women) resulted in prison terms; customers (mainly men) were more likely to be fined. During the same period in Alberta, 66% of prostitutes and 89% of customers were fined (Wolff & Geissel, 1994).

A bar prostitute is a variation of the streetwalker. She approaches men in a bar she frequents, rather than on the streets. Payoffs to bar owners or managers secure their cooperation, although the women are sometimes tolerated because they draw customers. Some streetwalkers work "adult" movie houses and may service patrons in their seats with manual or oral sex. Payoffs may secure the cooperation of the management.

Many streetwalkers support a pimp. A pimp acts as lover–father–companion–master. He provides streetwalkers with protection, bail, and sometimes room and board, in exchange for a high percentage of their earnings, often more than 90%. Prostitutes are often physically abused by their pimps, who may use threats and beatings as means of control. In a study of young streetwalkers in Boston, Price (1989) observed that as the relationship progressed, the beatings became more vicious. Romenesko and Miller (1989), who studied streetwalkers in Milwaukee, commented, "Clearly, 'men' are the rulers of the underworld" (p. 117).

Streetwalkers do not tend to remain in the business (sometimes referred to as "the life") very long (Edgley, 1989). Some make the transition to a more traditional life or get married. Others die young from drug abuse, disease, suicide, or physical abuse from pimps or customers. Those who survive become less marketable with age.

Prostitutes who work hotels and conventions generally hold a higher status than those who work the streets or bars. Clients are typically conventioneers or businessmen travelling away from home. Some hotel managers will tolerate known prostitutes (usually for a payoff under the table), so long as the woman conducts herself discreetly.

Brothel Prostitution *Cathouse, bordello, cat wagon, parlour house, whorehouse, bawdy house, joy house, house of ill repute*—these are but a handful of names given to brothels, houses in which many prostitutes work. Brothel prostitutes occupy a middle status in the hierarchy of prostitutes, between streetwalkers on one end and call girls on the other (Edgley, 1989). Some work in a massage parlour or for an "escort service."

Some brothel prostitutes lead lives of complete degradation. Many poor Asian women have been lured to North America by promises of the good life. Upon arrival, they have found themselves enslaved in brothels—working for tips and not allowed to leave. Such a brothel was closed by police in New York City. It housed more than 30 women smuggled from Thailand and came to the attention of police when one woman jumped from a window (Goldberg, 1995).

Generally, though, the life of the brothel (or "house") prostitute is neither as lucrative as that of the call girl nor as degrading as that of the streetwalker. Some prostitutes in massage parlours or working for escort services may not consider themselves to be "real prostitutes" because they do not walk the streets and because their businesses present a legitimate front (Edgley, 1989). The heyday of the brothel is all but over in North America. Formal brothels today are rare, except in Nevada.

"Massage parlours" are a variation on the brothel that sprang up to fill the gap. Many massage parlours are legitimate establishments that provide massage, and only massage, to customers. Registered massage therapists (RMT) are just what the name suggests—trained therapists. Other masseurs and masseuses, too, offer simple massage.

However, some businesses offering "massage" are fronts for prostitution. In these establishments, clients typically pay fees for a standard massage and then tip the workers for sexual extras. Massage parlour prostitutes generally offer to perform manual stimulation of the penis ("a local"), oral sex, or, less frequently, coitus. Some massage parlour prostitutes are better educated than streetwalkers and brothel workers and would not work in these other venues.

Escort Services Conventioneers and businessmen are more likely to turn to the listings for "escort services" in the telephone directory or under the personal ads in local newspapers than to seek hotel prostitutes. Services that provide "outcall" send masseuses (or masseurs) or escorts to the hotel room.

Escort services are typically (but not always) fronts for prostitution. Escort services are found in every major North American city and present themselves as legitimate businesses providing escorts for men. Indeed, one will find female companionship for corporate functions and for unattached men travelling away from home under "escort services." Many escort services provide only prostitution, however, and clients of other escort services sometimes negotiate sexual services after formal escort duties are completed—or in their stead.

Prostitutes who work for escort services often come from middle-class backgrounds and are well educated—so much the better to help prepare them to hold their own in social conversation. Escort services may establish arrangements with legitimate companies to provide "escorts" for visiting customers or potential clients. They also provide female escorts to "entertain" at conventions.

Call Girls **Call girls** occupy the highest status on the social ladder of female prostitution. Many of them overlap with escorts. Call girls tend to be the most attractive and well-educated prostitutes and tend to charge more for their services. Many come from middle-class backgrounds (Edgley, 1989). Unlike other types of prostitutes, call girls

Call girls Prostitutes who arrange for their sexual contacts by telephone. *Call* refers both to telephone calls and to being "on call."

usually work on their own. Thus, they need not split their income with a pimp, escort service, or massage parlour. Many lead a luxurious lifestyle. They live in expensive neighbourhoods, wear stylish clothes, and are more selective about customers. Yet they incur expenses for laundry services and for payoffs to landlords, doormen, and sometimes to police.

Call girls often escort their clients to dinner and social functions, and are expected to provide not only sex but also charming and gracious company and conversation (Edgley, 1989). Call girls often give clients the feeling that they are important and attractive. They may effectively simulate pleasure and orgasm and can create the illusion that time does not matter. It does, of course. To the call girl, as to other entrepreneurs, time is money.

Call girls may receive clients in their apartments or make "outcalls" to clients' homes and hotels. Call girls may trade or sell "black books" that list clients and their sexual preferences. To protect themselves from police and abusive clients, call girls may insist on reviewing a client's business card or learning his home telephone number before personal contact is made. They may investigate whether the customer is in fact the person he purports to be.

Characteristics of Female Prostitutes

No single factor explains entry into female prostitution. Yet, poverty and sexual and/or physical abuse figure prominently in the backgrounds of many prostitutes. They often come from conflict-ridden or one-parent homes in poor urban areas or rural farming communities.

Studies have found that for young women of impoverished backgrounds and marginal skills, the life of the prostitute may seem alluring. It is an alternative to the menial and dismal work that is otherwise available.

Researchers also find a high level of psychological disturbance among streetwalkers. Exner and his colleagues (1977) found that call girls and brothel prostitutes could not be distinguished from nonprostitutes on their psychological characteristics. Streetwalkers and drug-addicted prostitutes showed higher rates of psychological disturbance than comparison groups, however. In another study, teenage female prostitutes were more likely than normal female adolescents or delinquents who did not engage in prostitution to show signs of psychological disturbance and to have been placed in special-education classes in school (Gibson et al., 1988).

Poverty accounts for the entry of young women into prostitution in many countries. In some Third World nations, such as Thailand, rural, impoverished parents may in effect sell daughters to recruiters who place them in brothels in cities (Erlanger, 1991; Goldberg, 1995). Many of the women send home whatever money they can and also work hard to try to pay off the procurers and break free of their financial bonds.

In the United States and Canada, many initiates into prostitution are teenage runaways. The family backgrounds of teenage runaways vary in socioeconomic status (some come from middle-class or affluent homes, whereas others are reared in poverty). However, family discord and dysfunction frequently set the stage for their entry to street life and prostitution (Price, 1989). A study of female street youth in Montreal found that those involved in prostitution were more likely to report having run away from home or having been kicked out of their home. When compared to female street youth not involved in prostitution, they were also more likely to report incidents of sexual abuse, earlier experiences of consensual sex, and a history of injection drug use (Weber et al., 2002). Teenage runaways are at particularly high risk of unsafe sexual practices, such as unprotected sex with multiple partners. The average male teenage runaway in a New York City study reported having had 11 female sexual partners in his lifetime (Rotheram-Borus et al., 1992). Only 8% of the teenage boys reported using condoms consistently.

Teenage runaways with marginal skills and limited means of support may find few alternatives to prostitution. Adolescent prostitution results from the "necessities of street life—it is survival behavior more than it is sexual behavior" (Seng, 1989, p. 674).

It is not long before the teenage runaway is approached by a pimp or a john. A study of 149 teenage runaways in Toronto found that 67% of the boys and 82% of the girls who had been away from home for more than a year had been offered money to engage in sexual activity with an adult (Hartman et al., 1987).

Studies of teenage prostitutes show that perhaps as many as half to two-thirds of female prostitutes had been sexually abused as children (Seng, 1989). One sample of 45 former prostitutes in Canada showed that 73% had been sexually abused in childhood (Bagley & Young, 1987).

Not all sexually abused children become prostitutes, of course. In one sample of predominantly female 16- to 18-year-olds who had been sexually abused, 12% became involved in prostitution (Seng, 1989). Nor do all teenage runaways become prostitutes. A Boston study of homeless street youth in the mid-1980s found that fewer than 20% had engaged in prostitution (Price, 1989). Though most had been approached for prostitution within a few days of living on the streets, the overwhelming majority refused.

In sum, evidence suggests that most female prostitutes are survivors of sexual abuse or incest. Running away from home appears to funnel many survivors of childhood sexual abuse into prostitution, yet not all survivors of sexual abuse, nor all teenage runaways, become prostitutes.

Customers of Female Prostitutes

Many prostitutes refer to a customer as a "john" or a "trick." Terms such as *patron, meatball, sucker,* and *beefbuyer* are also heard. Men who use female prostitutes come from all walks of life and all socioeconomic and racial groups. Many, perhaps most, are married men of middle-class background. A study of the address listings of customers (seized by the local police) of an "escort service" in one city showed that most of the clients lived in relatively affluent neighbourhoods consisting of a high percentage of well-educated, largely white, and married residents (Adams, 1987).

Most patrons are "occasional johns." Examples include travelling salesmen or military personnel who are stopping over in town and away from their regular sex partners. One study of 30 occasional johns showed that all had regular sex partners. They used prostitutes because they desired novelty or sexual variety, not because they lacked other sexual outlets (Holzman & Pines, 1982).

"Habitual johns" use prostitutes as their major or exclusive sexual outlet. Some habitual johns have never established an intimate sexual relationship. Some wealthy men who wish to avoid intimate relationships habitually patronize call girls.

"Compulsive johns" feel driven to prostitutes to meet some psychological or sexual need. They may repeatedly resolve to stop using prostitutes but feel unable to control their compulsions. Some compulsive johns engage in acts of fetishism or transvestism with prostitutes but would not inform their wives or girlfriends of their variant interests. Some men who are compulsive users of prostitutes suffer from a **whore–madonna complex**. They see women as either sinners or saints. They can permit themselves to enjoy sex only with prostitutes or would ask only prostitutes to engage in acts such as fellatio. They see marital coitus as a duty or obligation.

Whore–madonna complex A rigid stereotyping of women as either sinners or saints.

Motives for Using Prostitutes Though the reasons for using prostitutes vary, researchers have identified six of the most common motives (Edgley, 1989; Gagnon, 1977):

1. *Sex without negotiation.* Prostitution may be attractive to men who do not want to spend the time, effort, and money involved in dating and getting to know someone simply to obtain sex.

2. *Sex without commitment.* Prostitutes require no commitment from the man other than payment for services rendered.

3. *Sex for eroticism and variety.* Many prostitutes offer "something extra" in the way of novel or kinky sex—for example, use of costumes (e.g., leather attire) and S&M

rituals (bondage and discipline or spanking). Men may not be able to obtain such activities with their regular partners.

4. *Prostitution as sociability.* In the nineteenth and early twentieth centuries, the brothel served not only as a place to obtain sex, but also as a kind of "stopping off" place between home and work. At times, sex was secondary to the companionship and amiable conversation that men would find in brothels. Today, however, such sociability is more likely to be found among call girls and escort prostitutes who offer social companionship, with or without sex.

5. *Sex away from home.* The greatest contemporary use of prostitution occurs among men who are away from home, such as businessmen attending conventions and sports fans attending out-of-town sporting events.

6. *Problematical sex.* Persons with physical disabilities or disfiguring conditions sometimes seek the services of prostitutes because of difficulty attracting other partners or because of fears of rejection. Men with sexual dysfunctions may also turn to prostitutes to help them overcome their problems.

Male Prostitution

Male prostitution includes both male–male and male–female activities. Male prostitutes who service female clients—*gigolos*—are rare. Gigolos' clients are typically older, wealthy, unattached women. Gigolos may serve as escorts or as surrogate sons for the women, and may or may not offer sexual services. Many gigolos are struggling actors or models.

The overwhelming majority of male prostitutes service gay men. Men who engage in male prostitution are called **hustlers**. Their patrons are typically called **scores**. Hustlers average 17 to 18 years of age and become initiated into prostitution at an average age of 14 or so (Coleman, 1989). They typically have less than eleventh-grade education and few, if any, marketable skills. The majority come from working-class and lower-class backgrounds. Many male prostitutes, like many female prostitutes, come from families troubled by conflict, alcoholism, or abuse (Boyer, 1989; Coleman, 1989).

Hustlers may be gay, bisexual, or heterosexual in orientation. At least half of the male prostitutes surveyed are gay.

The major motive for male prostitution, like female prostitution, is money. In one study, 69% of male prostitutes cited money as their principal motive (Fisher et al., 1982). Running away from home typically serves as an entry point for male as well as female prostitution. In one study, three of four male prostitutes had run away by an average age of 15 (Weisberg, 1985). Some had run away because of family problems; others, because of a desire for adventure or independence (Coleman, 1989). Some gay male prostitutes are thrown out because their families cannot accept their sexual orientation (Coleman, 1989; Kruks, 1991).

Heterosexual hustlers may try to psychologically detach themselves from male clients by refusing to kiss or hug them or to perform fellatio. Gagnon (1977) writes that, "As long as the [client's] head is below the [hustler's] belly button and contact is on the penis, it is the other person who is [gay]" (p. 264). To become aroused, heterosexual hustlers may fantasize about women while the "score" is fellating them.

Most hustlers are part-timers who continue some form of educational or vocational activity as they support themselves through prostitution. Drug dealing and drug use are also common among hustlers (Coleman, 1989).

Unlike female prostitutes, hustlers typically are not attached to a pimp (Luckenbill, 1985). They generally make contacts with clients in gay bars and social clubs, or by working the streets in areas frequented by gay men. They typically learn to hustle through their interactions with other hustlers and by watching other hustlers ply their trade (Luckenbill, 1985).

Coleman (1989) identifies several types of male prostitutes:

- *Kept boys* have relationships with older, economically secure men who keep them in an affluent lifestyle. The older male, or "sugar daddy," often assumes a parental role.

Hustlers Men who engage in prostitution with male customers.

Scores Customers of hustlers.

- *Call boys*, like call girls, may work on their own or through an agency or escort service.

- *Punks* are prison inmates who are used sexually by other inmates and rewarded with protection or goods such as cigarettes or drugs.

- *Drag prostitutes* are transvestites or presurgical male-to-female transsexuals who impersonate female prostitutes and have sex with men who may be unaware of their gender.

- *Brothel prostitutes* are rarer than their female counterparts. Fewer houses of male prostitution exist.

- *Bar hustlers* and *street hustlers*, like their female counterparts, occupy the lowest status and ply their trade in gay bars or on streets frequented by gay passersby. Street hustlers are the most common and typically the youngest subtype.

A World of Diversity

AIDS and Prostitution in Thailand

HIV may have been brought to Thailand by gay Thais who lived for a while in the West (Erlanger, 1991). Through the 1980s, HIV was spread in Thailand mostly via gay male sexual activity and injectable drug use. In the 1990s, however—in a progression that is found in many other nations—the central route of infection has become male–female sexual intercourse.

Whereas only a minority of Westerners visit (or admit to visiting) prostitutes, prostitution is a way of life in Thailand. About three in four Thai men—at a rate of 450 000 a day—avail themselves of prostitutes. As well, global sex tourism brings many men from other countries of the world to Thailand. In many brothels in northwest Thailand, such as in the city of Chiang Mai, where the epidemic is most advanced, 80% of the "working women" test positive for HIV antibodies (Erlanger, 1991). In populous Bangkok, the figure now exceeds 20%. HIV is leapfrogging from prostitutes to customers to the customers' wives, lovers, and—often—to their children.

Yet there are some signs of hope. During the 1990s, for example, the Thai Ministry of Public Health began an educational program to encourage army recruits to use condoms during sexual contacts with prostitutes. In 1991 and 1993, soldiers from northern Thailand were found to have HIV infection rates of 10.4% and 12.5%, respectively (Nelson et al., 1996). Moreover, only 61% of the men reported using condoms during recent contacts with prostitutes. By 1995, however, 92.5% of the men were using condoms reliably, and the infection rate among new recruits had fallen to 6.7%.

a number of Thai sex workers noted that women do not insist on condoms because "their fear of poverty is greater than their fear of AIDS" (Wawer et al., 1996). One of the prostitutes explained, "Sometimes I will allow it (sex without condom). Sometimes not. If I have no alternative, no money to buy food, I would accept" (Wawer et al., 1996, p. 459).

Prostitution in Thailand. Many prostitutes in Thailand are infected with HIV. It is common for their customers to become infected and to then transmit HIV to their wives.

Yet many Thai men still refuse to wear condoms. Nor do prostitutes always insist on them. If a client will not use a condom, a prostitute must make a choice between refusing her services and thus not receiving payment, or engaging in unsafe sex. A researcher who interviewed

Some prostitutes mistakenly believe that a man who appears to be healthy can not have AIDS. As says Daeng, a Bangkok bar girl, "If the man seems clean and healthy, I say, OK. If the man comes to me often and is nice to me, I say, OK. If he offers me more money, I say, OK" (Erlanger, 1991, p. 49).

Prostitution and HIV/AIDS
www.aidslaw.ca/
Maincontent/issues/
prostitution.htm
This site features three
documents on the legal,
ethical, and human rights issues
raised by HIV/AIDS in the
context of prostitution.

Male prostitutes typically have shorter careers than their female counterparts (Price, 1989). By and large, male prostitution is an adolescent enterprise.

HIV, AIDS, and Prostitution

The risk of HIV transmission has been linked to both male and female prostitution (Bloor et al., 1990; Campbell, 1991; Van den Hoek et al., 1990; Yates et al., 1991). Sex with prostitutes is an important factor in the male–female transmission of HIV in Africa, where researchers have speculated that the infection is spread predominantly via male–female sexual intercourse. A study showed that regular contact with female street prostitutes was a risk factor in the transmission of HIV in U.S. men (Castro et al., 1988). Prostitutes incur a greater risk of HIV transmission because they have sexual relations with a great many partners, often without protection (Quadagno et al., 1991). Moreover, many prostitutes and their clients and other sex partners inject drugs and share contaminated needles (Bloor et al., 1990; Freund et al., 1989). HIV may be spread by unprotected sex from prostitutes to customers, then to the customers' wives or lovers.

The rate of HIV infection is high among male prostitutes, and many, if not most, of their male customers describe themselves as either bisexual or heterosexual (Morse et al., 1992). One study found that the rate of HIV infection was 50% for gay male prostitutes, 36.5% for bisexual male prostitutes, and 18.5% for heterosexual male prostitutes (Boles & Elifson, 1994). Customers of such men may thus be exposing their wives and girlfriends to HIV.

Despite the danger of HIV transmission, many prostitutes have not altered either their sexual behaviour or their patterns of drug use to any large extent. For example, only 30% of a sample of 20 street prostitutes reported always using condoms (Freund et al., 1989). A study of 72 heroin-addicted female street prostitutes showed a high level of knowledge and fear about AIDS but a failure to change patterns of sexual behaviour or drug use (Bellis, 1990). Research has shown that the most disadvantaged sex workers are the ones least likely to be able to negotiate the use of a condom with a client. Threats of violence, economic necessity, and drug dependence are all factors that influence a pattern of risky sexual behaviour (Chan & Reidpath, 2003; Vanwesenbeeck, 2001).

Pornography and Obscenity

The production and distribution of sexually explicit materials has become a boom industry. Adult movies (also called *porn* movies or X-rated movies in the U.S.) have moved from sleazy adult theatres to living rooms in the form of videocassette rentals and sales. According to a Gallup poll, X-rated films account for about one in five U.S. video sales (Linsley, 1989). Data from a national American survey conducted in 2000 found that 32% of men and 17% of women questioned had viewed an X-rated film in the last year (American Porn, 2002). Pornography is indeed popular, but also highly controversial. Many people in our society are opposed to pornography on moral grounds. Many people oppose pornography on the grounds that it degrades and dehumanizes women. It portrays women as objects who are subservient to men's sexual wishes, as sexually insatiable nymphomaniacs, or as sexual masochists who enjoy being sexually assaulted and violated. Moreover, some people believe that depictions of women in sexually subordinate roles may encourage men to treat them as sex objects and may increase the potential for sexual assault (Scott & Schwalm, 1988).

What is pornography? How is it defined? Who uses it? Why? How does it affect users?

What Is Pornographic?

Webster's Deluxe Unabridged Dictionary defines **pornography** as "writing, pictures, etc., intended to arouse sexual desire." The inclusion of the word *intended* places the determination of what is pornographic in the mind of the person composing the work.

Pornography Written, visual, or audiotaped material that is sexually explicit and produced for purposes of eliciting or enhancing sexual arousal. (From Greek roots meaning "to write about prostitutes.")

Applying this definition makes it all but impossible to determine what is pornographic. If a filmmaker admits that he or she wanted to arouse the audience sexually, we may judge the work to be pornographic, even if no naked bodies or explicit sex scenes are shown. On the other hand, explicit representations of people engaged in sexual activity would not be pornographic if the work was intended as an artistic expression, rather than created for its **prurient** value. Many works that were once prohibited in this country because of explicit sexual content, such as the novels *Tropic of Cancer* by Henry Miller, *Lady Chatterley's Lover* by D. H. Lawrence, and *Ulysses* by James Joyce, are now generally considered literary works rather than pornography. Even Mark Twain's *Huckleberry Finn*, John Steinbeck's *The Grapes of Wrath*, and Ernest Hemingway's *For Whom the Bell Tolls* have been banned from place to place because local citizens found them to be offensive, obscene, or morally objectionable (Linsley, 1989).

There is thus a subjective element in the definition of pornography. An erotic statue that sexually arouses viewers may not be considered pornographic if the sculptor's intent was artistic. A grainy photograph of a naked body that was intended to excite sexually may be pornographic. One alternative definition finds material pornographic when it is judged to be offensive by others. This definition, too, relies on the subjective judgment of the person exposed to the material. In other words, one person's pornography is another person's work of art.

Pornography is often classified as either "hard-core" or "soft-core." Hard-core pornography includes graphic and sexually explicit depictions of sex organs and sexual acts. Soft-core porn, as represented by *Playboy* or *Penthouse* photo spreads, features more stylized nude photos and suggestive (or simulated) rather than explicit sexual acts.

Legislative bodies usually write laws about **obscenity** rather than pornography. In Canada, an obscene publication is "…any publication a dominant characteristic of which is the undue exploitation of sex, or of sex and any one or more of the following subjects, namely, crime, horror, cruelty and violence…" (Criminal Code, section 163, paragraph 8).

Child pornography and violent, degrading, or dehumanizing pornography complicate matters further. People who do not find depictions, however explicit, of consensual sexual activity between adults to be obscene may regard child pornography or violent pornography to be obscene. Child pornography is clearly psychologically harmful to the juvenile actors (Silbert, 1989) and is illegal in Canada. (The Supreme Court of Canada, in a 2001 decision, allowed two narrow exemptions: one allows expressive material, such

Prurient Tending to excite lust; lewd. (From the Latin *prurire*, meaning "to itch" in the sense of "to long for.")

Obscenity That which offends people's feelings or goes beyond prevailing standards of decency or modesty.

Adults Only: 2003. The VCR has already brought explicit sex from the red-light district into Canada's living rooms—or bedrooms. Now the home computer is getting involved as people surf the internet and engage in cybersex.

as journal writings or drawings, to be kept for the author's private use; the other allows teenagers to keep visual records of themselves engaged in legal, consensual sexual acts for their own use.)

Prevalence and Use of Pornography

Most of us have been exposed to sexually explicit materials, whether in the form of a novel, an article in *Playboy* or *Playgirl* (purchased, no doubt, for its literary value), or a sexually explicit film. The NHSLS study found that about one American man in four (23%) and one American woman in ten (11%) had bought an X-rated movie or video within the past year (Michael et al., 1994). Sixteen percent of the men and 4% of the women had bought sexually explicit magazines or books.

People are typically introduced to pornography by their high school years, often by peers (Bryant & Brown, 1989). Females are more likely to have been exposed to pornography by their boyfriends than the reverse (Bryant & Brown, 1989).

Pornography is typically used to elicit or enhance sexual arousal, often as a masturbation aid (Michael et al., 1994). Pornographic materials may also be used by couples to enhance sexual arousal during lovemaking. Couples may find that viewing a soft- or hard-core video, or reading an erotic story aloud, enlivens their sexual appetite or suggests novel sexual techniques.

Researchers have found that both men and women are physiologically sexually aroused by pornographic pictures, movies, or audiotaped passages (Goleman, 1995). That is, both men and women respond to pornographic stimuli with vasocongestion of the genitals and myotonia (muscle tension). However, there is a significant difference between physiological response and subjective feelings of arousal in women. Despite what is happening within their bodies, women tend to rate romantic scenes as more sexually arousing than sexually explicit scenes (Laan & Heiman, 1994).

Women are less accepting of sex without emotional involvement (Townsend, 1995). "Women like sex to come from an emotional connection," says marital and sex therapist Lonnie Barbach (1995). "For women there's a predisposition to allowing themselves to become turned on that romance allows. This wouldn't necessarily be measured by genital arousal."

Repeated exposure to the same pornographic materials progressively lessens the sexual response to them. People may become aroused by the familiar materials again if some time is allowed to go by. Novel materials are also likely to reactivate a sexual response (Meuwissen & Over, 1990; Zillmann, 1989).

Gender Differences in Response to Pornography

Both genders can become physiologically aroused by erotic materials. Yet men and women do not necessarily share the same subjective response to them or level of interest in them. Visual pornography (sexually explicit pictures or films) is actually largely a male preserve (Symons, 1995; Winick, 1985). The majority of erotic visual materials are produced by men for men. Attempts to market visual materials to females have been largely unsuccessful (Symons, 1995). Women may read erotic romance novels, but they show little interest in acquiring erotic pictures, films, or videotapes (Lawrence & Herold, 1988).

The reasons for these gender differences remain unclear (Bryant & Brown, 1989). Women may find such material a "turn-off" when it portrays women in unflattering roles, as "whorish," as subservient to the sexual demands of men, and as sexually aroused by male domination and coercion. Symons (1979), a sociobiologist, believes that a basic evolutionary process is at work. He argues that ancestral men who were more sexually aroused by the sight of a passing female may have had reproductive advantages over their less arousable peers:

> The male's desire to look at female genitals, especially genitals he has not seen before, and to seek out opportunities to do so, is part of the motivational process that maximizes male reproductive opportunities. (p. 181)

Women, however, have fewer mating opportunities than men and must make the most of any reproductive opportunity by selecting the best possible mate and provider. To be sexually aroused by the sight of male genitalia might encourage random matings, which would undermine their reproductive success.

Pornography and Sexual Coercion

Is pornography a harmless diversion or an impetus to sexual violence or other antisocial acts? Let us consider several sources of evidence in examining these highly charged questions, beginning with the findings of a 1970 U.S. government commission and of the Canadian Fraser Commission of 1985.

A U.S. Congressional Commission on Obscenity and Pornography studied the effects of pornography. Upon reviewing the existing research, the commission (Abelson et al., 1970) concluded that there was no evidence that pornography led to crimes of violence or sexual offences such as exhibitionism, voyeurism, or child molestation. Some people were sexually aroused by pornography and increased the frequency of their usual sexual activity, such as masturbation or coitus with regular partners, following exposure. They did not engage in antisocial behaviour, however. These results have been replicated many times.

The commission found no causal link between pornography and delinquent behaviour or sexual violence against women. However, Congress and then-president Richard Nixon rejected the commission's findings and recommendations on moral and political—not scientific—grounds.

In 1985, U.S. president Ronald Reagan appointed a committee to reexamine the effects of pornography. This committee, known as the Meese commission, claimed to find a causal link between sexual violence and exposure to violent pornography (U.S. Department of Justice, 1986). The report concluded that exposure to pornography that portrayed women in degrading or subservient roles increased acceptability of rape in the minds of viewers.

These findings are controversial. Critics claim that the conclusions reflected an overgeneralization of laboratory-based findings (Wilcox, 1987). Other researchers contended that the Meese commission failed to distinguish between the effects of sexually explicit materials per se and the effects of violent materials. They claim that evidence of the link between exposure to sexually explicit material (without violent content) and sexual aggression is lacking, and it is the violence, not the sex, that is problematic (Donnerstein & Linz, 1987). Let us take a look both at the scientific evidence on the effects of violent and nonviolent pornography and at the relationship between pornography and sex offenders.

In the early 1980s, the Canadian government established a Special Committee on Pornography and Prostitution (the Fraser Commission) to examine public, legal, and research implications. The Commission's report pointed out that most research examined the effects of exposure to considerable amounts of pornography over short periods of time and did not address the issue of long-term use of pornography. They also discussed the problem of defining what constituted pornography. Although the state of research at the time was described as "inadequate and chaotic," the report concluded that the available evidence did not support the conclusion that pornography contributed to violent crime, the sexual abuse of children, or the disintegration of communities and society (Special Committee on Pornography and Prostitution, 1985).

Pornography and Sex Offenders Another approach to examining the role of pornography in crimes of sexual violence involves comparing the experience of sex offenders and nonoffenders with pornographic materials. A review of the research literature by William Marshall of Queen's University found little or no difference in the level of exposure to pornography between incarcerated sex offenders and comparison groups of men who were incarcerated for nonsexual crimes (Marshall, 1989). Yet evidence also shows that as many as one in three sexual assaulters and child molesters use pornography to become sexually aroused immediately preceding, and during the commission of, their crimes. These findings suggest that pornography may stimulate sexually deviant urges in certain subgroups of men who are predisposed to commit crimes of sexual violence (Marshall, 1989).

Violent Pornography Laboratory-based studies have shown that men exposed to violent pornography are more likely to become aggressive against females and to show less sensitivity toward women who have been sexually assaulted (Donnerstein, 1980; Donnerstein & Berkowitz, 1981).

Exposure to violent pornography may lead men to become more accepting of sexual assault, less sensitive to women survivors of sexual assault, and more accepting of the use of violence in interpersonal relationships (Donnerstein & Linz, 1987; Malamuth, 1984).

Yet research suggests that it is the violence in violent pornography, and not sexual explicitness, that hardens men's attitudes toward survivors of sexual assault. In one study (Donnerstein & Linz, 1987), male university students were exposed to films consisting of either violent pornography, nonviolent pornography (a couple having consensual intercourse), or a violent film that was not sexually explicit. The violent pornographic and nonpornographic films both showed a woman being tied up and slapped at gunpoint, but the nonpornographic version contained no nudity or explicit sexual activity. The men had first been either angered or treated in a neutral manner by a female confederate of the experimenter. The results showed that, in comparison with nonviolent pornography, both violent pornographic films and violent *non*pornographic films produced greater acceptance of rape myths, increased reported willingness to force a woman into sexual activity, and increased reported likelihood of engaging in sexual assault (if the man also knew that he could get away with it). These effects occurred regardless of whether the man was angered by the woman or not.

Based on a review of the research literature, Linz (1989) concluded that short-term and prolonged exposure to sexual violence, whether sexually explicit or not, lessens sensitivity toward survivors of sexual assault and increases acceptance of the use of force in sexual encounters. Research on the effects of pornography should be interpreted with caution, however. Most of it has employed university and college students, whose behaviour may or may not be typical of people in general or of people with tendencies toward sexual violence. Another issue is that most studies in this area are laboratory-based experiments that involve simulated aggression or judgments of sympathy toward hypothetical women who have been portrayed as victims of sexual assault. None measured actual violence against women outside the lab.

And not all research supports these findings. Fisher suggests that there are a number of serious methodological and conceptual limitations that must be considered before concluding that pornography has harmful effects (Fisher & Barak, 1991; Fisher & Grenier, 1994). These factors include subjects' awareness of the purpose of the experiment, selective attrition rates as men who do not enjoy watching violent pornography drop out of research studies, and ecological validity. Laboratory situations are not all representative of the real world, and thus may tell us little about what happens in real situations. Fisher and Grenier (1994) report that in two experiments designed to take these and other methodological factors into account, they were unable to demonstrate any effect of violent pornography to increase anti-woman thoughts (sexual fantasies) or anti-woman acts (willingness to administer electric shock to a female confederate of the researchers).

Nonviolent Pornography Even nonviolent pornography typically portrays women in degrading or dehumanizing roles—as sexually promiscuous, insatiable, and subservient. Might such portrayals of women reinforce traditional stereotypes of women as sex objects? Might they lead viewers to condone sexual assault by suggesting that women are essentially promiscuous? Might the depiction of women as readily sexually accessible inspire men to refuse to take no for an answer on dates?

Zillmann and Bryant (1982, 1984) exposed male and female study participants to six sessions of pornography over six consecutive weeks. Participants were exposed to either a massive dose of pornography, consisting of six nonviolent pornographic films

What Sexual Scientists Know About Pornography www.sexscience.org/ publications
This article evaluates the ability of pornography to cause harm to society.

("Swedish erotica") during each weekly session; to an intermediate dose consisting of three pornographic and three neutral films each session; or to a no-dose control, consisting of six nonsexual films each session. When later tested in a purportedly independent study, both males and females who received extended exposure to pornography, especially those receiving the massive dose, gave more lenient punishments to a rapist who was depicted in a newspaper article. Moreover, males became more callous in their attitudes toward women.

Zillmann and Weaver (1989) argue that making women appear sexually permissive and promiscuous increases men's callousness toward women who have been sexually assaulted. Once men brand women as promiscuous, they lose respect for them and see them as "public property" who have forfeited their rights to exercise choice in sex partners.

Not all researchers, however, find exposure to nonviolent pornography to increase callousness toward women. Some report finding that nonviolent pornography did not reduce the sensitivity of men (Linz et al., 1988) or women (Krafka, 1985) to female victims of sexual assault. Others report that nonviolent pornography did not increase men's aggression toward women in laboratory studies (Malamuth & Ceniti, 1986). Still others did not find that repeated exposure to nonviolent pornography made men adopt more callous attitudes toward women or increase their acceptance of rape myths (Padgett et al., 1989).

Given the inconsistencies in the research findings and the limited amount of research on nonviolent pornography, Linz (1989) concludes that

> ... the data, *overall*, do not support the contention that exposure to nonviolent
> pornography has significant adverse effects on attitudes toward rape as a crime or
> more general evaluations of rape victims. (p. 74)

Moreover, if nonviolent pornography can be connected with negative attitudes toward women, Linz (1989) suggests that such attitudes may result from the demeaning portrayals of women as sexual playthings who are valued only for their physical attributes and sexual availability, rather than from sexual explicitness per se.

Zillmann (1989) argues that nonviolent pornography loosens traditional family values by projecting an image of sexual enjoyment without responsibility or obligations. Prolonged exposure to such pornography may also foster dissatisfaction with the physical appearance and sexual performance of one's intimate partners (Zillmann, 1989).

In sum, research on the effects of nonviolent pornography does not permit conclusions. The effects of nonviolent pornography may be more connected with whether or not women are presented in a dehumanizing manner than with sexual explicitness per se. No research has yet linked sexual explicitness itself with undesirable effects.

Sex in Advertising

In the 1980s a coquettish Brooke Shields was featured in a TV commercial that showed her spreading her denim-clad legs, smiling coyly at the camera, and murmuring that nothing came between her and her Calvins (Calvin Klein jeans, that is). The advertising campaign evoked a storm of complaints from viewers who felt that it was vulgar and obscene. Meanwhile, the sales of Calvin Klein jeans went through the roof. In short, sex sells.

The use of sexual imagery in advertising ranges from more subtle uses of innuendo and double entendre, such as slogans like "Take it off, take it all off" (for Noxema shaving cream) and "It's better in the Bahamas," to the use of attractive young women mimicking orgasm in Herbal Essence shampoo commercials. Sex in advertising operates according to the principle of association. Advertisers hope that people will link the product with the sexual imagery that is incorporated within the advertisement. Perhaps the use of a sexy ad will make consumers think that the product will make them more sexually alluring or enhance their sexual arousal, which, in turn, will prompt them to purchase the product rather than that of a competitor.

Advertisers may also need to consider the gender of the target audience. Researchers find that men tend to react more positively and women more negatively to various forms of sexual content in advertising, whether it be sexual innuendos uttered by female models in TV commercials (Bello et al., 1983) or female nudity in print advertising (LaTour, 1990).

Advertising and Gender-Role Stereotypes

The frequent use of sexy female models in advertisements raises broader concerns about the depiction of women in advertising. As Edgley notes, "Despite years of feminist consciousness-raising about the issue, commercials still tend to depict women in stereotypical ways" (Edgley, 1989). What Komisar said of advertising in 1971 may be as true today as it was then:

> If television commercials are to be believed, most American women go into uncontrollable ecstasies at the sight and smell of tables and cabinets that have been lovingly caressed with long-lasting, satin-finish, lemon-scented, spray-on furniture polish. Or they glow with rapture at the blinding whiteness of their wash—to the green-eyed envy of their neighbors.... it is an amazing feat of hocus-pocus worthy of Tom Sawyer and P. T. Barnum to lovingly declare that domestic labor is the true vocation of women wearing wedding bands. (p. 209)

Advertising Standards of Canada Gender Portrayal Guidelines
www.adstandards.com/en/ standards/gender.asp
This page gives guidelines for ads displayed in Canada.

"Pushing the Envelope." Sex is still used today to sell jeans. What do you think? How far is too far? Researchers caution, however, that sexy ads can backfire. Viewers may pay such careful attention to the sexy imagery that they tune out the advertising message or product claims, or even forget what the product is (Edgley, 1989; Severn et al., 1990). Sexy advertising may not only be distracting. It may also turn people off to the advertisement and, by extension, to the product, especially if the sexual image is unrelated to the nature of the product.

www.jeanmachine.com

Studies of TV commercials in the United States, Canada, the United Kingdom, and Italy show a consistent pattern: Females are more likely to be portrayed visually on screen, whereas males are more likely to do voice-overs as the "voice of authority" (Ferrante et al., 1988; Furnham & Voli, 1989; Lovdal, 1989). A study of 320 U.S. TV commercials employing voice-overs showed that 91% used male voices. Only 9% used female voices (Lovdal, 1989). In an updated study of gender representation in television commercials, researchers found an increase (30%) in female voice-overs and a decrease (71%) in male voice-overs (Bartsch & Burnett, 2000). However, the study also revealed a trend toward greater gender stereotyping in commercials featuring domestic products as compared to research findings from 1989.

TV commercials also tend to portray men in a wider variety of occupational roles than women (Bretl & Cantor, 1988; Lovdal, 1989). Women are still generally stereotyped in traditional roles as wives, mothers, brides, waitresses, actresses, and so on. Rarely are they photographers, athletes, or businesswomen. Still, we can report some signs of change, at least with respect to the portrayal of men's roles. Men today are increasingly represented in commercials as spouses and parents; however, they are more likely to be shown teaching, reading to, or playing with children rather than cooking, cleaning or shopping (Bretl & Cantor, 1988; Kaufman, 1999). Women are still more likely to be seen in domestic settings, advertising products that they can use in the home (Bretl & Cantor, 1988).

Summing Up

Commercial sex runs the gamut from "adult" movie theatres and bookshops to strip shows, sex toy shops, brothels, escort services, massage parlours, "900" telephone services, and the use of sex appeal in advertising.

Prostitution

The laws governing prostitution (the exchange of sex for money) in Canada are confusing because while prostitution itself is legal, almost all the activities that involve prostitution are illegal.

The major **types of female prostitutes** are streetwalkers, brothel prostitutes (many of whom work in massage parlours and for "escort services"), and call girls. Streetwalkers often support, and are abused by, pimps.

No single **characteristic** explains entry into **female prostitution**, but poverty and sexual and/or physical abuse figure prominently in the backgrounds of many prostitutes. Teenage runaways with marginal skills and limited means of support may find few alternatives to prostitution. **Customers of female prostitutes are** often referred to as "johns" or "tricks." Most patrons are "occasional johns" with regular sex partners. Some people use prostitutes habitually or compulsively, however. Most **male prostitutes** are "hustlers" who service male clients. Hustlers typically begin selling sex in their teens and may be gay or heterosexual in orientation.

Prostitutes are at greater risk of contracting **HIV infection** because they have sexual relations with many partners, often without protection. Many prostitutes and their clients and other sex partners also inject drugs and share contaminated needles. HIV may be spread by unprotected sex from prostitutes to customers, then to the customers' wives or lovers. Despite the dangers of HIV transmission, many prostitutes have not altered either their sexual behaviour or their patterns of drug use.

Pornography and Obscenity

Pornography is "writing, pictures, etc., intended to arouse sexual desire." Erotica, by contrast, consists of sexual materials that are artistically produced or motivated. The judgment of what is pornographic or obscene varies from person to person and from culture to culture. Pornography is fairly **prevalent;** Canadians are typically introduced to pornography by their high school years. **Pornography is used** to elicit or enhance sexual arousal. Although both genders can become physiologically aroused by erotic materials, **there are differences in response:** men are relatively more interested in sexually explicit pictures and films. The link, if any, between **pornography and sexual coercion** in the general population is unclear. Some researchers argue that it is the violence in violent pornography, and not sexual explicitness per se, that promotes violence against women.

Sex in Advertising Sex has long been used to sell everything from jeans to cars. Such ads provoke controversy, but may not always sell the product. Despite some changes, television commercials still display gender stereotyping.

Chapter Quiz

1. Which kind of prostitute is most likely to support a pimp?
   (a) The streetwalker
   (b) The call girl
   (c) The brothel prostitute
   (d) The masseuse

2. Conventioneers and businessmen who desire prostitutes are most likely to seek
   (a) bar girls.
   (b) escorts.
   (c) streetwalkers.
   (d) hustlers.

3. The text notes that the following factors are frequently found in the backgrounds of prostitutes, EXCEPT for
   (a) poverty.
   (b) a conflict-ridden home.
   (c) sexual abuse.
   (d) a religious upbringing.

4. Most customers of prostitutes are
   (a) compulsive johns.
   (b) occasional johns.
   (c) habitual johns.
   (d) sexually dysfunctional.

5. The most common use of prostitution occurs among men who
   (a) are away from home.
   (b) are seeking variety.

   (c) want sex without commitment.
   (d) want sex without negotiation.

6. The overwhelming majority of male prostitutes service
   (a) heterosexual men.
   (b) heterosexual women.
   (c) gay men.
   (d) lesbians.

7. _____ are most likely to have "sugar daddies."
   (a) Punks
   (b) Drag prostitutes
   (c) Call boys
   (d) Kept boys

8. Which of the following is true of women's response to pornography?
   (a) Women prefer explicit sex to romance.
   (b) Women are less accepting of sex without emotional involvement.
   (c) Women prefer violent pornography to nonviolent pornography.
   (d) Many people claim that pornography is degrading to men.

9. Social scientists criticize The Meese Commission Report on the grounds that
   (a) it studied the effects of obscene materials.
   (b) it failed to review a high number of research studies.
   (c) it did not adequately sort out the effects of sex from those of violence.
   (d) its recommendations were consistent with a conservative, traditional point of view.

Answers to Chapter Quizzes

Chapter 1
1. (d)
2. (a)
3. (b)
4. (c)
5. (a)
6. (d)
7. (a)
8. (c)
9. (b)
10. (d)

Chapter 2
1. (d)
2. (b)
3. (a)
4. (c)
5. (b)
6. (a)
7. (b)
8. (d)
9. (c)
10. (d)

Chapter 3
1. (b)
2. (c)
3. (a)
4. (a)
5. (c)
6. (b)
7. (a)
8. (d)
9. (b)
10. (c)

Chapter 4
1. (d)
2. (c)
3. (b)
4. (a)
5. (b)
6. (b)
7. (b)
8. (d)
9. (a)
10. (d)

Chapter 5
1. (d)
2. (b)
3. (c)
4. (d)
5. (d)
6. (b)
7. (a)
8. (c)
9. (b)

Chapter 6
1. (b)
2. (a)
3. (d)
4. (c)
5. (d)
6. (c)
7. (b)
8. (a)
9. (b)
10. (a)

Chapter 7
1. (a)
2. (d)
3. (c)
4. (b)
5. (a)
6. (d)
7. (a)
8. (a)
9. (c)
10. (b)

Chapter 8
1. (d)
2. (d)
3. (c)
4. (a)
5. (b)
6. (b)
7. (c)
8. (b)
9. (d)
10. (b)

Chapter 9

1. (d)
2. (b)
3. (c)
4. (c)
5. (a)
6. (c)
7. (a)
8. (d)
9. (d)
10. (b)

Chapter 10

1. (a)
2. (c)
3. (b)
4. (a)
5. (d)
6. (c)
7. (b)
8. (b)
9. (a)
10. (c)

Chapter 11

1. (a)
2. (d)
3. (d)
4. (c)
5. (b)
6. (c)
7. (a)
8. (d)
9. (c)

Chapter 12

1. (c)
2. (a)
3. (b)
4. (d)
5. (d)
6. (b)
7. (a)
8. (d)
9. (a)
10. (d)

Chapter 13

1. (d)
2. (b)
3. (a)
4. (b)
5. (c)
6. (a)
7. (c)
8. (a)
9. (c)
10. (d)

Chapter 14

1. (d)
2. (c)
3. (b)
4. (d)
5. (a)
6. (b)
7. (a)
8. (d)
9. (c)
10. (a)

Chapter 15

1. (d)
2. (d)
3. (a)
4. (a)
5. (c)
6. (c)
7. (b)
8. (a)
9. (a)
10. (c)

Chapter 16

1. (a)
2. (b)
3. (d)
4. (b)
5. (a)
6. (c)
7. (d)
8. (b)
9. (c)

References

Abel, G. G., et al. (1984). Complications, consent, and cognitions in sex between children and adults. *International Journal of Law and Psychiatry, 7*, 89–103.

Abelson, H., et al. (1970). Public attitudes toward and experience with erotic materials. In *Technical reports of the commission on obscenity and pornography*, (Vol. 6). Washington, DC: U.S. Government Printing Office.

Abramowitz, S. (1986). Psychosocial outcomes of sex reassignment surgery. *Journal of Consulting and Clinical Psychology, 54*, 183–189.

Acker, M., & Davis, M. H. (1992). Intimacy, passion and commitment in adult romantic relationships: A test of the triangular theory of love. *Journal of Social and Personal Relationships, 9*, 21–50.

Adams, H. E., et al. (1996). Is homophobia associated with homosexual arousal? *Journal of Abnormal Psychology, 105*, 440–445.

Adams, R. (1987). The role of prostitution in AIDS and other STDs. *Medical Aspects of Human Sexuality, 21*, 27–33.

Adelson, A. (1990, November 19). Study attacks women's roles in TV. *The New York Times*, p. C18.

Ahmed, R. A. (1991). Women in Egypt and the Sudan. In L. L. Adler (Ed.), *Women in cross-cultural perspective* (pp. 107–134). New York: Praeger.

Allen, J. R., & Setlow, V. P. (1991). Heterosexual transmission of HIV: A view of the future. *Journal of the American Medical Association, 266*, 1695–1696.

Alter-Reid, K., et al. (1986). Sexual abuse of children: A review of the empirical findings. *Clinical Psychology Review, 6*, 249–266.

Althof, S. E. (1994). Paper presented to the annual meeting of the American Urological Association. San Francisco, CA.

Altman, L. K. (1991, April 15). Study challenges federal research on risks of IUD's. *The New York Times*, p. A1.

Altman, L. K. (1993, February 17). 2 new studies link vasectomy to higher prostate cancer risk. *The New York Times*, p. C12.

Alzate, H. (1985). Vaginal eroticism: A replication study. *Archives of Sexual Behavior, 14*, 529–537.

Amato, P. R., & Keith, B. (1991). Parental divorce and the well-being of children: A meta-analysis. *Psychological Bulletin, 110*, 26–46.

Ambert, A. (2002). Divorce: Facts, causes and consequences. Accessed at **www.vifamily.ca/library/cft/divorce.html**, December 22, 2003.

American Porn. (2002, Feb. 2). Kirk, M. and Boyer, J. (writers) and Kirk, M. (producer) [Television series episode]. *Frontline*. Boston: WGBH Boston. Accessed at **www.pbs.org/wgbh/pages/frontline/shows/porn/**, November 13, 2003.

American Psychiatric Association. (1994). *Diagnostic and statistical manual of mental disorders* (4th ed.). Washington, DC: Author.

American Psychiatric Association. (2000). *Diagnostic and statistical manual of Mental Disorders DSM-IV-TR* (text revision). Washington, DC: Author.

American Psychological Association, Committee on Gay and Lesbian Concerns. (1991). Avoiding heterosexual bias in language. *American Psychologist, 46*, 973–974.

Ames, M. A., & Houston, D. A. (1990). Legal, social, and biological definitions of pedophilia. *Archives of Sexual Behavior, 19*, 333–342.

Anderson, B. J., & Wold, F. M. (1986). Chronic physical illness and sexual behavior. *Journal of Consulting and Clinical Psychology, 54*, 168–175.

Anderson, J. L., et al. (1992). Was the Duchess of Windsor right? A cross-cultural review of the socioecology of ideals of female body shape. *Ethology and Sociobiology, 13*, 197–227.

Anderson, S.E., et al. (2003). Relative weight and race influence average age at menarche: Research from two nationally representative surveys of US girls studied 25 years apart. *Pediatrics, 111*, 844–50.

Angier, N. (1990, July 19). Scientists say gene on Y chromosome makes a man a man. *The New York Times*, pp. A1, 19.

Angier, N. (1991, August 30). Zone of brain linked to men's sexual orientation. *The New York Times*, A1, D18.

Antill, J. K. (1983). Sex role complementarity versus similarity in married couples. *Journal of Personality and Social Psychology, 52*, 260–267.

Antonarakas, S. E., et al. (1991). Prenatal origin of the extra chromosome in trisomy 21 as indicated by analysis of DNA polymorphisms. *New England Journal of Medicine, 324*, 872–876.

Appell, R. A. (1986). Importance of the neurological examination in erectile dysfunction. *Medical Aspects of Human Sexuality, 20*, 32–36.

Arrindell, W., & Luteijn, F. (2000). Similarity between intimate partners for personality traits as related to individual levels of satisfaction with life. *Personality and Individual Differences, 28*, 629–637.

Asbell, B. (1995). *The pill: A biography of the drug that changed the world*. New York: Random House.

Asso, D., & Magos, A. (1992). Psychological and physiological changes in severe premenstrual syndrome. *Biological Psychology, 33*, 115–132.

Astley, S. J., et al. (1992). Analysis of facial shape in children gestationally exposed to marijuana, alcohol, and/or cocaine. *Pediatrics, 89*, 67–77.

Atkeson, B. M., et al. (1989). Victim resistance to rape: The relationship of previous victimization, demographics, and situational factors. *Archives of Sexual Behavior, 18*, 497–507.

Awad, G., et al. (1984). A clinical study of male adolescent sex offenders. *International Journal of Offender Therapy and Comparative Criminology, 28*, 116–123.

Ayres, B. D. (1996, August 27). California bill would require "chemical castration" for repeat sex offenders. *The New York Times*.

Bach, G. R., & Deutsch, R. M. (1970). *Pairing*. New York: Peter H. Wyden.

Baerwald, A. R., et al. (2003). A new model for ovarian follicular development during the human menstrual cycle. *Fertility and Sterility, 80*, 116–122.

Bagatell, C. J., & Bremner, W. J. (1996). Drug therapy: Androgens in men—Uses and abuses. *New England Journal of Medicine, 334*, 707–714.

Bagley, C., & Young, L. (1987). Juvenile prostitution and child sexual abuse: A controlled study. *Canadian Journal of Community Mental Health, 6*, 5–26.

Bailey, J. M., and Pillard, R. C. (1991). A genetic study of male sexual orientation. *Archives of General Psychiatry, 48*, 1089–1096.

Bailey, J. M., et al. (1993). Heritable factors influence sexual orientation in women. *Archives of General Psychiatry, 50,* 217–223.

Bailey, J.M., et al. (2000). Genetic and environmental influences on sexual orientation and its correlates in an Australian twin sample. *Journal of Personality and Social Psychology, 78,* 524–536.

Baird, V. (2001). *The no-nonsense guide to sexual diversity.* Toronto: New Internationalist Publications.

Baker, T. C., et al. (1990). Rape victims' concerns about possible exposure to HIV infection. *Journal of Interpersonal Violence, 5,* 49–60.

Baldwin, J. D., & Baldwin, J. I. (1989). The socialization of homosexuality and heterosexuality in a non-Western society. *Archives of Sexual Behavior, 18,* 13–29.

Bancroft, J. (1990). Commentary: Biological contributions to sexual orientation. In D. P. McWhirter, et al. (Eds.), *Homosexuality/heterosexuality: Concepts of sexual orientation* (pp. 101–111). New York: Oxford University Press.

Banning, A. (1989). Mother–son incest: Confronting a prejudice. *Child Abuse and Neglect, 13,* 563–570.

Barbach, L. G. (1975). *For yourself: The fulfillment of female sexuality.* New York: Doubleday.

Barbach, L. G. (1995). Cited in Goleman, D. (1995, June 14). Sex fantasy research said to neglect women. *The New York Times,* p. C14.

Barbaree, H. E., & Marshall, W. L. (1991). The role of male sexual arousal in rape: Six models. *Journal of Consulting and Clinical Psychology, 59,* 621–630.

Barlow, D. H. (1986). Causes of sexual dysfunction: The role of anxiety and cognitive interference. *Journal of Consulting and Clinical Psychology, 54,* 140–148.

Barlow, D. H., & Durand, V. M. (1995). *Abnormal psychology.* Pacific Grove, CA: Brooks/Cole.

Barr, H. M., et al. (1990). Prenatal exposure to alcohol, caffeine, tobacco, and aspirin. *Developmental Psychology, 26,* 339–348.

Barrett, M. (1994). Sexuality education in Canadian schools: An overview in 1994. *Canadian Journal of Human Sexuality, 3,* 199–208.

Barrett, M. B. (1990). *Invisible lives: The truth about millions of women-loving women.* New York: Harper & Row (Perennial Library).

Barringer, F. (1991, June 7). Changes in family patterns: Solitude and single parents. *The New York Times,* pp. A1, A18.

Bart, P. & O'Brien, P.H. (1984). Stopping rape: Effective avoidance strategies. *Signs, 10,* 83–101.

Bart, P. B., & O'Brien, P. B. (1985). *Stopping rape: Successful survival strategies.* Elmsford, NY: Pergamon Press.

Bar-Tal, D., & Saxe, L. (1976). Perceptions of similarly and dissimilarly physically attractive couples and individuals. *Journal of Personality and Social Psychology, 33,* 772–781.

Bartsch, R. & Burnett, T. (2000). Gender representation in television commercials: Updating an update. *Sex Roles, 42,* 735–743.

Basson, R. et al. (2000). Report of the International Consensus Development Conference on Female Sexual Dysfunction: Definitions and classifications. *The Journal of Urology, 163,* 888–893.

Basson, R. (2001). Women's sexual response and dysfunction: A reappraisal. Paper presented at the 36th Annual Review in Family Medicine, Vancouver, March 2001.

Baumeister, R. F. (1988). Gender differences in masochistic scripts. *Journal of Sex Research, 25,* 478–499.

Baxter, D. J., et al. (1986). Sexual responses to consenting and forced sex in a large sample of rapists and nonrapists. *Behaviour Research and Therapy, 17,* 215–222.

Baxter, N. (2001). Preventive health care, 2001 update: Should women be routinely taught breast self-examination to screen for breast cancer? *Canadian Medical Association Journal, 164,* 1837–1846. Accessed at **www.cmaj.ca/cgi/reprint/164/13/1837,** August 20, 2003.

Beck, A. (1988). *Love is never enough.* New York: Harper & Row.

Beck, J. G. (1993). Vaginismus. In W. O'Donohue & J. H. Geer (Eds.), *Handbook of sexual dysfunctions: Assessment and treatment* (pp. 381–397). Boston: Allyn & Bacon.

Becker, J. V., et al. (1986). Level of post-assault sexual functioning in rape and incest victims. *Archives of Sexual Behavior, 15,* 37–49.

Becker, J. V., et al. (1989). Factors associated with erection in adolescent sex offenders. *Journal of Psychopathology and Behavioral Assessment, 11,* 353–362.

Beichuan, Z., et al. (2000). A survey of men who have sex with men: Mainland China. *American Journal of Public Health, 90 (12),* 1949–1950.

Beitchman, J. H., et al. (1992). A review of the long-term effects of child sexual abuse. *Child Abuse and Neglect, 16,* 101–118.

Bell, A. P., & Weinberg, M. S. (1978). *Homosexualities: A study of diversity among men and women.* New York: Simon & Schuster.

Bell, A. P., et al. (1981). *Sexual preference: Its development in men and women.* Bloomington: University of Indiana Press.

Bell, S., et al. (1994). Understanding attributions of blame in stranger rape and date rape situations: An examination of gender, race, identification, and students' social perceptions of rape victims. *Journal of Applied Social Psychology, 24 (19),* 1719–1734.

Bellis, D. J. (1990). Fear of AIDS and risk reduction among heroin-addicted female street prostitutes: Personal interviews with 72 Southern California subjects. *Journal of Alcohol and Drug Education, 35,* 26–37.

Bello, D. C., et al. (1983). The communications effects of controversial sexual content in television programs and commercials. *Journal of Advertising, 12(3),* 32–42.

Bem, S. L. (1975). Sex role adaptability: One consequence of psychological androgyny. *Journal of Personality and Social Psychology, 31,* 634–643.

Bem, S. L. (1981). Gender schema theory: A cognitive account of sex typing. *Psychological Review, 88,* 354–364.

Bem, S. L. (1985). Androgyny and gender schema theory: A conceptual and empirical integration. In T. B. Sonderegger (Ed.), *Nebraska symposium on motivation, 1984: Psychology and gender.* Lincoln: University of Nebraska Press.

Bem, S. L. (1993). *The lenses of gender.* New Haven: Yale University Press.

Bem, S. L., et al. (1976). Sex typing and androgyny: Further explorations of the expressive domain. *Journal of Personality and Social Psychology, 34,* 1016–1023.

Bennett, N. G., et al. (1988). Commitment and the modern union: Assessing the link between premarital cohabitation and subsequent marital stability. *American Sociological Review, 53,* 127–138.

Berlin, F. S. (1983). Sex offenders: A biomedical perspective and a status report of biomedical treatment. In J. G. Greer & I. R. Stuart (Eds.), *The sexual aggressor* (pp. 83–123). New York: Van Nostrand Reinhold.

Berliner, D. (1993). Cited in Blakeslee, S. (1993, September 7). Human nose may hold an additional organ for a real sixth sense. *The New York Times,* p. C3.

Bernstein, S. J., et al. (1993). The appropriateness of hysterectomy: A comparison of care in seven health plans. *Journal of the American Medical Association, 269,* 2398–2402.

Bernstein, W. M., et al. (1983). Causal ambiguity and heterosexual affiliation. *Journal of Experimental Social Psychology, 19,* 78–92.

Berscheid, E. (1988). Some comments on love's anatomy: Or, whatever happened to old-fashioned lust? In R. J. Sternberg & M. L. Barnes (Eds.), *The psychology of love* (pp. 359–374). New Haven: Yale University Press.

Berscheid, E., & Walster, E. (1978). *Interpersonal attraction.* Reading, MA: Addison-Wesley.

Bieber, I. (1976). A discussion of "Homosexuality: The ethical challenge." *Journal of Consulting and Clinical Psychology, 44,* 163–166.

Bibby, R. (1995). *The Bibby report: Social trends Canadian style.* Toronto: Stoddart.

Bibby, R. (2001). Canada's teens: *Today, Yesterday, and Tomorrow.* Toronto: Stoddart.

Bieber, I., et al. (1962). *Homosexuality.* New York: Basic Books.

Bixler, R. H. (1989). Diversity: A historical/comparative perspective. *Behaviorial and Brain Sciences, 12,* 15–16.

Bjorklund, D. F., & Kipp, K. (1996). Parental investment theory and gender differences in the evolution of inhibition mechanisms. *Psychological Bulletin, 120,* 163–188.

Blair, C. D., & Lanyon, R. I. (1981). Exhibitionism: A critical review of the etiology and treatment. *Psychological Bulletin, 89,* 439–463.

Blake, J. M., et al. (2002). The SOGC statement on the WHI report on estrogen and progestin use in menopausal women. *Journal of Obstetrics and Gynecology Canada, 24* (10), 783–787.

Blakeslee, S. (1992, January 22). An epidemic of genital warts raises concern but not alarm. *The New York Times,* p. C12.

Blanchard, R., & Hucker, S. J. (1991). Age, transvestism, bondage, and concurrent paraphilic activities in 117 fatal cases of autoerotic asphyxia. *British Journal of Psychiatry, 159,* 371–377.

Blanchard, R., et al. (1985). Gender dysphoria, gender reorientation, and the clinical management of transsexualism. *Journal of Consulting and Clinical Psychology, 53,* 295–304.

Blenner, J. L. (1992). Stress and mediators: Patients' perceptions of infertility treatment. *Nursing Research, 41,* 92–97.

Bleustein, C. B., et al. (2003). Effects of circumcision on male penile sensitivity. Poster presented at the American Urological Association 98th Annual Meeting at Chicago, Illinois, April 26–May 1, 2003: Publishing ID 1260, Abstract ID: 100769.

Bloom, B. J., et al. (1978). Marital disruption as a stressor: A review and analysis. *Psychological Bulletin, 85,* 867–894.

Bloor, M., et al. (1990). An ethnographic study of HIV-related risk practices among Glasgow rent boys and their clients: Report of a pilot study. *AIDS Care, 2,* 17–24.

Blumstein, P., & Schwartz, P. (1983). *American couples: Money, work, sex.* New York: William Morrow.

Blumstein, P. & Schwartz, P. (1990). Intimate relationships and the creation of sexuality. In D. P. McWhirter, et al. (Eds.), *Homosexuality/heterosexuality: Concepts of sexual orientation* (pp. 307–320). New York: Oxford University Press.

Boles, J., & Elifson, K. W. (1994). Sexual identity and HIV: The male prostitute. *Journal of Sex Research, 31,* 39–46.

Bollinger, D. (2004). *Normal versus Circumcised: U.S. Neonatal Male Genital Ratio,* 2004, white paper, 2/12/04. Paper prepared for the Circumcision Information Resource Pages.

Bondurant, B. (2001). University women's acknowledgement of rape: Individual, situational, and social factors. *Violence against women, 7,* 294–314.

Boston Women's Health Book Collective. (1992). *The new our bodies, ourselves.* New York: Simon & Schuster.

Both-Orthman, B., et al. (1988). Menstrual cycle phase: Related changes in appetite in patients with premenstrual syndrome and in control subjects. *American Journal of Psychiatry, 145,* 628–631.

Bourgeois-Law, G. (2001). Dyspareunia: Eliciting the source of the pain. *Medical aspects of human sexuality, 1,* 35–44.

Bowie, W. R. (1990). Approach to men with urethritis and urologic complications of sexually transmitted diseases. *Medical Clinics of North America, 74,* 1543–1557.

Boyer, D. (1989). Male prostitution and homosexual identity. [Special issue: Gay and lesbian youth: I.]. *Journal of Homosexuality, 17,* 151–184.

Bozzette, S. A., et al. (1995). A randomized trial of three antipneumocystis agents in patients with advanced human immunodeficiency virus infection. *New England Journal of Medicine, 332,* 693–699.

Bradford, J. (1992). The paraphilias: A multiplicity of deviant behaviors. *Canadian Journal of Psychiatry, 37,* 104–108.

Bradford, J. (2001). The neurobiology, neuropharmacology, and pharmacological treatment of the paraphilias and compulsive sexual behaviour. *Canadian Journal of Psychiatry, 46,* 26–34.

Brady, E. C., et al. (1991). Date rape: Expectations, avoidance strategies, and attitudes toward victims. *Journal of Social Psychology, 131,* 427–429.

Brecher, E. M, and the Editors of Consumer Reports Books. (1984). *Love, sex, and aging.* Boston: Little, Brown.

Breslow, N. (1989). Sources of confusion in the study and treatment of sadomasochism. *Journal of Social Behavior and Personality, 4,* 263–274.

Breslow, N., et al. (1986). Comparisons among heterosexual, bisexual and homosexual male sadomasochists. *Journal of Homosexuality, 13,* 83–107.

Bretl, D. J., & Cantor, J. (1988). The portrayal of men and women in U.S. television commercials: A recent content analysis and trends over 15 years. *Sex Roles, 18,* 595–609.

Bretschneider, J., & McCoy, N. (1988). Sexual interest and behavior in healthy 80- to 102-year-olds. *Archives of Sexual Behavior, 17,* 109.

Briere, J., & Runtz, M. (1987). Post sexual abuse trauma: Data and implications for clinical practice. *Journal of Interpersonal Violence, 2,* 367–379.

Briere, J., & Runtz, M. (1989). University males' sexual interest in children: Predicting potential indices of "pedophilia" in a nonforensic sample. *Child Abuse and Neglect, 13,* 65–75.

Brody, J. E. (1989, January 5). How women can begin to cope with premenstrual syndrome, a biological mystery. *The New York Times,* p. B12.

Brody, J. E. (1990, January 23). Scientists trace aberrant sexuality. *The New York Times,* pp. C11, C12.

Brody, J. E. (1992, April 29). How to outwit a rapist: Rehearse. *The New York Times,* p. C13.

Brody, J. E. (1993a, July 7). Genital herpes drug found safe for daily use. *The New York Times,* p. C11.

Brody, J. E. (1993b, August 4). A new look at an old quest for sexual stimulants. *The New York Times,* p. C12.

Brody, J. E. (1995a, May 3). Breast scans may indeed help women under 50. *The New York Times,* p. C11.

Brody, J. E. (1995b, August 30). Hormone replacement therapy for men: When does it help? *The New York Times,* p. C8.

Brody, J. E. (1996, August 28). PMS need not be the worry it was just decades ago. *The New York Times*, p. C9.

Brooks, V. R. (1982). Sex differences in student dominance behavior in female and male professors' classrooms. *Sex Roles, 8,* 683–690.

Brooks-Gunn, J., & Furstenberg, F. F. (1989). Adolescent sexual behavior. *American Psychologist, 44,* 249–257.

Brooks-Gunn, J., & Matthews, W. S. (1979). *He and she: How children develop their sex-role identity.* Englewood Cliffs, NJ: Spectrum.

Broude, G. J., & Green, S. J. (1976). Cross-cultural codes on twenty sexual attitudes and practices. *Ethnology, 15,* 409–429.

Brown, R. A. (1994). Romantic love and the spouse selection criteria of male and female Korean college students. *Journal of Social Psychology, 134*(2), 183–189.

Bryant, J., & Brown, D. (1989). Uses of pornography. In D. Zillmann & J. Bryant (Eds.), *Pornography: Research advances and policy considerations* (pp. 25–55). Hillsdale, NJ: Erlbaum.

Bullough, V. L. (1990). The Kinsey Scale in historical perspective. In D. P. McWhirter, et al. (Eds.), *Homosexuality/heterosexuality: Concepts of sexual orientation* (pp. 3–14). New York: Oxford University Press.

Bullough, V. L. (1991). Transvestism: A reexamination. *Journal of Psychology and Human Sexuality, 4,* 53–67.

Bumiller, E. (1990, October 25). Japan's abortion agony: In a country that prohibits the pill, reality collides with religion. *The Washington Post.*

Bumpass, L. (1995). Cited in Steinhauer, J. (1995, July 6). No marriage, no apologies. *The New York Times,* pp. C1, C7.

Burgess, A. W., & Holmstrom, L. L. (1974). Rape trauma syndrome. *American Journal of Psychiatry, 131,* 981–986.

Burkhart, B., & Fromuth, M. E. (1991). Individual psychological and social psychological understandings of sexual coercion. In E. Grauerholz & M. A. Koralewski (Eds.), *Sexual coercion: A sourcebook on its nature, causes, and prevention* (pp. 7–89). Lexington, MA: Lexington Books.

Burt, M. R. (1980). Cultural myths and supports for rape. *Journal of Personality and Social Psychology, 38,* 217–230.

Buss, D. M. (1994). *The evolution of desire: Strategies of human mating.* New York: Basic Books.

Buxton, A. P. (1994). *The other side of the closet.* New York: Wiley.

Byers, E. S., & Lewis, K. (1988). Dating couples' disagreements over the desired level of sexual intimacy. *Journal of Sex Research, 24,* 15–29.

Byers, S. (2001) Evidence for the importance of relationship satisfaction for women's sexual functioning. *Women & Therapy, 24,* 23–26.

Byrnes, J., & Takahira, S. (1993). Explaining gender differences on SAT-math items. *Developmental Psychology, 29,* 805–810.

Caceres, C. F., & van-Griensven, G. J. P. (1994). Male homosexual transmission of HIV-1. *AIDS, 8* (8), 1051–1061.

Calderone, M. S., & Johnson, E. W. (1989). *Family book about sexuality* (rev. ed.). New York: Harper & Row.

Calhoun, K. S., & Atkeson, B. M. (1991). *Treatment of rape victims: Facilitating social adjustment.* New York: Pergamon Press.

Call, V., et al. (1995). The incidence and frequency of marital sex in a national sample. *Journal of Marriage and the Family, 57,* 639–652.

Campbell, C. A. (1991). Prostitution, AIDS, and preventive health behavior. *Social Science and Medicine, 32,* 1367–1378.

Canadian Association for Adolescent Health. (2004). Violence in adolescent dating relationships.PDF. Accessed from PDF at **www.acsa-caah.ca/pdf/ang/violenceinadorelation,** January 16, 2004.

Canadian Cancer Society (2000). **http://www.cancer.ca**

Canadian Cancer Society. (2003a). Breast cancer stats. Accessed at **www. cancer. ca / ccs / internet / standard/0,3182,3172_14435__langId-en,00.html,** August 16, 2003.

Canadian Cancer Society. (2003b). The Canadian Cancer Society's perspective on early detection and screening of breast cancer (updated July 19, 2003). Accessed at **www. cancer.ca/ccs/internet/standard/0,3182,3172_83256703_275174_langId-en,00.html** August 20, 2003.

Canadian Cancer Society. (2003c). Signs and symptoms of testicular cancer. Accessed at **www.cancer.ca/ ccs/internet/standard/0,3182,3172_10175_33369935_langId-en,00.html,** August 23, 2003.

Canadian Cancer Society. (2003d). Signs and symptoms of prostate cancer. Accessed at **www.cancer.ca/ccs/internet/standard/0,3182,3172_10175_266226_langId-en,00.html,** August 23, 2003.

Canadian Centre for Justice Statistics. (1999). Sex offenders. *Juristat 19* (3).

Canadian Institute for Health Information. (2000). Health System Performance. **http://www.cihi.ca/hirpt/jsp/HIDispatcher.jsp**

Canadian Medical Association. (2000, August). Rate of HIV infection is on the rise among Ontario gay men (1996 and 1999 data). *Canadian Medical Association Journal, 163,* 321.

Canadian Paraplegic Association. (2000, March 1). *Spinal cord injury.* Author.

Canadian Press Newswire. (2000, August 21). Unsafe sex on the rise among men hopeful of AIDS cure, study says.

Canadian Press Newswire. (2002, April 4). Supreme court refuses to reduce sentence of castrated child molester. Accession # 5337178. Accessed August 24, 2003 from CBCA.

Candib, L. (2001). A new view of women's sexual problems—A family physician's response. *Women and Therapy, 24,* 9–15, p. 13.

Cappella, J. N., & Palmer, M. T. (1990). Attitude similarity, relational history, and attraction: The mediating effects of kinesic and vocal behaviors. *Communication Monographs, 5,* 161–183.

Carani, C., et al. (1990). Effects of androgen treatment in impotent men with normal and low levels of free testosterone. *Archives of Sexual Behavior, 19,* 223–234.

Carmignani, G., et al. (1987). Cavernous artery revascularization in vasculogenic impotence: New simplified technique. *Urology, 30,* 23–26.

Carrera, M. (1981). *Sex: The facts, the acts and your feelings.* New York: Crown.

Casey, R. (1998). Oral medications for erectile dysfunction: Mode of action and treatment issues. *The Canadian Journal of Human Sexuality, 7,* 203–212.

Castro, K. G., et al. (1988). Transmission of HIV in Belle Glade, Florida: Lessons for other communities in the United States. *Science, 239,* 193–197.

Catalan, J., et al. (1990). Couples referred to a sexual dysfunction clinic: Psychological and physical morbidity. *British Journal of Psychiatry, 156,* 61–67.

Catania, J. A., et al. (1991). Changes in condom use among homosexual men in San Francisco. *Health Psychology, 10,* 190–199.

Cates, W., Jr., & Stone, K. M. (1992a). Family planning, sexually transmitted diseases, and contraceptive choice: A literature update. *Family Planning Perspectives, 24,* 75–84.

Cates, W., Jr., & Stone, K. M. (1992b). Family planning, sexually transmitted diseases, and contraceptive choice: A literature update—Part II. *Family Planning Perspectives, 24,* 122–127.

Cates, W., Jr., & Wasserheit, J. N. (1991). Genital chlamydial infections: Epidemiology and reproductive sequelae. *American Journal of Obstetrics and Gynecology, 164*, 1171–1181.

Catlin, G., ed. (2000). The health divide: How the sexes differ. *Health Reports Special Issue, 12(3)*, Statistics Canada Catalogue 82-003 XIE.

Centers for Disease Control. (1985). Chlamydia trachomatis infections. *Morbidity and Mortality Weekly Report, 34*, 53.

Centers for Disease Control. (1989). Treatment guidelines for sexually transmitted diseases. *Morbidity and Mortality Weekly Report, 38*, No. S-8.

Centers for Disease Control. (1990a). Progress toward achieving the 1990 objectives for the nation for sexually transmitted diseases. *Morbidity and Mortality Weekly Report 39*, 53–57.

Centers for Disease Control. (1992, January). HIV infection and AIDS: Are you at risk? Atlanta: Author.

Chan, K., & Reidpath, D. (2003). "Typhoid Mary" and "HIV Jane": Responsibility, agency and disease prevention. *Reproductive Health Matters, 11*, 40–50.

Chance of breast cancer is figured at 1 in 8. (1992, September 27). *The New York Times*, p. A30.

Charny, I. W., & Parnass, S. (1995). The impact of extramarital relationships on the continuation of marriages. *Journal of Sex and Marital Therapy, 21*, 100–115.

Cheating going out of style but sex is popular as ever. (1993, October 19). *New York Newsday*, p. 2.

Check, J. V. P., & Malamuth, N. M. (1983). Sex-role stereotyping and reactions to depictions of stranger versus acquaintance rape. *Journal of Personality and Social Psychology, 45*, 344–356.

Cherniak, D. (1999). *Birth control handbook, 30th anniversary edition*. Montreal: Montreal Health Press.

Childbirth by Choice Trust. (1998). *No Choice: Canadian women tell their stories of illegal abortion*. Toronto: Author.

Choi, K. H., et al. (2003). Emerging HIV epidemic in China in men who have sex with men. *The Lancet, 361*, 2125–2126.

Choi, P. Y. (1992). The psychological benefits of physical exercise: Implications for women and the menstrual cycle. [Special issue: The menstrual cycle]. *Journal of Reproductive and Infant Psychology, 10*, 111–115.

Chrisler, J. C. & Caplan, P. (2002). The strange case of Dr. Jekyll and Ms. Hyde: How PMS became a cultural phenome-

non and a psychiatric disorder. *Annual Review of Sex Research, 13*, 274–306. Accessed from ProQuest database, August 21, 2003.

CIA (2003). Rank order—Infant mortality rate. *The World Factbook*. Updated to January 1, 2003. Accessed at **www.cia.gov/cia/publications/factbook /rankorder/2091rank.html**, January 26, 2004.

Clark, M. S., et al. (1989). Keeping track of needs and inputs of friends and strangers. *Personality and Social Psychology Bulletin, 15*, 533–542.

Clumeck, N. (1995). Primary prophylaxis against opportunistic infections in patients with AIDS. *New England Journal of Medicine, 332*, 739–740.

Cobb, M., & Jallon, J. M. (1990). Pheromones, mate recognition and courtship stimulation in the Drosophila melanogaster species sub-group. *Animal Behaviour, 39*, 1058–1067.

Cochrane, S. (2001). Emerging issues in research on lesbians' and gay men's mental health: Does sexual orientation really matter? *American Psychologist, 56*, 931–947.

Cohen, J. Personal communication.

Colapinto, J. (2000). *As nature made him: The boy who was raised as a girl*. New York: HarperCollins.

Colditz, G.A., et al. (1993). Family history, age, and risk of breast cancer: Prospective data from the nurses' health study. *Journal of the American Medical Association, 270*, 338–343.

Colditz, G. A., et al. (1995). The use of estrogens and progestins and the risk of breast cancer in postmenopausal women. *New England Journal of Medicine, 332*, 1589–1593.

Cole, S. S. (1988). Women's sexuality, and disabilities. *Women and Therapy, 7*, 277–294.

Coleman, E. (1989). The development of male prostitution activity among gay and bisexual adolescents [Special issue: Gay and lesbian youth]. *Journal of Homosexuality, 17*, 131–149.

Coleman, M., & Ganong, L. H. (1985). Love and sex role stereotypes: Do macho men and feminine women make better lovers? *Journal of Personality and Social Psychology, 49*, 170–176.

Coles, C. (1994). Critical periods for prenatal alcohol exposure: Evidence from animal and human studies. *Alcohol Health and Research World, 18*(1), 22–29.

Coles, R., & Stokes, G. (1985). *Sex and the American teenager*. New York: Harper & Row.

Collaer, M. L., & Hines, M. (1995). Human behavioral sex differences: A role for gonadal hormones during early development? *Psychological Bulletin, 118*, 55–107.

Collins, N. L., & Miller, L. C. (1994). Self-disclosure and liking: A meta-analytic review. *Psychological Bulletin, 116*, 457–475.

COMPAS. (1998, October 30). Sexual athletics and performance of sexually active men and women—the myths and the realities. Report 6 from a national study of sex and relationships conducted for the *Toronto Sun* by COMPAS Inc. October 30, 1998. Accessed from **www.compas.ca/html/archivesdocume nt.asp?offset=230&compasID=77**, August 29, 2003.

Condon, J. W., & Crano, W. D. (1988). Inferred evaluation and the relation between attitude similarity and interpersonal attraction. *Journal of Personality and Social Psychology, 54*, 789–797.

Connor, E. M., et al. (1994). Reduction of maternal–infant transmission of human immunodeficiency virus type 1 with zidovudine treatment. *New England Journal of Medicine, 331*, 1173–1180.

Consumer's Union. (1995, May). Consumer reports: How reliable are condoms? America Online.

Cooper, A. J. (1986). Progestogens in the treatment of male sex offenders: A review. *Canadian Journal of Psychiatry, 31*, 73–79.

Cooper, A. J., et al. (1990). A female sex offender with multiple paraphilias: A psychologic, physiologic (laboratory sexual arousal) and endocrine case study. *Canadian Journal of Psychiatry, 35*, 334–337.

Cooper, D. A., et al. (1993). Zidovudine in persons with asymptomatic HIV infection and CD4 cell counts greater than 400 per cubic millimeter. *New England Journal of Medicine, 329*, 297–303.

Corey, L., & Holmes, K. K. (1996). Therapy for HIV infection—What have we learned? *New England Journal of Medicine, 335*, 1142–1144.

Cosgray, R. E., et al. (1991). Death from auto-erotic asphyxiation in a long-term psychiatric setting. *Perspectives in Psychiatric Care, 27*, 21–24.

Council of Ministers of Education. (2003). Canadian youth, sexual health and HIV study. Toronto: Council of Ministers of Education, Canada. Available online at **www.cmec.ca/publications/aids/**.

Cox, D. J. (1988). Incidence and nature of male genital exposure behavior as reported by college women. *Journal of Sex Research, 24*, 227–234.

Crews, D. (1994). Animal sexuality. *Scientific America, 270*(1), 108–114.

Cronin, A. (1993, June 27). Two viewfinders, two views of Gay America. *The New York Times*, Section 4, p. 10.

Crum, C., & Ellner, P. (1985). Chlamydia infections: Making the diagnosis. *Contemporary Obstetrics and Gynecology, 25*, 153–159, 163, 165, 168.

CTV/Angus Reid. (1998, March 3). Let's talk about sex.

Cunningham, M. R., et al. (1995). "Their ideas of beauty are, on the whole, the same as ours": Consistency and variability in the cross-cultural perception of female physical attractiveness. *Journal of Personality and Social Psychology, 68*(2), 261–279.

Cunningham, A. (2000). Adolescent female aggression: Proposal for a research agenda. Paper presented at the annual convention of the Canadian Psychological Association, June 29–July 1, 2000.

Curtis, R. C., & Miller, K. (1986). Believing another likes or dislikes you: Behavior making the beliefs come true. *Journal of Personality and Social Psychology, 51*, 284–290.

Cutrona, C. E. (1983). Causal attributions and perinatal depression. *Journal of Abnormal Psychology, 92*, 161–172.

Dabbs, J. M., Jr., & Morris, R. (1990). Testosterone, social class, and antisocial behavior in a sample of 4,462 men. *Psychological Science, 1*, 1–3.

Darby, R. (2003). The masturbation taboo and the rise of routine male circumcision: A review of the historiography. *Journal of Social History, 36*(3), 737–757.

Darling, C. A., et al. (1991). The female sexual response revisited: Understanding the multiorgasmic experience in women. *Archives of Sexual Behavior, 20*, 527–540.

DATTA (Diagnostic and Theapeutic Technology Assessment). (1988). Questions and answers: Penile implants for erectile impotence. *Journal of the American Medical Association, 260*, 997–1000.

Davenport, W. (1977). Sex in cross-cultural perspective. In F. Beach (Ed.), *Human sexuality in four perspectives* (pp. 115–163). Baltimore: Johns Hopkins University Press.

Davidson, J. K., & Hoffman, L. E. (1986). Sexual fantasies and sexual satisfaction: An empirical analysis of erotic thought. *Journal of Sex Research, 22*, 184–205.

Davidson, K. J., et al. (1989). The role of the Grafenberg spot and female ejaculation in the female orgasmic response: An empirical analysis. *Journal of Sex and Marital Therapy, 15*, 102–119.

Davies, P. T., & Cummings, E. M. (1994). Marital conflict and child adjustment. *Psychological Bulletin, 116*, 387–411.

Davis, J. A., & Smith, T. (1987). *General social surveys, 1972–1987: Cumulative data.* Storrs, CT: University of Connecticut, Roper Center for Public Opinion Research.

Dawes, R. M. (1989). Statistical criteria for establishing a truly false consensus effect. *Journal of Experimental Social Psychology, 25*, 1–17.

Day, N. L., & Richardson, G. A. (1994). Comparative teratogenicity of alcohol and other drugs. *Alcohol Health and Research World, 18*(1), 42–48.

Deaux, K. (1985). Sex and gender. *Annual Review of Psychology, 36*, 49–81.

Deaux, K., & Lewis, L. L. (1983). Assessment of gender stereotypes: Methodology and components. *Psychological Documents, 13*, 25 (Ms. No. 2583).

DeKeseredy, W. (2000). Guest editor's introduction. *Violence against Women, 6*, 915–917.

DeKeseredy, W. S., & Kelly, K. (1993). The incidence and prevalence of woman abuse in Canadian university and college dating relationships. *Canadian Journal of Sociology, 18*, 137–159.

Dekker, J. (1993). Inhibited male orgasm. In W. O'Donohue & J. H. Geer (Eds.), *Handbook of sexual dysfunctions: Assessment and treatment* (pp. 279–301). Boston: Allyn & Bacon.

Del Priore, G., et al. (1995). Risk of ovarian cancer after treatment for infertility. *New England Journal of Medicine, 332*, 1300.

de Luca, R. V., et al. (1992). Group treatment for child sexual abuse [Special issue: Violence and its aftermath]. *Canadian Psychology, 33*, 168–179.

Denny, N., et al. (1984). Sex differences in sexual needs and desires. *Archives of Sexual Behavior, 13*, 233–245.

de Raad, B., & Doddema-Winsemius, M. (1992). Factors in the assortment of human mates: Differential preferences in Germany and the Netherlands. *Personality and Individual Differences, 13*, 103–114.

Desmond, A. M. (1994). Adolescent pregnancy in the United States: Not a minority issue. *Health Care for Women International, 15*(4), 325–331.

Deutsch, F. M., et al. (1987). What is in a smile? *Psychology of Women Quarterly, 11*, 341–352.

de Young, M. (1982). *The sexual victimization of children.* Jefferson, NC: McFarland & Company.

Diamond, M. (1999). Sexual identity and sexual orientation in children with traumatized or ambiguous genitalia. *The Journal of Sex Research, 34*, 199–212.

Dick-Read, G. (1944). *Childbirth without fear: The principles and practices of natural childbirth.* New York: Harper & Bros.

Dietz, P. E., et al. (1990). The sexually sadistic criminal and his offenses. *Bulletin of the American Academy of Psychiatry and the Law, 18*, 163–178.

Digest: STD rates soar in China; Three in four new cases are among the unmarried. (2000). *Family Planning Perspectives, 26*(3) 141–142.

DiMatteo, M. R., et al. (1996). Cesarean childbirth and psychosocial outcomes: A meta-analysis. *Health Psychology, 15*, 303–314.

Dindia, K., & Allen, M. (1992). Sex differences in self-disclosure: A meta-analysis. *Psychological Bulletin, 112*, 106–124.

Doctors tie male mentality to shorter life span. (1995, June 14). *The New York Times*, p. C14.

Donnerstein, E. (1980). Aggressive erotica and violence against women. *Journal of Personality and Social Psychology, 39*, 269–277.

Donnerstein, E. & Berkowitz, L. (1981). Victim reactions in aggressive erotic films as a factor in violence against women. *Journal of Personality and Social Psychology, 41*, 710–724.

Donnerstein, E. I., & Linz, D. G. (1987). *The question of pornography.* New York: The Free Press.

Drews, C. D., et al. (1996, April). Pediatrics. Cited in "Smokers more likely to bear retarded babies, study says." (1996, April 10). *The New York Times*, p. B7.

Dube, R., & Hebert, M. (1988). Sexual abuse of children 12 years of age: A review of 511 cases. *Child Abuse and Neglect, 12*, 321–330.

Dugger, C. W. (1996, October 12). New law bans genital cutting in the United States. *The New York Times*, pp. A1, A28.

Dundas, S., & Kaufman, M. (2000). The Toronto lesbian family study. *Journal of Homosexuality, 40*, 65–79.

Dunn, M. E., & Trost, J. E. (1989). Male multiple orgasms: A descriptive study. *Archives of Sexual Behavior, 18*, 377–387.

Dunsmuir, W. D., & Gordon, E. M. (1999). The history of circumcision. *British Journal of Urology International, 83*, Supplement 1, 1–12.

DuRant, R. H., & Sanders, J. M. (1989). Sexual behavior and contraceptive risk taking among sexually active adolescent females. *Journal of Adolescent Health Care, 10*, 1–19.

Dwyer, M. (1988). Exhibitionism/voyeurism. *Journal of Social Work and Human Sexuality*, 7, 101–112.

Dziech, B. W., & Weiner, L. (1984). The lecherous professor: *Sexual harassment on campus*. Boston: Beacon Press.

Early prostate surgery is found very effective. (1996, August 28). *The New York Times*, p. C9.

Edgley, C. (1989). Commercial sex: Pornography, prostitution, and advertising. In K. McKinney & S. Sprecher (Eds.), *Human sexuality: The societal and interpersonal context* (pp. 370–424). Norwood, NJ: Ablex Publishing Corporation.

Edmonson, B. (1988). Disability and sexual adjustment. In V. B. Van Hasselt, et al. (Eds.), *Handbook of developmental and physical disabilities* (pp. 91–106). New York: Pergamon Press.

Eggert, A. K., & Muller, J. K. (1989). Mating success of pheromone-emitting necrophorus males: Do attracted females discriminate against resource owners? *Behaviour*, 110, 248–257.

Ehrlich, G. (1988, March). Sexual concerns of patients with arthritis. *Medical Aspects of Human Sexuality*, 10, 281–300.

Ellis, A. (1962). *Reason and emotion in psychotherapy*. New York: Lyle Stuart.

Ellis, A. (1977). The basic clinical theory of rational–emotive therapy. In A. Ellis & R. Grieger (eds.), *Handbook of rational–emotive therapy*. New York: Springer.

Ellis, L., & Ames, M. A. (1987). Neurohormonal functioning and sexual orientation: A theory of homosexuality–heterosexuality. *Psychological Bulletin*, 101, 233–258.

Elmer-Dewitt, P. (1991, September 30). Making babies. *Time*, 56–63.

Ember, C. R., & Ember, M. (1990). *Anthropology* (6th ed., instructor's edition). Englewood Cliffs, NJ: Prentice-Hall.

Emmanuel, N. P., et al. (1992). Fluoxetine treatment of voyeurism. *American Journal of Psychiatry*, 148, 950.

English, P. B., & Eskenazi, B. (1992). Reinterpreting the effects of maternal smoking on infant birthweight and perinatal mortality: A multivariate approach to birthweight standardization. *International Journal of Epidemiology*, 21, 1097–1105.

Erel, O., & Burman, B. (1995). Interrelatedness of marital relations and parent–child relations: A meta-analytic review. *Psychological Bulletin*, 118, 108–132.

Erlanger, S. (1991, July 14). A plague awaits. *The New York Times Magazine*, pp. 24, 26, 49, 53.

Erwin, P. (1994). First names and perceptions of physical attractiveness. *The Journal of Psychology*, 127, 625–631.

Eskenazi, G. (1990, June 3). The male athlete and sexual assault. *The New York Times*, pp. L1, L4.

Etaugh, C., & Rathus, S. A. (1995). *The world of children*. Fort Worth, TX: Harcourt Brace College Publishers.

Everaerd, W. (1993). Male erectile disorder. In W. O'Donohue & J. H. Geer (Eds.), *Handbook of sexual dysfunctions: Assessment and treatment* (pp. 201–224). Boston: Allyn & Bacon.

Exner, J. E., et al. (1977). Some psychological characteristics of prostitutes. *Journal of Personality Assessment*, 41, 474–485.

Faller, K. C. (1989). Why sexual abuse? An exploration of the intergenerational hypothesis. *Child Abuse and Neglect*, 13, 543–548.

Fallon, A. E., & Rozin, P. (1985). Sex differences in perceptions of desirable body shape. *Journal of Abnormal Psychology*, 94, 102–105.

Federal/Provincial Territorial Ministers Responsible for the Status of Women (Canada) (2002). *Assessing violence against women: A statistical profile*. Ottawa: Status of Women Canada.

Federman, D. D. (1994). Life without estrogen. *New England Journal of Medicine*, 331, 1088–1089.

Feingold, A. (1991). Sex differences in the effects of similarity and physical attractiveness on opposite-sex attraction. *Basic and Applied Social Psychology*, 12, 357–367.

Feingold, A. (1994). Gender differences in personality: A meta-analysis. *Psychological Bulletin*, 116, 429–456.

Feng, T. (1993). Substance abuse in pregnancy. Current Opinions in Obstetrics and Gynecology, 5, 16–23.

Fenichel, O. (1945). *The psychoanalytic theory of neurosis*. New York: Norton.

Fensterheimn, H., & Kantor, J. S. (1980). Behavioral approach to sexual disorders. In B. Wolman & J. Money (Eds.), *Handbook of human sexuality*. Englewood Cliffs, NJ: Prentice-Hall.

Ferrante, C. L., et al. (1988). Image of women in television advertising. *Journal of Broadcasting and Electronic Media*, 32, 231–237.

Fichner-Rathus, L. (1995). *Understanding art* (4th ed.). Englewood Cliffs, NJ: Prentice Hall.

Fink, K. S., et al. (2002). Adult circumcision outcomes study: Effect on Journal of Urology, 167(5), 2113–2116.

Finkelhor, D. (1984). *Child sexual abuse: Theory and research*. New York: The Free Press.

Fink, K. S., et al. (2002). Adult circumcision outcomes study: Effect on erectile function, penile sensitivity, sexual activity and satisfaction. *Journal of Urology*, 167(5), 2113–2116.

Finkelhor, D. et al. (1990). Sexual abuse in a national survey of adult men and women: Prevalence, characteristics, and risk factors. *Child Abuse and Neglect*, 14, 19–28.

Finkelhor, D., & Yllo, K. (1982). Rape in marriage: A sociological view. In D. Finkelhor, et al. (Eds.), *The dark side of families: Current family violence research* (pp. 119–130). Beverly Hills, CA: Sage.

Fish, L. S., et al. (1994). Structural couple therapy in the treatment of inhibited sexual drive. *American Journal of Family Therapy*, 22(2), 113–125.

Fisher, B., et al. (1982). *Report on adolescent male prostitution*. San Francisco: Urban and Rural Systems Associates.

Fisher, W. A., et al. (1999). The 1998 Canadian contraceptive study. *Canadian Journal of Human Sexuality*, 8(13), 161–216.

Fisher, W. A., & Barak, A. (1991). Pornography, erotica and behavior: More questions than answers. *International Journal of Law and Psychiatry*, 14, 65-83.

Fisher, W. A., & Fisher, J. D. (1998). Understanding and promoting sexual and reproductive health behaviour: Theory and method. *Annual Review of Sex Research*, 9, 38–76.

Fisher, W. A, & Grenier, G. (1994). Violent pornography, antiwoman thoughts and antiwoman acts: In search of reliable effects. *Journal of Sex Research*, 31, 23-38.

Fitzgerald, L. F. (1993a). *Sexual harassment in higher education: Concepts and issues*. Washington, DC: National Education Association.

Fitzgerald, L. F. (1993b). Sexual harassment: Violence against women in the workplace. *American Psychologist*, 48, 1070–1076.

Floyd, R. L., et al. (1993). A review of smoking in pregnancy: Effects on pregnancy outcomes and cessation efforts. *Annual Review of Public Health*, 14, 379–411.

Ford, C. S., & Beach, F. A. (1951). *Patterns of sexual behavior*. New York: Harper & Row.

Forster, P., & King, J. (1994). Fluoxetine for premature ejaculation. *American Journal of Psychiatry*, 151(10), 1523.

Franzoi, S. L., & Herzog, M. E. (1987). Judging physical attractiveness: What body aspects do we use? *Personality and Social Psychology Bulletin, 13,* 19–33.

Frayser, S. (1985). *Varieties of sexual experience: An anthropological perspective on human sexuality.* New Haven: Human Relations Area Files Press.

Frazier, P. A. (1990). Victim attributions and post-rape trauma. *Journal of Personality and Social Psychology, 59,* 298–304.

Freiberg, P. (1995). Psychologists examine attacks on homosexuals. *APA Monitor, 26*(6), 30–31.

Freud, S. (1922/1959). Analysis of a phobia in a 5-year-old boy. In A. & J. Strachey (Ed. & Trans.), *Collected papers* (Vol. 3). New York: Basic Books. (Original work published 1909.)

Freund, J., & Blanchard, R. (1986). The concept of courtship disorder. *Journal of Sex and Marital Therapy, 12,* 79–92.

Freund, K., et al. (1988). The value of self-reports in the study of voyeurism and exhibitionism. *Annals of Sex Research, 1,* 243–262.

Freund, M., et al. (1989). Sexual behavior of resident street prostitutes with their clients in Camden, New Jersey. *Journal of Sex Research, 26,* 460–478.

Fried, P. A. (1986). Marijuana use in pregancy. In I. J. Chasnott (Ed.), *Drug use in pregnancy: Mother and child.* Boston: MTP Press.

Friedman, D. M. (2003). *A mind of its own: A cultural history of the penis.* New York: Penguin Books.

Friedman, L. C., et al. (1994). Dispositional optimism, self-efficacy, and health beliefs as predictors of breast self-examination. *American Journal of Preventive Medicine, 10*(3), 130–135.

Friedman, R. C., & Downey, J. I. (1994). Homosexuality. *New England Journal of Medicine, 331,* 923–930.

Friedrich, E. (1985). Vaginitis. *American Journal of Obstetrics and Gynecology, 152,* 247–251.

Friedrich, W. N., & Gerber, P. N. (1994). Autoerotic asphyxia: The development of a paraphilia. *Journal of the American Academy of Child and Adolescent Psychiatry, 33*(7), 970–974.

Frisch, R. E. (1983). Fatness, puberty and fertility: The effects of nutrition and physical training on menarche and ovulation. In J. Brooks-Gunn & A. C. Petersen (Eds.), *Girls at puberty: Biological and psychosocial aspects.* New York: Plenum.

Fuchs, C. S., et al. (1995). Alcohol consumption and mortality among women. *New England Journal of Medicine, 332,* 1245–1250.

Furnham, A., & Voli, V. (1989). Gender stereotypes in Italian television advertisements. *Journal of Broadcasting and Electronic Media, 33,* 175–185.

Gabriel, T. (1995, April 23). When one spouse is gay and a marriage unravels. *The New York Times,* pp. A1, A22.

Gagnon, J. H. (1977). *Human sexualities.* Glenview, IL: Scott, Foresman.

Gagnon, J. H. (1990). Gender preferences in erotic relations: The Kinsey scale and sexual scripts. In D. P. McWhirter, et al. (Eds.), *Homosexuality/heterosexuality: Concepts of sexual orientation* (pp. 177–207). New York: Oxford University Press.

Gagnon, J. H., & Simon, W. (1973). *Sexual conduct: The social origins of human sexuality.* Chicago: Aldine.

Ganitsch, C. (1992, January 14). Personal communication.

Garber, M. (1995). *Vice versa.* New York: Simon & Schuster.

Garland, S. M., et al. (1990). Chlamydia trachomatis: Role in tubal infertility. *Australian and New Zealand Journal of Obstetrics and Gynaecology, 30,* 83–86.

Garwood, S. G., et al. (1980). Beauty is only "name deep": The effect of first name in ratings of physical attraction. *Journal of Applied Social Psychology, 10,* 431–435.

Gebhard, P. H. (1976). The institute. In M. S. Weinberg (Ed.), *Sex research: Studies from the Kinsey Institute.* New York: Oxford University Press.

Gebhard, P. H. (1977). *Memorandum on the incidence of homosexuals in the United States.* Bloomington, IN: Indiana University Institute for Sex Research.

Gebhard, P. H., et al. (1965). *Sex offenders: An analysis of types.* New York: Harper & Row.

Geer, J., et al. (1984). *Human sexuality.* Englewood Cliffs, NJ: Prentice-Hall.

Geiger, R. (1981). Neurophysiology of sexual response in spinal cord injury. In D. Bullard & S. Knight (Eds.), *Sexuality and physical disability: Personal perspectives.* St. Louis: C. V. Mosby.

Gelles, R. J., & Cornell, C. P. (1985). *Intimate violence in families.* Beverly Hills, CA: Sage.

Gelman, D., with P. Kandell. (1993, January 18). Isn't it romantic? *Newsweek,* 60–61.

Genes that protect against AIDS. (1996, August 14). *The New York Times,* p. A18.

Genuis, M., et al. (1991, Fall). Male victims of child sexual abuse: A brief overview of pertinent findings [Special issue: Child sexual abuse]. *Journal of Child and Youth-Care,* 1–6.

Gibbs, N. (1991, June 3). When is it rape? *Time,* pp. 48–54.

Gibson, A. I., et al. (1988). Adolescent female prostitutes. *Archives of Sexual Behavior, 17,* 431–438.

Gidycz, C. A., & Koss, M. P. (1990). A comparison of group and individual sexual assault victims. *Psychology of Women Quarterly, 14,* 325–342.

Gilbert, S. (1996, September 25). No long-term link is found between pill and breast cancer. *The New York Times,* p. C9.

Gillis, J. S., & Avis, W. E. (1980). The male-taller norm in mate selection. *Personality and Social Psychology Bulletin, 6,* 396–401.

Giovannucci, E., et al. (1993a). A prospective cohort study of vasectomy and prostate cancer in U.S. men. *Journal of the American Medical Association, 269,* 873–877.

Giovannucci, E., et al. (1993b). A retrospective cohort study of vasectomy and prostate cancer in U.S. men. *Journal of the American Medical Association, 269,* 878–882.

Gitlin, M. J., & Pasnau, R. O. (1989). Psychiatric syndromes linked to reproductive function in women: A review of current knowledge. *American Journal of Psychiatry, 146,* 1413–1422.

Glass, S. P., & Wright, T. L. (1992). Justifications of extramarital relationships: The association between attitudes, behaviors, and gender. *Journal of Sex Research, 29,* 361–387.

Gold, S. R., & Gold, R. G. (1993). Sexual aversions: A hidden disorder. In W. O'Donohue & J. H. Geer (Eds.), *Handbook of sexual dysfunctions: Assessment and treatment* (pp. 83–102). Boston: Allyn & Bacon.

Goldberg, C. (1995, September 11). Sex slavery, Thailand to New York. *The New York Times,* pp. B1, B6.

Goldberg, L. H., et al. (1993). Longterm suppression of recurrent genital herpes with acyclovir. *Archives of Dermatology, 129,* 582–587.

Goldberg, M. (1987). Understanding hypersexuality in men and women. In G. R. Weeks and Larry Hof (Eds.), *Integrating sex and marital therapy: A clinical guide* (pp. 202–220). New York: Brunner/Mazel.

Goldstein, A. M., & Clark, J. H. (1990). Treatment of uncomplicated gonococcal urethritis with single-dose ceftriaxone. *Sexually Transmitted Diseases, 17,* 181–183.

Goldstein, I. (1987). Penile revascularization. *Urologic Clinics of North America, 14,* 805–813.

Goleman, D. (1991, October 22). Sexual harassment: It's about power, not lust. *The New York Times,* pp. C1, C12.

Goleman, D. (1992). Therapies offer hope for sex offenders. *The New York Times,* pp. C1, C11.

Goleman, D. (1993, October 6). Abuse-prevention efforts aid children. *The New York Times,* p. C13.

Goleman, D. (1995, June 14). Sex fantasy research said to neglect women. *The New York Times,* p. C14.

Gollaher, D. L. (1994). From ritual to science. *Journal of Social History, 28,* 5–36.

Golombok, S., et al. (2003). Children with lesbian parents: A community study. *Developmental Psychology, 39,* 20–33.

Gomez-Schwartz, B., et al. (1990). *Child sexual abuse: The initial effects.* Newbury Park, CA: Sage.

Goodwin, J. M., et al. (1990). Borderline and other severe symptoms in adult survivors of incestuous abuse. *Psychiatric Annals, 20,* 22–32.

Gordon, S., & Snyder, C. W. (1989). *Personal issues in human sexuality: A guidebook for better sexual health* (2nd ed.). Boston: Allyn & Bacon.

Graber, B. (1993). Medical aspects of sexual arousal disorders. In W. O'Donohue & J. H. Geer (Eds.), *Handbook of sexual dysfunctions: Assessment and treatment* (pp. 103–156). Boston: Allyn & Bacon.

Graca, L. M., et al. (1991). Acute effects of maternal cigarette smoking on fetal heart rate and fetal body movements felt by the mother. *Journal of Perinatal Medicine, 19,* 385–390.

Grabrick, D. M., et al. (2000). Risk of breast cancer with oral contraceptive use in women with a family history of breast cancer. *Journal of the American Medical Association, 284,* 1791–1798.

Graham, L., & Metaxas, P. T. (2003). "Of course it's true; I saw it on the Internet!" *Communications of the ACM, 46,* 71–75.

Graham, S., et al. (1982). Sex patterns and herpes simplex virus type 2 in the epidemiology of cancer of the cervix. *American Journal of Epidemiology, 115,* 729–735.

Green, R. (1978). Sexual identity of 37 children raised by homosexual or transsexual parents. *American Journal of Psychiatry, 135,* 692–697.

Green, R. (2003). When therapists do not want their clients to be homosexual: A response to Rosik's article. *Journal of Marriage and Family Therapy, 29,* 29–38.

Greenberg, S. R. R., et al. (2002). Prediction of recidivism in exhibitionists: Psychological, phallometric, and offense factors. *Sexual Abuse: A Journal of Research and Treatment, 14,* 329–347.

Greenspan, S. L., et al. (2003). Combination therapy with hormone replacement and alendronate for prevention of bone loss in elderly women. *Journal of the American Medical Association, 289,* 2525–2533. Accessed from ProQuest database, August 21, 2003.

Greenwald, E., & Leitenberg, H. (1989). Long-term effects of sexual experiences with siblings and non-siblings during childhood. *Archives of Sexual Behavior, 18,* 389–399.

Greenwald, E., et al. (1990). Childhood sexual abuse: Long-term effects on psychological and sexual functioning in a nonclinical and nonstudent sample of adult women. *Child Abuse and Neglect, 14,* 503–513.

Griffin, E., & Sparks, G. G. (1990). Friends forever: A longitudinal exploration of intimacy in same-sex friends and platonic pairs. *Journal of Social and Personal Relationships, 7,* 29–46.

Grodstein, F., et al. (1993). Relation of tubal infertility to history of sexually transmitted diseases. *American Journal of Epidemiology, 137,* 577–584.

Groneman, C. (1994). Nymphomania: The historical construction of female sexuality. *Signs, 19*(2), 337–367.

Groth, A. N., & Birnbaum, H. J. (1979). *Men who rape: The psychology of the offender.* New York: Plenum.

Groth, A. N., & Hobson, W. (1983). The dynamics of sexual assault. In L. Schlesinger & E. Revitch (Eds.), *Sexual dynamics of antisocial behavior.* Springfield, IL: Thomas.

Grover, A., et al. (2000). The clinical burden of prostate cancer in Canada: Forecasts from the Montreal prostate cancer model. *Canadian Medical Association Journal, 162*(7), 977–983.

Grych, J. H., & Fincham, F. D. (1993). Children's appraisals of marital conflict. *Child Development, 64,* 215–230.

Grunseit, A. et al., (1997). Sexuality education and young people's sexual behavior: A review of studies. *Journal of Adolescent Research, 12,* 421–453.

Gupta, M. (1994). Sexuality in the Indian subcontinent. *Sexual and Marital Therapy, 9*(1), 57–69.

Haffner, D. (1993, August). Sex Education: Trends and issues. Paper presented at the meeting of the American Psychological Association, Toronto, Canada.

Haglund, B., & Cnattingius, S. (1990). Cigarette smoking as a risk factor for sudden infant death syndrome: A population based study. *American Journal of Public Health, 80,* 29–32.

Hall, C. S. (1984). "A ubiquitous sex difference in dreams" revisited. *Journal of Personality and Social Psychology, 46,* 1109–1117.

Hall, G. C. N. (1989). Sexual arousal and arousability in a sexual offender population. *Journal of Abnormal Psychology, 98,* 145–149.

Hall, G. C. N., & Hirschman, R. (1991). Toward a theory of sexual aggression: A quadripartite model. *Journal of Consulting and Clinical Psychology, 59,* 662–669.

Hall, M. (2002). Not tonight dear, I'm deconstructing a headache: Confessions of a lesbian sex therapist. *Women and Therapy, 24,* 161–172.

Halpern, D. F. (1997). Sex differences in intelligence: Implications for education. *American Psychologist, 52,* 1091–1092.

Hamer, D. H., et al. (1993, July 16). A linkage between DNA markers on the X chromosome and male sexual orientation. *Science, 261,* 321–327.

Handler, A. (1990). The correlates of the initiation of sexual intercourse among young urban Black females. *Journal of Youth and Adolescence, 19,* 159–170.

Hanrahan, J. P., et al. (1992). The effect of maternal smoking during pregnancy on early infant lung function. *American Review of Respiratory Disease, 145,* 1129–1135.

Harding, J. J. (1989). Postpartum psychiatric disorders: A review. *Comprehensive Psychiatry, 30,* 109–112.

Harney P. A., & Muehlenhard, C. L. (1991). Rape. In E. Grauerholz & M. A. Koralewski (Eds.), *Sexual coercion: A sourcebook on its nature, causes, and prevention* (pp. 3–16). Lexington, MA: Lexington Books.

Hart, J., et al. (1991). Sexual behavior in pregnancy: A study of 219 women. *Journal of Sex Education and Therapy, 17,* 86–90.

Hartman, C. R., et al. (1987). Pathways and cycles of runaways: A model for understanding repetitive runaway behavior. *Hospital and Community Psychiatry, 38,* 292–299.

Harvey, S. (1987). Female sexual behavior: Fluctuations during the menstrual cycle. *Journal of Psychosomatic Research, 31,* 101–110.

Hatcher, R. A., et al. (1990). *Contraceptive technology 1990–1992* (15th rev. ed.). New York: Irvington Publishers.

Hatcher, R. A., et al. (1994). *Contraceptive technology 1992–1994* (16th rev. ed.). New York: Irvington Publishers.

Hatfield, E. (1988). Passionate and companionate love. In R. J. Sternberg & M. L. Barnes (Eds.), *The psychology of love* (pp. 191–217). New Haven: Yale University Press.

Hatfield, E., & Sprecher, S. (1986). Measuring passionate love in intimate relationships. *Journal of Adolescence, 9,* 383–410.

Hausknecht, R. U. (1995). Methotrexate and misoprostol to terminate early pregnancy. *New England Journal of Medicine, 333,* 537–540.

Havemann, E., & Lehtinen, M. (1990). *Marriages and families: New problems, new opportunities* (2nd ed.). Englewood Cliffs, NJ: Prentice-Hall.

Hawton, K., and Catalan, J. (1990). Sex therapy for vaginismus: Characteristics of couples and treatment outcomes. *Sexual and Marital Therapy, 5,* 39–48.

Hazan, C., & Shaver, P. (1987). Love conceptualized as an attachment process. *Journal of Personality and Social Psychology, 52,* 511–524.

Health Canada. (1994). Health Products and Food Branch. Therapeutic Products Directorate, TPD-Web. Labelling standards for intravaginal antifungal agents (miconazole & clotrimazole). (Updated January 27, 2003.) Accessed at **www.hc-sc.gc.ca/hpfb-dgpsa/tpd-dpt/intravag_e.html**, January 29, 2004.

Health Canada. (1997). *Chlamydia trachomatis* in Canada: An update. *Canada Communicable Disease Report, 23*(15), August 1, 1997.

Health Canada. (1998a). Infant mortality. Canadian perinatal surveillance system fact sheet. Ottawa: Population and Public Health Branch.

Health Canada. (1998b). HIV and AIDS among women in Canada. STD Epi Update. Ottawa: Health Protection Branch. HIV Epidemiology, Bureau of HIV/AIDS, STD and TB, Laboratory Centre for Disease Control.

Health Canada. (1998c, November). Breastfeeding. Canadian perinatal surveillance system fact sheet. Ottawa: Population and Public Health Branch.

Health Canada. (1999a, May). Genital Chlamydia in Canada. STD Epi Update. Ottawa: Health Protection Branch. HIV Epidemiology, Bureau of HIV/AIDS and STD Update Series, Laboratory Centre for Disease Control.

Health Canada. (1999b, May). Syphilis in Canada: Elimination on the horizon? STD Epi Update. Ottawa: Health Protection Branch. HIV Epidemiology, Bureau of HIV/AIDS and STD Update Series, Laboratory Centre for Disease Control.

Health Canada (2000a). 1998/1999 Canadian Sexually Transmitted Diseases (STD) Surveillance Report. *Canada Communicable Disease Report,* volume 26S6. October 2000. Available at **www.hc-sc.gc.ca/pphb-dgspsp/publicat/ccdr-rmtc/00vol26/ 26s6/26s6h_e.html**.

Health Canada. (2000b). What everyone should know about human papillomavirus (HPV): Questions and answers. STD Epi Update. Centre for Infectious Disease Prevention and Control, Population and Public Health Branch, September 2000. Accessed at **www.hc-sc.gc.ca/pphb-dgspsp/publicat/epiu-aepi/std-mts/hpv_e.html**.

Health Canada. (2000c, April). HIV prevalence and incidence in Canada: 40,100 living with HIV infection and 4,200 new infections per year. HIV/AIDS Epi Update. Ottawa: Health Protection Branch. HIV Epidemiology, Bureau of HIV/AIDS and STD Update Series, Laboratory Centre for Disease Control.

Health Canada. (2000d, April). HIV and AIDS among Aboriginal people in Canada. HIV/AIDS Epi Update. Ottawa: Health Protection Branch. HIV Epidemiology, Bureau of HIV/AIDS and STD Update Series, Laboratory Centre for Disease Control.

Health Canada. (2000e, April). What everyone should know about human papillomavirus (HPV): Questions and answers. STD Epi Update. Ottawa: Health Protection Branch. HIV Epidemiology, Bureau of HIV/AIDS and STD Update Series, Laboratory Centre for Disease Control.

Health Canada. (2001). Non-insured health benefits. Drug Bulletin. Health Canada, October 2001.

Health Canada. (2003a). Centre for Infectious Disease Prevention and Control. HIV/AIDS EPI updates. Cat. H39-1/1-2003E-IN. April 2003. Accessed at **www.hc-sc.gc.ca/pphb-dgspsp/hast-vsmt/**, November 8, 2003.

Health Canada. (2003b). Population and Public Health Branch. Notifiable diseases by province for September 2003 (preliminary): Sexually transmitted and blood-borne pathogens. *Notifiable Diseases Monthly Report.* Accessed at **www.hc-sc.gc.ca/pphb-dgspsp/bid-bmi/dsd-dsm/ndmr-rmmdo/index.html#bbpathogens**, January 29, 2004.

Health Canada. (2003c). Incidence by province/territory: Gonococcal infections, both sexes combined (incl. not specified), all ages (inc. not specified), 2000. Rates per 100 000. *Notifiable Diseases Online.* Centre for Infectious Disease Prevention and Control, Health Canada, 2003. Accessed at **http://dsol-smed.hc-sc.gc.ca/dsol-smed/ndis/c_prv_e.html** (chart produced using OWTChart), January 29, 2004.

Health Canada. (2003d). Incidence by province/territory: Gonococcal infections, both sexes combined (incl. not specified), all ages (incl. not specified), 2000. Number of reported cases. *Notifiable Diseases Online.* Centre for Infectious Disease Prevention and Control, Health Canada, 2003. Accessed at **http://dsol-smed.hc-sc.gc.ca/dsol-smed/ndis/c_prv_e.html** (chart produced using OWTChart), January 29, 2004.

Health Canada. (2003e). Incidence by age group: Gonococcal infections, both sexes combined (incl. not specified), 2000, Canada. Number of reported cases. *Notifiable Diseases Online.* Centre for Infectious Disease Prevention and Control, Health Canada, 2003. Accessed at **http://dsol-smed.hc-sc.gc.ca/dsol-smed/ndis/c_prv_e.html** (chart produced using OWTChart), January 29, 2004.

Health Canada. (2003f). STD data tables, appendix 3.1: Reported infectious syphilis cases and rates in Canada by age group and sex, 1991–2000 (updated January 3, 2002). Accessed at **www. hc-sc.gc.ca/pphb-dgspsp/std-mts/stddata1201/tab3-1_e.html**, January 29, 2004.

Health Canada. (2003g). Sexual health and sexually transmitted infections section, Centre for Infectious Disease Prevention and Control, Health Canada. Reported cases and rates of notifiable STI from January 1 to June 30, 2003 and January 1 to June 30, 2002. Updated December 15, 2003. Accessed at **www.hc-sc.gc.ca/pphb-dgspsp/std-mts/stdcases-casmts/index.html**, January 29, 2004.

Health Canada. (2003h). Centre for Infectious Disease Prevention and Control. HIV infection reporting in Canada. *HIV/AIDS Epi Update,* April 2003. Accessed at **www.hc-sc.gc.ca/pphb-dgspsp/publicat/epiu-aepi/hiv-vih/hivrep_e.html**.

Health Canada. (2003i). Centre for Infectious Disease Prevention and Control. HIV infections among MSM in Canada. *HIV/AIDS Epi Update,* April 2003. Accessed at **www.hc-sc.gc.ca/pphb-dgspsp/publicat/epiu-aepi/hiv-vih/msm_e.html**.

Health Canada. (2003j). Centre for Infectious Disease Prevention and Control. HIV infections among injecting drug users in Canada. *HIV/AIDS Epi Update,* April 2003. Accessed at **www.hc-**

sc.gc.ca/pphb-dgspsp/publicat/epiu-aepi/hiv-vih/idus_e.html.

Health Canada. (2003k). Centre for Infectious Disease Prevention and Control. HIV infections among women in Canada. *HIV/AIDS Epi Update*, April 2003. Accessed at **www.hc-sc.gc.ca/pphb-dgspsp/publicat/epiu-aepi/hiv-vih/women_e.html**.

Health Canada. (2003l). Centre for Infectious Disease Prevention and Control. Perinatal transmission of HIV. *HIV/AIDS Epi Update*, April 2003. Accessed at **www.hc-sc.gc.ca/pphb-dgspsp/publicat/epiu-aepi/hiv-vih/peri_e.html**.

Health Canada. (2003m). Centre for Infectious Disease Prevention and Control. Ethnicity reporting for AIDS and HIV in Canada. *HIV/AIDS Epi Update*, April 2003. Accessed at **www.hc-sc.gc.ca/pphb-dgspsp/publicat/epiu-aepi/hiv-vih/hiveth_e.html**.

Health Canada. (2003n). Incidence over time: [hepatitis A, B, and C], both sexes combined (incl. not specified), Canada, 1988–2000. Number of reported cases. *Notifiable Diseases Online*. Centre for Infectious Disease Prevention and Control, Health Canada, 2003. Accessed at **http://dsol-smed.hc-sc.gc.ca/dsol-smed/ndis/c_prv_e.html**, January 29, 2004.

Health Canada. (2003o). Health Canada (2003l). Centre for Infectious Disease Prevention and Control. Nonoxynol-9 and the risk of HIV transmission. *HIV/AIDS Epi Update*, April 2003. Accessed at **www.hc-sc.gc.ca/pphb-dgspsp/publicat/epiu-aepi/hiv-vih/nonoxynol_e.html**.

Health Canada. (2003p). Nonoxynol-9 and the risk of HIV transmission. HIV/AIDS EPI Update, Centre for Infectious Disease Prevention and Control. Health Canada, April 2003.

Health Canada. (2004). Canadian Perinatal Surveillance System. **www.hc-sc.gc.ca/pphb-dgspsp/rhs-ssg/factshts/inabor_e.html**. Accessed February 22, 2004.

Hechtman, L. (1989). Teenage mothers and their children: Risks and problems: A review. *Canadian Journal of Psychiatry, 34*, 569–575.

Hedges, L. V., & Nowell, A. (1995). Sex differences in mental test scores, variability and numbers of high-scoring individuals. *Science, 269*, 41–45.

Heiman, J. R., & LoPiccolo, J. (1987). *Becoming orgasmic* (2nd ed.). Englewood Cliffs, NJ: Prentice-Hall.

Hendrick, C., & Hendrick, S. S. (1986). A theory and method of love. *Journal of Personality and Social Psychology, 50*, 392–402.

Hendrick, S. S., et al. (1988). Romantic relationships, love, satisfaction, and staying together. *Journal of Personality and Social Psychology, 54*, 980–988.

Hensley, W. E. (1992). Why does the best-looking person in the room always seem to be surrounded by admirers? *Psychological Reports, 70*, 457–458.

Hensley, W. E. (1994). Height as a basis for interpersonal attraction. *Adolescence, 29*, 469–474.

Herold, E. S. (1984). *Sexual behaviour in Canadian young people*. Markham: Fitzhenry and Whiteside.

Herold, E. S., & Way, L. (1983). Oral-genital behaviour in a sample of university females. *The Journal of Sex Research, 19*, 327–338.

Herdt, G. H. (1981). *Guardians of the flutes: Idioms of masculinity*. New York: McGraw-Hill.

Herold, E. S., & Byers, E. S. (1994). Sexology in China. *The Canadian Journal of Human Sexuality, 3*, 263–269.

Herzog, L. (1989). Urinary tract infections and circumcision. *American Journal of Diseases of Children, 143*, 348–350.

Hillier, S., & Holmes, K. K. (1990). Bacterial vaginosis. In K. K. Holmes, et al. (Eds.), *Sexually transmitted diseases* (2nd ed.) (pp. 547–560). New York: McGraw-Hill.

Hilton, E., et al. (1992). Ingestion of yogurt containing *Lactobacillus acidophilus* as prophylaxis for candidal vaginitis. *Annals of Internal Medicine, 116*, 353–357.

Hite, S. (1976). *The Hite report*. New York: Macmillan.

Hoagwood, K. (1990). Blame and adjustment among women sexually abused as children. *Women and Therapy, 9*, 89–110.

Hodge, S., & Canter, D. (1998). Victims and perpetrators of male sexual assault. *Journal of Interpersonal Violence, 13*, 222–239.

Hodgson, R., et al. (1990). Chlamydia trachomatis: The prevalence, trend and importance in initial infertility management. *Australian and New Zealand Journal of Obstetrics and Gynaecology, 30*, 251–254.

Hodson, D. S., & Skeen, P. (1994). Sexuality and aging: The hammerlock of myths. *Journal of Applied Gerontology, 13(3)*, 219–235.

Hofferth, S. L., & Hayes, C. D. (Eds.). (1987). *Risking the future: Adolescent sexuality, pregnancy, and childbearing*: Vol. 2. Working papers and statistical reports. Washington, DC: National Academy Press.

Hoffman, J. (1993, January 10). The morning after pill: A well-kept secret. *The New York Times Sunday Magazine*, p. 12.

Hogan, D. P. & Kitagawa, E. M. (1985). The impact of social status, family structure, and neighborhood on the fertility of black adolescents. *Family Planning Perspectives, 17*, 165–169.

Holden, G. W., & Ritchie, K. L. (1991). Linking extreme marital discord, child rearing, and child behavior problems. *Child Development, 62*, 311–327.

Holzman, H. R., & Pines, S. (1982). Buying sex: The phenomenology of being a john. *Deviant Behavior, 4*, 89–116.

Howard, J. A., et al. (1987). Social or evolutionary theories: Some observations on preferences in mate selection. *Journal of Personality and Social Psychology, 53*, 194–200.

Howards, S. S. (1995). Current concepts: Treatment of male infertility. *New England Journal of Medicine, 332*, 312–317.

Hsu, B., et al. (1994). Gender differences in sexual fantasy and behavior in a college population: A ten-year replication. *Journal of Sex and Marital Therapy, 20(2)*, 103–118.

Hubbard, R., & Wald, E. (1993). *Exploding the gene myth*. Boston: Beacon Press.

Huffman, T., et al. (1994). Gender differences and factors related to the disposition toward cohabitation. *Family Therapy, 21(3)*, 171–184.

Hunt, M. (1974). *Sexual behavior in the 1970's*. New York: Dell.

Hunter, D. J., et al. (1996). Cohort studies of fat intake and the risk of breast cancer—A pooled analysis. *New England Journal of Medicine, 334*, 356–361.

Hyde, J. S., & Plant, E. A. (1995). Magnitude of psychological gender differences: Another side to the story. *American Psychologist, 50*, 159–161.

Hyde, J. S., et al. (1990). Gender differences in mathematics performance: A meta-analysis. *Psychological Bulletin, 107*, 139–155.

Imperato-McGinley, J., et al. (1974). Steroid 5 reductase deficiency in man: An inherited form of male pseudohermaphroditism. *Science, 186*, 1213–1215.

Injections approved for child molesters. (1996, August 31). *The New York Times*, p. L7.

Ipsos-Reid/CTV Poll/ (2001). Marital infidelity. Available at **www.ipsos-na.com/news/pressrelease.cfm?id=1186**, accessed January 27, 2004.

Ipsos-Reid. (2003, August 8). Same-sex marriage: The debate enjoined. Accessed from PDF at **www. ipsos-reid.com/ search/pdf/media/mr030808-1.pdf**.

Isay, R. A. (1990). Psychoanalytic theory and the therapy of gay men. In D. P. McWhirter, et al. (Eds.), *Homosexuality/ heterosexuality: Concepts of sexual orientation* (pp. 283–303). New York: Oxford University Press.

Isay, R. A. (1993, April 23). Sex survey may say most about society's attitudes to gays [Letter]. *The New York Times*, Section 4, p. 16.

Islam, M. M., & Uddin, M. M. (2001). Female circumcision in Sudan: Future prospects and strategies for eradication. *International Family Planning Perspectives, 27*, 71–76. Accessed at **www. guttmach-er.org/pubs/journals/2707101.html**, July 21, 2003.

Jacklin, C. N., et al. (1984). Sex-typing behavior and sex-typing pressure in child–parent interaction. *Archives of Sexual Behavior, 13*, 413–425.

Jackson, J., et al. (1990). Young adult women who report childhood intrafamil-ial sexual abuse: Subsequent adjustment. *Archives of Sexual Behavior, 19*, 211–221.

Jackson, L. A., & Ervin, K. S. (1992). Height stereotypes of women and men: The liabilities of shortness for both sexes. *Journal of Social Psychology, 132*, 433–445.

Jacobson, J. L., & Jacobson, S. W. (1994). Prenatal alcohol exposure and neurobe-havioral development: Where is the threshold? *Alcohol Health and Research World, 18*(1), 30–36.

Jamison, P. L., & Gebhard, P. H. (1988). Penis size increase between flaccid and erect states: An analysis of the Kinsey data. *Journal of Sex Research, 24*, 177–183.

Jankowiak, W. R., & Fischer, E. F. (1992). A cross-cultural perspective on romantic love. *Ethnology, 31*, 149–155.

Janus, S. S., & Janus, C. L. (1993). *The Janus report on sexual behavior.* New York: Wiley.

Japanese Life Style. (2003). Japanese Christmas—Christmas in Japan. July 29, 2003, **www.japaneselifestyle. com.au/ culture/christmas.html**.

Johnson, K. A., & Williams, L. (1993). Risk of breast cancer in the nurses' health study: Applying the Gail model. *Journal of the American Medical Association, 270*, 2925–2926.

Jones, A., et al. (1994). Erectile disorder and the elderly: An analysis of the case for funding. *Sexual and Marital Therapy, 9*(1), 9–15.

Jones, H. W., & Toner, J. P. (1993). The infertile couple. *New England Journal of Medicine, 329*, 1710–1715.

Jorgensen, S. R., et al. (1980). Dyadic and social network influences on adolescent exposure to pregnancy risk. *Journal of Marriage and the Family, 42*, 141–155.

Kalick, S. M. (1988). Physical attractive-ness as a status cue. *Journal of Experimental Social Psychology, 24*, 469–489.

Kammeyer, K. C. W. (1990). *Marriage and family: A foundation for personal deci-sions* (2nd ed.). Boston: Allyn & Bacon.

Kammeyer, K. C. W., et al. (1990). *Sociology: Experiencing changing societies.* Boston: Allyn & Bacon.

Kaplan, D. (1993, January 18). The incor-rigibles. *Newsweek*, 48–50.

Kaplan, H. S. (1974). *The new sex therapy: Active treatment of sexual dysfunctions.* New York: Brunner/Mazel.

Kaplan, H. S. (1979). *Disorders of sexual desire.* New York: Simon and Schuster.

Kaplan, H. S. (1987). *Sexual aversion, sex-ual phobias, and panic disorder.* New York: Brunner/Mazel.

Karney, B. R., & Bradbury, T. N. (1995). The longitudinal course of marital quality and stability: A review of theory, method, and research. *Psychological Bulletin, 118*, 3–34.

Katz, J. N. (1995). *The invention of hetero-sexuality.* New York: Dutton.

Katz, R. C. (1990). Psychosocial adjust-ment in adolescent child molesters. *Child Abuse and Neglect, 14*, 567–575.

Kaufman, G. (1999). The portrayal of men's family roles in television commer-cials. *Sex Roles: A Journal of Research, 41*, 4399–4458.

Kedia, K. (1983). Ejaculation and emis-sion: Normal physiology, dysfunction, and therapy. In R. J. Krane, et al. (Eds.), *Male sexual dysfunction* (pp. 37–54). Boston: Little, Brown.

Kellerman, J., et al. (1989). Looking and loving: The effects of mutual gaze on feel-ings of romantic love. *Journal of Research in Personality, 23*, 145–161.

Kerns, J. G., & Fine, M. A. (1994). The relation between gender and negative attitudes toward gay men and lesbians: Do gender role attitudes mediate this rela-tion? *Sex Roles, 31*(5–6), 297–307.

Kettl, P., et al. (1991). Female sexuality after spinal cord injury. *Sexuality and Disability, 9*, 287–295.

Killmann, P. R., & Auerbach, R. (1979). Treatments of premature ejaculation and psychogenic impotence: A critical review of the literature. *Archives of Sexual Behavior, 8*, 81–100.

Killmann, P. R., et al. (1987). The treat-ment of secondary orgasmic dysfunction II. *Journal of Sex and Marital Therapy, 13*, 93–105.

Kilpatrick, D. G., et al. (1987, January). Rape in marriage and dating relation-ships: How bad are they for mental health? Paper presented at the meeting of the New York Academy of Science, New York, NY.

Kimlicka, T., et al. (1983). A comparison of androgynous, feminine, masculine, and undifferentiated women on self-esteem, body satisfaction, and sexual satisfaction. *Psychology of Women Quarterly, 1*, 291–294.

King, A. J. C., et al. (1988). *Canada youth and AIDS study.* Kingston, ON: Social Program Evaluation Group, Queens University.

King, L. (1988). Editorial comment in response to Wisell et al., 1987. *Journal of Urology, 139*, 883.

Kinloch-de Loes, S., et al. (1995). A con-trolled trial of zidovudine in primary human immunodeficiency virus infection. *New England Journal of Medicine, 333*, 408–413.

Kinsey, A. C., et al. (1948). *Sexual behavior in the human male.* Philadelphia: W. B. Saunders Co.

Kinsey, A. C., et al. (1953). *Sexual behavior in the human female.* Philadelphia: W. B. Saunders Co.

Kirby, D. (2000). School-based interven-tions to prevent unprotected sex and HIV among adolescents. In J. Peterson & R. Diclements (Eds.), *Handbook of HIV Prevention* (pp. 83–97). New York: Plenum Publishers.

Kleinplatz, P., & Moser, C. (2003). *DSM-IV-TR and the paraphilias: An argument for removal.* Accessed at **http: /home.net-com.com/~docx2/mk.html**, January 9, 2004.

Knapp, M. L. (1978). *Social intercourse: A behavioral approach to counseling.* Champaign, IL: Research Press.

Knight, R. A., et al. (1991). *Antisocial personality disorder and Hare assessments of psy-chopathy among sexual offenders.* Manuscript in preparation.

Knight, S. E. (1989). Sexual concerns of the physically disabled. In B. W. Heller, et al. (Eds.), *Psychosocial interventions with physical-ly disabled persons* (pp. 183–199). New Brunswick, NJ: Rutgers University Press.

Knox, D. (1988). *Choices in relationships.* St. Paul: West.

Knudsen, D. D. (1991). Child sexual coercion. In E. Grauerholz & M. A. Koralewski (Eds.), *Sexual coercion: A sourcebook on its nature, causes, and preven-tion* (pp. 17–28). Lexington, MA: Lexington Books.

Knussman, R., et al. (1986). Relations between sex hormone levels and sexual behavior in men. *Archives of Sexual Behavior*, *15*, 429–445.

Kockott, G., & Fahrner, E. (1987). Transsexuals who have not undergone surgery: A follow-up study. *Archives of Sexual Behavior*, *16*, 511–522.

Kohlberg, L. (1966). A cognitive–developmental analysis of children's sex-role concepts and attitudes. In E. E. Maccoby (Ed.), *The development of sex differences*. Stanford, CA: Stanford University Press.

Kohn, A. (1987, February). Shattered innocence. *Psychology Today*, 54–58.

Kolata, G. (1996, September 15). AIDS patients slipping through safety net. *The New York Times*, p. A24.

Kolodny, R. C. (1981). Evaluating sex therapy: Process and outcome at the Masters & Johnson Institute. *Journal of Sex Research*, *17*, 301–318.

Komisar, L. (1971). The image of women in advertising. In V. Gornick & B. Moran (Eds.), *Women in sexist society*. New York: Basic Books.

Kon, I. S. (1995). *The sexual revolution in Russia*. New York: The Free Press.

Kong, R. (1997, Autumn). *Criminal harassment in Canada. Canadian Social Trends*. Statistics Canada. Cat. No. 11-008 XPE.

Kong, R., et al. (2003) Sexual offences. *Juristat*, *23*(6). Ottawa: Canadian Centre for Justice Statistics.

Koss, M. P. (1993). Rape: Scope, impact, interventions, and public policy responses. *American Psychologist*, *48*, 1062–1069.

Koss, M. P., et al. (1987). The scope of rape: Incidence and prevalence of sexual aggression and victimization in a national sample of higher education students. *Journal of Consulting and Clinical Psychology*, *55*, 162–170.

Krafka, C. L. (1985). *Sexually explicit, sexually violent, and violent media: Effects of multiple naturalistic exposures and debriefing on female viewers*. Unpublished doctoral dissertation, University of Wisconsin-Madison.

Kresin, D. (1993). Medical aspects of inhibited sexual desire disorder. In W. O'Donohue & J. H. Geer (Eds.), *Handbook of sexual dysfunctions: Assessment and treatment* (pp. 15–52). Boston: Allyn & Bacon.

Kruks, G. (1991). Gay and lesbian homeless/street youth: Special issues and concerns [Special issue: Homeless youth]. *Journal of Adolescent Health*, *12*, 515–518.

Kuhn, D., et al. (1978). Sex-role concepts of two- and three-year olds. *Child Development*, *49*, 445–451.

Kuiper, B., & Cohen-Kettenis, P. (1988). Sex reassignment surgery: A study of 141 Dutch transsexuals. *Archives of Sexual Behavior*, *17*, 439–457.

Kulin, H., et al. (1989). The onset of sperm production in pubertal boys. *American Journal of Diseases of Children*, *143*, 190–193.

Laan, E., & Heiman, J. (1994). *Archives of Sexual Behavior*.

Lackie, L., & deMan, A. F. (1997). Correlations of sexual aggression among male university students. *Sex Roles*, *37*, 451–457.

Lackritz, E. M., et al. (1995). Estimated risk of transmission of the human immunodeficiency virus by screened blood in the United States. *New England Journal of Medicine*, *333*, 1721–1725.

Lamanna, M. A., & Riedmann, A. (1997). Marriages and families, 6th ed. Belmont, CA: Wadsworth.

Lamaze, F. (1981). *Painless childbirth*. New York: Simon & Schuster.

Lamke, L. K. (1982). The impact of sex-role orientation on self-esteem in early adolescence. *Child Development*, *53*, 1530–1535.

Lang, R. A., et al. (1989). An examination of sex hormones in genital exhibitionists. *Annals of Sex Research*, *2*, 67–75.

Langevin, R., et al. (1985). Sexual aggression: Constructing a predictive equation. In R. Langevin (Ed.), *Erotic preference, gender identity, and aggression in men: New research studies* (pp. 39–76). Hillsdale, NJ: Erlbaum.

Langevin, R., et al. (1989). Characteristics of sex offenders who were sexually victimized as children. *Annals of Sex Research*, *2*, 227–253.

LaTour, M. S. (1990). Female nudity in print advertising: An analysis of gender differences in arousal and ad response. *Psychology and Marketing*, *7*, 65–81.

Laumann, E. O., et al. (1994). *The social organization of sexuality: Sexual practices in the United States*. Chicago: University of Chicago Press.

Laviola, M. (1989). Effects of older brother–younger sister incest: A review of four cases. *Journal of Family Violence*, *4*, 259–274.

Lavoisier, P., et al. (1995). Clitoral blood flow increases following vaginal pressure stimulation. *Archives of Sexual Behavior*, *24*, 37–45.

Lawrence, K., & Herold, E. S. (1988). Women's attitudes toward and experience with sexually explicit materials. *Journal of Sex Research*, *24*, 161–169.

Leary, W. E. (1990, September 13). New focus on sperm brings fertility successes. *The New York Times*, p. B11.

Leary, W. E. (1992, December 10). Medical panel says most sexual impotence in men can be treated without surgery. *The New York Times*, p. D20.

Leary, W. E. (1993, April 28). Screening of all newborns urged for sickle cell disease. *The New York Times*, p. C11.

LeBourdais, C., et al. (2000). *The changing face of conjugal relationships. Canadian Social Trends*. Ottawa: Statistics Canada, Cat. No. 11-008.

Ledray, L. E. (1990). Counseling rape victims: The nursing challenge. *Perspectives in Psychiatric Care*, *26*, 21–27.

Lee, J. A. (1988). Love-styles. In R. J. Sternberg & M. L. Barnes (Eds.), The psychology of love (pp. 38–67). New Haven: Yale University Press.

Leiblum, S. R., & Rosen, R. C. (1988). *Sexual Desire Disorders*. New York: Guilford Press.

Léger Marketing. (2002). Canadians and immorality. Available as PDF at **www.legermarketing.com/documents/spclm/020218eng.pdf**.

Léger Marketing, (2003, June 21). Canadian perceptions of homosexuality. Accessed from PDF at **www.legermarketing.com/eng/tencan.asp**.

Leiblum, S. R., & Rosen, R. C. (1991). Couples therapy for erectile disorders: Conceptual and clinical considerations [Special issue: The treatment of male erectile disorders]. *Journal of Sex and Marital Therapy*, *17*, 147–159.

Leigh, B. C., et al. (1994). Sexual behavior of American adolescents: Results from a U.S. national survey. *Journal of Adolescent Health*, *15* (2) 117–125.

Leitenberg, H., & Henning, K. (1995). Sexual fantasy. *Psychological Bulletin*, *117*, 469–496.

Leitenberg, H., et al. (1989). The relation between sexual activity among children during preadolescence and/or early adolescence and sexual behavior and sexual adjustment in young adulthood. *Archives of Sexual Behavior*, *18*, 299–313.

Leitenberg, H., et al. (1993). Gender differences in masturbation and the relation of masturbation experience in preadolescence and/or early adolescence to sexual behavior and sexual adjustment in young adulthood. *Archives of Sexual Behavior*, *22*, 87–98.

Lemon, S. J., & Newbold, J. E. (1990). Viral hepatitis. In K. K. Holmes, et al. (Eds.), *Sexually transmitted diseases* (2nd ed.) (pp. 449–466). New York: McGraw-Hill.

Lenihan, G., et al. (1992). Gender differences in rape supportive attitudes before and after a date rape education intervention. *Journal of College Student Development, 33,* 331–338.

Lesnik-Oberstein, M., & Cohen, L. (1984). Cognitive style, sensation seeking, and assortive mating. *Journal of Personality and Social Psychology, 46,* 57–66.

Letourneau, E., & O'Donohue, W. (1993). Sexual desire disorders. In W. O'Donohue & J. H. Geer (Eds.), *Handbook of sexual dysfunctions: Assessment and treatment* (pp. 53–81). Boston: Allyn & Bacon.

LeVay, S. (1991). A difference in hypothalamic structure between heterosexual and homosexual men. *Science, 253,* 1034–1037.

Lever, J., et al. (1992). Behavior patterns and sexual identity of bisexual males. *Journal of Sex Research, 29,* 141–167.

Levine, G. I. (1991). Sexually transmitted parasitic diseases. *Primary Care: Clinics in Office Practice, 18,* 101–128.

Levinger, G. (1980). Toward the analysis of close relationships. *Journal of Experimental Social Psychology, 16,* 510–544.

Levy, D. S. (1991, September 16). Why Johnny might grow up violent and sexist. *Time,* 16–19.

Levy, J. (1985). Right brain, left brain: Fact and fiction. *Psychology Today, 19*(5), 38–44.

Lewin, T. (1991, February 8). Studies on teen-age sex cloud condom debate. *The New York Times,* p. A14.

Libman, E., et al. (1985). The role of therapeutic format in the treatment of sexual dysfunction: A review. *Clinical Psychology Review, 5,* 103–117.

Lief, H. I., & Hubschman, L. (1993). Orgasm in the postoperative transsexual. *Archives of Sexual Behavior, 22,* 145–155.

Linet, O. I., & Ogrinc, F. G. (1996). Efficacy and safety of intracavernosal alprostadil in men with erectile dysfunction. *New England Journal of Medicine, 334,* 873–877.

Linsley, W. A. (1989). The case against censorship of pornography. In D. Zillmann & J. Bryant (Eds.), *Pornography: Research advances and policy considerations* (pp. 343–359). Hillsdale, NJ: Erlbaum.

Linz, D. (1989). Exposure to sexually explicit materials and attitudes toward rape: A comparison of study results. *Journal of Sex Research, 26,* 50–84.

Linz, D., et al. (1988). The effects of long-term exposure to violent and sexually degrading depictions of women. *Journal of Personality and Social Psychology, 55,* 758–767.

Lipschultz, L. I. (1996). Injection therapy for erectile dysfunction. *New England Journal of Medicine, 334,* 913–914.

Lisak, D. (1991). Sexual aggression, masculinity, and fathers. *Signs, 16,* 238–262.

Lohr, J. (1989). The foreskin and urinary tract infections. *Journal of Pediatrics, 114,* 502–504.

Longmore, M., et al. (2001). Preadolescent parenting strategies and teens' dating and sexual initiation: A longitudinal analysis. *Journal of Marriage and Family, 63,* 322–335.

LoPiccolo, J. (1994). The evolution of sex therapy. *Sexual and Marital Therapy, 9*(1), 5–7.

LoPiccolo, J., & Friedman, J. (1988). Broad-spectrum treatment of low sexual desire: Integration of cognitive, behavioral, and systemic therapy. In S. Leiblum & R. Rosen (Eds.), *Sexual desire disorders.* New York: Guilford Press.

LoPiccolo, J., & Stock, W. E. (1986). Treatment of sexual dysfunction. *Journal of Consulting and Clinical Psychology, 54,* 158–167.

Lorefice, L. S. (1991). Fluoxetine treatment of a fetish. *Journal of Clinical Psychiatry, 52.*

Lottes, I. L., & Kuriloff, P. J. (1992). The effects of gender, race, religion, and political orientation on the sex role attitudes of college freshmen. *Adolescence, 27,* 675–688.

Lovdal, L. T. (1989). Sex role messages in television commercials: An update. *Sex Roles, 21,* 715–724.

Lown, J., & Dolan, E. (1988). Financial challenges in remarriage. *Lifestyles: Family and Economic Issues, 9,* 73–88.

Luckenbill, D. F. (1985). Entering male prostitution. *Urban Life, 14,* 131–153.

Lundstrom, B., et al. (1984). Outcome of sex reassignment surgery. *Acta Psychiatrica Scandinavica, 70,* 289–294.

Maccoby, E. E. (1990). Gender and relationships: A developmental account. *American Psychologist, 45,* 513–520.

Maccoby, E. E., & Jacklin, C. N. (1974). *The psychology of sex differences.* Stanford, CA: Stanford University Press.

MacFarquhar, N. (1996, August 8). Mutilation of Egyptian girls: Despite ban, it goes on. *The New York Times,* p. A3.

MacMillan, H. L., et al. (1996a). Aboriginal health. *Canadian Medical Association Journal, 155,* 1569–1598. http://www.cma.ca.

MacMillan, H. L., et al. (1996b). Relationship between history of childhood maltreatment and psychiatric disorder in a community sample: Results from the Ontario Health Supplement. International Family Violence Research Conference, Durham, NH.

MacNeil, S., & Byers, E. S. (1997). The relationships between sexual problems, communication and sexual satisfaction. *The Canadian Journal of Human Sexuality, 6,* 277–284.

Malamuth, N. M. (1981). Rape proclivity among males. *Journal of Social Issues, 37,* 138–157.

Malamuth, N. M. (1984). Aggression against women: Cultural and individual causes. In N. M. Malamuth & E. Donnerstein (Eds.), *Pornography and sexual aggression* (pp. 19–52). Orlando, FL: Academic Press.

Malamuth, N. M., & Ceniti, J. (1986). Repeated exposure to violent and nonviolent pornography: Likelihood of raping ratings and laboratory aggression against women. *Aggressive Behavior, 12,* 129–137.

Male birth control. (1995, August 1). *New York Newsday,* p. B31.

Maletzky, B. M. (1980). Self-referred vs. court-referred sexually deviant patients: Success with assisted covert sensitization. *Behavior Therapy, 11,* 306–314.

Malinowski, B. (1929). *The sexual life of savages in north-western Melanesia.* New York: Eugenics.

Malloy, M. H., et al. (1992). Sudden infant death syndrome and maternal smoking. *American Journal of Public Health, 82,* 1380–1382.

Manson, J. E., et al. (2003). Estrogen plus progestin and the risk of coronary heart disease. *The New England Journal of Medicine, 349,* 523–534. Accessed from PDF at **www.sogc. org/sogcnet/pdfs/ hormono1 pdf.pdf**, August 20, 2003.

Marchbanks, P., et al. (1988). Risk factors for ectopic pregnancy. *Journal of the American Medical Association, 259,* 1823–1827.

Marchbanks, P. A., et al. (2002). Oral contraceptives and the risk of breast cancer. *The New England Journal of Medicine, 346,* 2025–2032. Available online at **http:// content.nejm.org/cgi/content/short/3 46/26/2025.**

Margolin, L., et al. (1989). When a kiss is not just a kiss: Relating violations on consent in kissing to rape myth acceptance. *Sex Roles, 20,* 231–243.

Marks, G., et al. (1981). Effect of targets' physical attractiveness on assumption of similarity. *Journal of Personality and Social Psychology, 41,* 198–206.

Marshall, W. L. (1989). Pornography and sex offenders. In D. Zillmann & J. Bryant (Eds.), *Pornography: Research advances and policy considerations* (pp. 185–214). Hillsdale, NJ: Erlbaum.

Marshall, W. L., et al. (1991). Treatment outcome with sex offenders. *Clinical Psychology Review, 11*, 465–485.

Marsiglio, W. (1993a). Adolescent males' orientation toward paternity and contraception. *Family Planning Perpectives, 25*, 22–31.

Marsiglio, W. (1993b). Attitudes toward homosexual activity and gays as friends: A national survey of heterosexual 15- to 19-year-old males. *Journal of Sex Research, 30*, 12–17.

Martin, C. L., & Halverson, C. F., Jr. (1981). A schematic processing model of sex typing and stereotyping in children. *Child Development, 54*, 1119–1134.

Martin, D. H. (1990). Chlamydial infections. *Medical Clinics of North America, 74*, 1367–1387.

Martin, K., & Wu, Z. (2000, March). Contraceptive use in Canada: 1984–1995. *Family Planning Perspectives, 32*(2), 65–73.

Martinez, F. D., et al. (1992). Increased incidence of asthma in children of smoking mothers. *Pediatrics, 89*, 21–26.

Martinson, F. M. (1976). Eroticism in infancy and childhood. *The Journal of Sex Research, 2*, 251–262.

Mason, R. T., et al. (1989). Sex pheromones in snakes. *Science, 245*, 290–293.

Masters, W. H., & Johnson, V. E. (1966). *Human sexual response.* Boston: Little, Brown.

Masters, W. H., & Johnson, V. E. (1970). *Human sexual inadequacy.* Boston: Little, Brown.

Masters, W. H., & Johnson, V. E. (1979). *Homosexuality in perspective.* Boston: Little, Brown.

Matek, O. (1988). Obscene phone callers. *Journal of Social Work and Human Sexuality, 7*, 113–130.

Maticka-Tyndale, E. (1997). Reducing the incidence of sexually transmitted diseases through behavioural and social change. *Canadian Journal of Human Sexuality, 6*, 89–105.

Maticka-Tyndale, E. (2001). Sexual health and Canadian youth: How do we measure up? *Canadian Journal of Human Sexuality, 10*, 1–18.

Matthews, K. A., et al. (1990). Influences of natural menopause on psychological characteristics and symptoms of middle-aged healthy women. *Journal of Consulting and Clinical Psychology, 58*, 345–351.

Maybach, K. L., & Gold, S. R. (1994). Hyperfemininity and attraction to macho and non-macho men. *Journal of Sex Research, 31*(2), 91–98.

Mayer, J. P., et al. (1990). A randomized evaluation of smoking cessation interventions for pregnant women at a WIC [women, infants, and children] clinic. *American Journal of Public Health, 80*, 76–79.

McArthur, M. J. (1990). Reality therapy with rape victims. *Archives of Psychiatric Nursing, 4*, 360–365.

McConaghy, M. J. (1979). Gender performance and the genital basis of gender: Stages in the development of constancy of gender. *Child Development, 50*, 1223–1226.

McGuire, R. J., et al. (1965). Sexual deviation as conditioned behavior: A hypothesis. *Behaviour Research and Therapy, 2*, 185–190.

McKay, A., et al. (1998). Parents' opinions and attitudes towards sexuality education in the schools. *Canadian Journal of Human Sexuality, 6*, 139–146.

McKay, A., & Holowaty, P. (1997). Sexual health education: A study of adolescents' opinions, self-perceived needs and current and preferred sources of information. *Canadian Journal of Human Sexuality, 6*, 29–38.

McKenzie, S. (2003). Unpublished data.

McKenzie, S. (2004). Unpublished data.

McLaren, J., & Brown, R. E. (1989). Childhood problems associated with abuse and neglect. *Canada's Mental Health, 37*(3), 1–6.

McMahon, M. J., et al. (1996). Comparison of a trial of labor with an elective second cesarean section. *The New England Journal of Medicine, 335*, 689–695.

Mead, M. (1935). *Sex and temperament in three primitive societies.* New York: Dell.

Mead, M. (1967). *Male and female: A study of the sexes in a changing world.* New York: Morrow.

Meana, M., et al. (1997). Dyspareunia: Sexual dysfunction or pain syndrome? *Journal of Nervous and Mental Disease, 185*, 561–569.

Meana, M., & Binik, Y. M. (1994). Painful coitus: A review of female dyspareunia. *Journal of Nervous and Mental Disease, 182*(5), 264–272.

Meiselman, K. C. (1978). *Incest: A psychological study of causes and effects with treatment recommendations.* San Francisco: Jossey-Bass.

Meisler, A. W., & Carey, M. P. (1990). A critical reevaluation of nocturnal penile tumescence monitoring in the diagnosis of erectile dysfunction. *Journal of Nervous and Mental Disease, 178*, 78–89.

Mertz, G. J., et al. (1992). Risk factors for the sexual transmission of genital herpes. *Annals of Internal Medicine, 116*, 197–202.

Messenger, J. C. (1971). Sex and repression in an Irish folk community. In D. S. Marshall and R. C. Suggs (Eds.), *Human sexual behavior: Variations in the ethnographic spectrum* (pp. 3–37). New York: Basic Books.

Meston, C. M., & Frohlich, P. F. (2000). The neurobiology of sexual function. *Archives of General Psychology, 57*, 1012–1030.

Meston, C. M., & Gorzalka, B. B. (1992). Psychoactive drugs and human sexual behavior: The role of serotonergic activity. *Journal of Psychoactive Drugs, 24*, 1–40.

Meston, C. M., & Gorzalka, B. B. (1995). The effects of sympathetic activation on physiological and subjective sexual arousal in women. *Behaviour Research and Therapy 33*, 651–664.

Meston, C. M., et al. (1996). Ethnic and gender differences in sexuality: Variations in sexual behaviour between Asian and non-Asian university students. *Archives of Sexual Behavior, 25*, 33–72.

Meuwissen, I., & Over, R. (1990). Habituation and dishabituation of female sexual arousal. *Behaviour Research and Therapy, 28*, 217–226.

Meyer-Bahlburg, H. F. L., et al. (1995). Prenatal estrogens and the development of homosexual orientation. *Developmental Psychology, 31*(1), 12–21.

Michael, R. T., et al. (1994). *Sex in America: A definitive survey.* Boston: Little, Brown.

Milan, A. (2000). *One hundred years of families. Canadian Social Trends.* Ottawa: Statistics Canada, Cat. No. 11-008.

Miller, A. B., et al. (2000). Canadian national breast screening study-2: 13-year results of a randomized trial in women aged 50–59 years. *Journal of the National Cancer Institute, 92*, 1490–1499.

Miller, B. C., & Bingham, C. R. (1989). Family configuration in relation to the sexual behavior of female adolescents. *Journal of Marriage and the Family, 51*, 499–506.

Miller, B. C., et al. (1986). Dating age and stage as correlates of adolescent sexual attitudes and behavior. *Journal of Adolescent Research, 1*, 361–371.

Miller, B. C., et al. (1997). The timing of sexual intercourse among adolescents: Family, peer, and other antecedents. *Youth and Society, 29*, 55–83.

Miller, D. (1995). Personal communication.

Miller, S. M., et al. (1996). Applying cognitive–social theory to health-protective behavior: Breast self-examination in cancer screening. *Psychological Bulletin, 199,* 70–94.

Mills, J. L. (1995). Protecting the embryo from X-rated drugs. *New England Journal of Medicine, 333,* 124–125.

Minai, N. (1981). *Women in Islam: Tradition and transition in the Middle East.* London: John Murray.

Mishell, D. R., Jr. (1989). Medical progress: Contraception. *New England Journal of Medicine, 320,* 777–787.

Mohr, D. C., & Beutler, L. E. (1990). Erectile dysfunction: A review of diagnostic and treatment procedures. *Clinical Psychology Review, 10,* 123–150.

Moi, H., et al. (1989). Should male consorts of women with bacterial vaginosis be treated? *Genitourinary Medicine, 65,* 263–268.

Money, J. (1987a). Sin, sickness or status—Homosexual gender identity and psychoneuroendocrinology. *American Psychologist, 42,* 384–399.

Money, J. (1987b). Treatment guidelines: Antiandrogen and counseling of paraphiliac sex offenders. *Journal of Sex and Marital Therapy, 13,* 219–223.

Money, J. (1988). *Gay, straight, and in-between.* New York: Oxford University Press.

Money, J. (1990). Agenda and credenda of the Kinsey Scale. In D. P. McWhirter, et al. (Eds.), *Homosexuality/heterosexuality: Concepts of sexual orientation* (pp. 41–60). New York: Oxford University Press.

Money, J. (1994). The concept of gender identity disorder in childhood and adolescence after 39 years. *Journal of Sex and Marital Therapy, 20*(3), 163–177.

Money, J., & Ehrhardt, A. (1972). *Man and woman, boy and girl.* Baltimore: Johns Hopkins University Press.

Money, J., & Lamacz, M. (1989). *Vandalized lovemaps.* Buffalo, NY: Prometheus Books.

Money, J., & Wiedeking, C. (1980). Gender identity/role: Normal differentiation and its transpositions. In B. Wolman & J. Money (Eds.), *Handbook of human sexuality* (pp. 269–284). Englewood Cliffs, NJ: Prentice-Hall.

Money, J., et al. (1984). Micropenis: Adult follow-up and comparison of size against new norms. *Journal of Sex and Marital Therapy, 10,* 105–116.

Montreal Health Press. (1999). *Birth Control Handbook. 30th Anniversary Edition.* Montreal: author.

Morokoff, P. J. (1993). Female sexual arousal disorder. In W. Donohue and J. H. Greer (Eds.), *Handbook of sexual dysfunctions: Assessment and treatment* (pp. 157–199). Boston: Allyn & Bacon.

Morrison, B. (1994). Screening for breast cancer. In: Canadian Task Force on Preventive Health Care, *The Canadian guide to clinical preventive health care.* Ottawa: Canada Communication Group, 787–795.

Morse, E., et al. (1992). Sexual behavior patterns of customers of male street prostitutes. *Archives of Sexual Behavior, 21,* 347.

Mosher, W. D., & Bachrach, C. A. (1987). First premarital contraceptive use. *Studies in Family Planning, 18,* 83.

Motiuk, L. K., & Porporino, F. J. (1993, April). Examen des antécédents des agresseurs sexuels dans les établissements correctionnels fédéraux. Service correctionnel du Canada.

Muehlenhard, C. L., & Falcon, P. L. (1990). Men's heterosocial skill and attitudes toward women as predictors of verbal sexual coercion and forceful rape. *Sex Roles, 23,* 241–259.

Mueser, K. T., et al. (1984). You're only as pretty as you feel: Facial expression as a determinant of physical attractiveness. *Journal of Personality and Social Psychology, 46,* 469–478.

Murstein, B. I. (1988). A taxonomy of love. In R. J. Sternberg & M. L. Barnes (Eds.), *The psychology of love* (pp. 13–37). New Haven: Yale University Press.

Muster, N. J. (1992). Treating the adolescent victim-turned-offender. *Adolescence, 27,* 441–450.

Myers, T., et al. (1993). *The Canadian survey of gay and bisexual men and HIV infection: Men's survey.* Ottawa, ON: Canadian AIDS Society.

Myers, T., et al. (1999). Gay and bisexual men's sexual partnerships and variations in risk behaviour. *Canadian Journal of Human Sexuality, 8,* 115–126.

Nakanishi, M. (1986). Perceptions of self-disclosure in initial interaction: A Japanese sample. *Human Communication Research, 13,* 167–190.

National Academy of Sciences, Institute of Medicine. (1982). *Marijuana and health.* Washington, DC: National Academy Press.

National Cancer Institute of Canada. (2000). *Canadian cancer statistics, 2000.* Toronto: author.

National Cancer Institute of Canada. (2003). *Canadian Cancer Statistics 2003,* Toronto, Canada, 2003. Accessed from PDF at **www.ncic.cancer.ca/ncic/ internet/standard/0,3621,84658243_85787780__langI d-en,00.html,** August 16, 2003.

National Council of Welfare. (1997). *Healthy parents, healthy babies.* Accessed from **www.ncwcnbes.net/htmdocument/repo rtparenthealth/rephealthyparents.htm,** December 31, 2003.

National Research Council. (1993). *Losing generations: Adolescents in high risk settings.* Washington, DC: National Academy Press.

Nelson, K. E. (1996). Changes in sexual behavior and a decline in HIV infection among young men in Thailand. *New England Journal of Medicine, 335,* 297–303.

Nevid, J. S., (1984). Sex differences in factors of romantic attraction. *Sex Roles, 11,* 401–411.

Nevid, J. S. et al. (2000). *Abnormal psychology in a changing world* (4th ed.). Upper Saddle River, NJ: Prentice Hall.

NFO Cfgroup. (2003, September 5). Canadians split on same-sex marriage: poll. Accessed from PDF at **www.nfocfgroup.com/news/news.html #news_items.**

NGOs sceptical about discussions on Hudood law. (2003). *Dawn,* March 23, 2003, **www. dawn.com/2003/03/26/nat18.htm.**

Nichols, M. (1990). Lesbian relationships: Implications for the study of sexuality and gender. In D. P. McWhirter, et al. (Eds.), *Homosexuality/heterosexuality: Concepts of sexual orientation* (pp. 350–364). New York: Oxford University Press.

Nichols, M. (2000). Therapy with sexual minorities. In S. R. Leiblum and R. Rosen (Eds.), *Principles and Practice of Sex Therapy,* Third Edition (pp. 335–367). New York: The Guilford Press.

Nock, S. L. (1995). A comparison of marriages and cohabiting relationships. *Journal of Family Issues, 16*(1), 53–76.

Nosek, M. A., et al. (1994). Wellness models and sexuality among women with physical disabilities. *Journal of Applied Rehabilitation Counseling, 25*(1), 50–58.

Ochs, R. (1994, January 11). Cervical cancer comeback. *New York Newsday,* pp. 55, 57.

O'Donohue, W., et al. (1993). Premature ejaculation. In W. O'Donohue & J. H. Geer (Eds.), *Handbook of sexual dysfunctions: Assessment and treatment* (pp. 303–333). Boston: Allyn & Bacon.

O'Hara, M. W., et al. (1984). Prospective study of postpartum depression: Prevalence, course, and predictive factors. *Journal of Abnormal Psychology, 93,* 158–171.

O'Hara, M. W., et al. (1991). Prospective study of postpartum blues: Biological and psychosocial factors. *Archives of General Psychiatry, 48,* 801–806.

Okami, P., & Goldberg, A. (1992). Personality correlates of pedophilia: Are they reliable indicators? *Journal of Sex Research, 29,* 297–328.

Okami, P., & Shackelford, T. (2001). Human sex differences in sexual psychology and behavior. *Annual Review of Sex Research, 12,* 186–241.

Osborne, N. G., & Adelson, M. D. (1990). Herpes simplex and human papillomavirus genital infections: Controversy over obstetric management. *Clinical Obstetrics and Gynecology, 33*, 801–811.

Overholser, J. C., & Beck, S. (1986). Multimethod assessment of rapists, child molesters, and three control groups on behavioral and psychological measures. *Journal of Consulting and Clinical Psychology, 54*, 682–687.

Padesky, C. (1988). Attaining and maintaining positive lesbian self-identity: A cognitive therapy approach. *Women and Therapy, 8*, 145–156.

Padgett, V. R., et al. (1989). Pornography, erotica, and attitudes toward women: The effects of repeated exposure. *Journal of Sex Research, 26*, 479–491.

Palace, E. M. (1995). Modification of dysfunctional patterns of sexual arousal through autonomic arousal and false physiological feedback. *Journal of Consulting and Clinical Psychology, 63*, 604–615.

Panel says Pap tests could almost end cervical cancer deaths. (April 4, 1996). *The New York Times*, p. A18.

Parrinder, G. (1966). *Sexual morality in the world's religions*. Oxford, England: Oneworld.

Patrick, D. M., et al. (2000). Sexually transmitted infections: Recent resurgence threatens national goals. *Canadian Journal of Human Sexuality, 9*, 149–165.

Pauly, B., & Edgerton, M. (1986). The gender-identity movement. *Archives of Sexual Behavior, 15*, 315–329.

Pauly, I. B. (1974). Female transsexualism: Part 1. *Archives of Sexual Behavior, 3*, 487–508.

Peckham, C., & Gibb, D. (1995). Mother-to-child transmission of the human immunodeficiency virus. *New England Journal of Medicine, 333*, 298–302.

Penn, F. (1993, October 21). Cancer confusion: The risks and realities of human papilloma virus. *Manhattan Spirit*, pp. 14–15.

Peplau, L. A., & Cochran, S. D. (1990). A relationship perspective on homosexuality. In D. P. McWhirter, et al. (Eds.), *Homosexuality/heterosexuality: Concepts of sexual orientation* (pp. 321–349). New York: Oxford University Press.

Perduta-Fulginiti, P. S. (1992). Sexual functioning of women with complete spinal cord injury: Nursing implications [Special issue: Nursing roles and perspectives]. *Sexuality and Disability, 10*, 103–118.

Perrett, D. I. (1994). Nature. Cited in Brody, J. E. (1994, March 21). Notions of beauty transcend culture, new study suggests. *The New York Times*, p. A14.

Perry, D. G., & Bussey, K. (1979). The social learning theory of sex differences: Imitation is alive and well. *Journal of Personality and Social Psychology, 37*, 1699–1712.

Perry, J. D., & Whipple, B. (1981). Pelvic muscle strength of female ejaculation: Evidence in support of a new theory of orgasm. *Journal of Sex Research, 17*, 22–39.

Person, E. S., et al. (1989). Gender differences in sexual behaviors and fantasies in a college population. *Journal of Sex and Marital Therapy, 15*, 187–198.

Piasecna, M. A., et al. (2001). Longitudinal patterns of sexual behavior and condom use in a cohort of HIV-negative gay and bisexual men in Vancouver, British Columbia, Canada, 1995–2000. *Journal of Acquired Immune Deficiency Syndromes, 28*, 187–193.

Pillard, R. C. (1990). The Kinsey Scale: Is it familial? In D. P. McWhirter, et al. (Eds.), *Homosexuality/heterosexuality: Concepts of sexual orientation* (pp. 88–100). New York: Oxford University Press.

Pillard, R. C., & Weinrich, J. D. (1986). Evidence of familial nature of male homosexuality. *Archives of Sexual Behavior, 43*, 808–812.

Pines, A., & Aronson, E. (1983). Antecedents, correlates, and consequences of sexual jealousy. *Journal of Personality, 51*, 108–109.

Pinkerton, S., et al. (2002). Factors associated with masturbation in a collegiate sample. *Journal of Psychology and Human Sexuality, 14*, 103–121.

Population Council. (1995). Cited in Brody, J. E. (1995, August 31). Abortion method using two drugs gains in a study. *The New York Times*, pp. A1, B12.

Porter, N., et al. (1985). Androgyny and leadership in mixed-sex groups. *Journal of Personality and Social Psychology, 49*, 808–823.

Powderly, W. G., et al. (1995). A randomized trial comparing fluconazole with clotrimazole troches for the prevention of fungal infections in patients with advanced human immunodeficiency virus infection. *New England Journal of Medicine, 332*, 700–705.

Powell, E. (1991). *Talking back to sexual pressure*. Minneapolis: CompCare Publications.

Powell, E. (1996). *Sex on your terms*. Boston: Allyn & Bacon.

Prentky, R. A., & Knight, R. A. (1991). Identifying critical dimensions for discriminating among rapists. *Journal of Consulting and Clinical Psychology, 59*, 643–661.

Price, M., et al. (2002). Telephone scatologia comorbidity with other paraphilias and paraphilia-related disorders. *International Journal of Law and Psychiatry, 25*, 37–49.

Price, V. A. (1989). Characteristics and needs of Boston street youth: One agency's response [Special issue: Runaway, homeless, and shut-out children and youth in Canada, Europe, and the United States]. *Children and Youth Services Review, 11*, 75–90.

Proctor, F., et al. (1974). The differentiation of male and female orgasm: An experimental study. In N. Wagner (Ed.), *Perspectives on human sexuality*. New York: Behavioral Publications.

Prostate Cancer Research Foundation of Canada. (2000). Scientific facts. News and Facts. **http://www.prostatecancer.on.ca/news/facts/html**.

Purifoy, F. E., et al. (1992). The relationship of sexual daydreaming to sexual activity, sexual drive, and sexual attitudes for women across the life-span. *Archives of Sexual Behavior, 21*, 369–375.

Quadagno, D., et al. (1991). Women at risk for human immunodeficiency virus. *Journal of Psychology and Human Sexuality, 4*, 97–110.

Quevillon, R. P. (1993). Dyspareunia. In W. O'Donohue & J. H. Geer (Eds.), *Handbook of sexual dysfunctions: Assessment and treatment* (pp. 367–380). Boston: Allyn & Bacon.

Quinsey, V. L., et al. (1984). Sexual arousal to nonsexual violence and sadomasochistic themes among rapists and non-sex-offenders. *Journal of Consulting and Clinical Psychology, 52*, 651–657.

Radlove, S. (1983). Sexual response and gender roles. In E. R. Allgeier & N. B. McCormick (Eds.), *Changing boundaries: Gender roles and sexual behavior*. Palo Alto, CA: Mayfield.

Rajfer, J., et al. (1992). Nitric oxide as a mediator of relaxation of the corpus cavernosum in response to nonadrenergic, noncholinergic neurotransmission. *New England Journal of Medicine, 326*, 90–94.

Rathus, S. A. (1978). Treatment of recalcitrant ejaculatory incompetence. *Behavior Therapy, 9*, 962.

Rathus, S. A., & Fichner-Rathus, L. (1994). *Making the most of college* (2nd ed.). Englewood Cliffs, NJ: Prentice-Hall.

Ratican, K. L. (1992). Sexual abuse survivors: Identifying symptoms and special treatment considerations. *Journal of Counseling and Development, 71*, 33–38.

Reichart, C. A., et al. (1990). Evaluation of Abbott Testpack Chlamydia for detection of chlamydia trachomatis in patients attending sexually transmitted diseases clinics. *Sexually Transmitted Diseases, 17,* 147–151.

Rein, M. F., & Muller, M. (1990). Trichomonas vaginalis and trichomoniasis. In K. K. Holmes, et al. (Eds.), *Sexually transmitted diseases* (2nd ed.) (pp. 481–492). New York: McGraw-Hill.

Reinisch, J. M. (1990). *The Kinsey Institute new report on sex: What you must know to be sexually literate.* New York: St. Martin's Press.

Reiss, B. F. (1988, Spring/Summer). The long-lived person and sexuality. *Dynamic Psychotherapy, 6,* 79–86.

Reiss, I. L. (1980). *Family systems in America.* New York: Holt, Rinehart & Winston.

Renaud, C. A., & Byers, E. S. (1999). Exploring the frequency, diversity and content of university students' positive and negative sexual cognitions. *Canadian Journal of Human Sexuality, 8,* 17–30. Accessed from ProQuest database, August 15, 2003.

Renzetti, C. M., & Curran, D. J. (1989). *Women, men, and society: The sociology of gender.* Boston: Allyn & Bacon.

Resick, P. A., & Schnicke, M. K. (1990). Treating symptoms in adult victims of sexual assault. *Journal of Interpersonal Violence, 5,* 488–506.

Reuter. (1996, September 18). The RU-486 abortion pill got a tentative seal of approval. America Online.

Reuters. (2000, June 20). A woman's life in Iran unbearable for transsexual. *The Gazette* (Montreal), p. 36.

Ricci, E., et al. (2000). Caesarian section and antiretroviral treatment. *The Lancet, 355,* 496.

Rice, M. E., et al. (1990). A follow-up of rapists assessed in a maximum-security psychiatric facility. *Journal of Interpersonal Violence, 5,* 435–448.

Rice, M. E., et al. (1991). Sexual recidivism among child molesters released from a maximum security psychiatric institution. *Journal of Consulting and Clinical Psychology, 59,* 381–386.

Richardson, H., et al. (2000). Determinants of low risk and high risk human papilloma virus infections in Montreal university students. *Sexually Transmitted Diseases 27,* 79–86.

Rickwood, A. M. K., et al. (2000). Towards evidence based circumcision of English boys: Survey of trends in practice. *British Medical Journal, 321,* 792–793.

Riggio, R. E., & Woll, S. B. (1984). The role of nonverbal cues and physical attrac-tiveness in the selection of dating partners. *Journal of Social and Personal Relationships, 1,* 347–357.

Robert Koch Institut, Berlin. (2000). **http://www.rki.de/GESUND/ARCHIV/IES/CHINA.HTM**

Roberto, L. G. (1983). Issues in diagnosis and treatment of transsexualism. *Archives of Sexual Behavior, 12,* 445–473.

Rodgers, K. (1994). Wife assault: The findings of a national survey. *Juristat, 14*(6). Ottawa: Canadian Centre for Justice Statistics.

Roland, B., et al. (1989). MMPI correlates of college women who reported experiencing child/adult sexual contact with father, stepfather, or with other persons. *Psychological Reports, 64,* 1159–1162.

Rolfs, R. T., et al. (1990). Risk factors for syphilis: Cocaine use and prostitution. *American Journal of Public Health, 80,* 853–857.

Romenesko, K., & Miller, E. M. (1989). The second step in double jeopardy: Appropriating the labor of female street hustlers. *Crime and Delinquency, 35,* 109–135.

Roper Organization. (1985). *The Virginia Slims American women's poll.* New York: Author.

Rose, P. G. (1996). Endometrial carcinoma. *New England Journal of Medicine, 335,* 640–649.

Rose, R. J. (1995). Genes and human behavior. *Annual Review of Psychology, 46,* 625–654.

Rosen, I. (1967). *Pathology and treatment of sexual deviations.* London: Oxford University Press.

Rosen, R. C., et al. (1994). Psychologically based treatment for male erectile disorder: A cognitive–interpersonal model. *Journal of Sex and Marital Therapy, 20*(2), 67–85.

Rosenthal, A. M. (1994, September 6). A victory in Cairo. *The New York Times,* p. A19.

Rosenthal, A. M. (1995, June 13). The possible dream. *The New York Times,* p. A25.

Rosenthal, E. (1992, July 22). Her image of his ideal, in a faulty mirror. *The New York Times,* p. C12.

Rosman, J. P., & Resnick, P. J. (1989). Sexual attraction to corpses: A psychiatric review of necrophilia. *Bulletin of the American Academy of Psychiatry and the Law, 17,* 153–163.

Rothblum, E. (2000). Sexual orientation and sex in women's lives: Conceptual and methodological issues. *Journal of Social Issues, 56,* 193–204.

Rotheram-Borus, M. J., et al. (1992). Lifetime sexual behaviors among predominantly minority male runaways and gay/bisexual adolescents in New York City. *AIDS Education and Prevention* (Fall Suppl.), 34–42.

Rovet, J., & Ireland, L. (1994). Behavioral phenotype in children with Turner syndrome. *Journal of Pediatric Psychology, 19,* 779–790.

Roving mates called factor in cancer. (1996, August 7). *The New York Times,* p. A10.

Rozin, P., & Fallon, A. (1988). Body image, attitudes to weight, and misperceptions of figure preferences of the opposite sex: A comparison of men and women in two generations. *Journal of Abnormal Psychology, 97,* 342–345.

Rubinow, D. R., & Schmidt, P. J. (1995). The treatment of premenstrual syndrome—forward into the past. *New England Journal of Medicine, 332,* 1574–1575.

Ruble, D. N., & Ruble, T. L. (1982). Sex stereotypes. In A. G. Miller (Ed.), *In the eye of the beholder: Contemporary issues in stereotyping.* New York: Praeger.

Russell, D. (1982). *Rape in marriage.* New York: Macmillan.

Russo, N. F., Horn, J. D., & Schwartz, R. (1992). U.S. abortion in context: Selected characteristics and motivations of women seeking abortions. *Journal of Social Issues, 48,* 183–202.

Rust, P. C. (2002). Bisexuality: The state of the union. *Annual Review of Sex Research, 13,* 180–240.

Sadalla, E. K., et al. (1987). Dominance and heterosexual attraction. *Journal of Personality and Social Psychology, 52,* 730–738.

Sadker, M., & Sadker, D. (1994). *How America's schools cheat girls.* New York: Scribners.

Sagan, C., & Dryan, A. (1990, April 22). The question of abortion: A search for answers. *Parade Magazine,* 4–8.

St. Stephen's Community House. (2000). *The little black book: A book on healthy sexuality written by grrrls for grrrls.* Toronto: author.

Samuels, M., & Samuels, N. (1986). *The well pregnancy book.* New York: Simon & Schuster.

Sanday, P. R. (1981). The socio-cultural context of rape: A cross-cultural study. *Journal of Social Issues, 37,* 5–27.

Sanders, S. A., et al. (1990). Homosexuality/heterosexuality: An overview. In D. P. McWhirter, et al. (Eds.), *Homosexuality/heterosexuality: Concepts of sexual orientation* (pp. xix–xxvii). New York: Oxford University Press.

Sandfort, T., & de Keizer, M. (2001). Sexual problems in gay men: An overview of empirical research. *Annual Review of Sex Research, 12,* 93–120.

Sargent, T. O. (1988). Fetishism. *Journal of Social Work and Human Sexuality, 7,* 27–42.

Sarrel, P., & Masters, W. (1982). Sexual molestation of men by women. *Archives of Sexual Behavior, 11,* 117–131.

Sawyer, R., et al. (2002). Rape myth acceptance among intercollegiate student athletes: A preliminary examination. *American Journal of Health Studies, 18,* 19–26.

Schachter, J. (1989). Why we need a program for the control of *Chlamydia trachomatis. New England Journal of Medicine, 320,* 802–804.

Schafer, R. B., & Keith, P. M. (1990). Matching by weight in married couples: A life cycle perspective. *Journal of Social Psychology, 130,* 657–664.

Schiavi, R. C., et al. (1990). Healthy aging and male sexual function. *American Journal of Psychiatry, 147,* 766–771.

Schillinger, L. (1995, June 10). More sex please, we're Russian. *The New York Times Book Review,* p. 49.

Schmidt, G. (1994). Sex therapy, 1970–1994. *Nordisk-Sexologi, 12*(3), 178–183.

Schnirer, L. A. J. (1996). Adolescent sexuality in rural Alberta. Unpublished master's thesis, Department of Educational Psychology, University of Alberta, Edmonton, Alberta, Canada.

Schnirer, L. A. J. (2000, April). Late adolescent sexual activity in Alberta. Are they getting the message? Presentation to Moving Beyond Biology—Sexuality in the 21st Century: Fourth Western Canadian Sexual Health Conference, Edmonton, Alberta.

Schoendorf, K. C., & Kiely, J. L. (1992). Relationship of sudden infant death syndrome to maternal smoking during and after pregnancy. *Pediatrics, 90,* 905–908.

Schork, K. (1990, August 19). The despair of Pakistan's women: Not even Benazir Bhutto could stop the repression. *The Washington Post.*

Schott, R. L. (1995). The childhood and family dynamics of transvestites. *Archives of Sexual Behavior, 24,* 309–327.

Schreiber, G. B., et al. (1996). The risk of transfusion-transmitted viral infections. *The New England Journal of Medicine, 334,* 1685–1690.

Schreiner-Engle, P., & Schiavi, R. (1986). Lifetime psychopathology in individuals with low sexual desire. *Journal of Nervous and Mental Disease, 174,* 646–651.

Schreiner-Engle, P., et al. (1989). Low sexual desire in women: The role of reproductive hormones. *Hormones and Behavior, 23,* 221–234.

Schultz, N. R., & Moore, D. W. (1984). Loneliness: Correlates, attributions, and coping among older adults. *Personality and Social Psychology Bulletin, 10,* 67–77.

Schwartz, M. F., & Masters, W. H. (1984). The Masters and Johnson treatment program for dissatisfied homosexual men. *American Journal of Psychiatry, 141,* 173–181.

Scott, J. E., & Schwalm, L. A. (1988). Rape rates and the circulation rates of adult magazines. *Journal of Sex Research, 24,* 241–250.

Seftel, A. D., Oates, R. E., & Krane, R. J. (1991). Disturbed sexual function in patients with spinal cord disease. *Neurologic Clinics, 9,* 757–778.

Segal, Z. V., & Marshall, W. L. (1985). Heterosexual social skills in a population of rapists and child molesters. *Journal of Consulting and Clinical Psychology, 53,* 55–63.

Segraves, R. T. (1988a). Drugs and desire. In S. Leiblum & R. Rosen (Eds.), *Sexual desire disorders.* New York: Guilford Press.

Segraves, R. T. (1988b). Sexual side-effects of psychiatric drugs. *International Journal of Psychiatry in Medicine, 18,* 243–252.

Segraves, R. T., & Segraves, K. B. (1993). Medical aspects of orgasm disorders. In W. O'Donohue & J. H. Geer (Eds.), *Handbook of sexual dysfunctions: Assessment and treatment* (pp. 225–252). Boston: Allyn & Bacon.

Sell, R. (1997). Defining and measuring sexual orientation: A review. *Archives of Sexual Behavior, 26,* 643–658.

Sell, R. L., et al. (1995). The prevalence of homosexual behavior and attraction in the United States, the United Kingdom, and France: Results of national, population-based samples. *Archives of Sexual Behavior, 24,* 235–248.

Sellors, J. W., et al. (2000). Prevalence and predictors of human papilloma virus infection in women in Ontario, Canada. *Canadian Medical Association Journal, 163,* 503–508.

Semans, J. (1956). Premature ejaculation: A new approach. *Southern Medical Journal, 49,* 353–358.

Seng, M. J. (1989). Child sexual abuse and adolescent prostitution: A comparative analysis. *Adolescence, 24,* 665–675.

Serbin, L. A., et al. (2001). Gender stereotyping in infancy: Visual preferences and association of toys with gender in the second year. *International Journal of Behavioral Development, 25*(1), 7–15.

Severn, J., et al. (1990). The effects of sexual and non-sexual advertising appeals and information level on cognitive processing and communication effectiveness. *Journal of Advertising, 19,* 14–22.

Shaffer, D. R., et al. (1999). *Developmental Psychology: Childhood and Adolescence.* 1st Canadian Edition. Toronto: Thomson, Nelson.

Shaver, P., et al. (1988). Love as attachment. In R. J. Sternberg & M. L. Barnes (Eds.), *The psychology of love* (pp. 68–99). New Haven: Yale University Press.

Sheehy, G. (1995). *New passages: Mapping your life across time.* New York: Random House.

Shenon, P. (1995, July 15). New Zealand seeks causes of suicides by young. *The New York Times,* p. A3.

Sheppard, J. A., & Strathman, A. J. (1989). Attractiveness and height: The role of stature in dating preference, frequency of dating, and perceptions of attractiveness. *Personality and Social Psychology Bulletin, 15,* 17–627.

Sherman, K. J., et al. (1990). Sexually transmitted diseases and tubal pregnancy. *Sexually Transmitted Diseases, 17,* 115–121.

Sherman, M. C., et al. (1993). History of circumcision, medical conditions and sexual activity and risk of penile cancer. *Journal of the National Cancer Institute, 85,* 19–24.

Sherwin, B. B., et al. (1985). Androgen enhances sexual motivation in females: A prospective, crossover study of sex steroid administration in the surgical menopause. *Psychosomatic Medicine, 47,* 339–351.

Siegel, J., et al. (1989). Resistance to sexual assault: Who resists and what happens. *American Journal of Public Health, 79,* 27–31.

Signorielli, N., (1990). Children, television, and gender roles: Messages and impact. *Journal of Adolescent Health Care, 11*(1), 50–58.

Signorelli, N., & Kahlenberg, K. (2001). Television's world of work in the nineties. *Journal of Broadcasting and Electronic Media, 45*(1), 4–22.

Silber, S. J. (1991). *How to get pregnant with the new technology.* New York: Time Warner.

Silbert, M. H. (1989). The effects on juveniles of being used for pornography and prostitution. In D. Zillmann & J. Bryant (Eds.), *Pornography: Research advances and policy considerations* (pp. 215–234). Hillsdale, NJ: Erlbaum.

Simpson, J. A., et al. (1986). The association between romantic love and marriage: Kephart (1967) twice revisited. *Personality and Social Psychology Bulletin,* 363–372.

Singer, J., & Singer, I. (1972). Types of female orgasm. *Journal of Sex Research, 8*, 255–267.

Singh, D. (1994a). Body fat distribution and perception of desirable female body shape by young Black men and women. *International Journal of Eating Disorders, 16*(3), 289–294.

Singh, D. (1994b). Is thin really beautiful and good? Relationship between waist-to-hip ratio (WHR) and female attractiveness. *Personality and Individual Differences, 16*(1), 123–132.

Singh, G. K., & Yu, S. M. (1995). Cited in Pear, R. (1995, July 10). Infant mortality rate drops but racial disparity grows. *The New York Times*, p. B9.

Sirles, E. A., & Franke, P. J. (1989). Factors influencing mother's reactions to intrafamily sexual abuse. *Child Abuse & Neglect, 13*, 131–139.

Slattery, M. L., & Kerber, R. A. (1993). A comprehensive evaluation of family history and breast cancer risk: The Utah population database. *Journal of the American Medical Association, 270*, 1563–1568.

Smith, E. P., et al. (1994). Estrogen resistance caused by a mutation in the estrogen-receptor gene in a man. *The New England Journal of Medicine, 331*, 1056–1061.

Smolowe, J. (1993, June 14). New, improved and ready for battle. *Time*, pp. 48–51.

Solano, C. H., et al. (1982). Loneliness and patterns of self-disclosure. *Journal of Personality and Social Psychology, 43*, 524–531.

Sonenstein, F. L., et al. (1989). Sexual activity, condom use and AIDS awareness among adolescent males. *Family Planning Perspectives, 21*, 152–157.

Sourander, L. B. (1994). Geriatric aspects on estrogen effects and sexuality. *Gerontology, 40* (Suppl. 3), 14–17.

Southerland, D. (1990, May 27). Limited "sexual revolution" seen in China: Nationwide survey shows more liberal attitudes developing in conservative society. *The Washington Post*.

Spark, R. F. (1991). Male sexual health: A couple's guide. Mount Vernon, NY: Consumer Reports Books.

Special Committee on Pornography and Prostitution. (1985). *Report of the Special Committee on Pornography and Prostitution*, Vol. 1. Ottawa: Minister of Supply and Services.

Speckens, A. E. M., et al. (1995). Psychosexual functioning of partners of men with presumed non-organic erectile dysfunction: Cause or consequence of the disorder? *Archives of Sexual Behavior, 24*, 157–172.

Spitzer, R. L., et al. (1989). *DSM-III-R casebook*. Washington, DC: American Psychiatric Press.

Spong, J. S. (1988). *Living in sin: A bishop rethinks human sexuality*. San Francisco: Harper & Row.

Sprecher, S., et al. (1994). Mate selection preferences: Gender differences examined in a national sample. *Journal of Personality and Social Psychology, 66*(6), 1074–1080.

Starr, B. D., & Weiner, M. B. (1981). *The Starr-Weiner report on sex and sexuality in the mature years*. New York: Stein & Day.

Statistics Canada. *The Daily* (1999a). November 25, 1999.

Statistics Canada. Cited in Canadian Centre for Justice Statistics. (1999b). Sex offenders integration and analysis program. *Juristat, 19*(3). Cat. No. 85002-XPE.

Statistics Canada. (1999c). *Health Indicators, 1999*, Cat. No. 82 221.

Statistics Canada. (1999d). General Social Survey.

Statistics Canada. (2000a, July 24). *The Daily*.

Statistics Canada. (2000c). *Family violence in Canada: A statistical profile*. Cat. no. 85-224-XIE.

Statistics Canada. (2001). *Causes of death 2001*. Cat. No. 84-208-XIE. **http://www.statcan.ca/english/freepub/84-208-XIE/2001/index.htm**.

Statistics Canada. (2002a). *Family violence in Canada: A statistical profile*. Catalogue no. 85-224-XIE.

Statistics Canada. (2002b, October 22). *The Daily*. Available online at **www.statcan.ca/Daily/English/021022/td021022.htm**.

Statistics Canada. (2003a). Induced abortions by province and territory of report. Canadian Statistics. Updated March 23, 2003. Accessed at **www.statcan.ca/english/Pgdb/health40a.htm**.

Statistics Canada. (2003b). Teen pregnancy, by outcome of pregnancy and age group, count and rate per 1,000 women aged 15 to 19, Canada, provinces and territories, 1998–2000. Accessed at **www.statcan.ca/english/freepub/82-221-XIE/01103/tables/html/411.htm**, January 27, 2004.

Statistics Canada. (2003c, June 2). *The Daily*. Available online at **www.statcan.ca/Daily/English/030602/td030602.htm**.

Statistics Canada. (2004). Infant mortality, Canada, 1999. Canadian Statistics. Accessed at **www.statcan.ca/english/Pgdb/health21a.htm**, January 26, 2004.

Steben, M., & Sacks, S. S. (1997). Genital herpes: The epidemiology and control of a common sexually transmitted disease. *Canadian Journal of Human Sexuality, 6*, 127–134.

Steele, C. M., & Josephs, R. A. (1990). Alcohol myopia: Its prized and dangerous effects. *American Psychologist, 45*, 21–933.

Steiner, M., et al. (1995). Fluoxetine in the treatment of premenstrual dysphoria. *New England Journal of Medicine, 332*, 1529–1534.

Steinhauer, J. (1995, July 6). No marriage, no apologies. *The New York Times*, pp. C1, C7.

Stericker, A., & LeVesconte, S. (1982). Effect of brief training on sex-related differences in visual–spatial skill. *Journal of Personality and Social Psychology, 43*, 1018–1029.

Stermac, L., et al. (1996). Sexual assaults of adult males. *Journal of Interpersonal Violence, 11*, 52–64.

Sternberg, R. J. (1986). A triangular theory of love. *Psychological Review, 93*, 119–135.

Sternberg, R. J. (1987). Liking versus loving: A comparative evaluation of theories. *Psychological Bulletin, 102*, 331–345.

Sternberg, R. J. (1988). *The triangle of love: Intimacy, passion, commitment*. New York: Basic Books.

Sternberg, R. J. (2000). What's your love story? *Psychology Today, 33*, 52–59. Also at **www.psychologytoday.com/htdocs/prod/PTOArticle/PTO-20000701-000035.ASP**.

Sternberg, R. J., & Grajek, S. (1984). The nature of love. *Journal of Personality and Social Psychology, 47*, 312–329.

Stevenson, W., et al. (1999). Social support, relationship quality and well-being among pregnant adolescents. *Journal of Adolescence, 22*, 109–121.

Stewart, F. H. (1992). Cited in Leary, W. E. (1992, February 1). U.S. panel backs approval of first condom for women. *The New York Times*, p. 7.

Still no pill for Japan. (1992, March 22). *The New York Times*, Section 4, p. 7.

Stock, W. E. (1991). Feminist explanations: Male power, hostility, and sexual coercion. In E. Grauerholz & M. A. Koralewski (Eds.), *Sexual coercion: A sourcebook on its nature, causes, and prevention* (pp. 61–73). Lexington, MA: Lexington Books.

Stock, W. E. (1993). Inhibited female orgasm. In W. O'Donohue & J. H. Geer (Eds.), *Handbook of sexual dysfunctions:*

Assessment and treatment (pp. 253–301). Boston: Allyn & Bacon.

Stoller, R. J. (1969). Parental influences in male transsexualism. In R. Green & J. Money (Eds.), *Transsexualism and sex reassignment.* Baltimore: Johns Hopkins University Press.

Stoller, R. J. (1977). Sexual deviations. In R. Beach (Ed.), *Human sexuality in four perspectives* (pp. 190–214). Baltimore: Johns Hopkins University Press.

Stoller, R. J., & Herdt, G. H. (1985). Theories of origins of male homosexuality. *Archives of General Psychiatry, 42,* 399–404.

Storms, M. D. (1980). Theories of sexual orientation. *Journal of Personality and Social Psychology, 38,* 783–792.

Strickland, B. R. (1995). Research on sexual orientation and human development: A commentary. *Developmental Psychology, 31,* 137–140.

Strike, C. (1995, Spring). *Women assaulted by strangers. Canadian Social Trends.* Ottawa: Statistics Canada. Catalog No. 11-008E.

Struckman-Johnson, C. (1988). Forced sex on dates: It happens to men, too. *Journal of Sex Research, 24,* 234–241.

Stuart, F., et al. (1987). Inhibited sexual desire in women. *Archives of Sexual Behavior, 16,* 91–106.

Sue, D., et al. (1981). *Understanding abnormal behavior.* Boston: Houghton Mifflin Co.

Swann, W. B., Jr., et al. (1987). Cognitive–affective crossfire: When self-consistency meets self-enhancement. *Journal of Personality and Social Psychology, 52,* 881–889.

Symons, D. (1979). *The evolution of human sexuality.* New York: Oxford University Press.

Symons, D. (1995). Cited in Goleman, D. (1995, June 14). Sex fantasy research said to neglect women. *The New York Times,* p. C14.

Szasz, G., & Carpenter, C. (1989). Clinical observations in vibratory stimulation of the penis of men with spinal cord injury. *Archives of Sexual Behavior, 18,* 461–474.

Tannahill, R. (1980). *Sex in history.* Briarcliff Manor, NY: Stein & Day.

Tannen, D. (1990). *You just don't understand.* New York: Ballantine.

Tedeschi, J. T., & Felson, R. B. (1994). *Violence, aggression, & coercive actions.* Washington, DC: American Psychological Association.

Thomason, J. L., & Gelbart, S. M. (1989). *Trichomonas vaginalis. Obstetrics and Gynecology, 74,* 536–541.

Thomlison, B., et al. (1991, Fall). Characteristics of Canadian male and female child sexual abuse victims [Special issue: Child sexual abuse]. *Journal of Child and Youth Care,* 65–76.

Thompson, D. S. (Ed.). (1993). *Every woman's health: The complete guide to body and mind.* New York: Simon & Schuster.

Thompson, J. K., & Tantleff, S. (1992). Female and male ratings of upper torso: Actual, ideal, and stereotypical conceptions. *Journal of Social Behavior and Personality, 7,* 345–354.

Thompson, M. E. (1991). Self-defense against sexual coercion: Theory, research, and practice. In E. Grauerholz & M. A. Koralewski (Eds.), *Sexual coercion: A sourcebook on its nature, causes, and prevention* (pp. 111–121). Lexington, MA: Lexington Books.

Thompson, S. (1995). *Going all the way.* New York: Hill & Wang.

To, T., et al (1998). Cohort study on circumcision of newborn boys and subsequent risk of urinary tract infections. *The Lancet, 352,* 1813–1816.

Tobias, S. (1982). Sexist equations. *Psychology Today, 16*(1), pp. 14–17.

Tollison, C. D., & Adams, H. E. (1979). *Sexual disorders: Treatment, theory, and research.* New York: Gardner Press.

Toner, J. P., et al. (1991). Basal follicle-stimulating hormone level is a better predictor of in vitro fertilization performance than age. *Fertility and Sterility, 55,* 784–791.

Toomey, K. E., & Barnes, R. C. (1990). Treatment of chlamydia trachomatis genital infection. *Reviews of Infectious Diseases* (Suppl. 6), S645-S655.

Toubia, N. (1994). Female circumcision as a public health issue. *New England Journal of Medicine, 331,* 712–716.

Touchette, N. (1991). HIV-1 link prompts circumspection of circumcision. *Journal of NIH Research, 3,* 44–46.

Townsend, J. M. (1995). Sex without emotional involvement: An evolutionary interpretation of sex differences. *Archives of Sexual Behavior, 24,* 173–206.

Trovato, F. (1986). The relationship between marital dissolution and suicide: The Canadian case. *Journal of Marriage and the Family, 48,* 341–348.

Trussell, J., et al. (1993). Contraceptive efficacy of the diaphragm, the sponge, and the cervical cap. *Family Planning Perspectives, 25,* 100–105.

Turcotte, P., & Belanger, A. (1997). *Moving in together: The information of first common-law unions. Canadian Social Trends.* Ottawa: Statistics Canada, Cat. No. 11-008.

Tutty, L. M. (1992). The ability of elementary school children to learn child sexual abuse prevention concepts. *Child Abuse and Neglect, 16,* 369–384.

Udry, J. R., & Billy, J. O. G. (1987). Initiation of coitus in early adolescence. *American Sociological Review, 52,* 841–855.

Udry, J. R., et al. (1985). Serum androgenic hormones motivate sexual behavior in adolescent boys. *Fertility and Sterility, 43,* 90–94.

Udry, J. R., et al. (1986). Biosocial foundations for adolescent female sexuality. *Demography, 23*(2), 217–230.

Ulbrich, P. M., et al. (1990). Involuntary childlessness and marital adjustment: His and hers. *Journal of Sex & Marital Therapy, 16,* 147–158.

U.S. Department of Health and Human Services (USDHHS). (1990). *The health benefits of smoking cessation: A report of the Surgeon General.* (DHHS Publication No. CDC 90–8416). Rockville, MD: Public Health Service, Centers for Disease Control, Center for Chronic Disease Prevention and Health Promotion, Office on Smoking and Health.

U.S. Department of Health and Human Services (USDHHS). (1992). *Smoking and health in the Americas.* (DHHS Publication No. [CDC] 92–8419). Atlanta: Public Health Service, Centers for Disease Control, National Center for Chronic Disease Prevention and Health Promotion, Office on Smoking and Health.

U.S. Department of Justice. (1986). *Attorney general's commission on pornography: Final report.* Washington, DC: U.S. Government Printing Office.

Valentiner, D. P., et al. (1996). Coping strategies and posttraumatic stress disorder in female victims of sexual and nonsexual assault. *Journal of Abnormal Psychology, 105,* 455–458.

Van den Hoek, A., et al. (1990). Heterosexual behaviour of intravenous drug users in Amsterdam: Implications for the AIDS epidemic. *AIDS, 4,* 449–453.

Van Steirteghem, A. C., et al. (1993). High fertilization and implantation rates after intracytoplasmic sperm injection. *Human Reproduction, 8,* 1061–1066.

Vanwesenbeeck, I. (2001). Another decade of social scientific work on sex work: A review of research 1990–2000. *Annual Review of Sex Research, 12,* 242–289.

Vazi, R., et al. (1989). Evaluation of a testicular cancer curriculum for adolescents. *Journal of Pediatrics, 114,* 150–162.

Vinacke, W., et al. (1988). Similarity and complementarity in intimate couples. *Genetic, Social, and General Psychology Monographs, 114,* 51–76.

Voeller, B. (1991). AIDS and heterosexual anal intercourse. *Archives of Sexual Behavior, 20,* 33–276.

Voyer, D., et al. (1995). Magnitude of sex differences in spatial abilities: A meta-analysis and consideration of critical variables. *Psychological Bulletin, 117,* 250–270.

Vyas, G. N., et al. (1996). The risk of HIV transmission by screened blood. *New England Journal of Medicine, 334,* 992.

Wald, A., et al. (1995). Virologic characteristics of subclinical and symptomatic genital herpes infections. *New England Journal of Medicine, 333,* 770–775.

Waldinger, M. D., et al. (1994). Paroxetine treatment of premature ejaculation: A double-blind, randomized, placebo-controlled study. *American Journal of Psychiatry, 151* (9), 1377–1379.

Walfish, S., & Mayerson, M. (1980). Sex role identity and attitudes toward sexuality. *Archives of Sexual Behavior, 9,* 199–204.

Wallerstein, J. S., & Blakeslee, S. (1989). *Second chances: Women and children a decade after divorce.* New York: Ticknor & Fields.

Walsh, P. C. (1996). Treatment of benign prostatic hyperplasia. *New England Journal of Medicine, 335,* 586–587.

Walster, E., & Walster, G. W. (1978). *A new look at love.* Reading, MA: Addison-Wesley.

Walt, V. (1993, July 26). Some 2nd thoughts on Depo. *New York Newsday,* p. 13.

Waterman, J. (1986). Overview of treatment issues. In K. MacFarlane et al. (Eds.), *Sexual abuse of young children: Evaluation and treatment* (pp. 197–203). New York: Guilford Press.

Waterman, J., et al. (1986). Challenges for the future. In K. MacFarlane et al. (Eds.), *Sexual abuse of young children: Evaluation and treatment* (pp. 315–332). New York: Guilford.

Waterman, J., & Lusk, R. (1986). Scope of the problem. In K. MacFarlane et al. (Eds.), *Sexual abuse of young children: Evaluation and treatment* (pp. 3–14). New York: Guilford Press.

Wawer, M., et al. (1996). Origins and working conditions of female sex workers in urban Thailand: Consequences of social context for HIV transmission. *Social Sciences and Medicine, 42,* 453–464.

Weber, M., et al. (2002). HIV risk profile and prostitution among female street youths. *Journal of Urban Health, 79,* 525–535.

Weiler, A. (2001). Two-year college freshmen and the Internet: Do they really "know all that stuff?" *Libraries and the Academy 1,* 2.

Weinberg, M. S., et al. (1984). The social constituents of sadomasochism. *Social Problems, 31,* 379–389.

Weinberg, M. S., et al. (1994). Dual attraction. New York: Oxford University Press.

Weinberg, M. S., et al. (1999). Gendered sex work in the San Francisco tenderloin. *Archives of Sexual Behavior, 28,* 503–521.

Weinberg, T. S. (1987). Sadomasochism in the United States: A review of recent sociological literature. *Journal of Sex Research, 23,* 50–69.

Weisberg, D. K. (1985). Children of the night: A study of adolescent prostitution. Lexington, MA: Heath.

Weiss, R. D., & Mirin, S. M. (1987). *Cocaine.* Washington, DC: American Psychiatric Press.

Welsh, S. (2000). The multidimensional nature of sexual harassment. *Violence Against Women Quarterly, 6,* 118–141.

Whalen, R. E., et al. (1990). Models of sexuality. In D. P. McWhirter, et al. (Eds.), *Homosexuality/Heterosexuality: Concepts of sexual orientation* (pp. 61–70). New York: Oxford University Press.

Whiffen, V. E. (1992). Is postpartum depression a distinct diagnosis? *Clinical Psychology Review, 12,* 485–508.

Whipple, B., & Komisaruk, B. R. (1988). Analgesia produced in women by genital self-stimulation. *Journal of Sex Research, 24,* 130–140.

Whitam, F. L., et al. (1993). Homosexual orientation in twins: A report on 61 pairs and three triplet sets. *Archives of Sexual Behavior, 22,* 187–206.

White, G. L. (1981). Some correlates of romantic jealousy. *Journal of Personality, 49,* 129–146.

White, J. W. (1983). Sex and gender issues in aggression research. In R. G. Green & E. I. Donnerstein (Eds.), *Aggression: Theoretical and empirical reviews* (Vol. 2). New York: Academic Press.

White, S. D., & DeBlassie, R. R. (1992). Adolescent sexual behavior. *Adolescence, 27,* 183–191.

Whitley, B. E., Jr. (1983). Sex role orientation and self-esteem: A critical meta-analysis. *Journal of Personality and Social Psychology, 44,* 765–788.

Whitley, R., et al. (1991). Predictors of morbidity and mortality in infants with herpes simplex virus infections. *New England Journal of Medicine, 324,* 450–454.

Whittemore, A. S. (1994). The risk of ovarian cancer after treatment for infertility. *New England Journal of Medicine, 331,* 805–806.

WHO. (2002). AIDS epidemic update: December 2002. Joint United Nations Programme on HIV/AIDS (UNAIDS) and World Health Organization (WHO) 2002.

Accessed at **www. who.int/hiv/pub/ epidemiology/epi2002/en/**.

Wilcox, A. J., et al. (1995). Timing of sexual intercourse in relation to ovulation: Effects on the probability of conception, survival of the pregnancy, and sex of the baby. *New England Journal of Medicine, 333,* 1517–1521.

Wilcox, A. J., et al. (2000). The timing of the "fertile window" in the menstrual cycle: Day specific estimates from a prospective study. *British Medical Journal, 321,* 1259–1262.

Wilcox, B. L. (1987). Pornography, social science and politics: When research and ideology collide. *American Psychologist, 42,* 941, 943.

Wildman, B. G., & White, P. A. (1986). Assessment of dysmenorrhea using the Menstrual Symptom Questionnaire: Factor structure and validity. *Behaviour Research & Therapy, 24,* 547–551.

Wille, R., & Beier, K. M. (1989). Castration in Germany. *Annals of Sex Research, 2,* 103–133.

Williams, D. E., & D'Alessandro, J. D. (1994). A comparison of three measures of androgyny and their relationship to psychological adjustment. *Journal of Social Behavior and Personality, 9*(3) 469–480.

Williams, S., et al. (1997, August). *Aboriginal sex offenders: Melding spiritual healing with cognitive-behavioural treatment.* Ottawa: Corrections Service Canada.

Willis, F., & Henderson, M. (1994). Names associated with attractiveness. *Psychological Reports, 74,* 1275.

Willis, R. J., & Michael, R. T. (1994). Innovation in family formation: Evidence on cohabitation in the United States. In J. Eruisch & K. Ogawa (Eds.), *The family, the market and the state in aging societies.* London: Oxford University Press.

Wilson, G., & Cousins, J. (2003). Partner similarity and relationship satisfaction: Development of a compatibility quotient. *Sexual and Relationship Therapy, 18,* 161–170.

Wilson, G., & Cox, D. (1983). Personality of pedophile club members. *Personality and Individual Differences, 4,* 323–329.

Wilson, J. D. (1995). The promiscuous receptor: Prostate cancer comes of age. *New England Journal of Medicine, 332,* 1440–1441.

Wilson, M. R., & Filsinger, E. E. (1986). Religiosity and marital adjustment: Multidimensional interrelationships. *Journal of Marriage and the Family, 48,* 147–151.

Wilson, S. N., & Sanderson, C. A. (1988). The sex report curriculum: Is "just say no" effective? *SIECUS Report, 17,* 10–11.

Winick, C. (1985). A content analysis of sexually explicit magazines sold in an adult bookstore. *Journal of Sex Research, 21*, 206–210.

Wise, T. N. (1994). Sertraline as a treatment for premature ejaculation. *Journal of Clinical Psychiatry, 55*(9), 417.

Wisell, T. E., et al. (1987). Declining frequency of circumcision: Implications for changes in the absolute incidence and male to female sex ratio of urinary tract infections in early infancy. *Pediatrics, 79*, 338–342.

Wolff, L., & Geissel, D. (1994, Summer). *Street prostitution in Canada. Canadian Social Trends.* Statistics Canada Catalogue No. 11-008E.

The Working Group for a New View of Women's Sexual Problems. (2001). A new view of women's sexual problems. *Women & Therapy, 24*, 1–8.

Worling, J. R. (1995). Sexual abuse histories of adolescent male sex offenders: Differences on the basis of the age and gender of their victims. *Journal of Abnormal Psychology, 104*, 610–613.

Wortman, C. B., et al. (1976). Self-disclosure: An attributional perspective. *Journal of Personality and Social Psychology, 33*, 184–191.

WuDunn, S. (1996, January 25). In Japan, a ritual of mourning for abortions. *The New York Times*, A1, A8.

Wyatt, G. E., et al. (1990). Internal and external mediators of women's rape experiences. *Psychology of Women Quarterly, 14*, 153–176.

Yates, G. L., et al. (1991). A risk profile comparison of homeless youth involved in prostitution and homeless youth not involved [Special issue: Homeless youth]. *Journal of Adolescent Health, 12*, 545–548.

Yorburg, B. (1995, July 9). Why couples choose to live together. *The New York Times*, p. 14.

Young, T. K., & Katz, A. (1998). Survivors of sexual abuse: Clinical, lifestyle and reproductive consequences. *Canadian Medical Association Journal, 159*, 224–329.

Zaviacic, M., & Whipple, B. (1993). Update on the female prostate and the phenomenon of female ejaculation. *Journal of Sex Research, 30*, 148–151.

Zaviacic, M., et al. (1988a). Concentrations of fructose in female ejaculate and urine: A comparative biochemical study. *Journal of Sex Research, 24*, 319–325.

Zaviacic, M., et al. (1988b). Female urethral expulsions evoked by local digital stimulation of the G-spot: Differences in the response patterns. *Journal of Sex Research, 24*, 311–318.

Zhang, J., & Fried, D. B. (1992). Relationship of maternal smoking during pregnancy to placenta previa. *American Journal of Preventative Medicine, 8*, 278–282.

Zhang, K., et al. (1999). Changing sexual attitudes and behaviour in China: Implications for the spread of HIV and other sexually transmitted diseases. *AIDS Care, 11, 5*, 581—589.

Zilbergeld, B. (1978). *Male sexuality.* Boston: Little, Brown.

Zillman, D. (1989). Effects of prolonged consumption of pornography. In D. Zillman & J. Bryant (Eds.), *Pornography: Research advances and policy considerations* (pp. 127–157). Hillsdale, NJ: Erlbaum.

Zillmann, D., & Bryant, J. (1982, Autumn). Pornography, sexual callousness, and the trivialization of rape. *Journal of Communication*, 10–21.

Zillmann, D., & Bryant, J. (1984). Effects of massive exposure to pornography. In N. M. Malamuth & E. Donnerstein (Eds.), *Pornography and sexual aggression* (pp. 115–138). New York: Academic Press.

Zillmann, D., & Weaver, J. B. (1989). Pornography and men's sexual callousness toward women. In D. Zillmann & J. Bryant (Eds.), *Pornography: Research advances and policy considerations* (pp. 95–125). Hillsdale, NJ: Erlbaum.

Glossary

ABCDE model Levinger's view, which approaches romantic relationships in terms of five stages: attraction, building, continuation, deterioration, and ending.

Acquaintance sexual assault Sexual assault by an acquaintance of the person who is assaulted.

Acquired immunodeficiency syndrome (AIDS) A sexually transmitted infection that destroys white blood cells in the immune system, leaving the body vulnerable to various "opportunistic" diseases.

Activating effects Those effects of sex hormones that influence the level of the sex drive but not sexual orientation.

Agape (AH-gah-pay) Selfless love; a kind of loving that is similar to generosity and charity.

Age of viability The age at which a fetus can sustain independent life.

Aggravated sexual assault Sexual contact with a non-consenting person that results in wounding, maiming, disfigurement, or endangering the life of the victim.

Amenorrhea The absence of menstruation.

Amniocentesis A procedure for drawing off and examining fetal cells in the amniotic fluid to determine the presence of various disorders in the fetus.

Amniotic fluid Fluid within the amniotic sac that suspends and protects the fetus.

Amniotic sac The sac containing the fetus.

Ampulla A sac or dilated part of a tube or canal.

Ampulla The wide segment of a fallopian tube near the ovary. (A Latin word meaning "bottle.")

Analogous Similar in function.

Anaphrodisiacs Drugs or other agents that dull sexual arousal or sexual desire.

Androgen-insensitivity syndrome A form of pseudohermaphroditism in which a genetic male is prenatally insensitive to androgens. As a result his genitals do not become normally masculinized.

Androgenital syndrome A form of pseudohermaphroditism in which a genetic female has internal female sexual structures but masculinized external genitals.

Androgens Male sex hormones. (From the Greek *andros*, meaning "man" or "males," and -*gene*, meaning "born.")

Anilingus Oral stimulation of the anus.

Anorexia nervosa A potentially life-threatening eating disorder characterized by refusal to maintain a healthy body weight, intense fear of being overweight, a distorted body image, and, in females, lack of menstruation (amenorrhea).

Anorgasmic Never having reached orgasm. (Literally, "without orgasm.")

Anovulatory Without ovulation.

Anoxia Oxygen deprivation.

Anti-androgen drug A chemical substance that reduces the sex drive by lowering the level of testosterone in the bloodstream.

Anti-androgen A substance that decreases the levels of androgens in the bloodstream.

Antibodies Specialized proteins produced by the white blood cells of the immune system in response to disease organisms and other toxic substances. Antibodies recognize and attack the invading organisms or substances.

Antigen A protein, toxin, or other substance to which the body reacts by producing antibodies. (Combined word formed from *anti*body *gen*erator.)

Aphrodisiac Any drug or other agent that is sexually arousing or increases sexual desire. (From *Aphrodite*, the Greek goddess of love and beauty.)

Areola The dark ring on the breast that encircles the nipple.

Arthritis A progressive disease that is characterized by inflammation or pain in the joints.

Artificial insemination The introduction of sperm into the reproductive tract through means other than sexual intercourse.

Asexuals Bell and Weinberg's term for gay people who live alone and have few sexual contacts.

Asymptomatic Without symptoms.

Autoimmune response The production of antibodies that attack naturally occurring substances that are (incorrectly) recognized as being foreign or harmful.

Autonomic nervous system The division of the nervous system that regulates automatic bodily processes, such as heartbeat, pupil dilation, respiration, and digestion. Abbreviated *ANS*.

Aversion therapy A method for terminating undesirable sexual behaviour in which the behaviour is repeatedly paired with an aversive stimulus, such as electric shock, so that a conditioned aversion develops.

Bacteria Plural of *bacterium*, a class of one-celled micro-organisms that have no chlorophyll and can give rise to many illnesses. (From the Greek *baktron*, meaning—referring to the fact that many bacteria are rod-shaped.)

Bacterial vaginosis A form of vaginitis usually caused by the *Gardnerella vaginalis* bacterium.

Bartholin's glands Glands that lie just inside the minor lips and secrete fluid just before orgasm.

Basal body temperature (BBT) method A fertility awareness method of contraception that relies on prediction of ovulation by tracking the woman's temperature during the course of the menstrual cycle.

Behaviour therapy The systematic application of the principles of learning to help people modify problem behaviour.

Behaviourists Learning theorists who argue that a scientific approach to understanding behaviour must refer only to observable and measurable behaviours.

Benign prostatic hyperplasia Enlargement of the prostate gland due to hormonal changes associated with aging and characterized by symptoms such as urinary frequency, urinary urgency, and difficulty starting the flow of urine.

Benign Doing little or no harm.

Bisexual Sexually responsive to either gender. (From the Latin *bi-*, meaning "two.")

Bisexuality Erotic attraction to, and interest in developing romantic relationships with, both males and females.

Blastocyst A stage within the germinal stage of prenatal development, in which the embryo is a sphere of cells surrounding a cavity of fluid.

Bondage Ritual restraint, as by shackles, as practised by many sexual masochists.

Braxton-Hicks contractions So-called false labour contractions that are relatively painless.

Breech presentation Emergence of the baby bottom or feet first from the womb.

Bulbourethral glands Another term for Cowper's glands.

Butch A lesbian who assumes a traditional masculine gender role.

Caesarean section (C-section) A method of childbirth in which the fetus is delivered through a surgical incision in the abdomen.

Calendar method An abstinence-based method of contraception that relies on prediction of ovulation by tracking menstrual cycles, typically for a 10- to 12-month period, and assuming that ovulation occurs 14 days prior to menstruation.

Call girls Prostitutes who arrange for their sexual contacts by telephone. *Call* refers both to telephone calls and to being "on call."

Candidiasis A form of vaginitis caused by a yeastlike fungus, *Candida albicans*

Case study A carefully drawn, in-depth biography of an individual or a small group of individuals that may be obtained through interviews, questionnaires, and historical records.

Castration anxiety In psychoanalytic theory, a man's fear that his genitals will be removed. Castration anxiety is an element of the Oedipus complex and is implicated in the directionality of erotic interests.

Celibacy Complete sexual abstinence. (Sometimes used to describe the state of being unmarried, especially in the case of people who take vows to remain single.)

Cephalic presentation Emergence of the baby headfirst from the womb.

Cephalocaudal From the head downward. (From Latin roots meaning—and "tail.")

Cerebral palsy A muscular disorder that is caused by damage to the central nervous system (usually prior to or during birth) and characterized by spastic paralysis.

Cervicitis Inflammation of the cervix.

Cervix The lower end of the uterus. From the Latin for "neck."

Chancre A sore or ulcer.

Chancroid An STI caused by the *Hemophilus ducreyi* bacterium. Also called *soft chancre*.

Chlamydia A common STI caused by the *Chlamydia trachomatis* bacterium.

Chromosome One of the rodlike structures, found in the nucleus of every living cell, that carries the genetic code in the form of genes.

Cilia Hairlike projections from cells that beat rhythmically to produce locomotion or currents.

Circumcision Surgical removal of the foreskin of the penis. (From the Latin *circumcidere*, meaning "to cut around.")

Climacteric A long-term process, including menopause, that involves the gradual decline in the reproductive capacity of the ovaries.

Clitoridectomy Surgical removal of the clitoris.

Clitoris A female sex organ consisting of a shaft and glans located above the urethral opening. It is extremely sensitive to sexual sensations.

Clomiphene A synthetic hormone that is chemically similar to LH and induces ovulation.

Close couples Bell and Weinberg's term for gay couples whose relationships resemble marriage in their depth of commitment and exclusiveness.

Cohabitation Living together as though married but without legal sanction (also known as common-law relationship).

Coitus interruptus The practice of withdrawing the penis prior to ejaculation during sexual intercourse.

Coitus (co-it-us or co-EET-us). Sexual intercourse.

Combination pill A birth-control pill that contains synthetic estrogen and progesterone.

Complete hysterectomy Surgical removal of the ovaries, fallopian tubes, cervix, and uterus.

Concordance Agreement.

Concubine A secondary wife, usually of inferior legal and social status. (From Latin roots meaning "lying with.")

Condom A sheath made of animal membrane or latex that covers the penis during coitus and serves as a barrier to sperm following ejaculation.

Congenital syphilis A syphilis infection that is present at birth.

Consensual adultery Extramarital sex that is engaged in openly with the knowledge and consent of one's spouse.

Control group A group of study participants who do not receive the experimental treatment. However, other conditions are held comparable to those of individuals in the experimental group.

Conventional adultery Extramarital sex that is kept clandestine (hidden) from one's spouse.

Coprophilia A paraphilia in which sexual arousal is attained in connection with feces. (From the Greek *copros*, meaning "dung.")

Corona The ridge that separates the glans from the body of the penis. (From the Latin for "crown.")

Corpora cavernosa Masses of spongy tissue in the clitoral shaft that become engorged with blood and stiffen in response to sexual stimulation. (Latin for "cavernous bodies.") Also, cylinders of spongy tissue in the penis that become congested with blood and stiffen during sexual arousal.

Corpus luteum The follicle that has released an ovum and then produces copious amounts of progesterone and estrogen during the luteal phase of a woman's cycle. (From Latin roots meaning "yellow body.")

Corpus spongiosum The spongy body that runs along the bottom of the penis, contains the penile urethra, and enlarges at the tip of the penis to form the glans.

Correlation coefficient A statistic that expresses the strength and direction (positive or negative) of the relationship between two variables.

Correlation A statistical measure of the relationship between two variables.

Courtesan A prostitute—especially the mistress of a noble or wealthy man. (From Italian roots meaning "court lady.")

Covert sensitization A form of aversion therapy in which thoughts of engaging in undesirable behaviour are paired repeatedly with imagined aversive stimuli.

Cowper's glands Structures that lie below the prostate and empty their secretions into the urethra during sexual arousal.

Cremaster muscle The muscle that raises and lowers the testicle in response to temperature changes and sexual stimulation.

Crisis A highly stressful situation that can involve shock, loss of self-esteem, and lessened capacity for making decisions.

Critical period of vulnerability A period of time during which an embryo or fetus is vulnerable to the effects of a teratogen.

Cruising The name that gay people give to searching for a sex partner.

Crura Anatomical structures resembling legs that attach the clitoris to the pubic bone. (Singular: *crus*. A Latin word meaning "leg"; or "shank.")

Cryptorchidism A condition in which one or both testicles fail to descend from the abdomen into the scrotum.

Cryptorchidism The condition in which one or two testicles fail to descend from the abdomen into the scrotum.

Culpotomy A kind of tubal sterilization in which the fallopian tubes are approached through an incision in the back wall of the vagina.

Cunnilingus Oral stimulation of the female genitals.

Cyst a saclike structure filled with fluid or diseased material.

Cystitis An inflammation of the urinary bladder. (From the Greek *kystis*, meaning "sac.")

D&C Abbreviation for *dilation and curettage,* an operation in which the cervix is dilated and uterine contents are then gently scraped away.

D&E Abbreviation for *dilation and evacuation,* an abortion method in which the cervix is dilated prior to vacuum aspiration.

Dartos muscle The muscle in the middle layer of the scrotum that contracts and relaxes in response to temperature changes.

Defence mechanisms In psychoanalytic theory, automatic processes that protect the ego from anxiety by disguising or ejecting unacceptable ideas and urges.

Dependent variables The measured results of an experiment, which are believed to be a function of the independent variables.

DES Diethylstilbestrol: an estrogen that was once given to women at risk for miscarriage to help maintain pregnancy.

Diaphragm A shallow rubber cup or dome, fitted to the contour of a woman's vagina, that is coated with a spermicide and inserted prior to coitus to prevent conception.

Dilate To open or widen.

Dildo A penis-shaped object used in sexual activity.

Displacement In psychoanalytic theory, a defence mechanism that allows one to transfer unacceptable wishes or desires onto more appropriate or less threatening objects.

Dizygotic (DZ) twins Twins who develop from different fertilized ova; fraternal twins.

Dominican Republic syndrome A form of pseudohermaphroditism in which a genetic enzyme disorder prevents testosterone from masculinizing the external genitalia.

Don Juanism An excessive, insatiable sexual appetite or drive in men. (After the fictional Spanish nobleman who was unable to obtain true sexual gratification despite numerous affairs.)

Donor IVF A variation of in vitro fertilization in which the ovum is taken from one woman, fertilized, and then injected into the uterus or fallopian tube of another woman.

Douche Application of a jet of liquid to the vagina as a rinse. (From the Italian *doccia*, meaning "shower bath.")

Down syndrome A chromosomal abnormality that leads to mental retardation, caused by an extra chromosome on the 21st pair.

Dysfunctionals Bell and Weinberg's term for gay people who live alone and have sexual, social, or psychological problems.

Dysmenorrhea Pain or discomfort during menstruation.

Dyspareunia A sexual dysfunction characterized by persistent or recurrent pain during sexual intercourse. (From roots meaning "badly paired.")

Ectoparasites Parasites that live on the outside of the host's body—as opposed to *endo*parasites, which live within the body. (From the Greek *ektos*, meaning "outside.")

Ectopic pregnancy A pregnancy in which the fertilized ovum becomes implanted outside the uterus, usually in the fallopian tube. (*Ectopic* derives from Greek roots meaning "out of place.")

Efface To become thin.

Ego In Freud's theory, the second mental structure to develop, which is characterized by self-awareness, planning, and delay of gratification.

Ejaculatory duct A duct formed by the convergence of a vas deferens with a seminal vesicle through which sperm pass through the prostate gland and into the urethra.

Elephantiasis A disease characterized by enlargement of parts of the body, especially the legs and genitals, and by hardening and ulceration of the surrounding skin. (From the Greek *elephas*, meaning "elephant," referring to the resemblance of the affected skin areas to elephant hide.)

Embryo The stage of prenatal development that begins with implantation of a fertilized ovum in the uterus and concludes with development of the major organ systems at about two months after conception.

Embryonic stage The stage of prenatal development that lasts from implantation through the eighth week and is characterized by the differentiation of the major organ systems.

Embryonic transfer A method of conception in which a woman volunteer is artificially inseminated by the male partner of the intended mother, after which the embryo is removed from the volunteer and inserted within the uterus of the intended mother.

Emission stage The first phase of

ejaculation, which involves contractions of the prostate gland, seminal vesicles, and the upper part of the vas deferens.

Endocrine gland A ductless gland that releases its secretions directly into the bloodstream.

Endometriosis A condition caused by the growth of endometrial tissue in the abdominal cavity or elsewhere outside the uterus. Characterized by menstrual pain, it may cause infertility.

Endometrium The innermost layer of the uterus. (From Latin and Greek roots meaning "within the uterus.")

Epididymis A tube that lies against the back wall of each testicle and serves as a storage facility for sperm. (From Greek roots meaning "upon testicles.")

Epididymitis Inflammation of the epididymis.

Episiotomy A surgical incision in the perineum that may be made during childbirth to protect the vagina from tearing. (From Greek roots *epision*, meaning "pubic region," and *tome*, meaning "cutting.")

Erection The enlargement and stiffening of the penis as a consequence of engorgement with blood.

Erogenous zones Parts of the body that are especially sensitive to tactile sexual stimulation.

Eros The kind of love that is closest in meaning to the modern-day concept of passion.

Erotic Arousing sexual feelings or desires. (From the Greek word for love, *eros*.)

Estrogen A generic term for female sex hormones (including estradiol, estriol, estrone, and others) or synthetic compounds that promote the development of female sex characteristics and regulate the menstrual cycle. (From the roots meaning "generating" [*-gen*] and "estrus.")

Excitement phase The first phase of the sexual response cycle, which is characterized by erection in the male, vaginal lubrication in the female, and muscle tension and increases in heart rate in both males and females.

Exhibitionism A paraphilia characterized by persistent, powerful urges and sexual fantasies involving exposing one's genitals to unsuspecting strangers to achieve sexual arousal or gratification.

Experiment A scientific method that seeks to confirm cause-and-effect relationships by manipulating independent variables and observing their effects on dependent variables.

Experimental group A group of study participants who receive a treatment.

Expulsion stage The second stage of ejaculation, during which muscles at the base of the penis and elsewhere contract rhythmically, forcefully expelling semen and providing pleasurable sensations.

Extramarital sex Sexual relations between a married person and someone other than his or her spouse.

Fallopian tubes Tubes that extend from the upper uterus toward the ovaries and conduct ova to the uterus. (After the Italian anatomist Gabriel Fallopio, who is credited with their discovery.)

False positive An erroneous positive test result or clinical finding.

Fellatio Oral stimulation of the male genitals.

Femme A lesbian who assumes a traditional feminine gender role.

Fetal alcohol syndrome A cluster of symptoms caused by maternal drinking, in which the child shows developmental lags and characteristic facial features such as an underdeveloped upper jaw, flattened nose, and widely spaced eyes.

Fetishism A paraphilia in which an inanimate object, such as an article of clothing, or an item made of rubber, leather, or silk, elicits sexual arousal.

Fibroadenoma A benign, fibrous tumour.

Fimbriae Projections from a fallopian tube that extend toward an ovary. (Singular: *fimbria*. Latin for "fibre" or "fringe.")

Follicle-stimulating hormone (FSH) A gonadotropin that stimulates development of follicles in the ovaries.

Follicle A capsule within an ovary that contains an ovum. (From a Latin word meaning "small bag.")

Foreplay Mutual sexual stimulation that precedes sexual intercourse.

Foreskin The loose skin that covers the penile glans. Also referred to as the *prepuce*.

Frenulum The sensitive strip of tissue that connects the underside of the penile glans to the shaft. (From the

Latin *frenum*, meaning "bridle.")

Frequency The number of times an action is repeated within a given period.

Frotteurism A paraphilia characterized by recurrent, powerful sexual urges and related fantasies involving rubbing against or touching a nonconsenting person. (From the French *frotter*, meaning "to rub.")

Functionals Bell and Weinberg's term for gay people who live alone, have adapted well to a swinging lifestyle, and are sociable and well adjusted.

Fundus The uppermost part of the uterus. (*Fundus* is a Latin word meaning "base.")

Gamete intrafallopian transfer (GIFT) A method of conception in which mature sperm and ova are inserted into a fallopian tube to encourage conception.

Gay bashing Violence against homosexuals.

Gay males Males who are erotically attracted to and desire to form romantic relationships with other males.

Gender assignment The labelling of a newborn as a male or female.

Gender constancy The concept that people's genders do not change, even if they alter their dress or behaviour.

Gender dysphoria The subjective experience of incongruity between genital anatomy and gender identity or role.

Gender identity The psychological sense of being male or female.

Gender roles Complex clusters of ways in which males and females are expected to behave within a given culture.

Gender schema A cluster of mental representations about male and female physical qualities, behaviours, and personality traits.

Gender stability The concept that people retain their genders for a lifetime.

Gender typing The process by which children acquire behaviour that is deemed appropriate to their gender.

Gender One's personal, social, and legal status as male or female.

General anaesthesia The use of drugs to put people to sleep and eliminate pain, as during childbirth.

General paresis A progressive form of mental illness caused by neurosyphilis and characterized by gross confusion.

Generalize To go from the particular to the general.

Genes The basic units of heredity, which consist of chromosomal segments of DNA.

Genital herpes An STI caused by the *Herpes simplex* virus type 2 and characterized by painful shallow sores and blisters on the genitals. *Herpes simplex* virus type 2 The virus that causes genital herpes. Abbreviated *HSV-2.*

Genital warts An STI that is caused by the human papilloma virus and takes the form of warts that appear around the genitals and anus.

Germ cell A cell from which a new organism develops. (From the Latin *germen*, meaning "bud" or "sprout.")

Germinal stage The period of prenatal development prior to implantation in the uterus.

Gonadotropin-releasing hormone (Gn-RH) A hormone secreted by the hypothalamus that stimulates the pituitary gland to release gonadotropins.

Gonadotropins Pituitary hormones that stimulate the gonads. (Literally, "that which 'feeds' the gonads.")

Gonorrhea An STI caused by the *Neisseria gonorrhoeae* bacterium and characterized by a discharge and burning urination. Left untreated, gonorrhea can give rise to pelvic inflammatory disease (PID) and infertility. (From the Greek *gonos*, meaning "seed" and *rheein*, meaning "to flow," referring to the fact that in ancient times the penile discharge characteristic of the illness was erroneously interpreted as a loss of seminal fluid.)

Grafenberg spot A part of the anterior wall of the vagina, whose prolonged stimulation is theorized to cause particularly intense orgasms and a female ejaculation. Abbreviated as *G-spot.*

Granuloma inguinale A tropical STI caused by the *Calymmatobacterium granulomatis* bacterium.

Gynecologist A physician who treats women's diseases, especially of the reproductive tract. (From the Greek *gyne*, meaning "woman.")

Gynecomastia Overdevelopment of a male's breasts. (From Greek roots meaning "woman" [*gyne*] and "breast" [*mastos*].)

Hegar's sign Softness of a section of the uterus between the uterine body and the cervix, which indicates that a woman is pregnant.

Hepatitis An inflammation of the liver. (From the Greek *hepar*, meaning "liver.")

Hermaphrodite A person who possesses both ovarian and testicular tissue. (From the names of the male and female Greek gods Hermes and Aphrodite.)

Herpes simplex virus type 1 The virus that causes oral herpes, which is characterized by cold sores or fever blisters on the lips or mouth. Abbreviated *HSV-1.*

Heteroerotic Of an erotic nature and involving members of the other gender.

Heterosexism Oppression based on the assumption that heterosexuality is the norm in society and is therefore superior to gay, lesbian, bisexual, and transgendered sexual orientations.

Heterosexual orientation Erotic attraction to, and preference for, developing romantic relationships with members of the other gender.

Homoerotic Of an erotic nature and involving members of one's own gender.

Homogamy The practice of marrying people who are similar in social background and standing. (From Greek roots meaning "same" [*homos*] and "marriage" [*gamos*].)

Homologous Similar in structure; developing from the same embryonic tissue.

Homophobia A cluster of negative attitudes and feelings toward gay people, including intolerance, hatred, and fear. (From Greek roots meaning "fear" [of members of the] "same" [gender].)

Homosexual orientation Erotic attraction to, and preference for, developing romantic relationships with members of one's own gender. (From the Greek *homos*, meaning "same," not the Latin *homo*, which means "man.")

Hormone-replacement therapy (HRT) Replacement of naturally occurring estrogen, or estrogen and progesterone, with synthetic equivalents, following menopause.

Hormone A substance secreted by an endocrine gland that regulates various body functions. (From the Greek *horman*, meaning "to stimulate" or "to excite.")

Hormone A substance secreted by an endocrine gland that regulates various body functions. (From the Greek *horman*, meaning "to stimulate" or "to excite.")

Human chorionic gonadotropin A hormone produced by women shortly after conception, which stimulates the corpus luteum to continue to produce progesterone. The presence of HCG in a woman's urine indicates that she is pregnant.

Human immunodeficiency virus (HIV) A sexually transmitted virus that destroys white blood cells in the immune system, leaving the body vulnerable to life-threatening diseases.

Human sexuality The ways in which we experience and express ourselves as sexual beings.

Hustlers Men who engage in prostitution with male customers.

Hyaluronidase An enzyme that briefly thins the zona pellucida, enabling one sperm to penetrate. (From roots meaning "substance that breaks down a glasslike fluid.")

Hymen A fold of tissue across the vaginal opening that is usually present at birth and usually remains at least partly intact until a woman engages in coitus. (Greek for "membrane.")

Hypersexuality An excessive or apparently insatiable sex drive that disrupts the person's ability to concentrate on other needs or leads to self-defeating behaviour, such as indiscriminate sexual contacts.

Hypogonadism An endocrine disorder that reduces the output of testosterone.

Hypothalamus A bundle of neural cell bodies near the centre of the brain that are involved in regulating body temperature, motivation, and emotion.

Hypoxyphilia A practice in which a person seeks to enhance sexual arousal, usually during masturbation, by becoming deprived of oxygen. (From the Greek root meaning "under" [*hypo-*].)

Hysterectomy Surgical removal of the uterus.

Hysterotomy An abortion method in which the fetus is removed by caesarean section.

Id In Freud's theory, the mental structure that is present at birth, embodies physiological drives, and is fully unconscious.

Identification In psychoanalytic theory, the process of incorporating within our-

selves our perceptions of the behaviours, thoughts, and feelings of others.

Immune system A term for the body's complex of mechanisms for protecting itself from disease-causing agents.

In vitro fertilization A method of conception in which mature ova are surgically removed from an ovary and placed in a laboratory dish along with sperm.

Incest taboo The prohibition against intercourse and reproduction among close blood relatives.

Incest Marriage or sexual relations between people who are so closely related (by "blood") that sexual relations are prohibited and punishable by law. (From the Latin *in-*, meaning "not," and *castus*, meaning "chaste.")

Incidence A measure of the occurrence or the degree of occurrence of an event.

Independent variable A condition in a scientific study that is manipulated so that its effects may be observed.

Induced abortion The purposeful termination of a pregnancy before the embryo or fetus is capable of sustaining independent life. (From the Latin *abortio*, meaning "that which is miscarried.")

Infant mortality Usually defined as the number of deaths of babies under one year of age in a given year per live births in the same year

Infatuation A state of intense absorption in or focus on another person, which is usually accompanied by sexual desire, elation, and general physiological arousal or excitement; passion.

Infertility Inability to conceive a child.

Inflammation Redness and warmth that develop at the site of an injury, reflecting dilation of blood vessels that permits the expanded flow of leukocytes to the region.

Infundibulum The outer, funnel-shaped part of a fallopian tube. (A Latin word meaning "funnel.")

Inguinal canal A fetal canal that connects the scrotum and the testes, allowing their descent. (From the Latin inguinus, meaning "near the groin.")

Interstitial cells Cells that lie between the seminiferous tubules and secrete testosterone. (*Interstitial* means "set between.")

Intimacy Feelings of closeness and connectedness that are marked by sharing of inmost thoughts and feelings.

Intra-amniotic infusion An abortion method in which a substance is injected into the amniotic sac to induce premature labour. Also called *instillation*.

Intracytoplasmic injection A method of conception in which sperm is injected directly into an ovum.

Intrauterine device A small object that is inserted into the uterus and left in place to prevent conception. Abbreviated *IUD*.

Introitus The vaginal opening. (From the Latin for "entrance.")

Isthmus The segment of a fallopian tube closest to the uterus. (A Latin word meaning "narrow passage.")

Jaundice A yellowish discoloration of the skin and the whites of the eyes. (From the French *jaune*, meaning "yellow.")

Klinefelter's syndrome A sex-chromosomal disorder in males caused by an extra X sex chromosome.

Klismaphilia A paraphilia in which sexual arousal is derived from use of enemas.

Labia majora Large folds of skin that run downward from the mons along the sides of the vulva. (Latin for "large lips" or "major lips.")

Labia minora Hairless, light-coloured membranes, located between the labia majora. (Latin for "small lips" or "minor lips.")

Lactation Production of milk by the mammary glands.

Lamaze method A childbirth method in which women learn about childbirth, learn to relax and to breathe in patterns that conserve energy and lessen pain, and have a coach (usually the father) present at childbirth. Also termed *prepared childbirth*.

Laparoscopy 1. A medical procedure in which a long, narrow tube (laparoscope) is inserted through an incision in the navel, permitting visual inspection of organs in the pelvic cavity. (From the Greek *lapara*, meaning "flank.") 2. Tubal sterilization by means of a *laparoscope*, which is inserted through a small incision just below the navel and used to cauterize, cut, or clamp the fallopian tubes. Sometimes referred to as "belly button surgery."

Larynx A structure of muscle and cartilage at the upper end of the trachea that contains the vocal cords; the voice box.

Lesbians Females who are erotically attracted to and desire to form romantic relationships with other females. (After Lesbos, the Greek island on which, legend has it, female–female sexual activity was idealized.)

Leukocytes White blood cells that are essential to the body's defences against infection. (From the Greek *leukos*, meaning "white," and *kytos*, meaning "a hollow," and used in combination with other word forms to mean "cell.")

Leydig's cells Another term for interstitial cells.

Local anaesthesia Anaesthesia that eliminates pain in a specific area of the body, as during childbirth.

Lovemap A representation in the mind and in the brain of the idealized lover and the idealized erotic activity with the lover.

Lumpectomy Surgical removal of a lump from the breast.

Luteinizing hormone (LH) A gonadotropin that helps regulate the menstrual cycle by triggering ovulation.

Lymphogranuloma venereum A tropical STI caused by the *Chlamydia trachomatis* bacterium.

Male erectile disorder Persistent difficulty achieving or maintaining an erection sufficient to allow the man to engage in or complete sexual intercourse. Also termed *erectile dysfunction*.

Malignant Leading to invasive and destructive growth and metastasis; severe, tending to become worse.

Mammary glands Milk-secreting glands. (From the Latin *mamma*, which means both "breast" and "mother.")

Mammography A special type of X-ray test that detects cancerous lumps in the breast.

Mastalgia A swelling of the breasts that sometimes causes premenstrual discomfort.

Mastectomy Surgical removal of the entire breast.

Masturbation Sexual self-stimulation.

Matching hypothesis The concept that people tend to develop romantic relationships with people who are similar to themselves in attractiveness.

Mating gradient The tendency for women to "marry up" (in social or economic status) and for men to "marry down."

Menarche (pronounced men-AR-kee). The onset of menstruation; first menstruation. (From Greek roots meaning "month" [*men*] and "beginning" [*arche*].)

Menopause The cessation of menstruation.

Menstrual phase The fourth phase of the menstrual cycle, during which the endometrium is sloughed off in the menstrual flow.

Menstruation The cyclical bleeding that stems from the shedding of the uterine lining (endometrium).

Minilaparotomy A kind of tubal sterilization in which a small incision is made in the abdomen to provide access to the fallopian tubes.

Minipill A birth-control pill that contains synthetic progesterone but no estrogen.

Miscarriage A spontaneous abortion.

Missionary position The coital position in which the man is on top. Also termed the *male-superior position*.

Mittelschmerz Pain that occurs during ovulation. (German for "middle pain," reflecting the fact that the pain occurs midway between menstrual periods.)

Modelling Acquiring knowledge and skills by observing others.

Monozygotic (MZ) twins Twins who develop from the same fertilized ovum; identical twins.

Mons veneris A mound of fatty tissue that covers the joint of the pubic bones in front of the body, below the abdomen and above the clitoris. (The name is a Latin phrase meaning "hill" or "mount of Venus," the Roman goddess of love. Also known as the *mons pubis*, or simply *mons*.)

Morning sickness Symptoms of pregnancy, including nausea, aversions to specific foods, and vomiting.

Motility Self-propulsion. A measure of the viability of sperm cells.

Multiple orgasms One or more additional orgasms following the first, which occur within a short period of time and before the body has returned to a pre-plateau level of arousal.

Mutuality A phase in building a relationship in which members of a couple come to regard themselves as "we," no longer two "I's" who happen to be in the same place at the same time.

Myometrium The middle, well-muscled layer of the uterus. (*Myo-* stems from the Greek *mys*, meaning "muscle.")

Myotonia Muscle tension.

Natural childbirth A method of childbirth in which women use no anaesthesia but are given other strategies for coping with discomfort and are educated about childbirth.

Naturalistic observation A method in which organisms are observed in their natural environments.

Necrophilia A paraphilia characterized by desire for sexual activity with corpses. (From the Greek *nekros*, meaning "dead body.")

Neurosyphilis Syphilitic infection of the central nervous system, which can cause brain damage and death.

Nocturnal emission Involuntary ejaculation of seminal fluid while asleep. Also referred to as a "wet dream," although the individual need not be dreaming about sex, or dreaming at all, at the time.

Nymphomania An excessive, insatiable sexual appetite or drive in women. (From the Greek roots *nymphe*, meaning "a bride," and *mania*, which means "madness.")

Obscenity That which offends people's feelings or goes beyond prevailing standards of decency or modesty.

Observer effect A distortion of individuals' behaviour caused by the act of observation.

Ocular herpes A herpes infection of the eye, usually caused by touching an infected area of the body and then touching the eye.

Oedipus complex In psychoanalytic theory, a conflict of the phallic stage in which the boy wishes to possess his mother sexually and perceives his father as a rival in love. (The analogous conflict for girls is the *Electra complex*.)

Oedipus complex In psychoanalytic theory, a conflict of the phallic stage in which the boy wishes to possess his mother sexually and perceives his father as a rival in love. (The analogous conflict for girls is the Electra complex.)

Open couples Bell and Weinberg's term for gay couples who live together but engage in secret affairs.

Ophthalmia neonatorum A gonorrheal infection of the eyes of newborn children who contract the disease by passing through an infected birth canal. (From the Greek *ophthalmos*, meaning "eye.")

Opportunistic diseases Diseases that take hold only when the immune system is weakened and unable to fend them off.

Oral contraceptive A contraceptive, consisting of female sex hormones, which is taken by mouth.

Orgasm The climax of sexual excitement.

Orgasmic disorders Sexual dysfunctions in which people persistently or recurrently have difficulty reaching orgasm despite attaining a level of sexual stimulation of sufficient intensity to normally result in orgasm or reach orgasm more rapidly than they would like.

Orgasmic platform The thickening of the walls of the outer third of the vagina, due to vasocongestion, that occurs during the plateau phase of the sexual response cycle.

Orgasmic reconditioning A method for strengthening the connection between sexual arousal and appropriate sexual stimuli (such as fantasies about an adult of the other gender) by repeatedly pairing the desired stimuli with orgasm.

Os The opening in the middle of the cervix. (Latin for "mouth.")

Osteoporosis A condition characterized by a decline in bone density, such that bones become porous and brittle. (From the Greek *osteon*, meaning "bone," and the Latin *porus*, meaning "pore.")

Ova Egg cells. (Singular: ovum.)

Ovariectomy Surgical removal of the ovaries.

Ovaries Almond-shaped organs that produce ova and the hormones estrogen and progesterone.

Ovulation method A fertility awareness method of contraception that relies on prediction of ovulation by tracking the viscosity of the cervical mucus.

Ovulation The release of an ovum from an ovary.

Ovulatory phase The second stage of the menstrual cycle, during which a follicle ruptures and releases a mature ovum.

Oxytocin A pituitary hormone that stimulates uterine contractions in labour and the ejection of milk during nursing.

Pap test A test of a sample of cervical cells that screens for cervical cancer and certain other abnormalities, but not for STIs. (Named after the originator of the technique, Dr. Papanicolaou.)

Paraphilia A diagnostic category used by the American Psychiatric Association to describe atypical patterns of sexual arousal or behaviour that become problematic in the eyes of the individual or society, such as fetishism or exhibitionism. (From Greek roots meaning "to the side of" [*para-*] and "loving" [*philos*].)

Paraplegic A person with sensory and motor paralysis of the lower half of the body.

Parasympathetic The branch of the ANS most active during processes that restore the body's reserves of energy, such as digestion. The parasympathetic ANS largely controls erection.

Partialism A paraphilia related to fetishism, in which sexual arousal is exaggeratedly associated with a particular body part, such as feet, breasts, or buttocks.

Participant observation A method in which observers interact with the people they study as they collect data.

Pathogen An agent, especially a microorganism, that can cause a disease. (From the Greek *pathos*, meaning "suffering" or "disease," and *genic*, meaning "forming" or "coming into being.")

Peak days The days during the menstrual cycle during which a woman is most likely to be fertile.

Pederasty Sexual love of boys. (From the Greek *paidos*, meaning "boy.")

Pediculosis A parasitic infestation by pubic lice (*Pthirus pubis*) that causes itching.

Pedophiles Persons with pedophilia, a paraphilia involving sexual interest in children.

Pedophilia A type of paraphilia that is defined by sexual attraction to children. (From the Greek *paidos*, meaning "child," not the Latin *pedis*, meaning "foot.")

Pelvic inflammatory disease (PID) Inflammation of the pelvic region—possibly including the cervix, uterus, fallopian tubes, abdominal cavity, and ovaries—that can be caused by organisms such as *Neisseria gonorrhoeae*. Its symptoms are abdominal pain, tenderness, nausea, fever, and irregular menstrual cycles. The condition may lead to infertility.

Penis envy In psychoanalytic theory, the girl's wish to have a penis.

Penis The male organ of sexual intercourse. (From the Latin for "tail.")

Performance anxiety Feelings of dread and foreboding experienced in connection with sexual activity (or any other activity that might be judged by another person).

Performance anxiety Feelings of dread and foreboding experienced in connection with sexual activity (or any other activity that might be judged by another person).

Perimetrium The outer layer of the uterus. (From roots meaning "around the uterus.")

Perineum The skin and underlying tissue that lie between the vaginal opening and the anus. (From Greek roots meaning "around" and "to empty out.")

Perineum The skin and underlying tissue that lie between the vaginal opening and the anus. (From the Greek roots meaning "around" and "to empty out.")

Period of the ovum Germinal stage.

Peyronie's disease An abnormal condition characterized by an excessive curvature of the penis that can make erections painful.

Phallic symbols Images of the penis.

Phallic worship Worship of the penis as a symbol of generative power.

Pharyngeal gonorrhea A gonorrheal infection of the pharynx (the cavity leading from the mouth and nasal passages to the larynx and esophagus) that is characterized by a sore throat.

Pheromones Chemical substances secreted externally by certain animals, which convey information to, or produce specific responses in, other members of the same species. (From the Greek *pherein*, meaning "to bear [a message]" and *hormone*.)

Philia (FEEL-yuh) Friendship love, which is based on liking and respect rather than sexual desire.

Phimosis An abnormal condition in which the foreskin is so tight that it cannot be withdrawn from the glans. (From the Greek *phimos*, meaning "muzzle.")

Pimps Men who serve as agents for prostitutes and live off their earnings. (Possibly from the Middle French *pimper*, meaning "to dress smartly.")

Pituitary gland The gland that secretes growth hormone, prolactin, oxytocin, and others.

Placenta An organ connected to the fetus by the umbilical cord. The placenta serves as a relay station between mother and fetus, allowing the exchange of nutrients and wastes.

Plateau phase The second phase of the sexual response cycle, which is characterized by increases in vasocongestion, muscle tension, heart rate, and blood pressure in preparation for orgasm.

Poly-X or Superfemale Syndrome A sex chromosomal disorder in females caused by cells with at least three X chromosomes.

Polycystic ovary syndrome (PCOS) A condition whose exact causes are unknown. Characterized by infrequent or absent ovulation and menstrual periods, increased growth of facial and body hair, and obesity, it may cause infertility.

Polymorphously perverse In psychoanalytic theory, being receptive to all forms of sexual stimulation.

Population A complete group of organisms or events.

Pornography Written, visual, or audiotaped material that is sexually explicit and produced for purposes of eliciting or enhancing sexual arousal. (From Greek roots meaning "to write about prostitutes.")

Postpartum depression Persistent and severe mood changes during the postpartum period, involving feelings of despair and apathy and characterized by changes in appetite and sleep, low self-esteem, and difficulty in concentrating.

Postpartum Following birth.

Posttraumatic stress disorder (PTSD) A type of stress reaction brought on by a traumatic event and characterized by flashbacks of the experience in the form of disturbing dreams or intrusive recollections, a sense of emotional numbing or restricted range of feelings, and heightened body arousal. Abbreviated *PTSD*.

Premature ejaculation A sexual dysfunction in which the male persistently ejaculates too early to afford the couple adequate sexual gratification.

Premenstrual syndrome (PMS) A combination of physical and psychological symptoms (e.g., anxiety, depression, irritability, weight gain from fluid retention, and abdominal discomfort) that regularly afflicts many women during the four- to six-day interval that precedes their menses each month.

Prepuce The fold of skin covering the glans of the clitoris (or penis). (From Latin roots meaning "before a swelling.")

Preterm Born prior to 37 weeks of gestation.

Primary amenorrhea Lack of menstruation in a woman who has never menstruated.

Primary dysmenorrhea Menstrual pain or discomfort that occurs in the absence of known organic problems.

Primary erogenous zones Erogenous zones that are particularly sensitive because they are richly endowed with nerve endings.

Primary sex characteristics Physical characteristics that differentiate males and females and are directly involved in reproduction, such as the sex organs.

Progesterone A steroid hormone secreted by the corpus luteum or prepared synthetically that stimulates proliferation of the endometrium and is involved in regulation of the menstrual cycle. (From the root *pro-*, meaning "promoting," and the words *gestation, steroid,* and *one*.)

Prolactin A pituitary hormone that stimulates production of milk.

Proliferative phase The first phase of the menstrual cycle, which begins with the end of menstruation and lasts about 9 or 10 days. During this phase, the endometrium proliferates.

Prophylactic An agent that protects against disease.

Prostaglandins Hormones that cause muscle fibres in the uterine wall to contract, as during labour.

Prostate gland The gland that lies beneath the bladder and secretes prostatic fluid, which gives semen its characteristic odour and texture.

Prostatitis Inflammation of the prostate gland.

Prostitution The sale of sexual activity for money or goods of value, such as drugs. (From the Latin *prostituere,* meaning "to offer for sale.")

Proximodistal From the central axis of the body outward. (From Latin roots meaning "near" and "far.")

Prurient Tending to excite lust; lewd. (From the Latin *prurire,* meaning "to itch" in the sense of "to long for.")

Pseudohermaphrodites People who possess the gonads of one gender but external genitalia that are ambiguous or typical of the other gender.

Psychoanalysis The theory of personality originated by Sigmund Freud, which proposes that human behaviour represents the outcome of clashing inner forces.

Psychological androgyny Possession of stereotypical masculine traits, such as assertiveness and instrumental skills, along with stereotypical feminine traits, such as expressiveness, nurturance, and cooperation.

Psychosexual development In psychoanalytic theory, the process by which sexual feelings shift from one erogenous zone to another as a human being matures.

Puberty The stage of development during which reproduction first becomes possible. Puberty begins with the appearance of *secondary sex characteristics* and ends when the long bones make no further gains in length. (From the Latin *puber,* meaning "of ripe age.")

Pudendum The external genitals, especially the female genitals.

Radiotherapy Treatment of a disease by X-rays or by emissions from a radioactive substance.

Random sample A sample in which every member of a population has an equal chance of participating.

Rape trauma syndrome A two-phase reaction to sexual assault that is characterized by disruption of the survivor's lifestyle (the acute phase) and reorganization of the survivor's life (the long-term phase).

Rape Sexual assault involving penetration. (The term was removed from the Criminal Code of Canada in 1983 and replaced with *sexual assault*.)

Recessive trait A trait that is not expressed when the gene or genes involved have been paired with dominant genes. Recessive traits are transmitted to future generations, however, and are expressed if they are paired with other recessive genes.

Reciprocity Mutual exchange.

Reflex A simple, unlearned response to a stimulus that is mediated by the spine rather than the brain.

Refractory period A period of time following a response (e.g., orgasm) during which an individual is no longer responsive to stimulation (e.g., sexual stimulation).

Reliability The consistency of a measure.

Repression The automatic ejection of anxiety-evoking ideas from consciousness.

Resolution phase The fourth phase of the sexual response cycle, during which the body gradually returns to its prearoused state.

Respiratory distress syndrome A cluster of breathing problems, including weak and irregular breathing, to which preterm babies are especially vulnerable.

Retrograde ejaculation Ejaculation in which the ejaculate empties into the bladder. (From the Latin *retrogradi,* meaning "to go backward.")

Rh incompatibility A condition in which antibodies produced by a pregnant woman are transmitted to the fetus and may cause brain damage or death.

Romantic love A kind of love characterized by feelings of passion and intimacy.

Root The base of the penis, which extends into the pelvis.

Rubella A viral infection that can cause mental retardation and heart disease in an embryo. Also called *German measles*.

Sadism A paraphilia characterized by the desire or need to inflict pain or humiliation on others to enhance sexual arousal so that gratification is attained. (From the name of the author Marquis de Sade.)

Sadomasochism A mutually gratifying sexual interaction between consenting sex partners in which sexual arousal is associated with the infliction and receipt of pain or humiliation. Commonly known as *S&M*.

Sample Part of a population.

Satyriasis An excessive, insatiable sexual appetite or drive in men. (After *satyr,* a sexually insatiable, goat-legged creature with pointed ears and short horns in Greek mythology. Satyrs were part man, part beast.)

Scabies A parasitic infestation caused

by a tiny mite (*Sarcoptes scabiei*) that causes itching.

Scores Customers of hustlers.

Scrotum The pouch of loose skin that contains the testes. (From the same linguistic root as the word *shred*, meaning "a long, narrow strip," and probably referring to the long furrows on the scrotal sac.)

Secondary amenorrhea Lack of menstruation in a woman who has previously menstruated.

Secondary dysmenorrhea Menstrual pain or discomfort that is caused by identified organic problems.

Secondary erogenous zones Parts of the body that become erotically sensitized through experience.

Secondary sex characteristics Physical traits that distinguish men from women but are not directly involved in reproduction.

Secretory phase The third phase of the menstrual cycle, which follows ovulation. Also referred to as the luteal phase, after the corpus luteum, which begins to secrete large amounts of progesterone and estrogen following ovulation.

Selection factor A bias that may operate in research when people are allowed to determine whether or not they will receive a treatment.

Self-disclosure The revelation of personal, perhaps intimate, information.

Semen The whitish fluid that constitutes the ejaculate, consisting of sperm and secretions from the seminal vesicles, prostate, and Cowper's glands.

Seminal vesicles Small glands that lie behind the bladder and secrete fluids that combine with sperm in the ejaculatory ducts.

Seminiferous tubules Tiny, winding, sperm-producing tubes that are located within the lobes of the testes. (From Latin roots meaning "seed bearing.")

Sensate focus exercises Exercises in which sex partners take turns giving and receiving pleasurable stimulation in nongenital areas of the body.

Serial monogamy A pattern of involvement in one exclusive relationship after another, as opposed to engaging in multiple sexual relationships at the same time.

Sex flush A reddish rash that appears on the chest or breasts late in the excitement phase of the sexual response cycle.

Sex skin Reddening of the labia minora that occurs during the plateau phase.

Sex therapy A collective term for short-term behavioural models for treatment of sexual dysfunctions.

Sexism The prejudgment that because of gender, a person will possess negative traits.

Sexologist A person who engages in the scientific study of sexual behaviour.

Sexual arousal disorders Sexual dysfunctions in which people persistently or recurrently fail to become adequately sexually aroused to engage in or sustain sexual intercourse.

Sexual assault with a weapon Sexual contact with a non-consenting person involving a weapon, threats, or bodily harm.

Sexual assault Any form of sexual contact without voluntary consent.

Sexual desire disorders Sexual dysfunctions in which people have persistent or recurrent lack of sexual desire or aversion to sexual contact.

Sexual differentiation The process by which males and females develop distinct reproductive anatomy.

Sexual dysfunction A persistent or recurrent difficulty in becoming sexually aroused or reaching orgasm.

Sexual harassment Any sexually oriented conduct that is a condition of employment, interferes with job performance, or creates a hostile or offensive work environment is sexual harassment.

Sexual masochism A paraphilia characterized by the desire or need for pain or humiliation to enhance sexual arousal so that gratification may be attained. (From the name of the author Leopold von Sacher-Masoch.)

Sexual orientation The direction of one's sexual interests—toward members of the same gender, the other gender, or both genders.

Sexual pain disorders Sexual dysfunctions in which people persistently or recurrently experience pain during coitus.

Sexual response cycle Masters and Johnson's model of sexual response, which consists of four phases.

Sexual sadists People who become sexually aroused by inflicting pain or humiliation on others.

Sexually transmitted infections Infections that are communicated primarily through sexual contact. Abbreviated *STIs*.

Shaft The body of the penis, which expands as a result of vasocongestion.

Shigellosis An infection caused by the *Shigella* bacterium.

Small talk A superficial kind of conversation that allows exchange of information but stresses breadth of topic coverage rather than in-depth discussion.

Social-exchange theory The view that the development of a relationship reflects the unfolding of social exchanges—that is, the rewards and costs of maintaining the relationship as opposed to ending it.

Social-learning theory A cognitively oriented learning theory in which observational learning, values, and expectations play key roles in determining behaviour.

Social desirability A response bias to a questionnaire or interview, in which the person provides a socially acceptable response.

Social skills training Behaviour therapy methods for building social skills that rely on a therapist's coaching and practice.

Socialization The process of guiding people into socially acceptable behaviour patterns by means of information, rewards, and punishments.

Sociobiology The theory that dispositions toward behaviour patterns that enhance reproductive success may be genetically transmitted.

Spectator role A role, usually taken on because of performance anxiety, in which people mentally observe rather than fully participate in their sexual encounters.

Sperm The male germ cell. (From a Greek root meaning "seed.")

Spermatic cord The cord that suspends a testicle within the scrotum and contains a vas deferens, blood vessels, nerves, and the cremaster muscle.

Spermatids Cells formed by the division of spermatocytes. Each spermatid has 23 chromosomes.

Spermatocyte An early stage in the development of sperm cells, in which each parent cell has 46 chromosomes, including one X and one Y sex chromosome.

Spermatogenesis Process by which sperm cells are produced and developed.

Spermatozoa Mature sperm cells.

Sphincters Ring-shaped muscles that surround body openings and open or close them by expanding or contracting. (From the Greek for "that which draws close.")

Squeeze technique A method for treating premature ejaculation whereby the tip of the penis is squeezed temporarily to prevent ejaculation.

Stereotype A fixed, conventional idea about a group of people.

Sterilization Surgical procedures that render people incapable of reproduction without affecting sexual activity.

Stillbirth The birth of a dead fetus.

Storge (STORE-gay) Loving attachment and nonsexual affection; the type of emotion that binds parents to children.

Stranger sexual assault Sexual assault that is committed by someone previously unknown to the person who is assaulted.

Stratified random sample A random sample in which known subgroups in a population are represented in proportion to their numbers in the population.

Streetwalkers Prostitutes who solicit customers on the streets.

Superego In Freud's theory, the third mental structure, which functions as a moral guardian and sets forth high standards for behaviour.

Supermale syndrome A sex chromosomal disorder in males caused by an extra Y sex chromosome.

Surfactants Substances that prevent the walls of the airways from sticking together.

Surrogate mother A woman who is impregnated through artificial insemination with the sperm of a prospective father, carries the embryo and fetus to term, and then gives the child to the prospective parents.

Survey A detailed study of a sample obtained by means such as interviews and questionnaires.

Swinging A form of consensual adultery in which both spouses share extra-marital sexual experiences. Also referred to as *mate-swapping*.

Sympathetic pregnancy The experiencing of a number of signs of pregnancy by the father.

Sympathetic The branch of the ANS most active during emotional responses, such as fear and anxiety, that spend the body's reserves of energy. The sympathetic ANS largely controls ejaculation.

Syphilis A sexually transmitted infection caused by a bacterium.

Systematic desensitization A method for terminating the connection between a stimulus (such as a fetishistic object) and an inappropriate response (such as sexual arousal to the paraphilic stimulus). Muscle relaxation is practised in connection with each stimulus in a series of increasingly arousing stimuli, so that the person learns to remain relaxed (and not sexually aroused) in their presence.

Tampon A cylindrical plug of cotton that is inserted into the vagina and left in place to absorb menstrual fluid. (A French word, meaning a gun barrel "plug.")

Telephone scatologia A paraphilia characterized by the making of obscene telephone calls. (From the Greek *skatos*, meaning "excrement" and *logos*, meaning "speech.")

Teratogens Environmental influences or agents that can damage an embryo or fetus. (From the Greek *teras*, meaning "monster.")

Testes The male gonads. (Singular: testis.)

Testicles Testes.

Testosterone The male sex hormone that fosters the development of male sex characteristics and is connected with the sex drive.

Toucherism A practice related to frotteurism and characterized by the persistent urge to fondle nonconsenting strangers.

Toxemia A life-threatening condition that is characterized by high blood pressure.

Transition The process during which the cervix becomes nearly fully dilated and the head of the fetus begins to move into the birth canal.

Transsexuals People who have a gender-identity disorder in which they feel trapped in the body of the wrong gender.

Transverse position A crosswise birth position.

Transvestism A paraphilia in which a person repeatedly cross-dresses to achieve sexual arousal or gratification, or is troubled by persistent, recurring urges to cross-dress. (From the Latin roots *trans-*, meaning "cross," and *vestis*, meaning "garment.")

Treatment In experiments, an intervention that is administered to participants (e.g., a test, a drug, or a sex education program) so that its effects may be observed.

Trichomoniasis A form of vaginitis caused by the protozoan *Trichomonas vaginalis*.

Tubal sterilization The most common method of female sterilization, in which the fallopian tubes are surgically blocked to prevent the meeting of sperm and ova. Also called *tubal ligation*.

Tumescence Swelling; erection. (From the Latin *tumere*, meaning "to swell." *Tumour* has the same root.)

Turner syndrome A sex-chromosomal disorder in females caused by loss of some X chromosome material.

Umbilical cord A tube that connects the fetus to the placenta.

Unconscious mind Those parts or contents of the mind that lie outside of conscious awareness.

Urethral bulb The small tube that makes up the prostatic part of the urethral tract, which balloons out as muscles close at either end, trapping semen prior to ejaculation.

Urethral opening The opening through which urine passes from the female's body,

Urethritis An inflammation of the bladder or urethra.

Urologist A physician who specializes in the diagnosis and treatment of diseases of the urogenital system.

Urophilia A paraphilia in which sexual arousal is associated with urine.

Uterus The hollow, muscular, pear-shaped organ in which a fertilized ovum becomes implanted and develops until birth.

Vacuum aspiration Removal of the uterine contents by suction. An abortion method used early in pregnancy. (From the Latin *aspirare*, meaning "to breathe upon.")

Vagina The tubular female sex organ that contains the penis during sexual intercourse and through which a baby is born. (Latin for "sheath.")

Vaginismus A sexual dysfunction characterized by involuntary contraction of the muscles surrounding the vaginal barrel, preventing penile penetration or rendering penetration painful.

Vaginitis Vaginal inflammation.

Validity With respect to tests, the degree to which a particular test measures the constructs or traits it purports to measure.

Vas deferens A tube that conducts sperm from the testicle to the ejaculatory duct of the penis. (From Latin roots meaning "a vessel" that "carries down.")

Vasectomy A sterilization procedure in which the vas deferens is severed, preventing sperm from reaching the ejaculatory duct.

Vasocongestion The swelling of the genital tissues with blood, which causes erection of the penis and engorgement of the area surrounding the vaginal opening.

Vasovasotomy The surgical method of reversing vasectomy in which the cut or cauterized ends of the vas deferens are sewn together.

VDRL The test, named after the Venereal Disease Research Laboratory of the U.S. Public Health Service, that tests for the presence of antibodies to *Treponema pallidum* in the blood.

Vestibular bulbs Cavernous structures that extend downward along the sides of the introitus and swell during sexual arousal.

Viscosity Stickiness, consistency.

Volunteer bias A slanting of research data that is caused by the characteristics of individuals who volunteer to participate, such as willingness to discuss intimate behaviour.

Voyeurism A paraphilia characterized by strong, repetitive urges and related sexual fantasies of observing unsuspecting strangers who are naked, disrobing, or engaged in sexual relations. (From the French verb *voir*, meaning "to see.")

Vulva The external sexual structures of the female.

Whore–madonna complex A rigid stereotyping of women as either sinners or saints.

Zona pellucida A gelatinous layer that surrounds an ovum. (From roots meaning "zone that light can shine through.")

Zoophilia A paraphilia involving persistent or repeated sexual urges and related fantasies involving sexual contact with animals.

Zygote intrafallopian transfer (ZIFT) A method of conception in which an ovum is fertilized in a laboratory dish and then placed in a fallopian tube.

Zygote A fertilized ovum (egg cell).

Name Index

Subject Index